LIFE AN INTRODUCTION TO BIOLOGY

Shorter Edition

LIFE AN INTRO

HARCOURT, BRACE & WORLD, INC.
New York / Chicago / San Francisco / Atlanta

GEORGE GAYLORD SIMPSON

Harvard University
and The University of Arizona

WILLIAM S. BECK

Harvard University

DUCTION TO BIOLOGY

SHORTER EDITION

LIFE AN INTRODUCTION TO BIOLOGY

Shorter Edition, by George Gaylord Simpson and William S. Beck

Library of Congress Catalog Card Number: 69-14399

Printed in the United States of America

COVER: *Petrified Wood,* Harbrace Photo

PREFACE

This book and its predecessors are based on strong convictions. We believe that there is a unified science of biology, which embraces in one connected body of knowledge such specialties as biochemistry, botany, zoology, and ecology. We believe that this science has an established body of principles. We believe that knowledge of the principles of life is the most important thing that the living organism man can acquire.

Principles are more than summaries or descriptions of facts. They are, however, meaningless unless they arise from concrete data and are applicable to particular problems. We have tried to underpin the principles with facts and to show how the principles do arise from those facts. We have elucidated scientific method not as a catchword but by stating biological problems and illustrating the methods that have led to their solutions, partial or complete. In this lively science, we have avoided giving the impression that most solutions are complete. We have taken pains at various points to indicate where knowledge now ends and where new knowledge may be sought.

We have not concentrated on man as a biological specimen or on any list of "typical organisms," because we believe the former approach too limiting and the latter essentially fallacious. We believe that the main reason for studying biology is its human interest, but that interest is best served by a general view of the processes of life and its protean manifestations. The most logical approach to the subject of general biology is by levels of organization, and we have followed that approach as far as practicable. We do not think it necessary to stress one level at the expense of another, and we have tried to include, if not absolutely equal, at least adequate treatment at all levels from that of molecular biology to that of the history of life as a whole. The most general of all biological principles is evolution, and we have kept that as a central theme running through all others.

The present book is an abridgment and further revision of the second edition of *Life, An Introduction to Biology,* by the same authors. It is not intended to replace the unabridged version but to supply a shorter introduction along similar lines. Some reorganization of topics and, inevitably, many omissions have been made, but in general the approach, coverage, and sequence of the larger work are retained. This version is simpler in that a number of complicating details and special topics have been deleted and others treated more briefly, but it is not written down. We have tried to maintain the same level of intellectual interest and literacy. Readers and students who want further documentation of topics treated here and discussion of biological topics omitted here are referred to *Life,* Second Edition.

The basic labor of abridgment was performed by William K. Stephenson and Louis V. Wilcox, Jr. This task was considerably more demanding than a simple matter of striking out passages, and we are greatly indebted to them for their collaboration. The authors, however, approved the abridged text and remain responsible for it.

Those who particularly helped with the two previous full length versions should again be thanked, as their assistance is also reflected in this abridgment even though they have not been specifically concerned with it. Colin H. Pittendrigh and Lewis H. Tiffany were two of the three co-authors of the first edition. Others who helped extensively on the first or second editions include (in alphabetical order) J. T. Bonner, W. H. Camp, A. D. Chiquoine, W. H. Furgason, A. S. Gordon, A. D. Hershey, F. H. Johnson, D. L. Lindsley, A. E. Mirsky, A. Roe, E. T. Smith, O. T. Solbrig, K. V. Thimann, and M. D. F. Udvardy. We have also had the benefit of suggestions, criticisms, and corrections from readers, teachers, and students far too numerous to mention individually but greatly deserving collective thanks.

George Gaylord Simpson
William S. Beck

CONTENTS

PART ONE

INTRODUCTION

The picture introducing this part, which is itself an introduction to the whole book, is a photograph of a spider's web. The web is not alive, but it serves as a beautiful symbol of many of the general themes in the study of living things. It reflects the complexity and organization of the animal that made it. It has a function, which is to help provide food, and therefore both materials and energy for the maintenance of the spider. It is the product of its maker's behavior. It expresses the intricacy and precision of the spider's adaptation—its ability to live from and within its environment; an aspect of that adaptation—and of all adaptations whatever—is the ability to reproduce, and hence to maintain a population of spiders through the ages, a population that endures although the individuals in it perish. The web is finally but preeminently an outcome of a history of change, of organic evolution, that started long, long before there were any spiders and that continues to produce extraordinary results.

These are the major themes of life and of this text, and we shall examine them further in Chapter 1 as they are seen in a forest. We shall then organize the inquiry to be pursued throughout the rest of the book in terms both of these main themes and in terms of the levels of organization in nature, from molecules through cells, whole organisms, specific populations, and multispecific communities to the entire world of living things in time and space.

Then we shall consider the nature of our inquiry and of science itself as a way of knowing, understanding, and coping with the world in which we live. We shall also briefly trace the expanding scope and impact of science to its culmination when Darwin at last brought the phenomena of life fully into the domain of naturalistic study.

CHAPTER ONE

THE LIVING WORLD
AND ITS STUDY

"Know Thyself"

You are alive, and all around you are other living things. You would not yourself be alive if you were not part of the whole complex world of life. This is true not only in the sense that you depend on other forms of life for food but also in other and larger senses. You live in a community, a community of other humans and also of many other living things in greater diversity and of greater impact on your own life than you may have realized as yet. You share with them many processes of living. The study of these processes in other animals and in plants is necessary for an understanding of your own life. Moreover, you are literally related to all the other living things, just as truly as you are related to your sisters and your cousins and your aunts. You share a common ancestry with every other animal and every plant; you are a product of the same long, intricate history.

The real reason for studying biology is the old admonition "Know thyself." The better you know yourself, the happier, healthier, more comprehending, and richer will be your life. You cannot, however, really know yourself if that is *all* you know. True understanding can come only from knowledge of life in general. The meaning of biology is its human meaning, its significance to you as a person, but that meaning can be made clear only if human biology is seen as a part of the biology of all life.

Awareness of the world of life and knowledge of it begin when we look at living things and wonder about them. For a start, let us look at an example of a natural community, one abounding in a multiplicity of things alive.

A Forest

THE SCENE AND THE ACTORS

Here (Figure 1-1) is one of the beautiful forests of ponderosa pines in our Southwest. The stately old trees are 150 feet or more in height and 300 to 400 years old. They stand well apart, as if intolerant of each other's shadows, as indeed they are. They need full sunlight and, like all plants, have special requirements as to soil, slope, drainage, temperature, rainfall, and other conditions. We say that they have "preferences," but they make no choices, growing unconsciously when seeds fall where their needs are met.

The light that filters through the pines falls on a forest floor carpeted with herbaceous plants that make it green and flowery in summer. Along a nearby stream are other trees with different needs: alders, willows, narrow-leaf cottonwoods. On exposed, rocky slopes are still others: piñon pines, tree junipers, and oak scrub. There are plants everywhere, from the cactus on a sandy, dry, southern slope to the iris on the marshy bank of a pool, each in the particular place that best supplies its particular needs.

On a calm summer day the plants are motionless and silent. They seem to lack the ceaseless activity that we associate with being alive, but their external

FIG. 1-1 Upper left, the ponderosa pines stand well apart as if intolerant of each other's shadows. The stately trees are 150 feet or more in height and 300 to 400 years old.

Upper right, along the stream bank are different kinds of trees.

Lower left, wild turkeys flock in the oak and piñon pines to gorge themselves on acorns and pine nuts.

Middle, deer wander daintily, cropping leaves from the succulent vegetation.

Lower right, insects are everywhere and make up in numbers what they lack in bulk. Here one beetle larva preys upon another. (All photos U.S. Forest Service except wild turkeys, Lanks from Monkmeyer)

appearance is merely an illusion. Within them tremendous activity is going on. Water and chemicals are being drawn from the soil by roots, and gases are absorbed from the air by leaves. At the same time the leaves are capturing the energy of sunlight, energy released by fierce nuclear reactions in a star 93 million miles distant. From these materials and with this energy the plants are compounding special foods that, as we shall see, are the starting point for all the vital processes of the forest and its denizens.

Throughout the scene are animals whose most evident activity is consumption of the plants. Squirrels tear apart the pine cones and eat the nutritious seeds. Deer wander daintily along, cropping leaves from the lower, more succulent vegetation. Wild turkeys flock in the oaks and piñon pines to gorge themselves on acorns and pine nuts. The plant-eaters are preyed on by other animals. The deer are killed and eaten by mountain lions. Wildcats stalk the turkeys. Rabbits, a rich and perennial crop, fall prey to hawks, coyotes, weasels, and other hungry carnivores. The methods are endlessly varied, but the business is the same for all from pine tree to weasel: the gathering of materials and energy.

Everywhere there are plants and animals less obvious than the few so far noticed. There are literally hundreds of different insects, enough to occupy a whole congress of experts in their identification. They draw their materials and energy from every living thing in sight, their sources ranging from other insects to the nectar in flowers. Even the apparently lifeless soil is in fact swarming with life in forms often far too small to be detected by the unaided eye. Here, among many others, are mites and tiny worms, bacteria and molds. Even the clean mountain air is filled with such living things as spores, bacteria, and pollen.

SOME THEMES OF THE DRAMA

The extremely diverse forms and the no less diverse activities of the plants and animals of the forest may seem at first sight to be an ill-organized jumble. More thoughtful consideration quickly reveals that all, from bacterium in the soil to hawk in the sky, make up an integrated cast of actors playing in a unified drama. That drama has certain major themes in which every actor has his part.

Organization

We may view the drama at many different levels, and at each level we shall find that it is in fact intricately and extremely well organized. The structure of each actor is no hodgepodge but amazingly the contrary. The most complex and highly organized things in the world are the living things, to such an extent that the word *organism* has become synonymous with *living thing*. There is nothing random in the anatomy of a bacterium or a hawk. We see that the bacterium is a cell and that a hawk is made up of millions of cells. There is nothing random within a cell, either. We are here looking at a level of organization below that of the individual organism, but it is no less organized. At a level above that of the organism, we find the individuals living together in groups of their own kind, reproducing, and maintaining populations that endure although the individuals perish. Here organization differs greatly in degree and kind among the various groups. It is comparatively simple in bacteria and complex in hawks, but both populations are organized. A still higher level comprises the whole community as we first saw it, with its myriads of different species. Organization at this level is most evident in relationship to a second major theme of the drama.

Traffic in Materials and Energy

Organisms are obviously built of materials, and a study of organisms must sooner or later examine what those materials are at a level still lower than that of the cell—the molecular level. In our forest a part of the drama already glimpsed is the individual acquisition of materials, by plants from soil and air, by animals from plants or from other animals. Within the individual, at an appropriately lower level of observation, the materials thus acquired are transformed so as to be useful in the new system of organization that they have entered. In the community as a whole there is a constant flow of materials from soil and air to plant, from plant to animal, from animal to other animal, perhaps through a long sequence of animals, eventually from plant and animal to bacterium, and back to soil and air. That flow is the simplest element in organization at the community level.

Along with the materials goes *energy,* the capacity to do work. Every organism ceaselessly does work and so must ceaselessly acquire energy. A hawk obviously is doing work when it flies, screeches, or dives and seizes its prey. It is less obvious but still more important that a hawk is also expending energy when it simply sits still, or that a bacterium or a tree constantly utilizes energy. The fact is that energy is required not only to achieve but also to maintain organization. Unless work is put into them for maintenance, all systems tend toward disorder and eventual loss of organization. This is a bitter truth to the owner of a letter file, a house, or a factory. It is no less true of the systems that are organisms. They must spend energy or become disorganized, and disorganization is death.

With some exceptions of no importance at this point, all the energy used by all the organisms in the world (including industrial man) comes ultimately from the sun. In our forest we noted that the green leaves were capturing the radiant energy of sunlight. The plants transform that energy into a different form, into a successive series of chemical compounds, molecules that embody both materials and energy. The first step is the compounding of an energy-rich sugar, which later yields energy for other vital processes and materials for other organic compounds. All of the available energy and the most important of the materials in the entire forest community entered that organization through plants, which thus are the most essential actors in the entire drama. The flea that bites a mountain lion that ate a deer that browsed on leaves is acquiring energy from the sun, energy that would not be available for any other organisms if it had not been captured and transformed by plants.

Behavior

Behavior is not so much a theme of the drama as the way certain roles are played. As such it is a very necessary part of the drama, and we mention it here because it must also be one of the themes in our study of biology. In its overt forms—the browsing of the deer, the attack of the mountain lion, the hopping of the flea—it is practically confined to animals. It is essential to their acquisition of materials and energy, their reproduction, and many other of their life's activities. It depends on, and so its study becomes inseparable from, nonbehavioral activities at the lower levels of organization, for example, within the cells of muscles and nerves.

Organizing the Inquiry

We have introduced the living world as anyone is most likely to approach it—seen with the unaided eye in the communities of forest, shore, field, or park. On that basis we have encountered the major themes of biology as well as the concept of different levels of organization. There is no such thing as a wholly *separate* theme or level, in the sense of one that can be studied intelligently and understood without any reference to other themes and other levels. The hawk's behavior in seizing prey, for instance, becomes fully significant only when we follow the consequences of this action, in one direction down into the hawk's cells and the energetic molecular reactions there, and in another direction to the origin, reproduction, and destiny of the population of hawks. All biological subjects are interconnected in so many ways that comprehension of one demands a little knowledge, at least, of all. But one cannot study any broad field of science by learning something about every part of it all at once. To be effective and systematic, the procedure must be more like unraveling a tangled skein; one has to find an end and continue from there.

Among many possibilities, we have found it most practical and enlightening to orient our inquiry in large part by levels of organization. The level of communities was best for a first over-all glimpse of our themes, but it is not the best end for unraveling. The various levels in nature are not so distinct that a definitive and clear-cut sequence arises automatically, but for our purposes these levels can be listed:

Atoms
Molecules
Cells
Tissues
Organs and functional systems in individuals
Individual organisms as wholes
Populations (reproducing groups of organisms)
Phyletic lineages (evolving populations)
Communities (associations of different populations and lineages)
The world of life as a whole, in space and in time

Although our subject is life, our discussions will start at the top of this list. The first level at which life is present in the fullest sense is that of cells. Of course, what goes on within cells also involves the levels of atoms and molecules, and we must attend to those too, insofar as they are basic for life in the cells. We shall start at the level of the subliving and proceed in a general way upward through the scale of levels to its end.

At each level the various themes will appear as they are applicable and appropriate. All themes run through several if not through all levels. They thus supply a continuity or, in extension of the previous metaphor, a set of connecting threads as we weave the unraveled yarn into a fabric. Some themes distinctly belong to certain levels rather than to others; behavior, for example, emerges only when the level of the individual is reached. Other themes are highly pertinent at all levels but have different aspects at each level. The traffic in materials and energy, for instance, goes on at every level, but the forms it takes, the aspects of it that we examine, within a cell and within a community are quite different. The most omnipresent of all themes, the thread running through the entire fabric, is *evolution*.

Pursuing the Inquiry

THE NATURE OF SCIENCE

A visitor to a ponderosa pine forest experiences many emotions. He is awed by the vastness and strangeness. He rejoices in the beauty. He is curious about all the details of the scene. Each emotion is a basis for human institutions and activities. Man's highest response to the sense of awe is religion. Joy in beauty leads to art. Science is the systematized human activity that responds to man's curiosity.

Motivation

Science, a human activity, has varied human motivations. Curiosity, the desire to know, the pursuit of knowledge for its own sake, is a basic motivation. But it is at least equally human to want knowledge for our own material ends: to supply growing needs, to increase comfort, to amuse us, and even to kill our fellow men. It has been found that knowledge originally acquired for its own sake almost always, sooner or later, can be used to gain such material ends. It is, then, human to seek knowledge with those ends directly in view, motivated by gain rather than by curiosity. Whatever the motivation of the individual scientist may be, the tremendous increase in scientific activity that characterizes our civilization undoubtedly is due in largest measure to such material considerations. Science works. The methods of science yield knowledge that is both sound and materially useful. Certainly scientists do not scorn this outcome or consider material motivation unworthy. On the contrary, most of them rejoice that science is useful and are happy themselves to share in the benefits. (Of the science that we are now studying, health is one of the benefits—only one among a great many.)

The interrelationships between the pursuit and the application of knowledge are so close and numerous that the two sometimes seem indistinguishable. It is true that they intergrade so that no sharp line can be drawn between them, but that does not make them identical. Besides intergrading, science and technology also depend each on the other, but they are not the same. Science is a response to curiosity, a way to acquire new knowledge, a body of knowledge acquired, a means of insight into relationships among facts, an explanation of those facts. Technology is a response to felt needs, the application of knowledge to material ends. Biology has many extremely valuable technological applications, in agriculture, in medicine, and elsewhere, but those are not our subjects. We are concerned with biology as a science and as an indispensable basis for technologies, but we are not here concerned with the technologies themselves.

Question and Answer; Testability

Scientific method is refined common sense. In their examination of the world, the scientists' purpose is to ask sensible questions and to seek sensible answers. It is common sense that the questions should be about observable things, should arise from the phenomena of our world. What kind of coral is that? What does it eat? What happens to the food? How does it reproduce? Simple questions, but sensible ones, and scientific. How many invisible angels can dance on the point of a pin? We need not discuss whether this question is sensible or not, but we do insist that it is not scientific; it does not arise from an observed phenomenon. The first task of a scientist is learning to ask the right kinds of questions.

Scientific answers must also be sought in the right place, in the observation of the world. We consider this common sense too, but it has not always been so considered. During the Middle Ages, many highly intelligent men thought it sensible to seek answers about nature in the writings of ancient Greek philosophers rather than in nature itself. (And the ancient philosophers had rarely interrogated nature directly or asked the right questions.) Here the most important point is that to be scientific an answer must be testable, and must in fact be tested, by observation. The history of biology, more than that of most sciences, has been afflicted with untestable and therefore unscientific answers on various matters. For example, to the question "What causes evolu-

tion?" Henri Bergson, a French philosopher (1859–1941), proposed the answer "*Élan vital* [life drive]." But the *élan vital* was postulated as unobservable. The answer could, in some sense, be true for all we know, but that qualification is precisely what makes it unscientific; we cannot know, for there is no way to check it. Moreover—and this leads to our next point—even if true in some sense or other, the answer would not explain anything, any more than an *élan locomotif* could explain how a locomotive works.

Observation, Generalization, and Explanation

Observation of a particular object or occurrence is the fact, the datum, from which all scientific knowledge stems and to which all scientific theories must return. It is essential to the nature of science that an observation, against which the answers to scientific questions are tested, be repeatable. What a scientist has observed correctly, anyone else can observe and corroborate. This is the basis for one of many characterizations of the field of science: science deals with matters about which general agreement is possible. Nevertheless, an isolated fact, no matter how repeatable observation of it may be, is only a basis for science and is not the essence of scientific endeavor. It has little or no interest unless it can somehow be *generalized,* related to other facts, and ultimately *explained.*

The isolated observation of a hawk having a specific body form and color pattern and displaying a certain repertoire of behavior is generalized in one way when it is observed that the hawk is one of a large population of individuals with closely similar characteristics. This kind of generalization is widespread and fundamental in biology. A similar kind of biological generalization is embodied in the statement that all normal mammals have sex (the concept of sex is itself a generalization) and in this respect fall into one of two categories, male and female. Once reached, such a generalization leads to a search for extensions of it; in this example the generalization about sex was found to apply also to most (but not all) organisms other than mammals.

Such generalizations involve only the extension of observation to cover a large group of individual facts. The extension may even legitimately go beyond the range of observations actually made. If we have examined a million normal mammals of many species and found that all of them are either male or female, we run little risk of error if we conclude that those we have not examined follow the same pattern. Still, all we have done is to establish some characteristics of a group rather than of an individual. We are still describing, not explaining.

Another kind, or level, of generalization deals with relationships between phenomena or between generalizations of different orders. Usually, although not quite invariably (few biological generalizations are absolutely invariable), offspring of sexual organisms are produced after, and only after, some form of union of male and female elements has occurred. Here the nature and sequence of the phenomena are such that we feel that the generalization does have explanatory meaning. We feel entitled to say that offspring are produced *because* the two sexes come together. Given a particular observation of reproduction, we may cite this generalization as an explanation of the single incident.

Biology is characterized by three kinds of explanations. One kind is shared by the biological and the physical sciences and constitutes the connection between the two. It relates organic structures and activities to the chemical structures and physical activities that compose or underlie them and that in this special sense *cause* them. For example, as we shall see later in this book, essential features in reproduction are explicable by the properties of a remarkable substance called deoxyribonucleic acid, or DNA. This kind of explanation may be called *physiological,* with the word applied more broadly than usual.

The term *teleonomic* has been proposed for a second kind of explanation in biology. This relates organic structures and activities to the functions served in or for organisms. Physiologically, digestion is explained as the action of enzymes and other chemicals on food. Teleonomically, it is explained as a step in the process of providing the organism with needed materials and energy. Part of the teleonomic explanation of reproduction is that it leads to perpetuation of populations.

The third kind of explanation in biology is *historical.* This relates organic structures and activities to their evolutionary origins. The processes of diges-

tion and reproduction in us are different from those in our most remote ancestors. Tracing their origins and changes through the evolutionary sequence results in an explanation different from the physiological and teleonomic explanations.

Most biological facts and generalizations can be understood adequately only when all three explanations are provided. There are still many phenomena in biology for which these are not yet available.

Hypothesis and Theory

The goal of science is to establish generalizations and explanations for observed facts. The mere gathering of facts and descriptions is quite useless unless the observations are directed toward this goal and, indeed, dictated by it. Many of the most creative scientists have remarked that hunch and sudden inspiration have been instrumental in their discoveries of explanations. It must, however, be noted that the hunch or inspiration came only when they knew some pertinent facts and were seeking an explanation for them. And that is only the beginning of the process that produces an accepted scientific theory.

The first step toward explanation is taken when a *hypothesis* is formed. A hypothesis is a statement of an explanation that a scientist considers possible. It may be only a hunch or an informed guess, or it may seem inevitable as the only conceivable explanation of the facts at hand. We need not emphasize again that a hypothesis, as a suggested answer to a scientific question, must be testable by observation if it is to become a scientific explanation. The next step, then, is the testing. This involves seeking exceptions to generalizations embodied in the hypothesis. It also involves logical deduction of consequences from the hypothesis and observation of whether these consequences occur. The more consequences a hypothesis entails, the better it is, not only because it can be more thoroughly tested but also because it leads to new useful observations, to the formulation of still other good hypotheses, and to a general increase in knowledge. By way of example, we shall later in this book consider the hypothesis—now an accepted theory—of chromosomal inheritance.

If exceptions are found or if deductions fail to hold during the testing of a hypothesis, the hypothesis must be modified accordingly or rejected altogether. If the hypothesis does meet extended tests, our confidence in it grows. At some not precisely definable point, we feel justified in accepting it as the most probable explanation and in proceeding as if it were true. Then we begin to speak of the hypothesis as a *theory*. A theory is simply a hypothesis tested sufficiently for a scientist to have confidence in its probability. We speak in terms of "acceptance," "confidence," and "probability," not of "proof." If by proof is meant the establishment of eternal and absolute truth, open to no possible exception or modification, then proof has no place in the natural sciences. Alternatively, proof in a natural science, such

as biology, must be defined as the attainment of a high degree of confidence. A theory proved in this sense is still open to possible exception, which could amount to disproof and, even more often, to modification. A good scientist must be prepared to change, sometimes even to discard, his most prized theories, sustained by the conviction that we thus advance in knowledge and toward truth.

The fact that theories are not subject to absolute and final proof has led to a serious misapprehension. Theory is contrasted with fact as if the two had no relationship or were antitheses: "Evolution is *only* a theory, not a fact." Of course, theories are not facts. They are generalizations about facts and explanations of facts, based on and tested by facts. As such, they may be just as certain—merit just as much confidence—as what are popularly termed "facts." Belief that the sun will rise tomorrow is the confident application of a generalization. The theory that life has evolved is founded on much more evidence than supports the generalization that the sun rises every day. In the vernacular, both are "facts."

Biology and the Scientific Conceptual Scheme

ORIGINS OF SCIENCE

Men surely have been asking questions about the world and proposing answers ever since the human species began. Which questions are asked and how answers are sought always depend on a conceptual scheme, an attitude toward the world and a set of postulates or beliefs about it. A conceptual scheme that sees the world as capricious and chaotic gives rise to no questions about order and natural law. A conceptual scheme that embraces magic and invisible spirits as causes of phenomena does not evoke answers testable by the phenomena themselves. Some such primitive conceptual schemes still have a lingering influence, but in the light of present knowledge, the result of science, we consider them superstitions. At a more sophisticated level are conceptual schemes that seek answers to questions about the material world not from that world but from dogmatic authority or by deduction from

subjective philosophical premises. Such answers, not even regarded as subject to observational test, cannot be scientific.

The ancient world of Babylonia, Egypt, and Greece made great advances in knowledge of the world and laid the foundations for science and technology, but the ancients never developed a fully scientific conceptual scheme. Europe of the Middle Ages inherited from the ancient world a conceptual scheme that pictured the world as orderly but that sought answers about its orderliness in authority and in philosophical deduction more than in the world itself. It is an extraordinary fact that the scientific conceptual scheme arose so late in human history, within a single culture, that of western Europe, and over a comparatively brief span of time, roughly definable as from Nicolaus Copernicus (1473–1543) to Charles Darwin (1809–1882). Beyond the already general concept of order in the world, the whole basis of this scheme was the strict relation of questions and answers to the observation of the world, the seeking of natural explanations for natural phenomena, the proposal of testable hypotheses, and the testing of them.

It seems quite obvious to us that the only logical means of investigating the material world is by observing it. But we have grown up in a civilization in which the scientific conceptual scheme already existed and was generally (although not exclusively) accepted as the effective way of acquiring knowledge. Copernicus' scientific theory that the earth circles the sun was firmly grounded in observation, but it was violently rejected by those whose conceptual scheme was still based on authority and philosophical deduction.

EARLY, INCOMPLETELY SCIENTIFIC BIOLOGY

The scientific conceptual scheme arose first in the physical sciences. It brought about a revolution in human thought. Its insistence that natural phenomena obey natural, impersonal laws was a bitter and, at first, deeply resented blow to age-old superstitions embedded in nonscientific conceptual schemes. Nevertheless, the scientific scheme responded to a refined concept of common sense, and it worked. As regards the physical aspects of the world, acceptance of the scientific scheme was soon general, if not quite universal. Yet well into the nineteenth century the great majority of people—even among the most intelligent and most learned—clung to a conceptual scheme in which essential phenomena of life, and most particularly of human life, were believed to transcend physical laws and not to be amenable to strictly scientific explanation. Biology is as old a science as any. It had its roots in antiquity, and in its physical or plainly material aspects it became a true science along with physics, chemistry, astronomy, and the rest when the scientific conceptual scheme was developed in the sixteenth and seventeenth centuries. Until 1859, however, it was impeded by

the common view that some of its subject matter did not fit into that scheme.

BIOLOGY FULLY ENTERS THE SCHEME

It was in 1859 that Darwin's book *The Origin of Species* was published. This book accomplished two main objectives. First, it established the *theory of evolution,* the broadest generalization ever made about the interrelationships of living things. This theory (which in common speech we are now justified in calling a fact) states that all organisms have arisen from common ancestors by a natural, historical process of change and diversification. Second, the book propounded a theory to explain the *causes and results of evolution.* The most important point that had to be explained was the apparent purposiveness of life, the observation that organisms seem to be designed precisely for the functions they carry out. It was this, more than anything else, that had supported the claim that vital structures and processes could not have entirely natural causes and hence did not fit the scientific conceptual scheme.

Darwin's complex explanation was only partially successful, but its most essential element, *natural selection,* has stood the test of time and is accepted today in a somewhat modified form. We shall return to that subject, and to the problem of purpose in nature, after a sufficient basis for comprehension has been laid. What is significant here is that Darwin sufficiently demonstrated that *natural* explanations for *all* of the material phenomena of life should be sought and can be found. Thus, *The Origin of Species* actually accomplished a third objective, most important of all: it finally brought biology as a whole, in all its aspects, within the conceptual scheme of science.

Summary

Life seen in communities: a ponderosa pine forest as an example.

Major themes in the drama of life: organization; levels of organization and of study; traffic in materials and energy; behavior; reproduction; evolution.

Organization of this book: by levels and by themes within each level and between levels.

Nature of science: a human activity motivated by curiosity and by a desire to supply needs and wants; science and technology interdependent but distinct; science a system of questions and answers arising from observation and tested by observation; generalizations as extended observations and as explanations; three kinds of explanations in biology—physiological, teleonomic, and historical; hypothesis, a proposed answer to a scientific question; theory, a hypothesis in which we have confidence; the relationship of theory and fact.

Biology and the scientific conceptual scheme: the dependence of the pursuit of knowledge on conceptual schemes; superstitions and the nonscientific nature of old schemes; the rise of the scientific scheme from Copernicus to Darwin; the incomplete incorporation of biology in the scheme until 1859; Darwin's accomplishments—the theory of evolution, the theory of natural selection, and the inclusion of all biological phenomena in the scientific conceptual scheme.

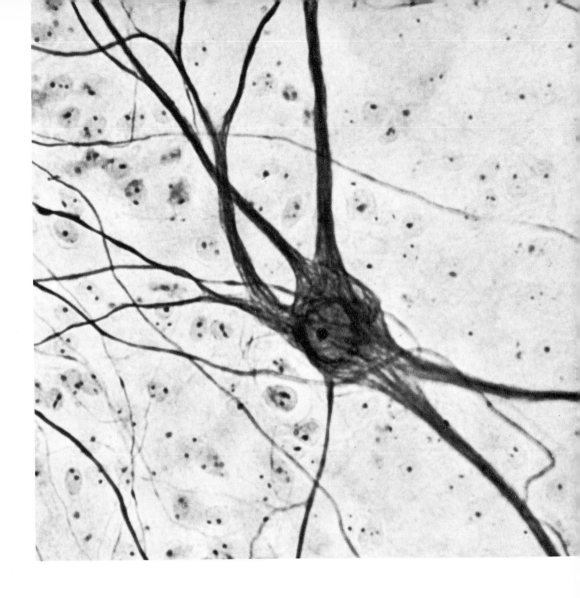

PART TWO

THE BASIS OF LIFE

Organisms are composed of cells. Plant or animal, large or small, the generalization holds for *all* living things; they are either single cells or groups of cells. The discovery of this great truth, which is the heart of the cell theory, was one of the outstanding achievements of the nineteenth century and ranks with the theory of evolution as a cornerstone of modern biology.

Every cell is, so to speak, a world of life in miniature. Like the organism of which it is a part—or even the whole—the cell is complex and organized. It responds to stimuli and is capable of movement; it feeds and respires, expending energy to maintain its ordered state and execute other work such as secretion; and, like other larger living systems, it can reproduce itself. In large and structurally complex organisms like ourselves, all special parts such as bones, muscles, and nerves are composed of special cells—bone cells, muscle cells, and nerve cells.

Although the cell is the basic unit of life, it is made up of units still lower in the hierarchic sequence. For full comprehension, the search for knowledge of life must start at those levels even below the cell, with a study of the atoms, molecules, and chemical reactions that enter into the structures and the activities of cells. These are the subjects of Chapter 2.

Chapter 3 describes the organization of cells, so intricate at microscopic and submicroscopic levels. It also discusses the differentiation of cells of different kinds and their organization into tissues of diverse functions in various organisms.

In Chapter 4 some of the most essential and widespread functions of cells are outlined. Here are the dynamic reactions that are the basis of the activities we call life.

MOLECULAR ASPECTS
OF BIOLOGY

The preceding chapter spoke of the hierarchical arrangement within and among living organisms. The cell, it was noted, is the simplest structure in which life is unambiguously present, existing at a certain level of the organizational ladder. But cells are components of more complex structures, tissues and organs, and these in turn are parts of still higher organizations—and so on up the ladder. It is obvious that one can also begin with the cell and descend the ladder, for within the cell are substructures such as the nucleus, its component parts, and the parts within those parts. Eventually, one reaches the molecules and atoms.

One of the most fruitful and exciting chapters of contemporary biology has been the study of the molecules of living organisms and the recognition of their importance to those wishing to understand how organisms function. Early scientific study of living things consisted mainly of descriptive and rather static observations of *structure,* or *morphology.* But investigators were not content merely with anatomical data revealed by the eye, the knife, and the microscope, and there arose a second great movement which sought to comprehend the *function,* or *physiology,* of living things. This involved the application of the techniques of chemistry and physics and resulted in the new and still actively growing disciplines of *biochemistry* and *biophysics.*

One of the most stimulating results of the biochemical approach to biological problems was the discovery that despite the great diversity in the size, form, and structure of living organisms as a group, they have a great deal in common—much more, in fact, than was suspected following the discovery of the fundamental sameness of all cells. Although each type of living thing is unique in its particular combination of materials, processes, and relationships, all require just the same general sorts of chemical materials. They require them in amounts and proportions that vary considerably, to be sure, but that vary within prescribed limits. Yet what any two kinds of organism do with these materials is never precisely the same.

This unity-with-diversity can be strikingly illustrated by two exceptional cases. One would say—and, up to a point, quite correctly—that cellulose, the material of many plant cell walls and hence of wood, is a substance peculiar to plants rather than to animals. Similarly, hemoglobin, the chemical that makes the blood red, seems completely characteristic of animals rather than plants. Yet cellulose occurs in a group of animals, the odd marine forms called *tunicates* (Chapter 17), and hemoglobin has been found in the root nodules of some leguminous plants.

This chapter summarizes the elementary chemical and biochemical principles necessary for an understanding of certain basic principles of biology. You will quickly discover that many of the molecules described, particularly the proteins and nucleic acids, are uniquely associated with living organisms. So, though we speak here of molecules, we are off on an exploration of the molecular basis of *life,* and the living organism must stay in the forefront of our thoughts.

ATOMS

You surely know that the smallest particles in nature, electrons, protons, and the rest, are commonly organized into *atoms.* Atoms represent in most basic form the chemical *elements,* the building blocks for all larger chemical units. In view of the tremendous complexity of the matter composed of them, the number of elements is surprisingly small. Only 103 are known, and 11 of these have been made artificially and may not occur in nature. About 35 are common in nature and important for life.

You also doubtless know that two or more atoms (up to thousands) can combine with each other to form a *molecule.* As we shall see below, the atoms of a molecule are held together by specific forces called *bonds.* Atoms or molecules, or both, can *react* with each other and produce different kinds of molecules.

Each element has a name and a symbolic abbreviation which stands for that name. The elements most important in biology are hydrogen, abbreviation H; oxygen, O; phosphorus, P; carbon, C; and nitro-

gen, N. The simple (or empirical) formula for a molecule shows what atoms it contains. Water is H_2O because it contains two atoms of hydrogen for every one of oxygen.

Atoms, the smallest units capable of retaining their elemental identity when chemical reactions take place, are constructed of smaller diverse components known collectively as *elementary particles.* The elementary particles that concern us are the *protons, electrons,* and *neutrons.* Every atom consists of a single *nucleus* and one or more electrons. The atomic nucleus contains the protons and neutrons. The mass or weight of every proton is the same, and it is given the arbitrary value of 1. A proton has a positive electric charge. A neutron also has a mass of 1, but it is electrically neutral. The mass of an electron is very much less than 1—it is 1/1836 that of the lightest nucleus—hence its weight is almost negligible. An electron bears a negative electric charge equal in magnitude to the positive charge of the proton.

Although nuclei are extremely small, the total mass of a whole atom is concentrated almost entirely in its nucleus. The total mass of the nucleus—that is, the number of protons and neutrons present—determines its *atomic weight.* For example, the simplest atom, that of hydrogen, has a nucleus consisting of a single proton; neutrons are absent (Figure 2-1). Since the nucleus has a mass of 1, the atomic weight of hydrogen is said to be 1. By contrast, the nucleus of an atom of sodium contains 11 protons and 12 neutrons. Therefore, the atomic weight of sodium is 23. Note that the number of protons defines the *atomic number* of an element. The atomic number of hydrogen is 1; the atomic number of sodium is 11.

Ordinary matter is electrically neutral; that is, it contains equal amounts of positive and negative electric charges. Normally, the number of protons exactly equals the number of electrons. The electronegative electrons in an atom are attracted by the positively charged nucleus and move rapidly about it in variously located orbital pathways. In fact, electrons travel only at certain fixed distances from the nucleus, the paths of the electrons in these orbits marking out a series of specific concentric *shells.* Each shell can hold only a fixed maximum number of electrons. Thus, the first shell, proximal to the atomic nucleus, can hold a maximum of 2 electrons, the second shell can hold 8, the third can hold 8, and so on (Figure 2-1).

The hydrogen atom has a single electron orbiting in its first shell. Since this shell can hold 2 electrons, hydrogen is said to have an *incomplete* shell. An atom of helium (He) does have 2 electrons in the first shell (Figure 2-1). Because this is the maximum possible number for this shell, it is said to be complete. Oxygen has 8 electrons, 2 in the first shell and 6 in the second. Since the second shell can hold a maximum of 8 electrons, it is incomplete in the oxygen atom.

Atoms whose electron shells are complete are

notably stable. This means that they are chemically inert and rarely react with other atoms. Helium with its 2 electrons is such a substance.

The atoms of most elements have incomplete outermost shells and are therefore unstable; that is, they are chemically reactive and they can gain or lose electrons from the outermost shell. The following section on molecules and bonds will bring out the full significance of the outer shell of electrons, but

FIG. 2-1 Atomic structures of various elements. The symbol e^- denotes an electron, p^+ a proton, and n a neutron. The nucleus of a hydrogen atom contains only 1 proton. Compare hydrogen with the other atoms shown.

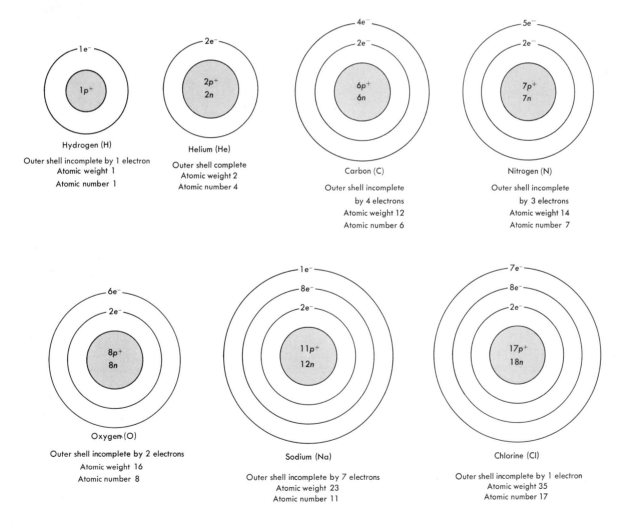

Hydrogen (H)
Outer shell incomplete by 1 electron
Atomic weight 1
Atomic number 1

Helium (He)
Outer shell complete
Atomic weight 2
Atomic number 4

Carbon (C)
Outer shell incomplete
by 4 electrons
Atomic weight 12
Atomic number 6

Nitrogen (N)
Outer shell incomplete
by 3 electrons
Atomic weight 14
Atomic number 7

Oxygen (O)
Outer shell incomplete by 2 electrons
Atomic weight 16
Atomic number 8

Sodium (Na)
Outer shell incomplete by 7 electrons
Atomic weight 23
Atomic number 11

Chlorine (Cl)
Outer shell incomplete by 1 electron
Atomic weight 35
Atomic number 17

first you must learn some shorthand notation for working with atoms and molecules. Electron-dot symbols are one way of representing atoms:

$$\text{H} \qquad \overset{..}{\text{He}}\cdot \qquad :\overset{..}{\text{A}}: \qquad :\overset{..}{\text{O}}\cdot \qquad \cdot\overset{.}{\text{C}}\cdot$$

$$:\overset{..}{\text{F}}\cdot \qquad :\overset{..}{\text{Cl}}\cdot \qquad \text{Na} \qquad \text{Mg}\cdot$$

Note that only the outer shell electrons are shown.

MOLECULES

Chemical reactions occur because every atom tends to complete its outer electron shell. An outer shell originally incomplete can become complete in several ways; therefore, the resulting *bonds* that hold the atoms together in a compound are of several distinct types.

Covalent Bond

Atoms may become electronically stable by *sharing* electrons. Atoms of elements of the halogen family, such as fluorine (F), have outer shells with 1 less than the complete number of electrons. One way in which a fluorine atom can achieve completeness is by reacting with another fluorine atom. The atoms share electrons in such a way that each behaves as if it actually possessed a complete outer shell.

$$:\overset{..}{\text{F}}\cdot + :\overset{..}{\text{F}}\cdot \rightarrow :\overset{..}{\text{F}}:\overset{..}{\text{F}}:$$

The combination is stable, and we say that a *covalent bond* has been formed. This type of bond may also form between atoms of different kinds. An example is hydrogen sulfide:

$$\text{H} + \cdot\overset{..}{\text{S}}\cdot + \text{H} \rightarrow \text{H}:\overset{..}{\text{S}}:\text{H}$$

Since making all the dots for electrons becomes rather laborious, it is customary to represent a covalent bond (one pair of shared electrons) by a dash:

$$\text{H—S—H}$$

Note that unshared electrons are not represented in this type of notation. Functionally, covalent bonds are notable for the large amount of energy needed

to break them. This means that they hold atoms together very tightly.

Ionic Bond

An *ion* is an atom or a group of atoms that has either acquired or lost 1 or more electrons. For example, consider the outer shells of the sodium and chlorine atoms:

$$\text{Na} \qquad \cdot\overset{..}{\text{Cl}}:$$

The chlorine atom is unstable because it has 1 electron too few in its outer shell. The sodium atom is unstable because it has 7 electrons too few—or, to put it another way, because it has 1 electron too many, since it is considerably easier for sodium to achieve a complete outer shell by losing 1 electron than by gaining 7. Under these circumstances, both atoms can attain stability simultaneously if a single electron is transferred from sodium to chlorine. Note that before the transfer of the electron the sodium atom is electrically neutral, its 11 orbiting electrons being counterbalanced exactly by the 11 positively charged protons in the nucleus. During the reaction, the sodium loses one negative charge when it loses an electron. Therefore, the sodium atom becomes positively charged, because the 11 protons are still present though there are only 10 electrons.

$$\text{Na} \rightleftharpoons e^- + \text{Na}^+$$

Conversely, chlorine loses its initial electrical neutrality by acquiring a single negative charge.

$$\text{Cl} + e^- \rightleftharpoons \text{Cl}^-$$

The charged forms, Na^+ and Cl^-, are ions. Negatively charged ions are called *anions,* and positively charged ions, *cations.* A symbol such as Na^+, Mg^{++}, or Cl^- denotes an ion and indicates the size and electrical character of the charge. Oppositely charged ions are attracted to one another, and the strong electrostatic force of attraction that binds them together is the *ionic bond.* A group of ions so bonded is an *ionic compound.* For example, in the reaction

$$\text{Na}^+ + \text{Cl}^- \rightarrow \text{NaCl}$$

the product is the ionic compound NaCl, or sodium chloride. Such an anion-cation combination is called a *salt;* salts are noted for their solubility in water and the ability of their solutions to conduct electric currents.

The formation of NaCl from Na^+ and Cl^- is an *electron-transfer* or *ionic reaction.* In such a reaction, the total number of positive charges carried by the cation equals the total number of negative charges carried by the anion. Every electron transferred establishes one ionic bond. For example, the magnesium ion, Mg^{++}, resulting from the transfer of 2 electrons, forms two ionic bonds with other ions.

Hydrogen Bond

Still another type of chemical bond, the H bond, though weaker in strength than a covalent or ionic bond, holds electrically charged groups together under certain circumstances. To understand the *hydrogen bond,* consider a molecule of water:

$$H : \overset{\cdot\cdot}{\underset{\cdot\cdot}{O}} : H$$

Each of the hydrogen atoms has a slight positive charge, and the oxygen has a slight negative charge. This is because the oxygen has a greater affinity for electrons than the hydrogen. Thus, we say that a molecule of water has a *dipole,* or a positive and a negative portion. In a glass of water, the water molecules are oriented as follows:

The slightly negative oxygens are attracted to the slightly positive hydrogens. This is an example of a *hydrogen bond* between molecules. The ability of water to form hydrogen bonds accounts for many of its extraordinary properties. Hydrogen bonds can also form within molecules, as you will see in your study of proteins. The hydrogen bond is relatively weak and can be broken easily.

Major Elements of the Living Organism

All the materials of life are ultimately derived from relatively simple elements and compounds. Once they are assimilated by a living organism, these ultimate materials often become elaborated into extremely complex forms, which are passed on from one organism to another. Most of these elaborated chemicals are eventually broken down into simple elemental forms again. There is, then, a cycle, with simple materials at the beginning and end; it thus seems logical to begin a consideration of life's materials with them. They include *carbon, oxygen, hydrogen, nitrogen,* and a great variety of what may be called, as a group, *minerals.*

CARBON

Once it has been incorporated into a living thing, a carbon atom may enter hundreds or thousands of different combinations within one organism and then, commonly, within others and yet still others as the materials are passed on. Carbon derives its unique ability to form these many different combinations from the nature of the carbon atom. Carbon has but 4 electrons in its outermost shell, which could hold 8. Therefore, carbon can form four covalent bonds.

Not only can these bonds be with atoms of other elements, but a carbon atom can also form a bond with another carbon atom.

Note that each carbon atom is bonded to four other atoms. Under certain circumstances, two carbon atoms can form two covalent bonds or a *double bond.*

The beginning and the end of the cycle in the inorganic environment involve carbon in the simple compound carbon dioxide (CO_2). CO_2 is produced when pure elemental carbon burns. It also forms within organisms. Under ordinary conditions, CO_2 is a gas. (At temperatures lower than those in nature it solidifies; solid CO_2 is called *dry ice*.) The gas makes up about 0.03 per cent of the atmosphere. This tiny fraction is the main inorganic reservoir of carbon as a material for life.

The gas CO_2 does not usually enter directly into chemical reactions. However, it dissolves in water (as everyone knows who has opened a bottle containing a carbonated drink) and then reacts readily in various ways. This activity is due in part to the fact that CO_2 in solution reacts with water itself to form a weak acid, carbonic acid (H_2CO_3), in accordance with the following equation:

$$CO_2 + H_2O \rightleftharpoons H_2CO_3$$

This equation, like many of those important in life processes, can readily go in either direction. Slight changes in pressure, heat, or concentration, or presence of other chemicals, can reverse the reaction.

The beginning of the incorporation of atmospheric CO_2 into the materials of life involves a more complex series of reactions with water. In green plants these two raw materials are combined into simple sugars in the process called *photosynthesis,* which is discussed in a later chapter. From the simple sugars, carbon is converted into many other substances.

The end of carbon's participation in the chemistry of life usually involves its withdrawal from the more complex compounds and its combination with oxygen. This yields CO_2 again, most of which finds its way more or less directly back into the atmosphere.

HYDROGEN AND OXYGEN

The great majority of the compounds involved in the substances and processes of life contain carbon, hydrogen, and oxygen. Some contain no other elements. Others contain quantities, usually much smaller quantities, of various additional elements.

Hydrogen, the lightest element, is unique in nature. Free H_2, a colorless, odorless gas, does not occur in living tissue. Instead, hydrogen atoms are extensively combined with carbon, oxygen, and the other elements. As we shall presently see, the ability to form hydrogen ions (H^+) is a characteristic property of a particular class of compounds.

The inorganic source of most oxygen in organic compounds is carbon dioxide. In addition, most organisms require more water than they get in their organic foods, and extra oxygen in the form of the element itself, O_2 molecules. Along with water and some salts, O_2 is an inorganic material that can be utilized *directly* by animals as well as plants, in marked contrast to the carbon source, CO_2. (There are, however, some lower organisms, mainly bacteria and parasites, that can live without oxygen and may even be killed by it.)

Oxygen is a gas, and its great inorganic reservoir is the atmosphere, which contains about 20 per cent (by volume) of elemental oxygen (that is, not combined with other elements). Oxygen dissolves in water, remaining in the elemental form and thus available to aquatic organisms. In fact, oxygen must be in solution in water to enter organisms living in air.

The principal role of elemental oxygen in cells is to combine with carbon and hydrogen from the breakdown of organic compounds, producing carbon dioxide and water. The water so formed may be further utilized by the organism, but the carbon dioxide is almost entirely eliminated. The input of oxygen and output of carbon dioxide depend on the chemical activity of the cells and of the organism as a whole. Oxygen consumption is a fairly good measure of total metabolism in most organisms. This is the principle involved in the clinical procedure known as the basal metabolism test.

NITROGEN

After carbon, hydrogen, and oxygen, the most common element in the materials of life is nitrogen. It is, in particular, a constituent of all proteins, an important class of organic compounds to be discussed later in this chapter.

There is a tremendous store of nitrogen in the atmosphere, which is (by volume) almost 80 per cent elemental nitrogen. Yet no animals and few plants can make direct use of this nitrogen. Most plants can utilize nitrogen from the environment only if it is in the form of various inorganic compounds: *ammonia* (NH_3) or its compounds; *nitrates* (salts containing NO_3); or *nitrites* (salts containing NO_2). Animals acquire their nitrogen in the form of compounds, especially proteins, which they obtain from plants or from other animals. The withdrawal of nitrogen from the atmospheric reservoir and its incorporation into life thus depend entirely on processes that make ammonia, nitrates, and nitrites. Some inorganic processes do this, especially lightning, but formation of these compounds is due mainly to a few kinds of organisms that are able to convert elemental nitrogen into ammonia, nitrates, and nitrites through the process known as *nitrogen fixation*. Some bacteria and simple plants (some fungi and algae) can do this. Most noteworthy are the bacteria that live in nodules in the roots of beans and related plants (legumes).

On the other hand, few organisms decompose compounds of nitrogen completely and produce the element nitrogen. Some denitrifying bacteria do this, but the end products of nitrogen metabolism in most organisms are still organic compounds, such as urea or uric acid in animals, or, at the simplest level, ammonia. Because even ammonia can be utilized by some plants and is readily turned into nitrates and nitrites by certain bacteria, the nitrogen remains available to life for long periods of time and passes through many different organisms.

MINERALS

Besides carbon, oxygen, hydrogen, and nitrogen, many other elements are required in smaller amounts by all forms of life. The inorganic sources of these are, in most cases, salts dissolved in water—

water in the soil or in lakes, streams, and seas. Plants and, to some degree, aquatic animals usually acquire these salts directly from the water of the environment. Land animals also acquire and utilize salts directly to some extent but obtain much of their mineral requirement more or less incidentally along with their organic food.

The large number of necessary mineral elements is often divided into two broad groups: the *macronutrients,* which are required in large quantities; and the *micronutrients,* which are needed only in small amounts. The latter are also known as *trace elements.* Although mineral needs vary from cell to cell, and particularly from plant cell to animal cell, the essential macronutrients for most cells include calcium, phosphorus, chlorine, sulfur, potassium, sodium (plants do not need sodium), magnesium, iodine, and iron. Micronutrients that are widely required, but perhaps not by all forms of life, include manganese, copper, zinc, fluorine, cobalt, and possibly vanadium and selenium. In addition, plants require boron and molybdenum, and, for some species, vanadium.

It should be remembered that about 99 per cent of the mineral content of most organisms consists of the so-called macronutrient elements. Nevertheless, the micronutrient elements have great significance. For example, we shall see later that micronutrients have an indispensable catalytic function in many enzyme systems (p. 40). Much research is currently being done on these interesting trace components of the living organism.

Properties of Compounds

Most elements, as we have seen, are electronically unstable and therefore chemically reactive. For this reason, these elements almost without exception do not exist as free atoms on the earth's surface. Surely this is true of elements composing the living organism, for they are joined together in innumerable chemical compounds.

It is useful to separate chemical compounds into two general categories: *electrolytes* and *nonelectrolytes.* Electrolytes (or ionic compounds) are compounds containing ionic bonds (p. 18), that is, bonds formed through electron transfer. We can easily identify electrolytes in the laboratory by demonstrating that solutions in which they are dissolved permit the passage of electric currents. Nonelectrolytes are compounds that have bonds of the covalent type (p. 18);

that is, their stability has been achieved through the sharing of electrons. Their solutions do not transmit electric currents.

We must consider these two groups of compounds because their properties (and particularly certain *differences* in their properties) are of great biological importance. However, let us first consider that often-neglected substance whose unusual behavior helps us distinguish electrolytes from nonelectrolytes, *water.*

UNUSUAL PROPERTIES OF WATER

It is a notable fact that the major portion of the total weight of living tissue consists of water. In man, about 60 per cent of the red blood cells and 92 per cent of the blood plasma are water; and water makes up considerably more than half—often more than three-quarters—of most other tissues. The only exceptions are such relatively inert tissues as hair, nails, and the solid portion of bone. The spores of certain plants and bacteria have low water contents, but these are comparatively inactive cells. When they are transformed into cells that show active metabolism and growth, their water contents must increase. Thus, water appears to be the indispensable matrix for the structural components, as well as for the functioning, of living cells. We are all familiar with the discomfort of animals (such as humans) and the wilting of plants when deprived of water. Indeed, all organisms die if their water supply continues to be inadequate. Water is also a principal constituent of the environment in which organisms live. Although much of the earth's water is liquid, large portions of it are in the vapor and solid phases. These forms of water are also of profound significance to the living world.

To the biologist, water is a strange and unusual substance with behavior full of apparent anomalies. This uniqueness has given water a key role in shaping the character of the physical and biological worlds and in guiding the course of their evolutionary development. Some characteristics of water are: (1) its expansion on freezing, (2) its uniquely high surface tension, (3) its odd thermal properties, and (4) its power as a solvent. Let us briefly examine these phenomena.

It is well known that most substances decrease in volume and therefore increase in density as their temperature decreases. Water is remarkable in that there is a temperature at which its density exceeds that at higher or lower temperatures. This temperature is 4°C. With further cooling, the volume of a sample of water *increases.* This extraordinary property of water is related to an unusual facility of formation of hydrogen bonds between water molecules. This causes ice to have an unusually open structure and, hence, a lower density than if the molecules were more closely packed. As ice melts, the open crystal structure is partially destroyed, and the molecules move closer together. This explains why cool water is denser than ice. Only at 4°C does the expansion from increasing molecular agitation start to overcome this effect and cause water to show the usual decrease of density with increasing temperature.

Very few molecular compounds have the property of expanding on freezing. The fact that water does has deep biological meaning. If ice were heavier than water, it would sink to the bottom on freezing. In fact, water just above the freezing point is heavier than water at the freezing point; therefore, it moves toward the bottom, freezing begins at the surface, and the bottom is last to freeze. Organisms living at the bottoms of fresh-water lakes are thereby protected from freezing. Organisms in the primitive ocean of the world, if they existed there before it was made salty by the erosion of the land surfaces, probably enjoyed the same protection.

Surface Tension

The surface of a liquid, like a stretched membrane, tends to contract in area as much as possible. The phenomenon is called *surface tension.* With no important exceptions, water has the highest surface tension of any known liquid. One consequence of the high surface tension of water is that water rises to unusually high levels in narrow capillary tubes, a fact of great significance in plant physiology (although surface tension alone does not account for the rise of water in tall plants and trees).

It is also of interest that most substances lower the surface tension of water when they dissolve in it. This means that such substances tend to collect at the interfaces between water's liquid phase and other phases. This tendency must be remembered in considering the passage of substances through a membrane and the formation and structure of the membrane itself.

Thermal Properties

The thermal properties of water have helped to make it such an excellent medium for the origin, development, and maintenance of life. Because of them, water plays a major part in keeping the earth's surface at a relatively constant temperature. Since organisms can survive only within a restricted temperature range, this is a matter of the greatest possible importance.

Much more heat is necessary to increase the temperature of a given amount of water by a given number of degrees than is necessary to heat most other substances. Stated another way, a given amount of heat produces a smaller temperature rise in water than in most other substances. Thus water acts as a temperature buffer, maintaining its temperature against the challenge of shifting environmental temperature more successfully than most other substances. We say that water has a high *heat capacity*.

We know that the air above a body of water takes up an increasing amount of water vapor as the temperature rises. Because water enters the atmosphere by evaporation from the sea, and because water evaporation utilizes large amounts of heat, the net result is another mechanism whereby water tends to prevent rapid rises in temperature at times of sudden heat input (such as sunrise). This property of water is called a high *heat of vaporization*. Likewise, the high heat transfers involved in the freezing of water explain why large bodies of water seldom develop temperatures below the freezing point.

Solvent Power

For reasons too complex to explain here, water is a solvent for an extraordinarily large variety of molecules, which form ionized solutions in water. This property is essential to the chemistry of organisms.

IONIC DISSOCIATION

The electrostatic attraction existing between the sodium and chloride atoms in NaCl accounts for

the regularities that manifest themselves in the characteristic structure of the NaCl crystal. But when solid NaCl dissolves in water, Na^+ and Cl^- ions leave the crystal and roam randomly among the water molecules. This separation into free ions is termed *ionic dissociation* and is a result of the high ability of water to weaken the attraction between ions of opposite charge, such as Na^+ and Cl^-.

Dissociation of Salts in Water

Let us consider what happens when the ions of a salt dissolve in water. We may picture the simple ions as if they were tiny charged spheres. The positive charge on the sodium ion tends to attract water molecules around it, the negative (oxygen) ends of the water molecules pointing toward the cation. The electric field around the ion is very intense, and so the orienting force is very great; a whole cluster of water molecules becomes arranged around the ion, and the intense electric field causes them to pack very closely. Similarly, water molecules cluster around the anion, in this case with their positive (hydrogen) ends pointing toward the ion. These shells of water molecules around the ions produce electric fields of their own, and these fields are so oriented as to oppose the fields arising from the ions themselves. Hence the forces of attraction between the ions are weakened; the ions are, as it were, *kept apart* from one another by the water molecules gathered around them. Thus water is an effective solvent for salts not only because it weakens ionic attraction, but also because water molecules tend to combine with ions to form *hydrated* ions.

Almost all chemical reactions of biological importance occur in aqueous solutions. Ionic compounds dissociate in water and yield free ions.

$$CH_3COOH \rightleftharpoons CH_3COO^- + H^+$$

| Acetic acid | Acetate ion | Hydrogen ion |

$$NH_4OH \rightleftharpoons NH_4^+ + OH^-$$

| Ammonium hydroxide | Ammonium ion | Hydroxyl ion |

Since the dissociated ions permit the passage of

electric currents, the compounds are electrolytes. Water is also an excellent solvent for many nonelectrolytes.

Acids and Bases

The equation showing the dissociation of acetic acid reveals that a hydrogen ion (H^+) is liberated. Indeed, this is why the compound is called an *acid.* An acid is strictly defined as any compound that can liberate a hydrogen ion. Thus hydrochloric acid (HCl) is an acid because it dissociates in water to form H^+ and Cl^-. A *base* is characterized by the ability to accept and combine with the hydrogen ion furnished by an acid. Note in the following examples of acids and bases that water can serve as an acid *and* a base. Any substance performing in such a dual capacity is said to be *amphoteric.* Note also that acids and bases can be either neutral molecules (for example, HCl and NaOH) or charged ions (for example, NH_4^+ and HPO_4^{--}), since both can liberate or accept hydrogen ions.

Acids

$$HCl \rightleftharpoons H^+ + Cl^-$$
$$H_2CO_3 \rightleftharpoons H^+ + HCO_3^-$$
$$NH_4^+ \rightleftharpoons H^+ + NH_3$$
$$H_2O \rightleftharpoons H^+ + OH^-$$

Bases

$$NH_3 + H^+ \rightleftharpoons NH_4^+$$
$$NaOH + H^+ \rightleftharpoons Na^+ + H_2O$$
$$HPO_4^{--} + H^+ \rightleftharpoons H_2PO_4^-$$
$$H_2O + H^+ \rightleftharpoons H_3O^+$$

Acids and bases vary significantly in the *extent* to which they dissociate into free ions in aqueous solutions. Those that dissociate completely are called *strong* acids or bases. *Weak* acids and bases dissociate only to a limited and varying degree.

The strength of an acid depends on the concentration of hydrogen ions in it. Since that concentration can vary enormously, from 1 gram of H^+ per liter to 0.00000000000001 grams per liter, it is convenient to represent it on a logarithmic scale. Thus, if a solution contained 0.01 grams of H^+ per liter, the logarithm of this number would be -2 (10^{-2} grams H^+ per liter). Since it is inconvenient to work with

negative numbers, we take the negative logarithm which converts -2 into $+2$. This value is called the pH and is defined as the negative logarithm of the H^+ concentration in grams per liter of solution. For a concentration of 1 gram of H^+ per liter, the pH is 0, and for a concentration of 0.00000000000001 grams per liter, the pH is 14.

Pure water at ordinary temperatures dissociates to free H^+ and OH^-, but only to a slight extent. Its pH is 7, and this is defined as *neutrality.* Solutions with pH's below 7 are acidic, and they are more acidic the lower the figure. Solutions with pH's above 7 are *basic* or *alkaline,* and they are more basic the higher the figure. Since the scale is logarithmic, a change of 1 pH unit indicates a 10-fold change in absolute concentration of H^+, or in acidity versus alkalinity.

Buffers

The pH's of fluids in living organisms are usually near neutrality. For instance, the pH of human blood is 7.4, just slightly alkaline. There are some exceptions (such as some strongly acidic digestive fluids), but an organism ordinarily cannot tolerate significant alterations of internal pH's. The main devices for preserving nearly constant pH's in the face of varying chemical circumstances are the *buffers* of the organism.

Changes in pH in a dynamic chemical system depend on the ratios of the concentration of H^+ acceptors, which are bases, to the concentration of H^+ donors, which are acids. For example, in a solution of carbonic acid (H_2CO_3), the pH depends on the ratio $[HCO_3^-]/[H_2CO_3]$, where the brackets denote concentrations. In order to produce a pH of 7.4, the ratio would have to be 20, but since H_2CO_3 dissociates only slightly, so high a proportion of HCO_3^- cannot arise from its dissociation alone. If, however, the salt sodium bicarbonate ($NaHCO_3$) is added to the solution, it dissociates completely into Na^+ and HCO_3^-. The concentration of HCO_3^- ions from this source can readily be adjusted to make the ratio $[HCO_3^-]/[H_2CO_3]$ equal 20 and thus to produce a pH of 7.4. In the absence of such a salt, the addition of some other substance, such as the strong base sodium hydroxide (NaOH), may cause a radical change in pH. In such a case, the further addition of a completely dissociated salt of the weak acid minimizes, that is, buffers, the effect on the pH.

A biological buffering system, then, is one that achieves and maintains a pH adaptive for the organism in question. It consists of a solution containing a mixture of a slightly ionized weak acid with one of its completely ionized salts. The bicarbonate buffer (HCO_3^-/H_2CO_3) and a phosphate buffer ($HPO_4^{--}/H_2PO_4^-$) are particularly important in living organisms.

PROPERTIES OF ORGANIC COMPOUNDS

A large percentage of the biologically important inorganic molecules are electrolytes, or ionic compounds. In contrast, organic molecular compounds are usually built up by covalent bonds. However, even though most organic molecules are considered to be nonelectrolytes, it would be incorrect to state that they do not undergo ionization at all. A compound held together by covalent bonds may possess certain groupings in one or more regions of the molecule that do undergo ionization. These groupings will be dealt with later. The discussion in this section concerns mainly the covalently bonded portions of an organic molecule. Since many hundreds of thousands of kinds of pure substances (and hence of molecules) exist but only a hundred-odd kinds of atoms from which they can be constructed, it follows that the uniqueness of a molecule must depend upon the *number, type,* and *spatial arrangement* of its component atoms. The ordinary chemical formula merely indicates the numbers and types of atoms present in each molecule; thus carbonic acid is H_2CO_3.

The three-dimensional structure of a molecule must be compatible with the covalences of its component atoms. The two hydrogens of water, for example, cannot be attached to one another because no means for attaching oxygen would remain. We would have H_2 and O, not H_2O. The structure of a water molecule is H—O—H, with each of the two hydrogens attached directly to the oxygen. Similarly, in methane (CH_4), each of the hydrogens must attach to the carbon and not to each other, so that the atoms necessarily are combined and distributed in space as follows:

$$H-\underset{\displaystyle H}{\overset{\displaystyle H}{C}}-H$$

When molecular structures include atoms of valences higher than 1, the possible arrangements become elaborate. Carbon dioxide (CO_2) is straightforward enough, the two oxygens being attached to the carbon by two double bonds, O=C=O. However, one of the bonds can open and still leave the oxygen and carbon firmly held together by the other. This happens when CO_2 is dissolved in water. The two molecules combine to form carbonic acid (H_2CO_3), or

$$\underset{\displaystyle O=C-O}{\overset{\displaystyle H-O\ \ \ H}{}}$$

The H and OH of the water molecule are added to the O and C ends, respectively, of the opened bond.

This depiction of carbonic acid constitutes a *structural formula.* The *empirical formula* merely gives the ratio of atoms in a molecule. The structural formula indicates the spatial distribution of the atoms or atomic groupings. Even more precise representations are possible. Actually, the atoms within a molecule do not lie within a single plane as a printed structural formula might suggest.

Structural formulas and molecular models make it readily apparent that a given empirical formula may represent more than one structural arrangement. Consider the formula C_2H_6O. The principles of bonding indicate that all the hydrogens must be attached to oxygen or carbon and that the carbons must be bonded together, but two different structures are still possible.

$$H-\overset{H}{\underset{H}{C}}-O-\overset{H}{\underset{H}{C}}-H \quad or \quad H-\overset{H}{\underset{H}{C}}-\overset{H}{\underset{H}{C}}-O-H$$

Methyl ether   Ethanol

Two such compounds with differing structural formulas and identical molecular formulas are *isomers* of one another. Given these two isomers, the only two known substances with the formula C_2H_6O, the chemist must use special chemical techniques to detect which is which.

Functional Groups

Organic compounds would consist solely of carbon (and its associated hydrogens) in chains and rings of varying sizes were it not for certain distinctive groupings of atoms that recur frequently in organic structural formulas. In the compounds just discussed, for example, we encountered the hydroxyl (—OH) group, which replaces one hydrogen in ethane,

$$\begin{array}{c} H \quad H \\ | \quad | \\ H-C-C-H \\ | \quad | \\ H \quad H \end{array}$$

to make ethanol,

$$\begin{array}{c} H \quad H \\ | \quad | \\ H-C-C-OH \\ | \quad | \\ H \quad H \end{array}$$

The chemical properties of such groups play a large role in determining the chemical behavior of the molecules of which they are a part. Hence, they are called *functional groups* (or *radicals*).

The terminal functional group is essential in establishing the chemical behavior of the compounds in the following series:

$CH_3-CH_2-CH_3$	Propane
$CH_3-CH_2-CH_2-OH$	Propanol
CH_3-CH_2-CHO	Propionaldehyde
CH_3-CH_2-COOH	Propionic acid

Note that the last-named compound is an acid because it possesses a *carboxyl* group (—COOH), which dissociates to yield a hydrogen ion (R denotes CH_3-CH_2-):

$$R-COOH \rightleftharpoons R-COO^- + H^+$$

The carboxyl group is the hallmark of the organic acid. All organic acids, incidentally, are weak acids. Even though their carbon-to-carbon bonds are all covalent, they can possess one or more functional groups containing ionic bonds that dissociate in water. Indeed, in some of the most biologically important organic molecules (for example, amino acids), there is one acidic functional group (that liberates H^+ in water) *and* one basic functional group (that accepts H^+).

Table 2-1 lists some of the more common organic functional groups. The open bonds in the second and third columns of the table are a reminder that functional groups do not occur by themselves. To understand modern biology, it is helpful to recognize these few functional groups.

TABLE 2-1   *Some Organic Functional Groups*

Name of group	Molecular formula	Structural formula
Methyl	$-CH_3$	$\begin{array}{c} H \\ | \\ -C-H \\ | \\ H \end{array}$
Ethyl	$-C_2H_5$	$\begin{array}{c} H \quad H \\ | \quad | \\ -C-C-H \\ | \quad | \\ H \quad H \end{array}$
Hydroxyl	$-OH$	$-O-H$
Carboxyl	$-COOH$	$\begin{array}{c} O \\ \| \\ -C-O-H \end{array}$
Aldehyde	$-CHO$	$\begin{array}{c} O \\ \| \\ -C-H \end{array}$
Keto (carbonyl)	$=O$	$=O$
Amino	$-NH_2$	$\begin{array}{c} H \\ | \\ -N-H \end{array}$
Sulfhrydryl (thiol)	$-SH$	$-S-H$
Phenyl	$-C_6H_5$	(ring structure) or (hexagon)

Organic Compounds in Living Organisms

It is now believed that the origin of life on earth was the result of a long series of chemical reactions of gradually increasing complexity. We have every reason to suppose that only simple organic molecules existed on and above the surface of the primitive earth—compounds such as methane (CH_4), carbon monoxide (CO), and perhaps some carbon dioxide (CO_2). There was a great deal of free hydrogen, nitrogen was mainly in the form of ammonia (NH_3), and oxygen was almost all in the form of water. We shall consider the origin of life in a later chapter. But in anticipation of the following discussion of the major types of organic molecules within living organisms, we should note here that these complex organic chemical structures had themselves to evolve before the first living organisms came into being.

One might reasonably ask why the bulk of living organisms is fabricated of compounds of carbon. Why were the earliest living organisms not made primarily of compounds of silicon (Si), another element of valence 4, one that the earth possesses in abundance far beyond that of carbon? In fact, writers of science fiction have already reviewed the prospects of siliceous beings in which quartz, or SiO_2, is analogous to the CO_2 of real life.

Part of the answer is simply that, for a variety of reasons, carbon atoms bond together to form chains more readily than do silicon atoms. Hence, larger and more varied molecular structures may develop from carbon. These include long and short chains, straight and branched chains, and ring structures of all descriptions. In addition, many (but not all) carbon compounds are readily soluble in water. The same is not true of silicon compounds. Carbon, though present in many rocks as carbonate, has remained in the earth's water and atmosphere as a constituent of reactive small molecules capable of further combination into countless numbers of organic compounds.

Many of the details of early chemical evolution are not yet known. But the point is worth making that the relatively few kinds of compounds that we shall treat here are found in *all* living organisms. We must conclude, therefore, that these compounds were uniquely suited to form the coherent, self-duplicating system, or organism, that emerged from a diffuse background, succeeded, and survived. We may assume that there existed some process that caused these molecules destined for perpetuation to be selected from the welter of useless compounds.

Whatever the nature of this selective process, it centered on four major groups of simple organic molecules (and a number of minor ones) (Table 2-2).

TABLE 2-2   *Four Major Groups of Organic Compounds*

Simple organic compounds in living organisms	Macromolecules formed from these compounds
Monosaccharide sugars	Polysaccharides
Fatty acids	Simple and complex lipids
Amino acids	Proteins
Nucleotides	Nucleic acids

The simple molecules linked together in various ways to produce the large, so-called *macromolecules* that are such prominent objects of contemporary biochemical research.

We shall attempt here simply to familiarize ourselves with the chemical natures of these substances. Later chapters will describe the metabolic activities in which they are involved. We shall also consider the reasons that the gross structure of an organism persists while its individual chemical components are undergoing continuous synthesis, modification, and replacement. As you survey these compounds and classes of compounds, it will be helpful to bear in mind that most of the organic molecules of living organisms have four broad functions: (1) some are essential to body structure; (2) some serve primarily as energy-rich fuels; (3) some convey information controlling growth, differentiation, and biological specificity from one generation to another; and (4) some operate primarily as catalytic agents in the body's chemical processes.

SIMPLE AND COMPLEX CARBOHYDRATES

The *carbohydrates,* comprising the sugars and their many derivatives, consist of carbon, hydrogen, and oxygen, the last two elements ordinarily being present in the same proportions as in water. Most simple carbohydrates can therefore be represented by the empirical formula $C_x(H_2O)_y$. This makes it seem that they are *hydrates* of carbon, whence the name "carbohydrate." However, a carbohydrate is made up fundamentally of short carbon chains bearing many hydroxyl groups plus a single *aldehyde* or *keto* group.

Simple sugars are called *monosaccharides*. As noted earlier, these can join in long complex chains called *polysaccharides*. Monosaccharides function chiefly as immediate sources of energy. Polysaccharides are storage forms of carbohydrate and, in plants, structural elements.

Monosaccharides are usually named according to the number of carbon atoms in each molecule, with the characteristic *-ose* ending of all carbohydrate nomenclature. Thus there are *trioses* $(C_3H_6O_3)$, *tetroses* $(C_4H_8O_4)$, *pentoses* $(C_5H_{10}O_5)$, and *hexoses* $(C_6H_{12}O_6)$. The monosaccharides are not divisible into smaller carbohydrate units. We shall consider several monosaccharides important to living organisms. *Glucose* (a six-carbon sugar) is one of the most common carbohydrates in living organisms. It is a fundamental fuel in the cells of both higher plants and animals.

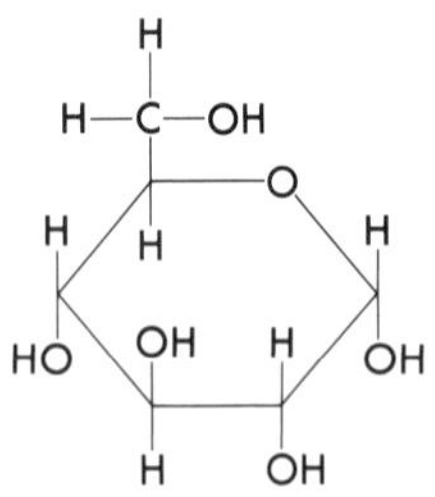

Galactose (another six-carbon sugar) differs from glucose only in the spatial orientation of the hydroxyl on the left side of the molecule.

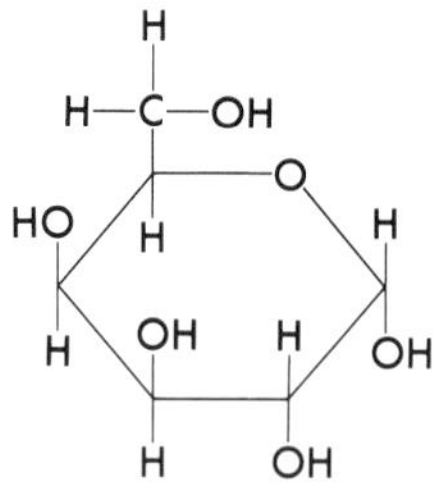

GALACTOSE

Galactose, as you will note later, is functional in forming the milk sugar, lactose.

Fructose (still another six-carbon sugar) is an important intermediate in plants in the processes of photosynthesis and respiration.

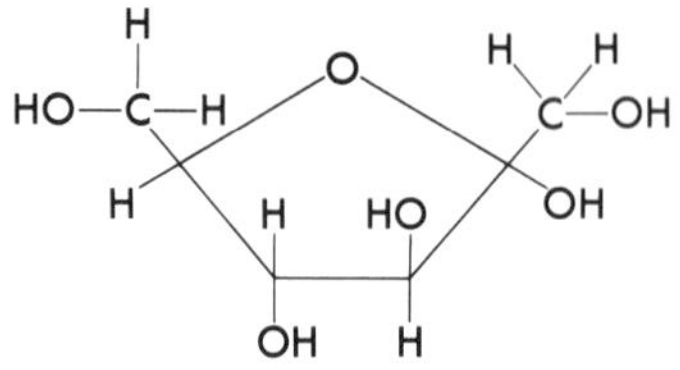

FRUCTOSE

Glyceraldehyde (a three-carbon sugar) is fundamental in the process of respiration and in lipid formation.

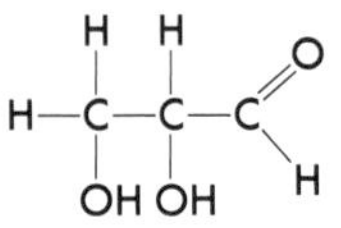

or $CH_2OHCHOHCHO$

GLYCERALDEHYDE

Related to glyceraldehyde and the trioses are two acidic three-carbon compounds, *pyruvic acid* and *lactic acid*. Pyruvic acid is important in energy production in living cells, and the accumulation of lactic acid in man is a cause of muscle fatigue.

GLUCOSE

H—C—C—C or $CH_2CHOHCOOH$
LACTIC ACID

H—C—C—C or $CH_3COCOOH$
PYRUVIC ACID

Ribose (a five-carbon sugar) and *deoxyribose* (another five-carbon sugar) are both important in the formation of nucleic acids, which are fundamental genetic materials.

RIBOSE

DEOXYRIBOSE

Disaccharides contain two monosaccharide molecules. A disaccharide arises when two simple sugars are linked together. When such a linkage takes place, one hydrogen atom and one hydroxyl group are lost from the sites of attachment in the carbohydrate molecule and combined to form water. Thus, sucrose (glucose-fructose) is produced, as in Figure 2-2. The process as it actually occurs is far more complex than the simple one-step reaction shown. The equation gives only the net reaction, summing up what goes into the complex process and what results from it. Other common disaccharides are *lactose* (glucose-galactose) and *maltose* (glucose-glucose).

A similar process can link together several monosaccharide molecules, one molecule of water being eliminated for each unit added.

$$n(C_6H_{12}O_6) \xrightarrow{\text{condensation}} (C_6H_{10}O_5)_n + (n-1)H_2O$$

n Glucose   Starch $(n-1)$ Water
molecules   molecules

This process as it actually occurs in cells also goes through many steps and is even more complicated than the last. Here n indicates the number of hexose

units involved, which is large in this case. The result is a relatively large, complex polysaccharide. The building up of a large molecule from simple sugar units is called *condensation*; it is a *dehydration* synthesis, that is, one involving the elimination of water. This is one of the principal ways in which the materials of life are compounded.

Like simple sugars, polysaccharides may have the same empirical formula and yet be quite different because the atoms are arranged differently. Thus, the many polysaccharides with the same general formula $(C_6H_{10}O_5)_n$ include *glycogen, cellulose,* and the *starches.*

FIG. 2-2 Carbohydrate molecules. Glucose, fructose, and their combination, with dehydration, to form sucrose.

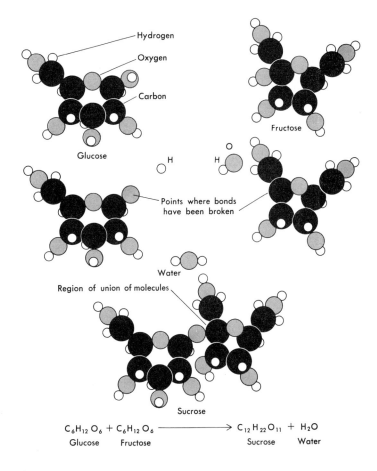

$C_6H_{12}O_6 + C_6H_{12}O_6 \longrightarrow C_{12}H_{22}O_{11} + H_2O$
Glucose Fructose   Sucrose Water

All are polyglucoses, but they differ in molecular weight, branching structure, and solubility. Cellulose, the tough insoluble constituent of cell walls in plants and a very few animals (for example, tunicates or sea squirts) has a primarily structural function. It has no importance for most animals, except as a food for some herbivores. Starch, on the other hand, has no structural function in plants and animals but is a major form of *storage* carbohydrate in plants and a food source of carbohydrate for animals. The potato consists mainly of starch stores. Glycogen is the insoluble glucose polymer that is produced in animals as a carbohydrate reservoir. It resembles starch in structure, but its molecules are smaller. Glycogen is stored mainly in the liver and muscle.

When additional supplies of glucose are needed, these polysaccharides are broken down in a series of reactions whose net effect is the reverse of the condensation reaction.

$$(C_6H_{10}O_5)_n + (n-1)H_2O \xrightarrow{\text{hydrolysis}} n(C_6H_{12}O_6)$$

Starch or glycogen (insoluble) $(n-1)$ Water molecules n Glucose molecules (soluble)

This reversal of condensation involves *hydrolysis,* that is, the cleavage of a molecule by the incorporation into it of the elements of water.

LIPIDS

The *lipids,* or *fats,* are a heterogeneous collection of organic substances that are generally insoluble or sparingly soluble in water but freely soluble in organic solvents such as ethanol and ether. These substances owe some of their biological significance to the fact that as a group they can bridge the gap from water-soluble to water-insoluble phases without a sharp line of demarcation. In addition, they are important fuels whose metabolic oxidation provides cells with a large proportion of their energy.

The group includes a variety of fats, oils, waxes, and related compounds. Many of these are extremely complex. However, the most abundant lipids, and the ones with which we are mainly concerned, are referred to as *simple lipids.* Simple lipids contain only carbon, hydrogen, and oxygen; compared to carbohydrates, they have less oxygen relative to carbon and hydrogen.

A simple lipid contains *glycerol* and *fatty acids.* Glycerol contains three hydroxyl groups and is an alcohol. A simple lipid, or *triglyceride,* results when the acidic —COOH groups of fatty acids react with the three alcoholic —OH groups of glycerol.

$$
\begin{array}{l}
H_2C\!-\!\boxed{OH \quad H}\!-\!OOC\!-\!R^1 \\
HC\!-\!\boxed{OH + H}\!-\!OOC\!-\!R^2 \rightarrow \\
H_2C\!-\!\boxed{OH \quad H}\!-\!OOC\!-\!R^3
\end{array}
$$

Glycerol   Fatty acids

$$
\begin{array}{l}
H_2C\!-\!OOC\!-\!R^1 \\
HC\!-\!OOC\!-\!R^2 + 3H_2O \\
H_2C\!-\!OOC\!-\!R^3
\end{array}
$$

Triglyceride   Water

The R^1, R^2, and R^3 compounds can be identical or different fatty acids. The more common fatty acids are palmitic acid, $CH_3(CH_2)_{14}COOH$ (or $C_{15}H_{31}COOH$), and stearic acid, $CH_3(CH_2)_{16}COOH$ (or $C_{17}H_{35}COOH$).

Fatty acids are divided into two classes depending on whether or not the carbon chain carries the maximum possible number of attached hydrogens. The *saturated* fatty acids have structures like

$$
\begin{array}{c}
H \;\; H \;\; H \;\; H \\
| \;\;\; | \;\;\; | \;\;\; | \\
-C\!-\!C\!-\!C\!-\!C\!-\!COOH \\
| \;\;\; | \;\;\; | \;\;\; | \\
H \;\; H \;\; H \;\; H
\end{array}
$$

In the *unsaturated* fatty acids, double bonds join the carbon atoms that are not fully saturated with hydrogen, as in

$$
\begin{array}{c}
H \;\; H \;\; H \;\; H \\
| \;\;\; | \;\;\; | \;\;\; | \\
-C\!-\!C\!=\!C\!-\!C\!-\!COOH \\
| \quad\quad\quad\quad\; | \\
H \quad\quad\quad\quad H
\end{array}
$$

A well-known unsaturated fatty acid is oleic acid, $CH_3(CH_2)_7CH\!=\!CH(CH_2)_7COOH$ (or $C_{17}H_{33}COOH$). If the double bond in oleic acid were eliminated by the addition of two hydrogens, the product would be stearic acid.

The higher members of the saturated class of fatty acids (lauric, myristic, palmitic, stearic, etc., acids) in combination with glycerol form the bulk of the body fat in most organisms. The short-chain fatty acids are not widely distributed in nature. Lipids are important components of cell membranes and membranous submicroscopic cellular particles.

One of the fatty acids making up a simple lipid may be replaced by a compound containing phosphorus and nitrogen. The result is a *phospholipid.* Members of this category also constitute an important part of the tissue lipids. The additional group makes them soluble in both water and organic solvents. For this reason, they serve to bind water-soluble compounds (such as proteins) to water-insoluble compounds.

The *steroids* are fat-soluble complex organic molecules widely distributed in nature and often associated with body fat. Hence, they are usually discussed with the lipids. They include cholesterol, vitamin D, and a large number of animal hormones.

AMINO ACIDS AND PROTEINS

Proteins are large, complex, and fragile chainlike linkages or *polymers* of *amino acids.* When proteins are broken down into their low-molecular weight components, the amino acids, it is found that these links in the chain all contain *nitrogen* as well as carbon and hydrogen.

Proteins have a unique role in biology. To a large extent, the complexity and the diversity of life itself are dependent upon the complexity and the diversity of proteins. In order to appreciate this singular fact, we must first learn how protein molecules are constructed.

The amino acids are organic acids with the general formula

$$R-\overset{\overset{\displaystyle H}{|}}{\underset{\underset{\displaystyle NH_2}{|}}{C}}-COOH$$

Note that the amino group ($-NH_2$) is attached to the carbon adjacent to the carboxyl group

($-COOH$). All the amino acids in proteins have this structure. The individual amino acids differ only in the composition of the R group. This may have any of two dozen or so structures, according to current knowledge. Some of the most commonly encountered R groups are listed in Table 2-3. When R is simply a hydrogen atom, we have glycine,

$$H-\overset{\overset{\displaystyle H}{|}}{\underset{\underset{\displaystyle NH_2}{|}}{C}}-COOH$$

Note that each amino acid has a basic $-NH_2$ group on the carbon next to the acidic $-COOH$ carbon. An amino acid containing no other acidic or basic functional groups is called *neutral* because it possesses one basic group and one acidic group. An amino acid designated as *basic* or *acidic* possesses an additional basic (for example, $-NH_2$) or acidic (for example, $-COOH$) functional group elsewhere in the molecule.

The amino acids linked together in a protein molecule have been joined end to end. The carboxyl group of one amino acid combines with the amino group of the next to form a *peptide bond* ($-CO-NH-$), and a molecule of water is liberated.

$$R-\overset{\overset{\displaystyle H}{|}}{\underset{\underset{\displaystyle NH_2}{|}}{C}}-\overset{\overset{\displaystyle O}{\|}}{C}-\boxed{OH+H}-\overset{\displaystyle H}{N}-\overset{\overset{\displaystyle H}{|}}{\underset{\underset{\displaystyle COOH}{|}}{C}}-R' \rightarrow$$

$$R-\overset{\overset{\displaystyle H}{|}}{\underset{\underset{\displaystyle NH_2}{|}}{C}}-\overset{\overset{\displaystyle O}{\|}}{C}-\overset{\displaystyle H}{N}-\overset{\overset{\displaystyle H}{|}}{\underset{\underset{\displaystyle COOH}{|}}{C}}-R' + H_2O$$

Short chains of amino acids are *peptides;* two amino acids linked together constitute a *dipeptide,* and a large number a *polypeptide.* Polypeptide chains combine to form proteins.

An outstanding recent development was the discovery of methods for determining the amino-acid sequence of an entire protein molecule. Because of the enormous amount of work involved, few proteins have yet been studied completely. *Insulin,* a hormone

TABLE 2-3 *Major Amino Acids*

Category	Name	Structure
Neutral	Glycine (GLY)	$H-\underset{\underset{NH_2}{\vert}}{CH}-COOH$
	Alanine (ALA)	$CH_3-\underset{\underset{NH_2}{\vert}}{CH}-COOH$
	Valine (VAL)	$CH_3-\underset{\underset{CH_3}{\vert}}{CH}-\underset{\underset{NH_2}{\vert}}{CH}-COOH$
	Leucine (LEU)	$CH_3-\underset{\underset{CH_3}{\vert}}{CH}-CH_2-\underset{\underset{NH_2}{\vert}}{CH}-COOH$
	Isoleucine (ILEU)	$CH_3-CH_2-\underset{\underset{CH_3}{\vert}}{CH}-\underset{\underset{NH_2}{\vert}}{CH}-COOH$
Acidic	Aspartic acid (ASP)	$HOOC-CH_2-\underset{\underset{NH_2}{\vert}}{CH}-COOH$
	Glutamic acid (GLU)	$HOOC-CH_2-CH_2-\underset{\underset{NH_2}{\vert}}{CH}-COOH$
Basic	Lysine (LYS)	$H_2N-CH_2-CH_2-CH_2-CH_2-\underset{\underset{NH_2}{\vert}}{CH}-COOH$
	Arginine (ARG)	$H_2N-\overset{\overset{NH}{\vert\vert}}{C}-NH-CH_2-CH_2-CH_2-\underset{\underset{NH_2}{\vert}}{CH}-COOH$
	Asparagine (ASP—NH$_2$)	$H_2N-CO-CH_2-\underset{\underset{NH_2}{\vert}}{CH}-COOH$
	Glutamine (GLU—NH$_2$)	$NH_2-CO-CH_2-CH_2-\underset{\underset{NH_2}{\vert}}{CH}-COOH$
Hydroxy	Serine (SER)	$HO-CH_2-\underset{\underset{NH_2}{\vert}}{OH}-COOH$
	Threonine (THR)	$CH_3-\overset{\overset{OH}{\vert}}{\underset{\underset{NH_2}{\vert}}{CH}}-CH-COOH$
Sulfur Containing	Cysteine (CYS)	$HS-CH_2-\underset{\underset{NH_2}{\vert}}{CH}-COOH$

Category	Name	Structure
	Methionine (MET)	CH_3—S—CH_2—CH_2—CH—COOH (NH_2)
	Cystine	HOOC—CH—CH_2—S—S—CH_2—CH—COOH (NH_2) ... (NH_2)
Cyclic	Phenylalanine (PHE)	—CH_2—CH—COOH (NH_2)
	Tyrosine (TYR)	OH——CH_2—CH—COOH (NH_2)
	Tryptophan (TRY)	C—CH_2—CH—COOH (NH_2)
	Histidine (HIS)	C=C—CH_2—CH—COOH (NH_2)
	Proline (PRO)	CH_2—CH—COOH CH_2 CH_2—NH

of the animal pancreas, was the first protein to be fully analyzed (Figure 2-3). It was found that the insulin molecule consists of two chains of unequal length, held together by disulfide (—S—S—) bonds formed between the —SH groups of opposed cysteine residues. One chain contains 30 amino acid units, and the other 21 units.

The amino acid sequence is one aspect of protein structure; the *shape* of the molecule is another. Thus, we speak of *primary, secondary,* and *tertiary* protein

FIG. 2-3 The structure of insulin. The insulin molecule is a complex sequence of amino acids in two unequal chains joined by disulfide bridges.

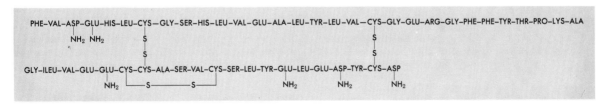

structures. Knowledge of the primary structure of a protein molecule requires information on the number of polypeptide chains, the amino acid sequence in each, and the natures and positions of the covalent cross links between different chains or different portions of the same chain. As in insulin, such cross links are usually disulfide bonds forming between —SH groups projecting from cysteine units. It is important to remember that a protein may

contain any or all of the approximately 24 known amino acids; that it may contain virtually any *number* of amino acids; and that these may occur in any *sequence.*

At the secondary-structure level, we consider the spatial arrangements of the individual polypeptide chains. For example, the polypeptide chains of many proteins exist as *helical coils* (Figure 2-4). These are stabilized by hydrogen bonds of the type NH --- OC—, which form between the CO— and NH— groups at each turn. The tertiary structure involves the foldings and loopings of the already coiled polypeptide chains. It too depends upon stabilizing bonds, which are of many types, including covalent disulfide bonds, hydrogen bonds between various groups, and others. Protein molecules whose stabilizing bonds have been irreversibly ruptured, such as happens to egg white when heated, are said to be *denatured.*

It would be difficult indeed to overstate the biological importance of protein structure. A large, complex molecule that consists of long chains of simple amino acids arranged in diverse patterns is ideally suited to extensive and subtle variation. We shall later find that amino acid sequences are involved in the enormous variety of living organisms.

Certain protein molecules are *enzymes,* the *catalysts* of chemical reactions in organisms. Enzymes make possible chemical reactions that would otherwise virtually fail to occur. We shall say more about them presently, but the point to be emphasized here is the great *specificity* of enzyme action. In general, every chemical reaction in the living organism is catalyzed by a specific enzyme. It is now known that this specificity is a consequence of a precise amino acid sequence in the polypeptide chain and its three-dimensional configuration.

One other fact will become increasingly significant as we go along. Besides the *simple proteins* just discussed—that is, those consisting entirely of amino acid chains in various arrangements—there are a large number of *conjugated proteins.* These have, in addition to the amino acids, nonprotein groups chemically bound onto their molecules. The nonprotein groups are called *prosthetic groups.* Among the important conjugated proteins are (1) *nucleoproteins,* compounds in which one or several molecules of protein are combined with a *nucleic acid;* (2) *glycoproteins,* compounds with polysaccharide prosthetic groups; (3)

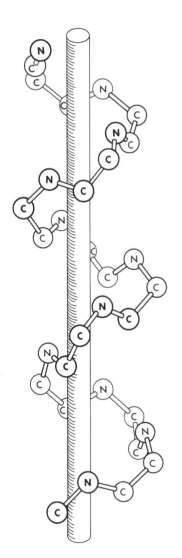

FIG. 2-4 The α helix, a hydrogen-bonded helical configuration of the polypeptide chain present in many proteins. The polypeptide chain is coiled as a left-handed screw, with about 3.6 amino-acids per turn of the helix. The sketch emphasizes the helical arrangement by picturing the carbon and nitrogen linkages circling a rod.

lipoproteins, proteins conjugated to triglycerides or other lipids; and (4) *chromoproteins,* compounds with colored prosthetic groups. The last category includes *hemoglobin,* the pigment upon which animal cells depend for oxygen.

NUCLEOTIDES AND NUCLEIC ACIDS

The nucleic acids are the largest biological molecules. Like polysaccharides and proteins, they are polymers made up of repeating small-molecule units (*monomers*). However, if proteins are viewed as long words composed from a 20-letter alphabet, the nucleic acids are longer words written from a 4-letter alphabet. The four repeating monomers are called *nucleotides.* Thus nucleic acids may alternatively be termed *polynucleotides.* In the organism nucleic acids, or polynucleotides, are attached to proteins, the resulting nucleoproteins comprising conjugated proteins whose prosthetic groups are the nucleic acid polymers. It is important to understand the nature of nucleotides, for they have at least one major physiological function other than that of links in the nucleic acid chain—they are often essential participants in enzyme reactions.

A nucleotide consists of three simpler molecules in direct linkage: a *nitrogen-containing organic base,* a *sugar* residue, and *phosphoric acid.* Since the identities of the base and sugar may vary, there are a number of nucleotides. The bases all fall into two groups, one containing the *purine* ring and the other the *pyrimidine* ring.

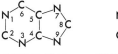

PURINE RING   PYRIMIDINE RING

As shown in Table 2-4, the bases found in nucleic acid nucleotides are the purines *adenine* and *guanine* and the pyrimidines *cytosine, thymine,* and *uracil.* The two main nucleic acid sugars are *deoxyribose* and *ribose,* both five-carbon monosaccharides or pentoses, the former differing from the latter only in lacking one oxygen atom. The deletion of an oxygen atom is implied by the *deoxy-* prefix.

Nucleic acids fall into two major classes depending on whether their nucleotides contain ribose (that is, are *ribonucleotides*) or deoxyribose (that is, are *deoxyribonucleotides*). Thus, there are *deoxyribonucleic acid,* or

TABLE 2-4   *Compositions of DNA and RNA*[a]

	DNA	RNA
Bases		
Purines	Adenine (A)	Adenine (A)
	Guanine (G)	Guanine (G)
Pyrimidines	Thymine (T)	Uracil (U)
	Cytosine (C)	Cytosine (C)
Sugar	Deoxyribose (dR)	Ribose (R)
Phosphoric acid	Phosphoric acid (P)	Phosphoric acid (P)

[a] The letters in parentheses are frequently used abbreviations.

DNA, and *ribonucleic acid,* or *RNA.* Interestingly, DNA and RNA have one other fundamental *chemical* difference (in addition to the physiological differences to be described later). Although both contain only four nitrogenous bases (of which three are adenine, guanine and cytosine), the fourth base is not the same in RNA and DNA. The second pyrimidine in RNA is uracil; in DNA it is thymine, a methyl derivative of uracil. Therefore, DNA may be represented as a chain of the following general structure, the base sequence being variable:

Deoxyribose—Adenine

Phosphate

Deoxyribose—Thymine

Phosphate

Deoxyribose—Guanine

Phosphate

Deoxyribose—Cytosine

Phosphate

Deoxyribose—Cytosine

And RNA may be represented similarly as follows:

```
          \
           \
            \Ribose—Adenine
           /
          /
Phosphate
          \
           \
            \Ribose—Uracil
           /
          /
Phosphate
          \
           \
            \Ribose—Guanine
           /
          /
Phosphate
          \
           \
            \Ribose—Adenine
           /
          /
Phosphate
          \
           \
            \Ribose—Cytosine
```

In 1953, J. D. Watson and F. H. C. Crick discovered that the DNA molecule consists of a *double-stranded helix* resembling a long twisted ladder (Figure 2-5) with two parallel nucleotide chains winding around a cylindrical space. The sides of the ladder are alternating deoxyribose and phosphate groups. The rungs between the sugars are *paired* purines and pyrimidines. Base pairing is the key to the structure, for it has been found that *bases can be paired only in certain ways*—adenine with thymine only and guanine with cytosine only. The positions of the two sugar-phosphate chains are so fixed that only pairings involving a "large" purine and a "small" pyrimidine will fit in the confined space. Moreover, a base with a keto group on carbon 6 must stand opposite one with an amino group on carbon 6, since only such a pair will form the hydrogen bond required to hold the two strands together. The two DNA strands are *complementary*, not identical, and if one strand contains genetic information in its base sequence, then the other strand must contain the identical information in a complementary code.

The cell contains at least three kinds of RNA, which differ in function and structure. At least some of the RNA is a single-stranded nonhelical polymer.

The principal function of RNA is in the control of *protein synthesis*. In Chapter 7 we shall encounter a most satisfying relationship among these isolated facts concerning DNA, RNA, and protein structure.

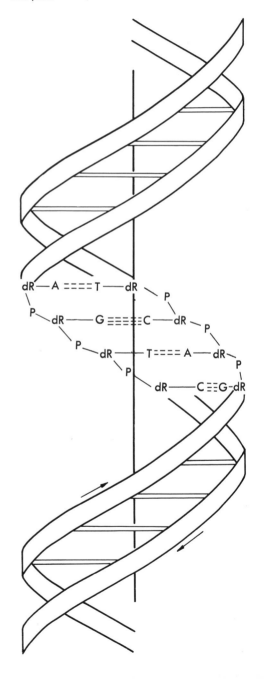

FIG. 2-5 The double-stranded helical configuration of the DNA molecule. The two nucleotide strands are held together by hydrogen bonds forming between complementary purine–pyrimidine pairs.

Properties of Chemical Reactions

We have remarked that enzymes catalyze biochemical reactions. So that we may understand the principles of enzyme action, let us briefly consider certain general properties of chemical reactions. What are chemical reactions? Why do they occur?

ENERGY AND WORK IN GENERAL

Energy and *work* are well enough defined by our ordinary use of both words: work is something accomplished (ultimately, something moved); and energy is something required to perform work. The physicist's definition of energy is different only in wording: energy is the capacity to accomplish work. This definition holds whether or not the work is done. A boulder at the top of a hill has *potential* energy while it is at rest—while not doing work; this energy becomes *kinetic* energy as the boulder does work in rolling down the hill. The work was performed at the expense of the boulder's potential energy inherent in its former position at the top of the hill.

Kinetic energy can be thought of as the motion of matter, and work as movement accomplished. Kinetic energy may take many forms. The movement of the boulder was *mechanical* energy. *Light* is kinetic energy and may be thought of as the movement of minute particles, *photons*. An *electric current* is another form of kinetic energy, the movement of electrons from atom to atom in the wire through which the current is flowing. The *chemical* form of kinetic energy is the movement of atoms within or between molecules that takes place in a chemical reaction. And, finally, *heat* is the ceaseless, random motion of atoms in all directions within a gas, liquid, or solid. Hot and cold water differ in the speed at which their molecules are moving; in the hot water the motion is faster.

All these forms of energy are interconvertible to some extent, and the conversions are governed by two general laws called the *first and second laws of thermodynamics*. The first law is all that we need at the moment, and it states that energy is neither lost nor gained when it is converted from one form to another. We may transform the mechanical energy of a waterfall into electricity by means of a turbine, but we will never get more energy out of the transformation than entered it. Nor will we lose any.

The form of energy with which the cell deals is principally chemical energy; its work is largely chemical work. Chemical work consists of the transformation of molecules in a chemical reaction such as

$$A + B \rightarrow C + D$$
Reactants Products

The formula sums up the fact that the two molecules A and B (the *reactants*) interact in such a way as to recombine their atomic parts, forming new molecules C and D (the *products*). Two groups of factors influence the reaction: (1) factors affecting the collision and contact of the molecules; and (2) factors relating to energy expenditures in the performance of the chemical work.

FACTORS GOVERNING REACTION VELOCITY

The molecules A and B are dispersed, undergoing continual random movements in all directions. Only when they collide and make contact can they react with each other. The dependence of the reaction on collision explains several laws governing chemical reactions. All those factors that increase collision frequency increase the rate at which the reaction proceeds. The more *concentrated* the reactants are in a solution, the greater is their chance of colliding, and the faster is the reaction. Accordingly, subjecting the solution to *pressure,* which effectively concentrates it, increases collision frequency and speeds up the reaction. An increase in *temperature* speeds up the movement of the molecules and thereby raises the probability that they will contact and react.

The contact necessary for a reaction between two

molecules can be facilitated in another way—by the *adsorption* of both reactants onto a surface where they are brought close together. This is what happens in *surface catalysis*. The adsorption to the catalyst surface has an effect similar to that of raising the pressure or temperature or concentrating the reactants. Usually, however, there is more to catalysis than this; and the effect of a catalyst is far greater than any other. It is a defining characteristic of a catalyst that it is never itself consumed in the course of a reaction. When the reaction is complete, the catalyst's surface is freed to act again. A minute amount of catalyst can thus do a great deal of work.

THE ENERGY OF CHEMICAL REACTION

Contact between molecules is necessary if they are to interact, but it is not sufficient. Energy considerations also play a dominant role in chemical reactions. Let us begin with the notion of the potential energy inherent in chemical structure.

Potential Energy of Chemical Structure

It is a familiar fact that useful kinetic energy can be obtained from chemical compounds such as sugar, coal, gas, or wood. When any of these compounds is burned, its complex molecular structure is destroyed, and energy is liberated. In summary, the burning of sugar can be written as follows:

$$C_6H_{12}O_6 + 6O_2 \rightarrow 6CO_2 + 6H_2O + \text{Energy}$$

Sugar Oxygen Carbon Water
         dioxide

The large sugar molecule is broken down by an *oxidation* process. The products of the reaction are the smaller, simpler molecules CO_2 and H_2O. The energy liberated takes the obvious forms of light and heat. The important point is that potential energy is inherent in the structure of the large molecule. The complicated positions of its atoms might be compared to the position of the boulder at the top of a hill, in which potential energy is inherent. When sugar is disintegrated by oxidation into the simple

constituents CO_2 and H_2O, the energy inherent in its complex chemical structure is freed, just as the boulder's energy is freed when it gives up its position on the hilltop and rolls down hill.

Work can be done with the kinetic energy liberated from both the boulder and the sugar. And both the boulder at the bottom of the hill and the collection of small CO_2 and H_2O molecules can be used for work again, but only if they are first restored to their original positions. The boulder must be pushed up the hill, and the CO_2 and H_2O must be pushed up a "chemical hill." These processes are both work, and both demand new energy resources. Notice that in repeatedly doing work the *same matter* can be used over and over. There may be a cycle of materials used, but there is *no cycle of energy*. It is a continuous expenditure of capital funds. Where does all this capital lie? Ultimately, all usable energy in nature comes from the sun; this is a theme that we shall develop in later chapters. For the moment it suffices to note that the relocation of matter to a position enabling it to do work demands fresh energy.

Energy of Activation

Let us return now to chemical reaction in general, keeping these energy ideas in mind. We must distinguish two kinds of energy function in the reaction. Once the boulder is started down the hill, it liberates huge quantities of energy; once sugar is started on its oxidation, it also liberates considerable energy. But both processes need a little energy to get them started. There is a little rise in front of the boulder that is, indeed, what keeps it in place. You must supply *activation energy* to push it over this rise and start it on its downward path. And so it is with a chemical reaction. There is always a need for activation energy to get the process under way.

Every molecule is in constant motion; this is true of the molecule as a whole and of the atomic parts within it. In terms of Figure 2-6, this means that the sugar molecule is constantly dancing about inside the "energy valley" that keeps it from uniting with O_2 and then rolling downhill to CO_2 and H_2O. Sometimes—very rarely—a random movement takes it over the energy barrier and on to the reaction

$$C_6H_{12}O_6 + 6O_2 \rightarrow 6CO_2 + 6H_2O + \text{Energy}$$

But this possibility is so extremely unlikely as to be

utterly negligible. If left to themselves, sugar and oxygen will effectively *never* interact. The reaction is encouraged by the application of just a little activation energy. The great kinetic energy liberated from the first full downhill roll activates the other molecules, and off they all go. The minute kinetic energy of a single spark can liberate untold amounts of energy once it is applied to a gasoline dump.

In the last section we noted that a catalyst can have an effect similar to that of raising concentration, pressure, or temperature. It brings molecules together by adsorbing them to a surface, but its effect is always greater than could be accounted for by this property alone. Now we can go further. Catalysts speed up chemical reactions by lowering the activation-energy requirements. How they do this is not entirely clear. One might think of them picturesquely as tunneling through the activation-energy barrier.

OXIDATION-REDUCTION: ENERGY EXCHANGE

The processes of burning sugar, coal, wood, and gasoline all consume oxygen and liberate energy. They are all special cases of the general process of oxidation, and all oxidations are energy-liberating chemical reactions. The reverse process is called *reduction,* and in it oxygen, instead of being consumed, is released, and energy, instead of being liberated, is bound into the chemical that is reduced. In the green leaves of plants, CO_2 and H_2O combine in a series of chemical reactions (*photosynthesis*) during which energy is consumed, CO_2 is reduced, and O_2 is liberated.

The oxidation or reduction of a compound can be accomplished in another way besides that of the addition or removal of oxygen—by the removal or addition of hydrogen. The removal of hydrogen is an oxidation; its addition is a reduction. When these alternative methods of oxidizing and reducing are analyzed and compared, they are found to be special cases of an even more general process of energy exchange: the transfer of electrons from one atom to another. Energy is released by the *removal of electrons;* this is the general definition of oxidation. Either the addition of oxygen or the removal of hydrogen effectively removes an electron from an oxidized compound and thus liberates energy. Simi-

larly, the general definition of reduction is the *addition of electrons;* either the removal of oxygen or the addition of hydrogen to a compound effectively adds an electron and thus binds energy.

In terms of the model in Figure 2-6, oxidation occurs as the molecule rolls downhill, liberating energy; and when the molecules at the bottom of the hill are reduced, they are pushed uphill again. *Oxidations* are *exergonic,* and *reductions* are *endergonic.*

The reason for going into these matters here is that they are fundamental in the energy economy of the living organism. Most biological energy transfers involve oxidation-reduction processes, and most of them are accomplished by the removal of hydrogen (*dehydrogenation*) from a compound. Thus, sugar is oxidized with a release of energy into the cell by the removal of hydrogen from the sugar molecule, not by the addition of oxygen to it. The oxygen consumed in degrading sugar in a cell acts as a hydrogen acceptor, not as an oxygen donor.

FIG. 2-6 Activation energy and reaction energy in the oxidation of sugar.

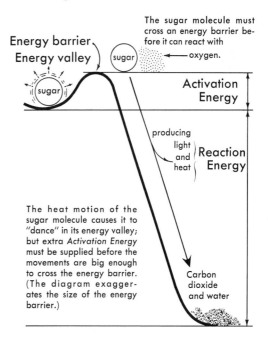

Energy barrier
Energy valley

sugar

sugar

The sugar molecule must cross an energy barrier before it can react with ← oxygen.

Activation Energy

producing light and heat

Reaction Energy

The heat motion of the sugar molecule causes it to "dance" in its energy valley; but extra *Activation Energy* must be supplied before the movements are big enough to cross the energy barrier. (The diagram exaggerates the size of the energy barrier.)

Carbon dioxide and water

CHEMICAL EQUILIBRIUM

Three questions can be raised about every proposed chemical reaction. Will it occur? If so, at what rate? And to what extent? We have just dealt with some aspects of the first question. *Chemical kinetics* is that branch of physical chemistry concerned with the rates of chemical reactions. It is important not to confuse the *rate* of a reaction with the *extent* of its progress toward completion. In reactions that can operate in both directions, the extent of the reaction depends upon the ratio between the rate constants of the forward and reverse reactions, k_1 and k_2. In a reversible second-order reaction,

$$A + B \underset{k_2}{\overset{k_1}{\rightleftharpoons}} C + D$$

the rate of the forward reaction is $k_1[A][B]$, and that of the backward reaction is $k_2[C][D]$. We say that reaction has attained equilibrium when the forward rate equals the backward rate.

$$k_1[A][B] = k_2[C][D]$$

At this point, $[A]$, $[B]$, $[C]$, and $[D]$ have reached fixed values, and the ratio $[C][D]/[A][B]$ is constant.

$$\frac{[C][D]}{[A][B]} = \frac{k_1}{k_2} = K$$

The new constant K is the *equilibrium constant.* Clearly the final concentrations of the reactants would be the same regardless of whether we started with A and B or C and D. We·now see why the reaction does not go to completion in one direction or the other. If it did in a forward direction, $[A]$ and $[B]$ would be zero, and K would be infinity. Since $K = k_1/k_2$, it could not equal infinity unless k_1 equaled infinity or k_2 equaled zero. This is not the case, for both the forward and backward reactions occur at finite rates.

A number of circumstances may intervene, however, to make such a reaction go to completion in actuality. If one of the products, C or D, is an escaping gas or an insoluble precipitate, it is in effect removed as quickly as it is formed, and its concentration drops to zero in the equilibrium equation. Thus, the reaction continues until the initial reactants are consumed. This situation is known as "pulling a reaction to the right." Such circumstances arise in living organisms in the decomposition of H_2CO_3 to CO_2 and H_2O and in the precipitation of Ca^{++} as insoluble bone salts.

Enzymes

One of the distinguishing characteristics of living organisms is the presence within them of the special catalysts called *enzymes*. The existence of these catalysts in living tissues accounts for the rapid execution and control of an exceedingly large number of biochemical reactions. They speed up reactions that are otherwise so slow that they would virtually never occur; they are not consumed in the reactions and in small amounts perform much work.

The names first given to enzymes, such as pepsin, trypsin, and ptyalin, offered no clues to their functions. The present convention of enzyme nomenclature often derives the name of an enzyme from that of the *substrate* (that is, the substance attacked by the enzyme), adding the suffix *-ase*. Thus, we speak of the enzymes that split starch as *amylases* (*amylum* is Latin for "starch"), and of the enzymes that split lipids as *lipases.* Enzymes may also be named according to the types of reactions they catalyze, for example, *hydrolases.*

MECHANISMS OF ENZYME ACTION

We have seen that a catalyst, whether enzymatic or not, affects only the occurrence and rate of a reaction. It has no effect on the equilibrium of a reaction—that is, on the extent to which it proceeds to completion. Enzymes represent a special class of catalysts in their outstanding catalytic efficiency as well as in their specificity; molecule for molecule, no inorganic catalyst even approaches an enzyme in catalytic efficiency. As in the case of inorganic catalysts, the mechanisms of action of enzymes are not completely understood, although they constitute an area of active research. In part, an enzyme functions like an inorganic catalyst by bringing reactants into contact on a surface. Then, somehow, the enzyme makes the substrate molecules more reactive to the other molecules in the environment than before. Perhaps this results from the fact that the enzyme combines chemically with the substrate for a brief moment. Good evidence exists that the following reaction takes place:

$$E + S \rightleftharpoons ES \rightarrow E + \text{Products}$$

where E is the enzyme, S the substrate, and ES an unstable enzyme-substrate complex.

The fact that enzymes are proteins is undoubtedly the key to any interpretation of their mode of action and specificity. Specificity remains one of the most

striking properties of enzymes: individual enzymes catalyze specific reactions of specific substrates. Enzymes differ in the degree of their specificity. For instance, lipases, which catalyze the breakdown of triglycerides to their constituents, glycerol and fatty acids, affect only the ester linkages in the triglycerides, the identity of the fatty acids being of no relative importance.

Diagrams such as those in Figure 2-7 are usually drawn to illustrate the concept of enzymatic specificity and to emphasize the importance of the enzyme surface. You should remember, however, that the shapes shown in the figure are purely imaginary. The active catalytic site on the enzyme is a unique three-dimensional configuration of the polypeptide chain whose various functional groups are precisely complementary to those of the substrate. This arrangement accounts for substrate specificity and for the formation of a temporary enzyme-substrate complex. In addition, it is now clear that the active center of the enzyme molecule, which chemically alters the substrate, comprises only a relatively small sector of the polypeptide chain, for investigators have been able to remove some amino acids from certain enzyme molecules without altering their catalytic activity. Thus, the entire molecule is not essential in the catalytic process.

Temperature affects enzyme-catalyzed reactions in the same way that it affects ordinary chemical reactions. High temperatures, however, inactivate most enzymes by destroying (denaturing) their tertiary structures. Biological phenomena thus have optimal temperatures. This fact places serious limitations on organisms. Only a few have heat-resistant enzymes capable of surviving high temperatures. Many cells lose the ability to carry on metabolic processes above 40°C.

COENZYMES

In the well-known technique called *dialysis* (Figure 2-8), a solution in which a mixture of large and small molecules is dissolved is placed in a bag made of cellophane or some other porous membrane.

FIG. 2-7 Enzyme catalysts bring reactants together in close contact and proper orientation for the reaction to proceed. The diagram merely illustrates the selective fitting of different complementary shapes; the real shapes of the molecules concerned are not like these.

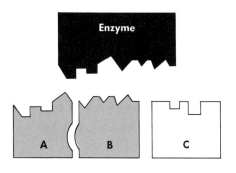

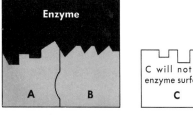

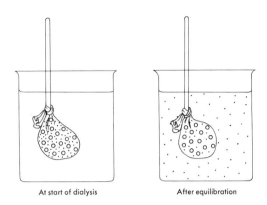

FIG. 2-8 Separation of large (O) and small (•) molecules by dialysis.

When the bag is immersed in water, the small molecules pass through the membrane into the surrounding water, leaving behind all the large molecules. In this manner low-molecular weight organic molecules such as monosaccharides, amino acids, and nucleotides are readily separated from macromolecules such as polysaccharides, proteins, and nucleic acids.

When early biochemists exhaustively dialyzed tissue extracts containing active oxidative enzymes, they observed a gradual loss of the catalytic power of the material remaining in the bag. They then found that activity was fully restored after the addition of a little boiled tissue juice. This effect could not have been due to the addition of new enzymes, since boiled enzymes are ordinarily denatured. The dialyzed enzymes in the bag could also be reactivated by the addition of the materials that had passed out of the bag—even though they had been boiled in the interim. It was concluded, therefore, that tissues contain molecules that are (1) essential for the catalytic activity of oxidative enzymes; (2) dialyzable and hence low in molecular weight; and (3) heat-stable and hence not proteins. The molecules were called *coenzymes*.

The major coenzymes of the dehydrogenases are two dinucleotides:

$\textcircled{P}$—Ribose—Nicotinamide

$\textcircled{P}$—Ribose—Adenine

Nicotinamide-adenine
dinucleotide (NAD)

and

$\textcircled{P}$—Ribose—Nicotinamide

$\textcircled{P}$—Ribose—Adenine

$\textcircled{P}$

Nicotinamide-adenine
dinucleotide phosphate (NADP)

Some dehydrogenases operate with NAD, and others with NADP, but all employ the nucleotide coenzymes as intermediary donor-acceptors of hydrogen in oxidation-reduction reactions. Note that *A*H transfers its

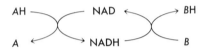

hydrogen to NAD to form NADH, which is converted back to NAD by the transfer of its hydrogen to *B* to form *B*H. NAD is not consumed in the reaction; its continuous regeneration requires that it be present in only small quantities. Thus it functions as if it were a catalyst.

Tissues also contain other nucleotides that function as coenzymes. One outstanding type comprises the ribonucleotides of adenine, particularly the di- and triphosphates.

Adenine—Ribose—$\textcircled{P}$
Adenosine monophosphate (AMP)

Adenine—Ribose—$\textcircled{P}$—$\textcircled{P}$
Adenosine diphosphate (ADP)

Adenine—Ribose—$\textcircled{P}$—$\textcircled{P}$—$\textcircled{P}$
Adenosine triphosphate (ATP)

ADP serves as a $\textcircled{P}$ acceptor in certain reactions, the result being ATP. Conversely, ATP donates $\textcircled{P}$ to become ADP.

$$X—\textcircled{P} + ADP \rightleftharpoons X + ATP$$
$$\underline{ATP + Y \rightleftharpoons ADP + Y—\textcircled{P}}$$
$$X—\textcircled{P} + Y \rightleftharpoons X + Y—\textcircled{P}$$

Here X and Y represent any of a large group of organic compounds. It should be noted that again the coenzymes are donor-acceptors of some group (as NAD and NADP are donor-acceptors of hydrogen). This is a recurrent phenomenon of great significance in biochemistry. We shall presently see that ADP and ATP, the donor-acceptors of phosphate groups, are of profound biological importance.

Although we shall consider *vitamins* later, it should be mentioned here that vitamins are converted in the body to coenzymes. Thus, NAD and NADP contain

the vitamin nicotinamide; FAD contains riboflavin; coenzyme A contains pantothenic acid; etc. The consequences of vitamin deficiency stem from deficiencies of specific coenzymes needed for enzyme function.

Summary

Importance of chemical and biochemical principles for an understanding of life.

Nature of chemical substances: atoms and atomic structure; chemical bonds; the covalent bond and its origin in electron sharing; the ionic bond and its origin in electron transfer; the hydrogen bond and its special biological significance.

Major elements of the living organism: carbon, the fundamental constituent of organic molecules; oxygen and hydrogen; nitrogen, a key constituent of proteins; minerals, required in small amounts by all organisms.

Properties of compounds: the unusual properties of water—its biological importance, its expansion on freezing, its uniquely high surface tension, its unusual thermal properties, its high solvent power; ionic dissociation—dissociation of salts in water, acids and bases, the concept of pH, buffers; properties of organic compounds— compounds that contain carbon and are synthesized by living systems, properties of organic molecules, structural and empirical formulas, isomers, functional groups.

Major organic compounds in living organisms: how they arose prior to the origin of life; carbohydrates—sugars and polysaccharides, energy sources and structural materials; lipids—high hydrogen content, high energy yield; amino acids and proteins—the largeness and complexity of proteins, how amino acids form chains linked together through peptide bonds, the importance of protein structure; nucleotides and nucleic acids—properties of nucleic acid chains, RNA and DNA, purines and pyrimidines.

Properties of chemical reactions: energy and work in general; collision and contact; the energy of chemical reaction—potential energy of chemical structure, energy of activation, chemical equilibrium.

Enzymes: classification and nomenclature; mechanisms of enzyme action; coenzymes—NAD, NADP, ATP, and ADP.

THE CELL:
UNIT OF LIFE

The Cell Theory

DEVELOPMENT OF THE CELL THEORY

"We have seen that all organisms are composed of essentially like parts, namely, of cells." (Schwann, 1839)

"Where a cell exists there must have been a pre-existing cell, just as the animal arises only from an animal and the plant only from a plant. The principle is thus established, even though the strict proof has not yet been produced for every detail, that throughout the whole series of living forms, whether entire animal or plant organisms, or their component parts, there rules an eternal law of continuous development [or continuous reproduction]." (Virchow, 1858)

These two statements, one made in 1839 and the other in 1858, mark the emergence of the *cell theory* in its definitive form. The cell theory is one of the two great foundations of modern biology; the other is the theory of evolution (1859). The two theories have much in common: they reached their definitive forms almost simultaneously, and both had been developing over a long period of time. In their modern forms they merge almost inextricably.

It is impossible to be sure when living cells were first observed. Certainly it was long after the necessary instruments were available. Simple lenses were known many years before the Christian era began, and spectacles were commonly worn by the wealthy of the fourteenth century. But there is no record of the use of optical instruments to examine living specimens before the curiosity of the Renaissance somehow suggested it. Two seventeenth-century biologists did see what we today call "cells." Robert Hooke (1635–1703) observed with a lens that wood charcoal, cork, and other plant tissues are made up of small cavities separated by walls; in 1665 he described cellular organization in plants (Figure 3-1). Hooke's original observations were made of plant cell walls whose living material had been lost, and he did not, therefore, understand the functional significance of the cellular organization he observed and described.

A few years later Anton van Leeuwenhoek first saw minute single-celled organisms in a drop of pond water. But neither of these men, nor the many others who saw and drew cells throughout the eighteenth century, realized the significance of their observations.

It was not until 1839, when Theodor Schwann published the book quoted at the beginning of this chapter, that any *generalization* was made. Schwann clearly perceived that *all living organisms consist of cells; they are either single cells or groups of cells.* Even in large and complex organisms like men or giant redwood trees, the whole body proves to be an aggregation of some billions of cells. Every specialized part of such an organism—skin, bone, muscle, nerve, and even blood; wood, bark, flower, and root—is composed of specialized cells plus a variety of intercellular materials that are largely produced by the cells.

It is a long way from merely observing cells to reaching the great inductive generalization that Schwann announced. A generalization as broad as Schwann's surely indicates some underlying natural process of still greater consequence than the generalization itself. The underlying process is made clear in Rudolf von Virchow's later statement that all cells arise only from preexisting cells. The full significance of this statement emerges when we consider how it relates the cell concept to two other major generalizations that appeared at about the same time. First, it conforms completely with the contemporary work

of the French scientist Louis Pasteur (1822–1895). Second, it merges with the theory of evolution published by Darwin in 1859, the year after Virchow's book.

Between 1859 and 1861 Pasteur proved as conclusively as science can that in the modern world no living thing arises except from other living things. It was the general opinion for many centuries that lower organisms could originate from mud or, especially, from the flesh of dead animals. Aristotle (384–322 B.C.) taught that fleas and mosquitoes arise from putrefying matter, and no one ventured to contradict him during the long course of antiquity and the Middle Ages. An eminent seventeenth-century scientist was certain he had seen rats develop from bran and old rags. It was even easier to be certain that maggots arose spontaneously in rotten meat. Another seventeenth-century scientist, Francesco Redi (1627–1697), disproved this idea. By careful experiments, he showed that maggots never appear unless flies have laid eggs in the meat.

Perhaps Redi's work should have settled the matter, but it did not. A really popular error dies hard, if it ever dies completely. This one is still alive, and some people in the United States still believe that

FIG. 3-1 **Hooke's drawings (1665) of the cellular organization in cork.** (Photo: from Hooke "Micrographia", 1665. New York Public Library)

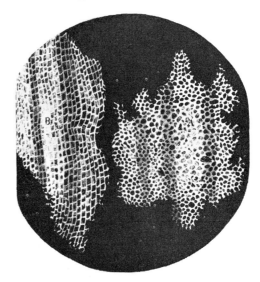

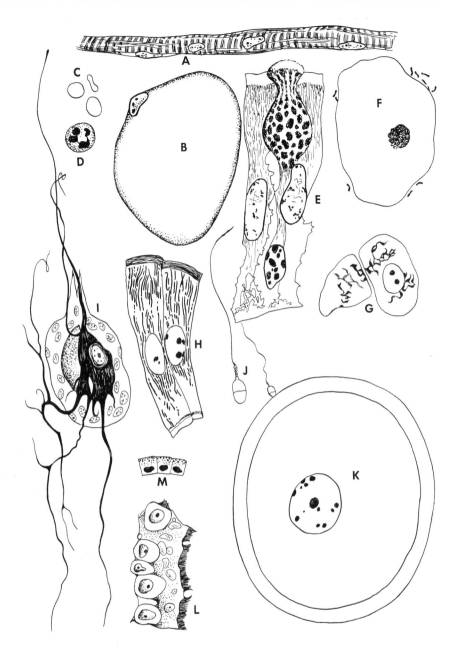

FIG. 3-2 A diversity of cells. All ×700 except J, which is ×1500. A. Human muscle cells. Note their elongate form. B. A fat storage cell from human connective tissue. The nucleus is a small body near the cell membrane. The whole of the (unstippled) central part of the cell is occupied by a large globule of fat. C. Human red blood cells. D. Human white blood cells. E. Three epithelial cells from the intestine of an axolotl, a larval salamander. The flask-shaped central cell secretes mucus, which provides lubrication for the passage of food. F. An epithelial cell from the lining of the human vagina. Several bacteria lie beside it. G. Two cells from the liver of a mouse; the Golgi element can be seen in both of them. H. Two epithelial cells from the rat's intestine; they contain threadlike mitochondria lying above and below the nucleus. I. A human nerve cell. Note how it is drawn out into fiberlike processes. The nerve cell itself (black in the figure) is encased by a second cell containing many nuclei. J. A human sperm cell (×1500). K. A human egg cell, with a sperm entering it. L. Part of the human placenta; five separate cells are overlaid by a syncytium that bears cilia. A syncytium is a multinucleate mass of protoplasm that is not separated by membranes into distinct cells. M. Three cells from the human eye (retina) containing pigment granules.

a horsehair can turn into a worm if soaked long enough in water. As far as biologists are concerned, however, the problem was finally resolved by the work of Pasteur. In his day it was known that microorganisms appeared in milk, wine, meat broth, and other substances even if they were protected from flies and other apparent sources. Pasteur examined every known example of such supposed spontaneous generation of living things. He showed that heating would kill any microorganisms present and that if the sterile substance were then protected from air, no other microorganisms would appear. (We still call this heating procedure *pasteurization.*) He demonstrated that microorganisms are carried through the air and that spontaneous generation does not occur in any known case.

Pasteur's critics were still inclined to accept the view that the living germs responsible for fermentation did not come from the air but arose spontaneously from the nonliving materials in the wine or milk. Pasteur won his point with a wonderfully simple and conclusive experiment. He took two sealed flasks that contained a nutrient broth infected with germs capable of causing putrefaction. One of these flasks was subjected to prolonged heating. The other flask was not heated. The unheated broth putrefied immediately. The heated broth remained free of putrefaction for months until the neck of the flask was broken, exposing it to the entry of germs from the air. Once the neck was broken, this broth also putrefied immediately, and Pasteur showed that its putrefaction was again caused by *germs*. Pasteur's experiments marked the end of a belief in spontaneous generation and the establishment of the principle of *biogenesis*—"all life comes from life." Virchow's principle that "all cells come from cells" is simply a more explicit form of this same truth, because all life takes the form of cells. Pasteur's minute "germs" were single-celled organisms, bacteria and yeasts.

The relationship of the cell theory to evolution follows from Virchow's statement "The principle is thus established . . . that throughout the whole series of living forms, whether entire animal or plant organisms, or their component parts, there rules an eternal law of *continuous development.*" Here Virchow is glimpsing, in his mind's eye, an unbroken continuity of cell generations stretching almost endlessly in time, back to the beginning of life. It is only a step

from this picture of all cells arising from other cells to the insight that all cells have a common ancestry. Schwann's perception "that all organisms are composed of essentially like parts, namely of cells" recalls the perception of the imaginative Comte de Buffon (1707–1788) that the structures of all vertebrate animals have much in common. Both insights are explained by the theory of evolution. Vertebrates, no matter how diverse, share a common structural plan because they share a common ancestry. In similar fashion, all living cells, no matter how diverse they may be (Figure 3-2), show structural resemblances that are their common inheritance from still earlier forms of life. In cell and organism, the novelty and diversity that have appeared in the course of evolution never obscure entirely those limitations imposed by an inheritance from ancient ancestors.

The transition from earlier investigators like Hooke and Leeuwenhoek to Schwann is a transition from simple observations to an inductive generalization of great breadth. And the transition from Schwann to Virchow is from a simple generalization to a *theory* of major importance that explains the generalization.

Before entering into a more detailed study of the cell, let us consider some of the principal implications of the cell theory.

THE CELL: THE MINIMUM MATERIAL ORGANIZATION POSSESSING LIFE

There are some particles that are smaller than any cells and that have been regarded by some biologists as alive. These are the *viruses* (Figure 3-3), familiar as the agents responsible for such human diseases as influenza, poliomyelitis, and virus pneumonia. Many different kinds of viruses exist; however, all of them are associated with and utterly dependent upon living cells. When ordinary viruses enter the living cells of organisms as invaders, they cause the biochemical machinery of the host cell to cease its normal activities and to produce new viruses. In the process, the host cell is destroyed. One could hardly term viral reproduction *self-reproduction* since it occurs only through the mechanisms of host cells.

A capacity for *self*-reproduction is surely one of the main characteristics of a living system. Another is a capacity for *self-regulation*. Neither of these attributes is possessed by the isolated virus. The cell, in fact, is the minimum organizational level of matter that, in the modern world, is capable of all those processes we refer to collectively as "life." In this generalization we include the qualification "in the modern world" because we are sure that life first arose from the nonliving world billions of years ago in much simpler form than the cell as we know it now. For, elementary as the cells appear in Figure 3-2, they represent an enormous degree of complexity and organization, something far more than a single step away from nonliving matter.

In the light of the important discoveries that began to emerge in the late 1950's and that are discussed on later pages, the boundary between the living and the nonliving is becoming increasingly indefinite. Today biochemists can place purified nucleic acids and other appropriate organic materials in a test-tube system and synthesize both duplicates of these nucleic acids and specific protein molecules. Many of the essential features of life thus can be made to arise experimentally without cellular organization. The various physical and chemical properties of living organisms did not originate all at once, and some, perhaps all, of the vital reactions can be made to occur separately and outside of cells. To this extent, there is a continuous spectrum from nonliving to living, with a middle ground between the two where application of either term is more or less arbitrary. Nevertheless, the combination of *all* vital phenomena within a single and *natural unit* occurs only with organization of the degree and kind seen at a minimum in a cell. It is therefore meaningful and useful to consider the cell as the basic unit of life.

There are several reasons why precellular organizations of the kind that led to living organisms no longer exist. In the first place, the environment has changed radically since life began; those conditions which made the precellular precursors of life possible have long since passed. Secondly, progressively more efficient reproducing systems have developed as a universal aspect of organic evolution. The cell as we know it today, then, is a highly evolved organization of matter in which basic processes characteristic of life are performed with precision and assurance—indeed, often with double assurance, as we shall see. It has long since replaced (probably for more than 3 billion years) the cruder precellular transitions between it and the nonliving world.

The past existence of precellular life must not blind us to the significance of our generalization about life today. The cell is life's minimum unit. In the cell and its relations with other cells, we must seek the organization and mechanisms that underlie all life's processes: the intake, storage, and release of energy; the intake of materials and their metabolism, leading to growth; sense perception and the response to stimuli; movement; and, above all, life's most distinctive process, reproduction.

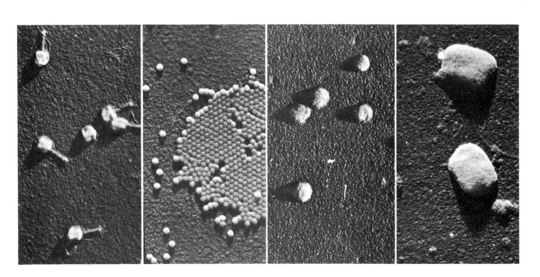

FIG. 3-3 Various viruses. Photographed by electron microscopy ($\times 50,000$) at the Virus Laboratory, University of California, Berkeley. Left to right, bacteriophage (by Dean Fraser and Robley C. Williams). Poliomyelitis (by C. E. Schmerdt and Robley C. Williams). Influenza (by Robley C. Williams). Vaccinia (by Robley C. Williams).

Organization of the Cell

It is not our present purpose to describe in detail the countless differences among the many kinds of cells. Rather, we propose to focus attention on those features of structural organization that are common to all cells and that are clearly related to the fundamental activities of life as a whole.

SIZES AND SHAPES OF CELLS

Although a few cells are visible to the naked eye, most are microscopic in size (Figure 3-4). In a large, multicellular animal like man, the average diameter of a cell is about 10 microns, that is, 0.01

FIG. 3-4   Objects, magnitudes, and appropriate microscopes.

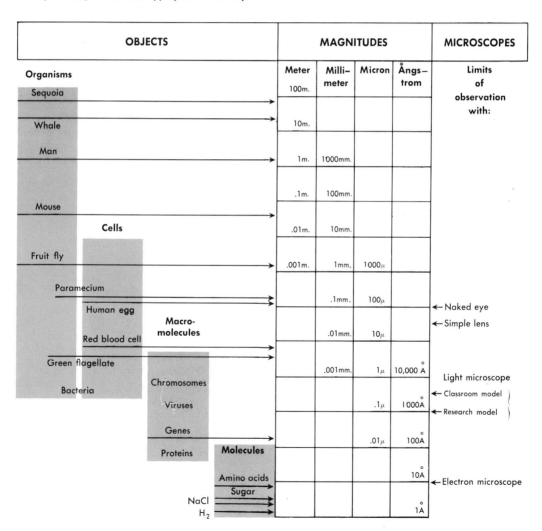

millimeter. A bacterial cell may be as small as 0.4 micron in diameter, which is near the limit of vision with an ordinary microscope. Some other cells are almost that small. There are, however, exceptions to the rule of small size. A single nerve cell in a large animal may reach a length of several feet, although its diameter is relatively small. Eggs of animals are single cells before development begins, and they are commonly visible to the naked eye. Human eggs, which are unusually small, can be seen without a lens but only as specks smaller than the periods on this page. The eggs of an extinct bird (*Aepyornis* of Madagascar) had capacities of more than 2 gallons and were, in volume, the largest known cells. Of course, only the yolk of a bird's egg is a cell. It is usually greatly inflated with stored food material and surrounded by accessory materials familiar as the "white" and the shell of the egg.

The Generalized Cell

Until the mid-1950's most textbooks of biology contained an old and familiar drawing which portrayed the "generalized" cell as it appeared through the ordinary *light microscope.* Unchanged for perhaps 30 years, and many times reprinted, it presented an idealized composite picture of an object that does not exist in reality. As we have seen (Figure 3-2), cells exhibit great variety in size and shape. But for all their variety, they possess certain features in common, and it is these that were depicted in the "generalized" cell. It showed, for example, a large central *nucleus* embedded in surrounding *cytoplasm,* the whole being encased in a *membrane.* And within the cytoplasm were various *organelles*—small particulate bodies that were really nondescript.

In recent years, new techniques of electron microscopy, giving much greater magnification than the old light-microscopic methods, have disclosed exquisite, fine structures in the subcellular particles, and it is now possible to present the contemporary diagram of the generalized cell shown in Figure 3-5. This illustration should be compared with the actual electron micrographs reproduced in subsequent figures.

THE CELL MEMBRANE AND WALL

The main chemical constituent of the cell is water, which may account for over 90 per cent of the cell's weight. Accordingly, cell contents always have a fluid character; the fact that cells maintain any individuality and form is due to the universal presence of a *cell membrane.* The membrane retains the rest of the living system within it. The cell membrane, however, is not something outside the living system but an integral part of it. Indeed, the membrane plays a vital role in regulating what passes into and out of the cell. The cell membrane, also called the *plasma membrane,* can hardly be seen with the ordinary light microscope, and the new science of electron microscopy had to solve some difficult technical problems before this remarkable boundary structure could be visualized.

Even before it was clearly seen, however, a complex functioning membrane was known to be present simply because certain substances could be shown to enter and leave cells freely, while others could not. Red blood cells and nerve cells, for example, distinguish between sodium and potassium ions, despite the similarities in size and charge of these ions. Potassium ions pass into the cells, and sodium ions are somehow forced out. This behavior implies the existence of both a selectively permeable barrier and an active mechanism analogous to a pump within the surface membrane. As we shall learn later, this distinction by the cell membrane between sodium and potassium is of great importance in the functioning of nerves, muscles, and many other cell types. The cell membrane is also capable of actively transporting certain large molecules and particles into the cell interior.

The peculiar structure of fatty acids (Chapter 2) ideally equips them to serve as building blocks in membranes. A long molecule such as oleic acid has, in fact, two functional groups: the carboxyl group, which is freely soluble in water, and the long hydro-

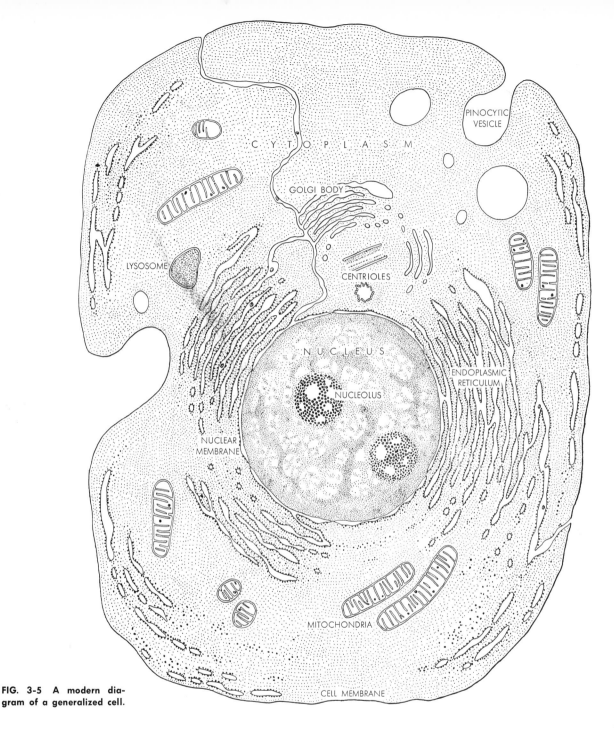

FIG. 3-5 A modern diagram of a generalized cell.

carbon chain, which is water-insoluble. These characteristics account for the solubility properties of lipids. As a result of the differences in solubility between the two ends of the molecules, fatty acids in an immiscible mixture of water and benzene (a fat solvent) orient themselves at the interface in a characteristic manner. The hydrocarbon chains project into the fat solvent, and the water-soluble carboxyl groups point toward the water layer. The affinity of the water-insoluble hydrocarbon residues for one another

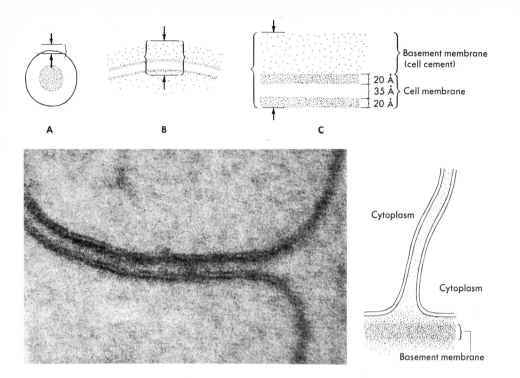

FIG. 3-6 The cell membrane. A. A cell membrane as seen by light microscopy. B. Low-power electron microscopy of the region delimited by arrows in A. C. High-power electron microscopy of the delimited area in B. D. The appearance of adjacent cell membranes of two neighboring cells (×333,000,000). The gap between cell membranes contains "cell cement." E. Demonstration of the fusion of cell cement into the basement membrane, which forms a supporting surface for a sheet of cells. (Photo, J. David Robertson)

tends to spread the fatty acids into a monomolecular film in which the hydrocarbon chains are parallel to one another. Such configurations are the basis of the functionally important membrane systems of all cells.

Electron microscopy has revealed that each cell membrane consists of two extremely thin dense layers separated by a less-dense material (Figure 3-6). There is reason to believe that the less-dense layers are composed of fatlike molecules lying side by side, and that the dense layers are outside sheaths of protein molecules (Figure 3-7). Presumably, minute pores exist through which molecules are selectively passed. On the cell surface is a cement-like substance that appears to hold neighboring cells together. When cells are arranged in sheets of tissue, this substance fuses them together into an underlying, supporting *basement membrane.*

Because of the fluid nature of the cell substance, nearly every organism is faced with mechanical problems in maintaining a definite form and chemical integrity. When a single cell lives its own, independent life, the cell membrane alone may suffice. But

FIG. 3-7 A diagrammatic representation of one theory of cell membrane structure. (Danielli, 1954.)

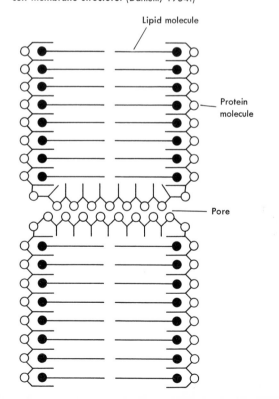

this is not true for a large multicellular organism, which would collapse under its own weight without a support of greater rigidity than the fluid protoplasm. In multicellular animals, generally, this problem is met by the development of special *skeletons,* such as our own bones. In plants, however, mechanical support is not derived from wholly separate skeletal systems. Support comes from the *cell wall* that lies outside the membrane of each cell. Although some cells specialize in producing extra thick and strong walls, benefiting the whole organism, *each* plant cell has a wall of its own. This wall is the most distinctive feature of a plant cell.

The cell wall should be distinguished from the cell membrane that lies within it. The wall is much thicker than the membrane. Moreover, it plays a smaller part than the membrane in controlling the passage of materials in and out of the cell; its function is mainly mechanical. The great functional differences between the wall and the membrane are reflected by the relatively simple structure of the wall (which is generally composed mostly of cellulose and related molecules) and by its durability, which contrast so sharply with the extremely complex and fragile nature of the membrane.

THE NUCLEUS

Inside the membrane of plant and animal cells, the nucleus is usually the largest distinct body. It is a roughly spherical body, denser than the cytoplasm in which it is embedded, and surrounded by a thin *nuclear membrane.* Its position is commonly central, and its role in the life of the cell is certainly central in the metaphoric sense, for it is the governing headquarters of the cell. It contains within it a tangled network of material called *chromatin,* which is darkly stained by certain dyes in preparations for microscopic study. Chromatin strands coalesce during cell division to form a definite number of distinct linear or threadlike bodies, the *chromosomes,* which are the carriers of the cell's hereditary material. The chromosomes' affinity for certain dyes is the property from which they derive their name—"chromosomes," from the Greek *chroma* (color) and *soma* (body). The chromosomes guide the development of the organism and maintain the order and organization of the entire living system. How they effect this control is a topic

for later chapters. In essence, they manufacture special chemical compounds that enter the cytoplasm as the agents of control, regulating the chemical processes that go on there.

Usually the chromosomes are seen only when the cell and its nucleus are dividing. When the nucleus is not dividing, a spherical body, the *nucleolus,* can be distinguished (see Figure 3-5). It disappears during nuclear division. Special staining techniques have shown that most of the deoxyribonucleic acid (DNA) of the cell is in the chromosomes. The nucleolus also contains much ribonucleic acid (RNA) and is considered a site of RNA synthesis.

Electron microscopy has added some information to this picture. As shown in Figures 3-5, 3-8, and 3-9, the nucleus is surrounded by an envelope consist-

FIG. 3-8   An electron micrograph of a liver cell. The nucleus (N), nuclear membrane (Nm), rough endoplasmic reticulum (Er), ribosomes, and mitochondria (M) are shown (×11,000). (Photo, D. W. Fawcett)

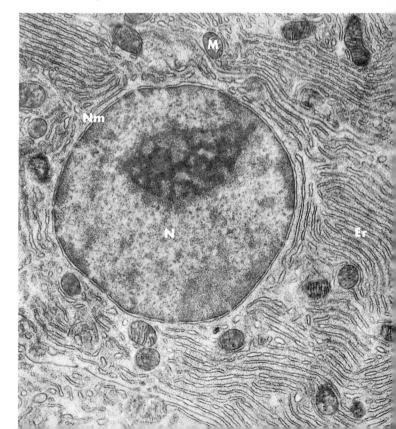

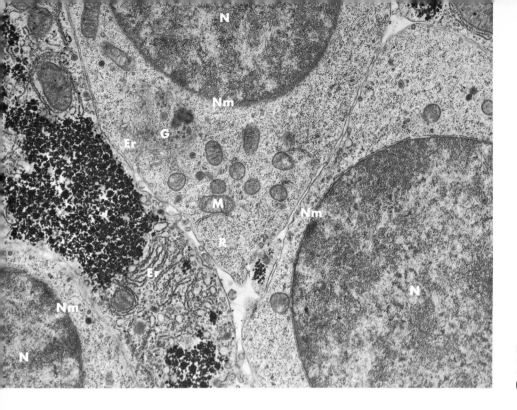

FIG. 3-9 An electron micrograph of blood-forming cells. Nuclei, nuclear membranes, scant endoplasmic reticulum, free ribosomes (R), mitochondria, and parts of Golgi complex (G) are visible (× 10,000). (Photo, Wincenty Kilarski)

ing of an inner membrane and an outer membrane. At certain sites the two membranes of the nucleus are joined together around small pores (see Figure 3-8). Through these pores the nucleus may communicate directly with the cytoplasm. The interior of the nucleus, in sharp contrast with the cytoplasmic interior, is free of membranes.

THE CYTOPLASM

The cell substance outside the nucleus is the complex, viscous, fluidlike material called "cytoplasm." Of the several cytological discoveries that can be credited to electron microscopy, surely the most significant is that of the cytoplasm's rich content of membranes and membrane-limited elements, unsuspected from light microscopy. The only membranes visible with the light microscope were the external cell membrane and the nuclear envelope; the cytoplasmic organelles were depicted as solid granules or filaments.

In disclosing the true *membranous* structure of each of the classic organelles, electron microscopy revealed the existence within the cytoplasm of a rich and diverse system of membrane-enclosed spaces. When cut across, these structures appear as narrow tubules, but when the dimension of depth is added, their walls are found to be connecting and sheetlike membranes which extend into all parts of the cytoplasm.

Ribosomes and the Endoplasmic Reticulum

Almost every cell—and especially one engaged actively in the synthesis of protein—contains this labyrinthine system of membrane-limited channels that follow a meandering course throughout the cytoplasm (Figures 3-5, 3-8, 3-9, 3-10, and 3-11). The system, a revelation wholly attributable to electron microscopy, is called the *endoplasmic reticulum*. As shown diagrammatically in Figure 3-5, the tubelike passageways of the endoplasmic reticulum open into the space between the two layers of the nuclear envelope. Conceivably, the cytoplasmic part of the system is an outgrowth of the nuclear envelope. The connection seems to provide a channel between nucleus and cytoplasm. It is thought also that the tubules may connect with the exterior of the cell through small pores in the cell membrane.

Two forms of endoplasmic reticulum are encountered: a *rough* or *granular* form and a *smooth* or *agranular* form. Typical granular endoplasmic reticu-

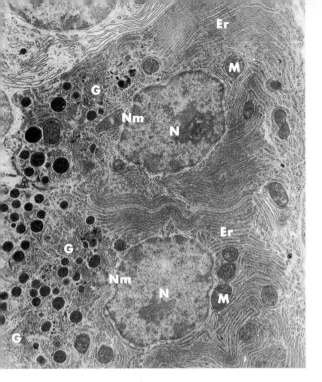

(2) those destined to be extruded through the cell membrane. The extrusion process, called *secretion,* is characteristic of certain types of cells (for example, gland cells). These are the cells with the most profuse systems of granular endoplasmic reticulum.

Agranular endoplasmic reticulum has been less well studied than granular endoplasmic reticulum, but it is equally common and may appear in the same cell with the granular form (see Figure 3-11). The agranular form displays smooth membranous surfaces that are devoid of ribosomal granules. Various theories implicating agranular endoplasmic reticulum in lipid, steroid, and polysaccharide metabolism are as yet unsubstantiated. Finally, it should be mentioned that in some cells the endoplasmic reticulum is represented almost solely by the nuclear envelope, other parts having disappeared in the course of cellular development (see Figure 3-9).

FIG. 3-10 An electron micrograph of pancreatic glandular cells of a bat. Nuclei, nuclear membranes, profuse rough endoplasmic reticulum, ribosomes, mitochondria, and Golgi complexes are shown ($\times$3,260). (Photo, Keith R. Porter and Mary A. Bonneville)

FIG. 3-11 An electron micrograph of a rat liver cell. Rough and smooth endoplasmic reticulum and mitochondria are present ($\times$16,000). (Photo, Keith R. Porter)

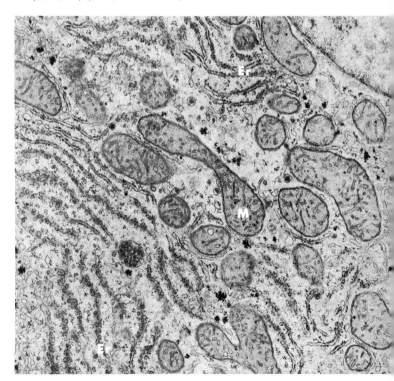

lum (see Figures 3-8 and 3-10) contains many parallel reticular membranes encrusted with minute dense particles visible at high magnifications. These are the *ribosomes,* the ribonucleoprotein particles whose role in protein synthesis has been so brilliantly elucidated in recent years (Chapter 7). Although located chiefly in the cytoplasm—indeed, most of the cell's RNA is within cytoplasmic ribosomes—similar particles are found in the nucleus (see Figure 3-8), particularly in the nucleolus. These account in part for the high RNA content of the nucleolus. Although the function of the nucleolar ribosome is not clearly understood, the cytoplasmic ribosomes are the major sites of protein synthesis. Protein molecules synthesized on the ribosomes are moved through the supporting membrane and are segregated from the rest of the cytoplasm within the membrane-limited spaces of the endoplasmic reticulum. We shall discuss protein synthesis in a later chapter, but it is useful to recognize at this point that cells synthesize two classes of materials: (1) those that remain within the cell; and

The Golgi Complex

Another interesting cytoplasmic component is the *Golgi complex,* or *Golgi body,* first noted in 1898 in nerve cells of barn owls by the Italian cytologist Camille Golgi. Light microscopists suspected that it was involved in secretory mechanisms but were unable to delineate its ultrastructure. Electron microscopy revealed that the multilayered complex is made of smooth membranes that are probably continuous with the endoplasmic reticulum (see Figures 3-5, 3-9, and 3-10).

It is possible that the Golgi complex participates in the secretion of proteins destined to leave the cell—probably not as a site of synthesis but as a sort of collecting and packaging station, where particles of matter to be secreted are somehow enclosed in membranous envelopes capable of fusing with the external cell membrane and, ultimately, of passing through it. These *secretory granules* occur only in specialized secretory cells (see Figure 3-10). However, Golgi bodies themselves occur also in nonsecretory cells, and their function is still disputed.

Mitochondria

The cytoplasm of nearly all cells contains small bodies called *mitochondria* (see Figures 3-5, 3-8, 3-9, 3-10, and 3-11). Though barely visible with the light microscope, they exhibit highly intricate fine structures in electron micrographs. Their numbers vary from cell to cell, a fact of interest since recent studies of isolated mitochondria have identified them as centers of cellular respiration and energy-yielding metabolism. It seems logical, therefore, that mitochondria tend to aggregate in those regions of the cell that are most actively engaged in metabolic processes. The occasional cell types containing no mitochondria (such as red blood cells) are biological curiosities, and they must rely upon notably less efficient means of energy production.

Electron microscopy discloses a remarkable internal structure in a mitochondrion (Figure 3-12). The individual mitochondrion is bounded by a double-walled surface membrane, flattened infoldings of the inner wall form perpendicular platelike *cristae,* and the internal space is filled with fluid. We shall

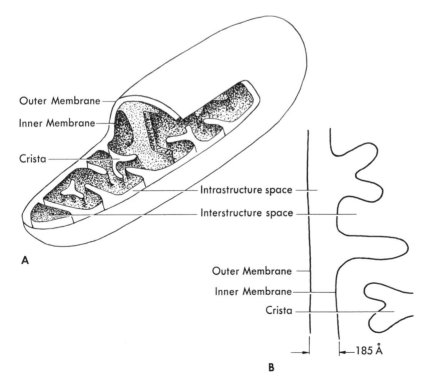

Outer Membrane
Inner Membrane
Crista
Intrastructure space
Interstructure space

A

Outer Membrane
Inner Membrane
Crista

185 Å

B

FIG. 3-12 The structure of a mitochondrion at different levels of magnification. A. A cutaway drawing showing two membrane layers separated by a fluid-filled intrastructure space and invaginations of inner membrane, the cristae. B. The same structures at a higher magnification.

presently encounter evidence indicating that the respiratory enzymes are anchored in or on these structures (Chapter 4). We should note, therefore, how much the *area* of the mitochondrial membrane is expanded by its architectural plan. Recent observations have shown that mitochondria swell and contract in the course of physiological activity. We shall later consider the possible meaning of these geometrical changes.

Lysosomes

The electron microscope clearly distinguishes between mitochondria and another newly identified group of bodies of similar size, the *lysosomes*. These curious particles contain many of the hydrolytic enzymes that cleave macromolecules into smaller molecules capable of being oxidized in the mitochondria—among them phosphatase, ribonuclease, and various proteases. The enzymes appear to be sheathed by lipoprotein envelopes, which isolate them from the rest of the cytoplasm. When rupture of the lysosomal membranes releases the enzymes, dissolution of the cell quickly follows. This phenomenon accounts for the breakdown of aging and dead cells.

Centrioles and Kinetosomes

The *centrioles* are a pair of small, cylindrical bodies lying near the nucleus. Electron microscopy reveals that a centriole consists of a cluster of exactly nine groups of delicate tubule-like structures, each group containing three tubules (Figures 3-5 and 3-13). Curiously, the elements of one member of a centriole pair always lie at right angles to those of the other. The significance of their orientation and their critical importance in cell division will be discussed in Chapter 5. Centrioles are rarely found in plant cells.

In cells equipped with *cilia* upon their surfaces there is a *kinetosome* whose structure precisely resembles that of the centriole at the base of each cilium. Since both cilia and certain components arising in cell division are contractile, it is conceivable that centrioles and kinetosomes function similarly as contractile or locomotory units within a cell.

Plastids and Vacuoles

In most plants and one-celled organisms, but not in higher animals, special bodies in the cytoplasm called *plastids* are often found. They are usually associated with the formation and storage of particular substances important in the metabolism of the organisms. They may be thought of as specialized factories and warehouses. The green pigment, *chlorophyll*, of green plants nearly always (invariably in higher plants) occurs in plastids, called *chloroplasts*, which are the sites of the fundamental process of photosynthesis (Chapter 4). There are other pigmented and unpigmented plastids in plants; starch and lipids are formed and stored in some of them, and pigments other than chlorophyll function in others.

Vacuoles are cavities in the cytoplasm bounded by definite membranes. They contain liquids with various substances in solution. They are absent from most animal cells and are submicroscopic in young plant cells, but in a mature plant cell one or more large vacuoles develop within the cytoplasm. The viscous part of the cytoplasm outside the vacuole membrane

FIG. 3-13 Sister centrioles in an animal cell (×90,000). They lie at right angles to each other. The cross section of the bottom one shows that a centriole is made up of nine groups, each containing three tubules. (Photo, Wilhelm Bernhard)

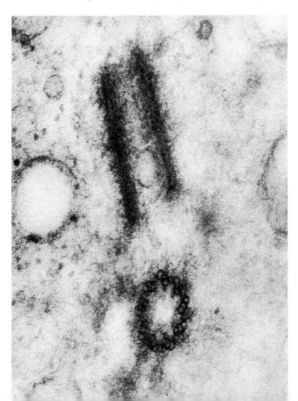

then becomes restricted to a thin layer just inside the cell membrane and wall. The nucleus always lies outside the vacuole in the viscous cytoplasm.

Large vacuoles rarely occur in animal cells, but smaller ones of various sorts may be present. In some cells the cell membrane forms a pouch around a food particle, which later separates and becomes a temporary *food vacuole*. The food is broken down in the vacuole by juices secreted into it from the cytoplasm. Another kind of vacuole is concerned with the maintenance of a proper water balance in the cell. Water continually passes into some single-celled organisms for physical reasons over which the cells have no control (cf. osmosis, p. 61). These cells meet the problem by continually bailing out excess water, which is first concentrated into *contractile vacuoles* whose rhythmic contractions eject the water.

PHYSICAL ORGANIZATION OF PROTOPLASM

Problem of Invisible Organization

Our survey of the visible structures within the cell strongly suggests that highly important features of the cell's organization exist beyond the limits of even the electron microscope. By indirect methods of analysis, we are beginning to understand aspects of the ultrastructure of protoplasm. The fact that it is not directly visible does not mean that it cannot be analyzed.

Table 3-1 gives the gross chemical composition of protoplasm from two different sources, a sea urchin and man. The predominance of water we have noted before. The proteins form the next largest protoplasmic constituent. Then follow carbohydrates and lipids, molecules of much smaller dimensions. The term "ash" includes a host of still smaller molecules, especially salts of various kinds. We are sure, to begin with, that protoplasm must be largely an aqueous solution of many kinds of molecules, but observation of its behavior indicates that there is more to it than that. For instance, even in its most fluid condition, protoplasm is thicker, that is, more viscous, than water or most solutions in water. Moreover, even within

TABLE 3-1   *Chemical Constituents of Protoplasm*

	Sea urchin	Man[a]
Water	78.3	66.0
Protein	15.2	16.0
Lipids	4.8	12.4
Carbohydrates	1.4	0.6
Ash[b]	0.3	5.0

[a]Data are for a newborn child.
[b]Ash includes all the elements not included in the other categories (iron, potassium, and other metals).

one and the same cell part, the viscosity varies; sometimes a piece of protoplasm flows freely, and at other times it acquires a thickly set jellylike consistency. Experiment shows that the viscosity is readily affected by acids and heat. This and other properties of protoplasm emphasize that it cannot be exclusively regarded as a simple solution of chemicals in water; it must be, in part, what is called a *colloidal system*. When we reach this conclusion, we see how a fine-scale structural organization may exist within the cell at the molecular level, far outside the range of direct vision. What is a *colloid?*

Colloidal Systems

Gases, liquids, and solids are the three most obvious phases of matter. The same substance may exist in any of the three phases. Water is a familiar example: it is a gas in clear air (or steam *before* the steam condenses and becomes visible), a liquid in a drink, a solid in an ice cube. There are, however, other phases of matter. Suppose that a cube of sugar, a solid, is dissolved in water. It is no longer a solid, and yet it is not exactly a liquid, either. It is in *solution* in a liquid. As we saw in Chapter 2, dissolved molecules are separate from each other, and each moves more or less independently through the *solvent*, the medium in which it is dissolved.

If instead of sugar fine sand is stirred in a glass of water, the sand particles do not dissolve. For a time many of the unchanged, solid particles remain in *suspension* in the water. The system is not stable, however, and the particles eventually settle out of suspension and collect at the bottom of the glass. If extremely fine clay particles are stirred in the glass of water, some may settle out, but many remain suspended indefinitely; in other words, the system is *stable*. If the particles are small enough, they never do settle out unless something is done to change the system—unless, that is, it is disturbed by an influence from outside. *A stable suspension is a colloid.*

A colloid may also be formed by two liquids instead of a liquid and a solid. If you stir kerosene into water, some small drops of kerosene remain suspended in the water for a while, but eventually they rise to the top. Such a system of one liquid dispersed in another is an *emulsion*. You will find it difficult or impossible to make drops of kerosene small enough to remain suspended in water indefinitely, so that a stable emulsion results. Stable emulsions— colloids of liquid in liquid—do exist, however. Homogenized milk is one; a special procedure makes the liquid fat globules so small that they remain in the milk and do not rise to the top as cream.

The differences among true solutions, colloids, and unstable suspensions or emulsions hinge on the sizes of the particles involved; and colloids are also dependent on the electric charges that the large particles carry. Consider the extreme cases first. Suspensions settle out eventually because of the pull of gravity on the large particles. Sugar molecules in water do not settle because the pull of gravity is negligible on particles so small. All the molecules in a liquid and true solution are constantly in random dancing movement in all directions. This random movement of the liquid (water) molecules is, in part, the reason colloidal particles, which are of intermediate size, are not settled out by the slight pull of gravity on them. The colloidal particles are constantly being bombarded and pushed in all directions, up as well as down, by the solvent molecules that surround them. They are also prevented from settling because their electric charges are all of the same sign (sometimes all positive and sometimes all negative); consequently, they mutually repel each other and stay uniformly dispersed. When chemicals added to a colloid neutralize the charges in the particles, they no longer repel each other, and then they precipitate.

There is no sharp line between the sizes of particles that form solutions, colloids, and unstable suspensions or emulsions. A substance is usually considered to be in true solution if it separates into individual molecules (or their ions) that are smaller than 0.001 micron. Aggregates of unseparated molecules are rarely as small as 0.001 micron and usually, therefore, form colloids. Larger aggregates form unstable suspensions or emulsions.

Proteins as Colloids and Fibers

Some single molecules are larger than 0.001 micron, and these include proteins, important constituents of protoplasm. Proteins usually dissolve in water and form solutions in the sense that their molecules do separate. Yet these molecules are often as large as the particles in colloids, and they do in fact form colloids in water. The result may be said to be simultaneously a solution and a colloid, or *chemically a solution* and *physically a colloid*.

Gelatin and albumen are proteins with very large molecules that form colloids in water. The white of an egg is a colloidal system of albumen in water, and gelatin is also an aqueous colloid. Gelatin, of course, can exist either as a freely flowing fluid (when the gelatin is dissolved in warm water) or as a thickly set jelly. This is a general property of colloids: they can assume either a *sol* or *gel* state and, moreover, can be transformed from one state to the other.

The colloidal properties of protoplasm account for some of its known organization and behavior. Its capacity to form semisolid gels helps us to understand how a system that is 90 per cent water can maintain any structure whatsoever. The integrity of the cell membrane as a retaining boundary depends on this ability of the protoplasmic proteins to form gels. And the variations in viscosity that are observable in different parts of a cell, and in the same part at different times, are reflections of reversible sol–gel changes.

Although we are now part way toward an understanding of the invisible ultrastructure of protoplasm, we are still far from our goal. The properties of protoplasm leave no doubt that it is simultaneously a complex solution and a colloid. That is, it consists of water in which small molecules (like sugars and salts) and their dissociated parts are dissolved and in which there are also dispersed much larger molecules (proteins and lipids) and molecular aggregates of colloidal size. What we ultimately must look for, then, is some basis for maintaining order and organization within a semifluid system. It is difficult to imagine how any order can be preserved in a true solution, the essence of which is the random movement and uniform distribution of its constituent molecules. Yet various hypotheses, all unproven as yet, have been advanced. Most of them relate to the remarkably large sizes of proteins and the diversity of shapes, including fibers, that they can assume. The hypotheses envisage a semisolid framework of fibers and colloidal particles as the basis for spatial order and organization.

Diffusion

Molecules move about continuously in colloids as well as in true solutions. It is essential to recognize the principles governing their movements because the processes of cellular metabolism depend upon this molecular traffic. In turn, the movements of molecules in protoplasm are affected by its physical organization.

It is a physical property of matter, even of solids, that molecules are always moving. This is simply demonstrated when a bottle of perfume is uncorked in a closed, still room. You may stand several feet from the bottle, but soon you will smell the perfume. Molecules have moved out of the bottle and through the air of the room. Your nose, which is one of the most sensitive chemical detection systems known, has recognized the dispersed molecules.

Molecular movement in gases, such as that of the perfume molecules in air, is considerably faster than in liquids. It is faster in liquids than in solids, although it still goes on in the densest solid. It is faster in hot than in cold substances; in fact, the movement of molecules *is* the phenomenon that is known by the name "heat."

Molecules are much too small to see. Consequently, we cannot actually or directly see molecular motion, but there are simple ways to see it indirectly by some of its visible results. Put a little face powder in a drop of water, and look at it under the high power of an ordinary microscope. The particles of face powder (which are composed of many molecules) will be seen darting about. They are being bombarded by the moving water molecules and are small enough to move when hit.

In a drop of water millions of molecules move about virtually at random. The *average* result, the net effect of these movements in every direction, is nil. In spite of all the activity within it, the drop does not go anywhere, nor do the molecules become more concentrated in one part of the drop than in another. This is the usual situation when molecules are evenly distributed through the space or substance being studied, even when there is a uniform mixture of different kinds of molecules.

When the perfume bottle was opened, however, something else happened. There was a change in net effect; the perfume molecules did go somewhere. When the bottle was first opened, there were no perfume molecules outside it. Soon there were such molecules at increasing distances away from the bottle. A short time later the molecules were still highly concentrated in the bottle but also were highly concentrated near it. Concentration away from the bottle was progressively lower, until it became zero in the farthest part of the room. The motion of the molecules was random. Some even moved back into the bottle, but more moved out. The net effect, the average over millions of molecules, was that more molecules moved from regions of high concentration to regions of low concentration than vice versa.

This tendency for molecules to spread from regions of higher to those of lower concentration is quite general and is called *diffusion*. If it continues, the concentration eventually becomes the same everywhere. The perfume molecules become evenly distributed throughout the room. There is a state of equilibrium. What happens then? Does diffusion stop? Do the perfume molecules stop moving?

Now consider another simple experiment. If a crystal of copper sulfate (or any soluble, colored compound) is put in the bottom of a glass and the glass is filled with clear water, the water soon begins to turn colored around the crystal. The zone of colored water becomes larger from day to day. What is happening? At the surface of the crystal, copper sulfate is going, molecule by molecule, into *solution* in the water, the *solvent*. Naturally the dissolved molecules are more concentrated right at the surface of the crystal than elsewhere. They therefore diffuse into the surrounding water, and so the colored zone spreads.

It spreads very slowly, however, much more slowly than the perfume molecules spread through the air. The perfume can be smelled 3 feet from the bottle within a few minutes, but it takes more than a year for copper sulfate in recognizable amounts to diffuse this far through water. If you have ever tried to run in shallow water, you know the reason for this difference in the rates of diffusion. Water is a *denser* medium than air. This means that in air the molecules are farther apart than in water. The molecules are thus less likely to collide, and the diffusing molecules are less often slowed down or bounced back, than in water. In either air or water, however, the molecules are very small in proportion to the space between them. There is plenty of room between them for the oncoming molecules of perfume or of copper sulfate, and the total volume of air or water is not increased by the diffusion.

In these examples, then, diffusion does not push the molecules of gas or liquid farther apart. On the other hand, in a solid or a dense colloid, the molecules are so close together that diffusion among them may force them apart. If a thin piece of dry gelatin is placed in water, it swells. Water has diffused into the gelatin and separated its molecules. The resulting volume of the piece of gelatin is greater than that of the dry gelatin alone but less than that of the dry gelatin plus the original volume of the water diffused into it. This particular sort of diffusion is called *imbibition*. The word simply means "drinking in." Imbibition is a familiar part of daily life and of life processes. It makes wooden doors stick in rainy weather, and it makes bean seeds swell and burst their seed coats just before they sprout. The pressures caused by imbibition may be enormous. Imbibition in starch can develop pressures up to 15 tons per square inch. Ships loaded with rice have been split when water got into the holds and was imbibed in the rice.

Diffusion plays a leading role in the organization of the protoplasm. Frequently, molecules within a cell are unevenly distributed. Diffusion then tends to equalize the distribution, providing one way for materials to move about within the cell.

Semipermeability

Now that we have discussed diffusion in general, we must consider diffusion through membranes, a special circumstance of peculiar importance in the lives of cells. Some substances diffuse quite readily through some membranes. If a membrane is no particular barrier to a given substance, it is said to be *permeable* to that substance. Of course, if a substance cannot pass through a membrane, the membrane is *impermeable* to it. If a membrane is permeable to some substances and less permeable or impermeable to others, it is called *semipermeable* (or *differentially permeable,* which may be more precise but is clumsier).

The relevance of these facts to our study of the cell is that a cell membrane is semipermeable. It is generally permeable to water and impermeable to colloids. The membrane holds in the colloidal elements of the cytoplasm and yet permits water to move rather freely into and out of the cell. The cell membrane is also more or less permeable to various materials dissolved in water. Thus needed materials from the outside can diffuse through the membrane. Once within the cell, they can be retained in the colloidal mesh or in compounds to which the membrane is not permeable. Waste products can be converted into forms to which the membrane is permeable and so can leave the cell.

Actually the situation is more complicated than this explanation indicates, and in a very interesting way. Like other parts of the cell, the membrane is in a continual state of flux. The degree of permeability to different substances is not constant, varying quite markedly from time to time. Thus, even without any change in its own state or composition, a substance may pass through the membrane at some times and be held back by it at others. The variation depends on many things, such as sugar content, acidity, electrical properties, and conditions of colloids within the cell and temperature, acidity, heat, light, concentrations of materials, and other factors outside the cell. Alterations in membrane permeability greatly influence the kinds and amounts of materials diffusing into and out of the cell. These processes are essential in the regulation of basic life processes in the cell.

Osmosis

Suppose that we make a container of a membrane permeable to water, such as a pig's bladder, a frog's skin, or collodion. If we fill it with water, close it tightly, and immerse it in water, nothing noticeable will happen. Although the container is permeable to

water, the concentration of water is the same inside as outside. Therefore, as many molecules move out as move in, and equilibrium or the status quo is maintained. However, if we put a sugar solution in the container (preferably leaving it somewhat slack but without air inside) and immerse it in water (preferably distilled water) again, the container will swell up (Figure 3-14).

What happens? Evidently more water moves in than out through the membrane. Why? What you already know of diffusion supplies the answer. Water molecules are less concentrated in the sugar solution than in pure water. Molecules move predominantly from the pure water into the solution. If the membrane were equally permeable to sugar and to water, sugar molecules would also move out. But the membrane is semipermeable, being much more permeable to water than to sugar. So no (or very little) sugar moves out of the container, more water moves in than out, the amount of fluid in the container increases, and the container swells. This is the process of *osmosis*.

The influx of water into the container produces pressure, *osmotic pressure*. The flow through the membrane continues until the pressure inside forces water molecules out through the membrane as fast as osmosis brings them in. The pressure then ceases to rise, becoming steady. A state of equilibrium has been reached. The amount of osmotic pressure that can develop in a solution separated from distilled water by a semipermeable membrane depends on the concentration of the solution, the temperature, and other factors.

Osmosis goes on, to some degree, most of the time in most of the cells of any living organism. It is essential to the movement of materials into and out of cells. It usually proceeds in a businesslike way, quietly and without any really striking results. Sometimes, however, its effects are clearly visible and even dramatic.

If a cell of almost any water plant—a filament of the little pond-scum alga *Spirogyra* will do nicely—is soaked in a 15 per cent solution of common sugar, the cell contents soon separate from the wall and form a mass in the center of the cell. The sugar solution soaks through the cell wall and comes in contact with the cell membrane. Remember that in plants the cell *wall* is different from the underlying

FIG. 3-14 Semipermeability and osmosis. A. Sugar molecules cannot cross the membrane; they are too big. Water molecules are less concentrated on the sugar-solution side of the membrane than on the other side, and the chance that they will hit pores in the membrane, and thus cross it, is consequently smaller on the sugar-solution side. More water therefore enters the solution than leaves it. B. The net movement of water into a sugar solution enclosed within a membrane container creates a pressure (osmotic pressure) that causes the container to swell.

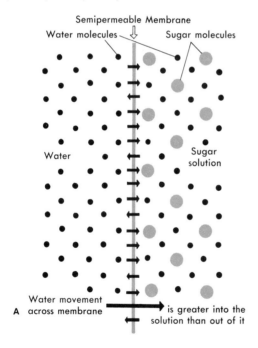

Semipermeable Membrane
Water molecules   Sugar molecules

Water   Sugar
                              solution

Water movement
A across membrane   is greater into the
                         solution than out of it

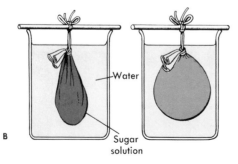

Water

B   Sugar
               solution

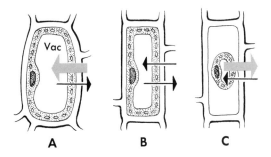

FIG. 3-15 Plasmolysis of a plant cell. Arrows indicate the relative amounts of inward and outward diffusion of water. In A water concentration outside the cell is greater than that inside. Hence, there is a net diffusion into the vacuole resulting in a swelling against the firm cell wall. In B the water concentration inside and outside are equal, with no net water movement and no volume change. In C the water concentration inside the cell is greater than that outside, and the vacuole and cell shrink away from the cell wall as water is lost. This shrinking is termed plasmolysis.

membrane. The cell wall, unlike the membrane, is not semipermeable; the membrane is permeable to water and impermeable to sugar. The large vacuole in the center of the cell contains a dilute solution, with a water concentration definitely higher than that of the sugar solution. Osmosis therefore occurs; water diffuses out of the vacuole through the membrane into the space between membrane and wall. As the vacuole loses water and becomes smaller, this space enlarges. The membrane and its contained protoplasm are finally crowded into a ball at the center of the cell. This phenomenon is called *plasmolysis* (Figure 3-15). Plasmolyzed cells ultimately die, but if you remove the cell from the sugar solution quickly enough and put it in pure water, it will recover, and the protoplasm will return to its position near the wall. Why?

You can demonstrate radical effects of osmosis even more simply in a kitchen. Put a leaf of lettuce in salt water. It will wilt, because the cells lose water by osmosis. Remove the leaf quickly, and put it in pure water. It will recover its crispness. The process is similar to the wilting of a plant on a dry, sunny day and its recovery when the plant is watered, to the extent that both involve the loss and gain of water by the cells; only the mechanism of water loss is different—it is osmosis between solutions in the lettuce and evaporation in the growing plant.

Summary

The cell theory and its relation to the theory of evolution—the foundations of modern biology.

The cell as the minimum organization of matter that is alive, the basic unit of life.

Protoplasm, not the name of a single substance, but a name loosely applied to the living organization of matter.

Visible structure of a cell: membrane, wall, nucleus, cytoplasm—ribosomes, endoplasmic reticulum, the Golgi complex, mitochondria, lysosomes, centrioles, plastids, and vacuoles.

Physical organization of protoplasm, colloids, and fibers.

Molecular movements in solutions: diffusion; semipermeability and osmosis, the movement (and its control) of water into and out of the living cell.

CHAPTER FOUR

THE CELL:

ITS METABOLIC MACHINERY

In Chapter 2 we were concerned with some of the basic chemical properties of living things, and in Chapter 3 with the structures of cells, the units of life. Both chapters were largely preliminary to a consideration of the dynamic processes that in a sense *are* life. Tissues and cells and their parts have *functions* in the lives of organisms. These functions include chemical processes that go on within cells, and this chapter is devoted to some of the most important of these processes.

Adaptation and Homeostasis

Every new organism is the product of reproduction. The individual then develops as did its parents and in the fashion characteristic of its species. Throughout its life it maintains and regulates the complex organization specific to it. There must obviously be some kind of program or information, a metaphorical blueprint, guiding development. This has been mentioned before and will be more fully dealt with in Part 3. Here we are more interested in the fact that throughout the whole history there must be a constant traffic in energy and materials if the organism is to exist, is to develop, and is to be maintained. We are now about to consider this traffic at one of its most significant levels: the events taking place within the cell. In approaching this subject, we first encounter two broad principles that will often reappear at other levels and in other contexts—those of *adaptation* and of *homeostasis*. Aspects of them occur in cells, in the tissues and organs of multicellular organisms, in whole individuals of all kinds, and in aggregations and communities of organisms. The word "adaptation" in this connection refers to the usefulness to an organism of its structures and functions. They tend, with more or less success, to enable the plant or animal to survive and maintain its normal form and activities in its given

64

environment. They often have the peculiarity of seeming to provide for some *future* need, seeming literally providential in the old colloquial sense, or teleological in the technical philosophical sense. Such apparently goal-directed structures and functions can be explained in historical, evolutionary terms without the postulate of an actual goal. We shall have more to say on this matter.

Homeostasis, which is itself an adaptation of life, is the tendency of an organism to maintain its internal composition and state with fair constancy and within a range suitable for its continued functioning. Processes such as respiration, digestion, metabolism, and

excretion all plainly contribute to homeostasis. Auto-regulation, the self-perpetuation of functional stability and structural integrity, or homeostasis in a broader sense, makes it possible for an organism to maintain itself in the face of a universe of destructive forces. Homeostasis is particularly evident in systems that involve feedback. Some biochemical examples of such systems within cells are discussed later in this chapter.

Cell Metabolism: Some Basic Principles

ANABOLISM AND CATABOLISM

The molecular components of cells are in a constant state of flux in which they undergo continuous and rapid chemical transformation, replacement, and renewal. We speak of this dynamic state of the molecular constituents as *metabolism*. In its broadest sense, metabolism includes all of the enzyme-catalyzed chemical reactions taking place within an organism or its individual cells, whether they are involved in growth, reproduction, tissue repair, or energy production.

Metabolic processes are conveniently divided into two categories. Those reactions concerned with the synthesis of cell constituents and cell products from simpler substances are referred to collectively as *anabolism*. In general, these do not supply the energy needed by the cell. Indeed, they are usually endergonic reactions requiring an input of energy (Chapter 2). Energy production is the function of the second category of metabolic reactions, collectively called *catabolism*. In catabolism, complex molecules are broken down to simpler ones by exergonic processes that ultimately involve energy-liberating oxidative reactions.

UNIVERSALITY OF FUNDAMENTAL METABOLIC PROCESSES

As we begin our survey of the main pathways of cellular metabolism, we should take note of the fact that most of these mechanisms were discovered

quite recently. The brilliant explorations of biochemists in the years since World War II comprise one of the most distinguished chapters in the history of science. The new knowledge of cell biochemistry would surely have delighted Darwin, Schwann, and Virchow, because it permits an extension down to the molecular level of a combination of the cell theory and the theory of evolution. The theory of evolution sees a living thing as an evolving organization of materials that in themselves are not alive; the cell theory sees the cell as the unit of that living organization. Together, the two theories predict fundamental similarities in the chemical constitutions and organizations of all living cells. It is this broad prediction that modern biochemistry has now fulfilled.

The common ancestry of all cells—protists, plants, and animals—accounts for their marked similarity in constituent chemicals and processes. We glimpsed this similarity in Chapter 2. The lives of all cells are founded on the chemistry of four major classes of molecules and their derivatives—carbohydrates, lipids, proteins, and nucleic acids. Biochemistry now tells us that the basic processes of carbohydrate, lipid, protein, and nucleic acid synthesis are virtually identical in all living cells, whether they be of plants or animals. We know, too, that all cells synthesize their large organic molecules from simpler molecules that are available in their physical environments. From these facts it is reasonable to conclude that long before the plant and animal kingdoms became separated in evolution, there existed in the ancient oceans various primitive forms of life that were endowed with most, if not all, of the principal metabolic processes occurring in contemporary living organisms.

One interesting practical consequence of this "biochemical brotherhood" of all protoplasm has been the frequency with which scientists have discovered important new principles relevant to animal cells from experiments performed with bacteria or other lower forms.

Obviously, differences developed among the early organisms, for an enormous number of diverse species arose. Their diversity is reflected in metabolic differences among cells and species. Nevertheless, the metabolic similarities of all cells are striking and fundamental, and it is to them that we shall give our attention in this chapter. Thus we shall ask, "How does the cell manufacture its characteristic organic chemicals?" This question will lead us to recognize that the synthesis of complex molecules from simpler ones involves chemical work and, like other forms of work, requires the expenditure of energy. The key to understanding the pattern underlying the cell's metabolic framework is the concept of energy, and we shall need to review the remarkable mechanisms by which the cell obtains its energy to do work and the way in which it uses its energy in the fabrication and organization of its chemical constituents.

CELLULAR ENVIRONMENT AND NUTRITION

All metabolism begins with the chemical raw materials that are referred to collectively as *food*. These material requirements of the organism are supplied in one form or another by the environment. The environment also, of course, affects the processes of metabolism by means of temperature, pressure, and other physical and chemical features of the background. But we are here concerned with the environment as the ultimate source of all raw materials.

It is fair to say that there are even more types of cellular environments than there are types of cells, for the environment of any one cell type is constantly changing. Moreover, the environment is determined not by physical, geological, and meteorological factors alone. Every cell, every group of cells, every organism is dependent upon and influenced by other cells, other groups of cells, other organisms. Every organism lives in an environment of which it is itself a part, along with others of its kind, organisms of other kinds, and many nonliving substances such as air, water, and soil. No organism lives alone, and no living thing is sufficient unto itself. To consider a cell or organism apart from its environment is to consider the nonexistent, an abstraction that is not a real form of life. Relationships between life and environment are so pervasive a part of living that they are involved in all aspects of biology.

The fact that these relationships are so complex and that they do somehow affect every process of life makes it virtually impossible to study them as a distinct and separate topic. It is necessary to take them up repeatedly, from different points of view and at different levels. In this part of the book we are interested mostly in life at the cellular and subcellular levels. The relationships to be discussed here are thus mainly the exchanges and other interrelationships between cells and their environments, which are composed of other cells and the various media (mainly fluids) in or on which cells live.

The degree of interdependence varies according to the properties of cells, their positions with respect to other cells, the kinds of organisms, and the surroundings of cells and organisms. One very important sort of interdependence results from the fact that cells arise only from other cells; they are derived from other cells in sequence through time and related in growth, reproduction, and heredity. Another sort of interdependence is involved in the integration of cells in multicellular organisms. Some cells secrete *hormones,* which modify the activities of other cells. Cells in organs and systems act to move or otherwise to affect the organism as a whole. Nerves (themselves cells) control and coordinate the activities of other cells.

Perhaps the most fundamental sort of interdependence of all is illustrated by the fact that organisms differ considerably in their ability to manufacture essential biomolecules with their own metabolic machinery. For example, *all* cells require certain sugars (and their derivatives) that are synthesized—or elaborated—*only* by the green cells of plants. These green plant cells synthesize the sugars from carbon dioxide (CO_2) molecules in the environment, provided there is adequate sunlight, and furnish them ready-made to animal cells. Similarly, some cells cannot make essential vitamins or amino acids from simple environmental precursors, whereas others can; again the nonsynthesizers must obtain the substances ready-made. We call the needed substances in such cases *essential nutrients* or *growth factors*.

The science of *nutrition* is the study of food requirements and of the methods by which foodstuffs are utilized. As we have just learned, organisms are either *autotrophic* (from the Greek words meaning "self-feeder") or *heterotrophic* (meaning "other-feeder"). Autotrophs are organisms that grow and thrive in a purely inorganic medium. This means that they produce their own sugars, lipids, amino acids, etc., from CO_2 (as the carbon source), ammonia (NH_3) or nitrate (NO_3^-) (as the nitrogen source), and H_2O. Heterotrophs require preexisting carbohydrates and other organic molecules. In general, heterotrophs are animals, and autotrophs are plants.

When put in such general terms, the difference between autotrophy and heterotrophy sounds clear-cut and absolute. So it is when we compare, say, a buttercup and a cow. If, however, we compare many different organisms, we find intergradations and a great diversity in powers of synthesis. *Photosynthetic* autotrophs convert light energy into chemical energy in the process of *photosynthesis*. Organisms in this group are the colored sulfur bacteria, blue-green, red, brown, and green algae, and complex green plants. The colors in these organisms result from a number of special *pigments,* including chlorophyll, which plays a critical role in trapping light. By means of chlorophyll-mediated photosynthesis, green plants absorb the energy of sunlight and combine CO_2 with hydrogen to build the sugars that serve as the major energy sources for all living things:

$$CO_2 + H_2O + Energy \rightarrow Sugars + O_2$$

Heterotrophs are also classifiable into various subdivisions, and we shall mention only some of them. There are, for example, organisms (like the bacterium *Azotobacter*) that require preformed sugars but that can convert gaseous atmospheric nitrogen

into inorganic or organic nitrogenous compounds. These *nitrogen-fixing* organisms are invaluable in agriculture because they are the natural fertilizers of soil. Other heterotrophs that do not require organic nitrogen sources can thrive on ammonia or nitrate (like the bacterium *Escherichia coli*). Still others require some of their nitrogen in the form of certain preformed amino acids, and others require certain vitamins or growth factors. It is generally assumed that if an organism requires a particular compound (such as a vitamin) in its food in order to survive and multiply, the organism cannot itself synthesize that compound. On the other hand, it is assumed that if a compound occurs and plays a vital role in an organism but is not required in its food, then the organism can and does synthesize it. Thus, nutritional experiments reveal that syntheses are performed in an organism. Humans require ascorbic acid (vitamin C) in their diets and cannot synthesize it. Rats, although rather closely related to us and generally similar biochemically, can synthesize ascorbic acid, as can most plants and animals. Man is actually a very complex and exacting heterotroph who requires a carbohydrate energy source, certain fatty acids, at least eight amino acids, and almost 20 vitamins.

There is some evidence that the ancestors of all living organisms went through autotrophic stages in which they could perform all necessary syntheses from elements and very simple inorganic compounds. The inability of present-day organisms to perform a particular synthesis may, then, demonstrate an evolutionary loss of a biosynthetic ability possessed by remote ancestors. We shall later learn that such a loss is a result of a genetic mutation resulting in a heritable inability to synthesize a specific enzyme. Although new syntheses have certainly developed in some lines of evolution, on the whole the loss of syntheses has probably been a ruling factor in the evolution of heterotrophic biochemical systems. There can, for instance, be little doubt that ancestors of ours could synthesize ascorbic acid and that we need it in our food because the synthetic capacity was lost somewhere along the line. In fact, it is even likely that other ancestors of ours, very remote ancestors indeed, had the power of photosynthesis and then lost it. Among the living protists called *flagellates,* there are pairs in which the forms are almost exactly alike, except that one has chlorophyll and performs photosynthesis and the other does not. It is probable in each case that the nonphotosynthetic form was directly derived from the photosynthetic one by loss of the power to perform this synthesis. By experimental procedures it is possible to take some of the photosynthetic flagellates and to breed from them a strain that lacks chloroplasts and, therefore, cannot perform photosynthesis. (Why not?) This artificial strain lives and reproduces perfectly well as long as it is fed either the carbohydrates that it cannot synthesize or some other organic molecule as an energy source.

This experiment actually turns an autotrophic "plant" into a heterotrophic "animal" as far as nutrition is concerned. Some such change probably took place in the distant past when plants and animals became distinct and began to diverge along their separate paths of biochemical and bodily evolution. The experiment actually may be repeating the beginning of that epochal event. There is, indeed, reason to believe that the organisms among which the separation began may have been similar to the flagellates of today. As to whether the flagellates themselves, as a group, are really animals or plants, we may call them what we please. Among these organisms the distinction is arbitrary if not meaningless.

An organism that loses its capacity for photosynthesis immediately becomes dependent for food on organisms retaining a capacity for that synthesis. This is, of course, the basis of the dependence of the animal kingdom on the plant kingdom. Loss of the ability to perform any synthesis—and it has been mentioned that this is a frequent occurrence in the history of organisms—leads to greater dependence on other organisms. Such loss and increased dependence might be considered degeneration, and they have been so considered by some students of the subject. It is true that the real end of the trail (or is it the end of only one of the trails?) can hardly be deemed

other than degenerate. This end is realized in some parasites that perform almost no syntheses and depend on the plants or animals within which they live for nearly all compounds. Nevertheless, the loss of synthetic capacity may be associated with increased activity, greater anatomical complexity, greater mobility, increased perceptiveness, and many other evolutionary changes that man, at least, considers progressive. Man himself, certainly the most intelligent if not in all respects the most advanced organism, has "degenerated" enormously by the loss of synthetic capacities and is as dependent on other organisms for food as most parasites.

HOW CELLS GET THEIR MATERIALS

In all cells, some of the essential organic molecules are fabricated within the cell, and others come from outside. As we have noted, cells vary enormously as to what they make and what they take in. They vary also in what they release. In multicellular organisms there is great diversity in these respects among the cells of one organism. Its cells are chemical specialists. There is also great diversity among different organisms. We have seen that green plants can make sugars and most of the other essential foods, whereas animals cannot. These are matters of nutrition and of *food chains* among organisms in communities, above the level of cells. A food chain is a series of organisms in a community, each of which devours the next in the series as its principal food source. The concept will be discussed in Chapter 19. Here we are most concerned with the fact that each cell must obtain materials from outside itself, regardless of what compounds it makes or what it does with materials taken in. The materials must also move within the cell.

Cells usually obtain their materials as molecules or as ions from watery solutions. There are some real and some merely apparent exceptions to this generalization. Cells in direct contact with air may acquire and lose gases in the absence of an external liquid solution. (The gases are usually in solution when *within* the cell.) Even in cases apparently of this sort an external solution may really be present. Your lungs do not extract oxygen directly from air, but from solution in a thin liquid film that covers the cells at the surfaces of the lungs. Cells may also take in undissolved material from their surroundings, small bits of solid food, globules of fat, or the like. You may see an ameba surrounding a food particle and taking it whole into its cell. There are cells in your own body that do the same thing. Among them are certain blood cells (*phagocytes*) that engulf and digest bacteria, thus providing resistance to bacterial disease. Their behavior is more of an apparent exception than a real one. The particles taken in whole by an ameba or other cell are reduced to molecules in solution before they actually enter the protoplasm and take part in its chemical activities.

Thus, even in these instances the rule holds that protoplasm usually obtains materials from a solution with which it is in contact. Cells in multicellular organisms are usually also in constant contact with solutions, solutions in adjacent cells or, commonly, in liquids moving outside but among the cells. These liquids, of which the sap of a tree and blood plasma are special examples, are generally very elaborate solutions, intricately influenced by the chemistry of the whole organism.

The question of how cells get their materials thus reduces to the question of how molecules move about, sometimes in gases, but more often in the liquids in which they are in solution. Some movements of molecules are sufficiently obvious to need little discussion. If a molecule is in solution in a liquid or is part of a gas, it is moved along by movements of the liquid or the gas. It is less obvious that molecules also move under their own power, so to speak. This movement is governed by the principles of diffusion, the semipermeability of membranes, and osmosis, which were treated in Chapter 3.

RELATIONS OF CELL STRUCTURE AND CELL METABOLISM

The remainder of this chapter will deal principally with the major pathways of metabolism, both catabolic and anabolic, and the mechanisms controlling them. In effect, we shall be studying $A \rightarrow B \rightarrow C \rightarrow D$ sequences so that we may become acquainted with the compounds in each sequence and the modes of their chemical transformation.

This is an appropriate moment for an admonition. Even though we display the various metabolic pathways as abstract series of compounds and arrows, we must never forget that all of the changes occur in

and on the many intricate subcellular structures described in Chapter 3 and so elegantly portrayed by electron micrography. The point to be stressed is that the cell is more than a mere bag of enzymes. It would be remarkable enough if it were. But, in fact, it is an intricate, highly compartmentalized structure, consisting of many membranes and membrane-limited spaces. None of its exquisite structure is without importance in the conduct of metabolic processes. The outer cell membrane actively determines what substances may enter the cell. Other cytoplasmic membranes act as barriers to random molecular motion and thus tend to segregate certain reactions into certain cell regions. Perhaps the perfect example of such a segregating boundary is the membrane surrounding the lysosome. As long as it is intact, the cell is spared destruction by enzymes within the lysosome. When the membrane is broken, the cell is killed.

We should also remember that specific metabolic processes take place in or on specific intracellular structures. Protein synthesis, we have seen, occurs on the ribosomes, and the new protein molecules have particular relations to the endoplasmic reticulum. The main oxidative reactions of cell metabolism occur in the mitochondria, and we shall presently discover that the configuration of the mitochondrial membrane is such as to permit a particular spatial organization of the many interacting oxidative enzymes. We shall also have reason to appreciate that photosynthesis is enormously facilitated by the complicated organization of the chloroplast.

As we survey the various energy-producing and synthetic pathways of metabolism, we should keep in mind that all of the processes are taking place in a structural system whose complex arrangement of materials and high degree of order is an extraordinarily improbable event. Moreover, it is a system of great instability, one that can be maintained only by constant input of energy and synthetic activity. Thus, metabolism depends for its continuance and efficiency on a complex physical structure, and, in turn, the structure depends for its continued existence on the transactions of metabolism.

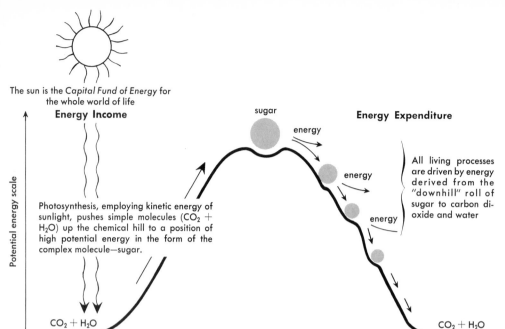

The sun is the *Capital Fund of Energy* for the whole world of life

Energy Income

sugar

Energy Expenditure

energy

energy

energy

All living processes are driven by energy derived from the "downhill" roll of sugar to carbon dioxide and water

Potential energy scale

Photosynthesis, employing kinetic energy of sunlight, pushes simple molecules (CO_2 + H_2O) up the chemical hill to a position of high potential energy in the form of the complex molecule—sugar.

$CO_2 + H_2O$

$CO_2 + H_2O$

FIG. 4-1 **Sugar: crossroads of metabolism.**

Chemical Work of the Cell

We learned in Chapter 2 that energy is defined as the capacity to do work, that large quantities of potential energy are inherent in the chemical structures of sugars and other nutrient materials, that the potential energy is invested in these molecules in the process of photosynthesis, the ultimate energy source being the sun, and that exergonic oxidative reactions convert this potential energy to free kinetic energy, although such reactions frequently require initial investments of activating energy. We must now consider further the metabolic processes that generate energy and the forms in which this energy is transported, stored, and released.

The fact that the cell's complex organic molecules—sugars, lipids, and proteins—have high contents of potential chemical energy has a twofold significance. First, as has been said, it is by the chemical breakdown of large molecules that kinetic energy is released to power all the cell's and organism's many activities. You are expending kinetic energy when you run, when you merely lift a finger, when your chest muscles move in breathing, or when your blood courses in your veins. And in every activity the energy derives from the potential chemical energy

in your own constituent molecules as they are oxidized. You literally consume yourself when you do work. It is, then, small wonder that you must constantly feed—and feed, moreover, by taking in some large and complex molecules.

But there is a second significance. *Only* living organisms possess these large molecules. It is true that after you have partly burned yourself up on hard work you can repair the damage by ingesting some other form of life. But it too did work and fed; where did its food come from? If the supply were limited, life would last just so long before it would stop because its chemical fuel resources had been expended. That life is not limited by a finite and expendable fuel source is due entirely to the existence of *some* living cells that can photosynthesize sugars. These cells can use the energy of sunlight to push CO_2 and H_2O uphill again into sugar (a reduction process). The chemical machinery in green plants is a turbine for the whole world of life. Just as the hydroelectric turbine exploits the resources of a waterfall, converting its energy into a form usable by other machines, so does the photosynthetic apparatus in a plant turn over the sun's energy to all other living things. It does so by transforming the kinetic energy of sunlight into the potential chemical energy that living systems can utilize.

There are many ways of looking at the metabolism of living cells and many details to fit together. But there is one feature that will always keep us oriented; like a major crossroads, it is the point to which we can always come back to find our way again. This feature is the central role of sugars in the economy of cells. In the balance sheet of life, all energy income leads to sugars, and all energy expenditures lead from them (Figure 4-1).

The sugar fuels made by a plant can be broken down in an oxidative process that releases energy. This is so both in the plant itself and in the animal that eats the plant. The oxidative release of energy is *respiration,* and it is in one form or another coextensive with life. In the vast majority of cases, respiration involves the consumption of oxygen; like the burning of coal or wood, respiration stops when oxygen is withheld.

In an over-all view, we can sum up the chemical processes underlying life's energy economy as in Table 4-1. Photosynthesis reduces CO_2 and binds energy with a release of O_2. Respiration oxidizes a carbon molecule (sugar) and releases energy and CO_2. These two simple equations summarize the end results but omit the numerous complex intermediate reactions. Furthermore, they make no reference to the chemical mechanisms by which the energy released in respiration is put to use and the cell functions in which it is utilized.

The great similarities in the chemical properties of all cells derive largely from the fact that they all have to start from the sugar crossroads. They resemble each other most markedly in how they break sugar down piecemeal, in how they trap and transfer the energy released, and in how they use the energy to compound their other constituents, the fats and proteins. Before we can investigate the general patterns of energy expenditure and utilization shared by most cells, we must first examine the income side of the ledger in greater detail.

ENERGY CAPTURE: PHOTOSYNTHESIS

General Plan of Photosynthesis

It would be difficult indeed to overstate the fundamental biological importance of photosynthesis. The world of life has found no substitute for it as an energy transformer. Knowledge of the photosynthetic process was only slowly acquired during the seventeenth and eighteenth centuries. Jan Baptista van Helmont demonstrated in the seventeenth century that a potted plant gained weight that could not be accounted for by the withdrawal of food from the soil in the pot. Using a willow tree, he discovered that in 5 years it gained pounds, while the soil lost only ounces. The gain in weight was evidently due to the uptake of gases from the atmosphere or of the water daily supplied to the pot or of both. The fact that a plant takes up CO_2 from the air and releases

TABLE 4-1   *Cyclic Interrelations of Carbon Dioxide, Oxygen, Sugar, Water, and Energy*

Photosynthesis in plants (endergonic) is an energy-binding *reduction.*

$$6CO_2 + 6H_2O \; + \text{Kinetic energy of sunlight} \xrightarrow{\text{enzymes}} C_6H_{12}O_6 + 6O_2$$

low potential energy   high potential energy

Respiration in plants and animals (exergonic) is an energy-releasing *oxidation.*

$$C_6H_{12}O_6 + 6O_2 \xrightarrow{\text{enzymes}} 6CO_2 + 6H_2O \; + \text{Kinetic energy of living processes}$$

high potential energy   low potential energy

O_2 was discovered by Joseph Priestley in experiments showing that plants and animals die when placed under bell jars separately but survive when placed together, as in Figure 4-2. The CO_2 given off by the respiring mouse supplies the plant with material for photosynthesis; the O_2 released by the plant's photosynthesis suffices for the respiration of both.

It was not, however, until the nineteenth century that these facts were understood. The weight gain van Helmont noted was due to the manufacture of organic molecules from the CO_2 and H_2O. This manufacture was found to be dependent on light and on the green pigment chlorophyll in the leaf. Precisely *how* the sugar is manufactured in the green leaf was only recently resolved, through ingenious experiments involving the use of CO_2 containing radioactive carbon. From the biochemical pathway of the radioactive carbon, we can trace the various compounds formed in the course of sugar synthesis.

For purposes of discussion, it is helpful to divide the story of photosynthesis into two major topics. First, how is the energy of sunlight captured and made available for the performance of chemical work? And second, what metabolic pathway is followed in the conversion of CO_2 to sugar? Let us briefly consider these questions in turn.

Absorption of Light Energy—
the Light Reaction

To be photochemically useful, light must first be absorbed. The particular molecules that are specially adapted to absorb visible light are the pigments. The color of any pigment is due to the fact that because of its molecule structure it absorbs some wavelengths of light more than others. Sunlight, as you doubtless recall, is a mixture of wavelengths ranging (as far as is visible to our eyes) from the long waves that we perceive as red to the short waves that we perceive as violet. When sunlight strikes a colored object, part of this wavelength mixture is absorbed. The remaining wavelengths are reflected toward our eyes, which thus receive more of some wavelengths than of others. We perceive these dominant wavelengths as color. Chlorophyll absorbs mostly red and violet and adjacent wavelengths from sunlight and so transmits or reflects mainly the wavelengths around the middle of the visible spectrum, which we see as green. In many organic compounds, color seems to be a purely incidental result of molecular structure and not, in itself, related to a biological function. In chlorophyll, however, the color is an indication that energy-rich radiation is being absorbed and used; the red and violet ends of the spectrum are the rays most strongly absorbed by chlorophyll. (What color would trees and fields be if plants contained a pigment which absorbed the middle and purple portions of the spectrum?)

Chlorophyll is commonly a mixture of two different compounds, chlorophyll a ($C_{55}H_{72}O_5N_4Mg$) and chlorophyll b ($C_{55}H_{70}O_6N_4Mg$). The chemical structure of chlorophyll a is given in Figure 4-3. All green plants have chlorophyll a; many algae and a few other green plants lack chlorophyll b and may have other, related compounds. Except in the blue-

FIG. 4-2 Priestley's experiments. In sealed chamber A the plant dies for lack of carbon dioxide; in B the mouse dies for lack of oxygen; in C both live. Priestley (1733–1804) did not know CO_2 and O_2 by the modern terms. He spoke of "fixed" and "good" air, respectively.

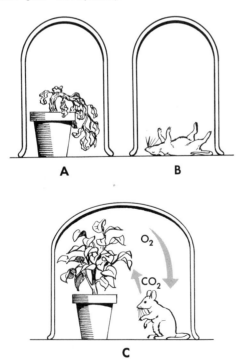

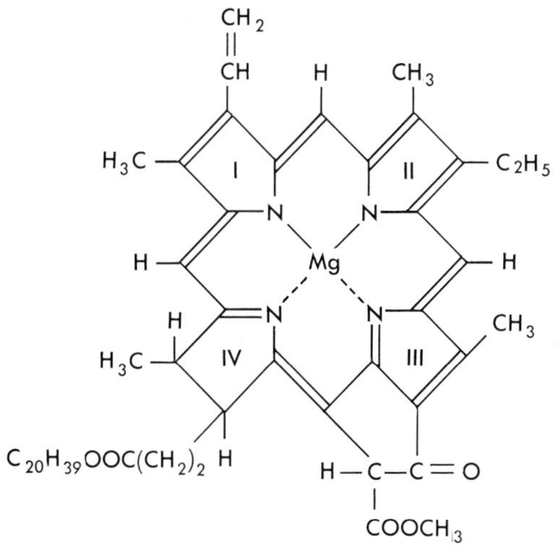

CH$_2$
CH
H   **CH$_3$**

H$_3$C — I   II — **C$_2$H$_5$**

N   N

H   **Mg**   **H**

N   N

H
H$_3$C — IV   III — **CH$_3$**

C$_{20}$H$_{39}$OOC(CH$_2$)$_2$ **H**   **H — C — C = O**

COOCH$_3$

Chlorophyll a

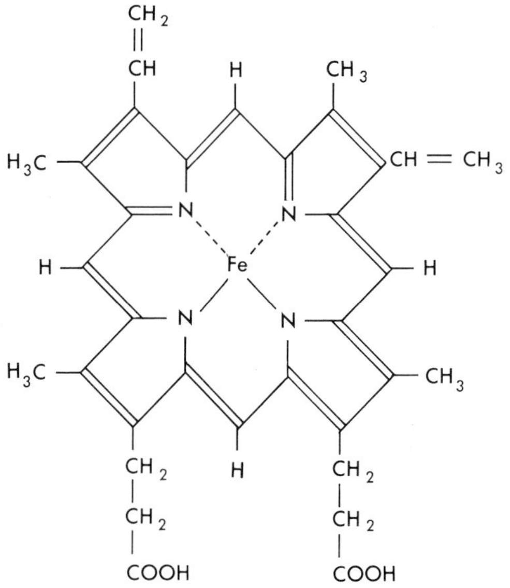

CH$_2$
CH
H   **CH$_3$**

H$_3$C —   — **CH = CH$_3$**

N   N

H —   **Fe**   — **H**

N   N

H$_3$C —   — **CH$_3$**

CH$_2$ **H**   **CH$_2$**

CH$_2$ **CH$_2$**

COOH   **COOH**

Heme

FIG. 4-3 Chemical structures of chlorophyll a and heme.
Note the close structural similarity between chlorophyll and heme,
with four identical rings (I to IV) contributing to the basic structure. The chief differences are (1) the Mg in chlorophyll and Fe
in heme, and (2) the proteins attached to chlorophyll and heme
are different.

green algae and bacteria, chlorophyll occurs within
cells only in the small bodies (plastids) called chloroplasts. Within the chloroplasts the pigment is found
in numerous still smaller bodies, the *grana* (Figure

4-4). A single plant cell may contain up to 80
chloroplasts, and a single mature chloroplast—for
instance, of spinach—may contain 40 to 60 grana.
Within a granum the flat chlorophyll molecules are
stacked in piles providing a relatively huge surface

FIG. 4-4 The chloroplast. Note the laminated structure as
shown by electron microscopy ($\times$22,000). The stacks of dense
lamellae are the grana, the main loci of the chlorophyll molecules. (Photo, A. E. Vatter)

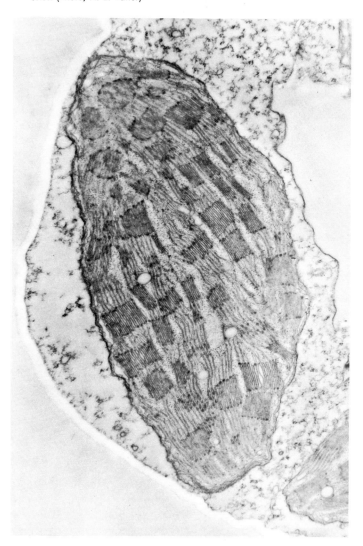

area. These molecules are the true loci of photosynthesis in the green plant.

In the first phase of photosynthesis, the radiant energy of sunlight activates or excites the chlorophyll molecule as follows:

$$Ch \quad + \quad Photon \rightarrow \quad Ch^*$$

Chlorophyll   Light   Activated chlorophyll

The absorption of light energy by the chlorophyll molecule raises it to a short-lived *excited* state (designated by an asterisk), in which the pigment has the capacity to serve as an *electron donor*. A similar phenomenon occurs in photoelectric cells whose light-sensitive chemical substances generate electric currents. However, only chlorophyll is useful as an electron donor in photosynthesis. Moreover, it is useful only when it is in its natural crystal-like arrangement within a granum. Free chlorophyll, extracted from the granum, although chemically intact, can no longer transfer energy to other molecules as in photosynthesis.

Organic *electron acceptors* within the granum accept the electrons (that is, they are *reduced*—see Chapter 2) from activated chlorophyll; the chlorophyll then replaces its lost electrons by splitting water and taking some from the cleavage products. Water, it will be recalled, can dissociate into H^+ and OH^- ions. These ions can react in a variety of ways. The H^+ ion can indirectly reduce the coenzyme NADP to form $NADPH_2$ (Chapter 2), which in turn can serve as an essential reducing agent (that is, electron donor) in the conversion of $6CO_2$ to sugar ($C_6H_{12}O_6$). Four OH^- ions can interact to form two molecules of H_2O and one of gaseous O_2, which escapes. This is the free oxygen known to be liberated in photosynthesis. The activated chlorophyll can also transfer energy to ADP and phosphate to form ATP; thus the two energy-rich molecules produced early in photosynthesis are $NADPH_2$ and ATP. Solar energy has been trapped in the structure of these two molecules.

Many of the details of these reactions are uncertain, but we may say in summary that (1) activated chlorophyll promotes the dissociation of water to H and OH; (2) the H of water provides the reducing power needed to transform the coenzyme NADP to $NADPH_2$, which then reduces CO_2 to sugar; (3) free O_2 is a by-product, whose ultimate source is the water molecule; (4) energy is transferred to ADP to produce ATP. Thus the net result of the light reaction in photosynthesis is

$$2H_2O + 2NADP \xrightarrow{\text{light}} 2NADPH_2 + O_2$$

$$ADP + \text{\textcircled{P}} \xrightarrow{\text{chlorophyll}} ATP$$

Light energy, through its effect on chlorophyll, thereby converts the cleavage products of water into two metabolically useful compounds. With the formation of $NADPH_2$ and ATP, the light-dependent phase of photosynthesis is completed.

Conversion of CO_2 to Sugar— the Dark Reaction

Present knowledge of the complex means whereby CO_2 is reduced to sugar has been achieved largely through the use of CO_2 containing the radioactive carbon isotope C^{14}. To the plant, $C^{14}O_2$ is chemically indistinguishable from ordinary CO_2 ($C^{12}O_2$); hence the metabolic fates of both types of CO_2 are identical. Thus, when $C^{14}O_2$ is supplied to green cells in the light, all the intermediary compounds on the pathway to sugar become radioactive through its incorporation and are thereby traceable with Geiger counters and other detecting devices.

This approach to the problem of identifying the metabolic pathway of CO_2 was launched in the late 1940's by Melvin Calvin and his associates at the University of California. In experiments performed mainly with the unicellular algae *Chlorella* and *Scenedesmus,* they found that within less than 1 minute after the introduction of $C^{14}O_2$, radioactivity could be detected in many molecules within the cells, including sugars, sugar phosphates, amino acids, and organic acids. One of the *first* compounds to become radioactive was phosphoglyceric acid, or PGA, a well-known three-carbon acid,

$$\begin{array}{c} COOH \\ | \\ H-C-OH \\ | \\ CH_2O-\text{\textcircled{P}} \end{array}$$

Moreover, almost all of the radioactivity in the

PGA formed during a brief exposure to $C^{14}O_2$ was located in its carboxyl (—COOH) carbon. We now know that a sequence of enzymatic reactions occurs in which the ketopentose ribulose diphosphate accepts the $C^{14}O_2$ to form an unstable six-carbon compound, which splits to give two molecules of PGA.

$$\begin{array}{c}
\text{CH}_2\text{O}—\text{P} \\
| \\
\text{C}=\text{O} \\
| \\
\text{H}—\text{C}—\text{OH} \\
| \\
\text{H}—\text{C}—\text{OH} \\
| \\
\text{CH}_2\text{O}—\text{P}
\end{array}
\xrightarrow{+\,C^{14}O_2}
\begin{array}{c}
\text{CH}_2\text{O}—\text{P} \\
| \\
\text{HO}—\text{C}—\text{C}^{14}\text{OOH} \\
| \\
\text{C}=\text{O} \\
| \\
\text{H}—\text{C}—\text{OH} \\
| \\
\text{CH}_2\text{O}—\text{P}
\end{array}
\xrightarrow{+\,H_2O}$$

$$\begin{array}{c}
\text{CH}_2\text{O}—\text{P} \\
| \\
\text{HO}—\text{C}—\text{H} \\
| \\
\text{C}^{14}\text{OOH}
\end{array}
+
\begin{array}{c}
\text{COOH} \\
| \\
\text{H}—\text{C}—\text{OH} \\
| \\
\text{CH}_2\text{O}—\text{P}
\end{array}$$

The photosynthetic process is completed by the conversion of PGA to glucose, through a series of reactions that is exactly the reverse of the pathway by which glucose is broken down to PGA in animal cells. An early step in the conversion of PGA to glucose requires the participation of the $NADPH_2$ formed in the first step of photosynthesis.

$$\begin{array}{c}
\text{COOH} \\
| \\
\text{H}—\text{C}—\text{OH} \\
| \\
\text{CH}_2\text{O}—\text{P}
\end{array}
+ NADPH_2 \rightarrow$$

Phosphoglyceric
acid

$$\begin{array}{c}
\text{CHO} \\
| \\
\text{H}—\text{C}—\text{OH} \\
| \\
\text{CH}_2\text{O}—\text{P}
\end{array}
+ NADP + H_2O$$

Phosphoglyceraldehyde

This reaction, the reduction of —COOH to —CHO, could not occur without the H atoms of $NADPH_2$.

ENERGY RELEASE AND EXPENDITURE

We have seen that the energy of sunlight is trapped by chlorophyll, transferred to $NADPH_2$ and ATP, and used by the plant to convert CO_2 into glucose. We must now ask a critical question: How

does the cell convert the potential energy of glucose into a chemically useful form? The remarkable answer, it turns out, is equally valid for all cells, plant and animal—a striking example of the cell theory manifesting its universality at the biochemical level. In a sense, we have reached the great crossroads of metabolism.

Analogy with a Business Economy

It is useful to think about cellular energy expenditure in terms of a business community. Like a member of such a community, a cell does work—movement, heat production, manufacture of new complex chemicals (lipids, proteins), and, occasionally, even light production. Also, as in a business community, there is the costly task of maintaining order. For all this work, which includes both production and maintenance, payment must be made.

In a community of people, payment is made in currency, but currency is only a token for energy of some kind. It is simply more convenient to pay a man a dollar for some goods or services than to pay him by spading his garden for an hour. It is also convenient to carry only small change in one's pocket for immediate use and to keep reserves either in the bank for quick withdrawal or more deeply stored in bonds or real estate.

In the cell's economy, we detect a similar over-all pattern. The cell keeps some of its energy-wealth in deep storage (especially starches and lipids), it keeps some on quick call (glucose and compounds called *phosphagens*), and it makes immediate payments in what proves to be small change (phosphate groups). Thus payments are made by the cell directly in energy—energy in the form of chemical structures.

Analogies are always dangerous when carried too far, but the present one does help us keep the details in perspective. Let us then look at this cellular economy, being careful to distinguish the following aspects: (1) the nature of work done; (2) methods of payment; (3) methods of currency (energy) conversion; (4) phosphate radicals as general currency; (5) glucose and phosphagens as current accounts; (6) starches and lipids as reserves.

well-known nucleotide adenosine triphosphate, abbreviated ATP, which is adenine—ribose—$\text{P} \sim \text{P} \sim \text{P}$ (see Chapter 2).

The ATP molecule has a high potential-energy content, largely concentrated in the bonds attaching the two terminal phosphates. An energy-rich bond is represented by a wavy line, $\sim$ (in contrast to the conventional bond, —). Energy transfer in a synthetic reaction might be illustrated thus:

$$\text{glucose} + \text{ATP} \xrightarrow{\text{enzyme}} \text{starch} + \text{ADP} + \text{P}$$

In this reaction, energy is transferred from ATP to the bonds joining the glucose units in the larger starch molecule. We might say that the conversion of glucose to starch is an endergonic process, but that the over-all reaction shown above is exergonic.

In summary, the function of ATP is as follows: it pays out energy, in a currency of $\sim \text{P}$ radicals, to molecules unable themselves to react exergonically. It is as though $\sim \text{P}$ were the extra capital needed to allow a project to go ahead.

Let us now develop a more detailed view of cellular economy by returning to glucose. We have mentioned that the oxidative breakdown of glucose (respiration) is the source of cellular energy. How is the energy released in the oxidation of sugar converted into the usable currency of ATP?

Currency of Energy Exchange:
Energy-rich Chemical Bonds

When the cell executes any of the thousands upon thousands of endergonic reactions necessary for its organized chemical life, it must supply energy for two distinct operations: (1) energy of activation and (2) energy of reaction. Cells meet these energetic needs in two ways.

First, the cell employs enzymes to reduce the need for *activation energy.* As we have noted, enzymes catalyze specific reactions. You will now appreciate the significance of enzyme specificity; order would not be preserved within the cell if there were a "universal enzyme" simultaneously catalyzing all reactions.

Second, the cell pays in the *reaction energy* by the exchange of energy from special energy-transfer molecules. This principle of molecular energy transfer is the heart of the cell's mechanisms. One of the great unifying themes in the chemical life of all cells is the common nature of the energy-transfer mechanism. The most important such molecule of the cell is the

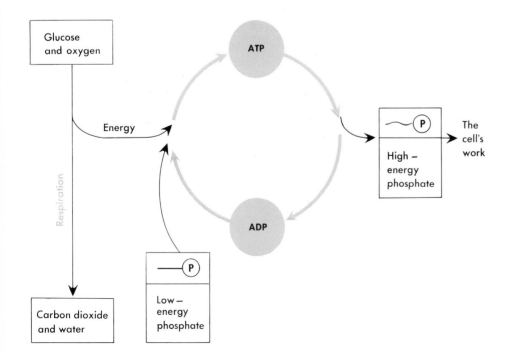

FIG. 4-5 The ADP-ATP cycle.

Figure 4-5 shows in outline form how energy liberated in the respiration of glucose is ultimately converted to energy-rich phosphate groups. The oxidation of glucose proceeds stepwise, releasing small packets of energy adequate to regenerate ATP from ADP and —$\circledP$. The reconstituted ATP then can make further payments by donating $\sim\circledP$ to other compounds that require energy.

In seeking to understand how the oxidation of sugar generates utilizable energy as energy-rich phosphate bonds in ATP, it is helpful to consider a few simple quantitative relationships. We learned earlier (Table 4-1) that glucose is oxidized according to the following reaction:

$$C_6H_{12}O_6 + 6O_2 \rightarrow 6CO_2 + 6H_2O + \text{Energy}$$

Thermodynamics tells us that the amount of energy liberated in the combustion of a substance is always the same, no matter what means is used to accomplish the combustion. When a mole of glucose (180 grams) is oxidized by actual burning, 690,000 calories are released. We may assume, therefore, that this much free energy is liberated in the stepwise metabolic oxidation of glucose.

In the late 1930's, it was found that when simple suspensions of ground muscle or kidney tissue are incubated with glucose in the presence of oxygen, glucose is oxidized, and inorganic phosphate is added to ADP to make ATP. Furthermore, it was found that the utilization of oxygen and the disappearance of inorganic phosphate are coupled; for each atom of oxygen utilized, three phosphate groups are incorporated into three ATP molecules. It was this discovery of *oxidative phosphorylation* that led to the realization that ATP production is dependent upon oxidative metabolism. A P/O ratio of 3 means that the utilization of 12 atoms of oxygen in the total oxidation of glucose (see the equation) must be accompanied by the production of 36 molecules of ATP. Subsequent experiments showed that, in fact, 38 molecules of ADP are converted to ATP; the extra two will be explained later. These considerations indicate that the net equation of glucose oxidation should be expanded as follows:

$$C_6H_{12}O_6 + 6O_2 + 38ADP + 38P \rightarrow$$
$$6CO_2 + 6H_2O + 38ATP$$

These figures permit some interesting calculations. Since the terminal $\sim\circledP$ group of the number of grams equal to the molecular weight of ATP contains about 10,000 calories, 38 times that amount of ATP represents an energy yield of 380,000 calories, or 55 per cent of the 690,000 calories originally present in the glucose. The remainder is dissipated as heat. Even the best modern steam-generating plants convert no more than 30 per cent of the invested energy to useful work!

The many individual transformations summarized in the net equation just given occur in four major stages (Figure 4-6). In inspecting the figure, you should attempt to identify the stage at which each of the several components of the net reaction makes its entrance and exit. In particular, note what happens to the carbon skeleton of glucose and at what point electrons or hydrogen atoms are transferred and $\sim\circledP$ groups created from —$\circledP$ groups.

In the first stage, the six-carbon glucose molecule is split into two molecules of three carbons each, and these are converted at length into the three-carbon compound pyruvic acid. This process, involving no less than 10 sequential enzymatic steps, is called *glycolysis,* which produces a net gain of two ATP molecules per molecule of glucose cleaved. Note also that glycolysis involves the oxidative transfer of four hydrogens. In this preliminary stage, no CO_2 is produced, all the carbons being accounted for in pyruvic acid, and no O_2 is utilized. In sum, stage one involves the following net transformations:

$$\text{Glucose} + 2ADP + 2P \rightarrow 2 \text{ Pyruvic acid} + 2ATP + 4H$$

One of the three-carbon intermediates of glycolysis is phosphoglyceraldehyde. This compound is oxidized to phosphoglyceric acid (PGA) on its way to pyruvic acid. Note that this oxidative step is a reversal of the $NADPH_2$-dependent reduction occuring early in the conversion of CO_2 to glucose in photosynthesis (see p. 74). The reaction sequence from phosphoglyceraldehyde to glucose in photosynthesis is also exactly the reverse of the glucose-to-phosphoglyceraldehyde sequence in glycolysis.

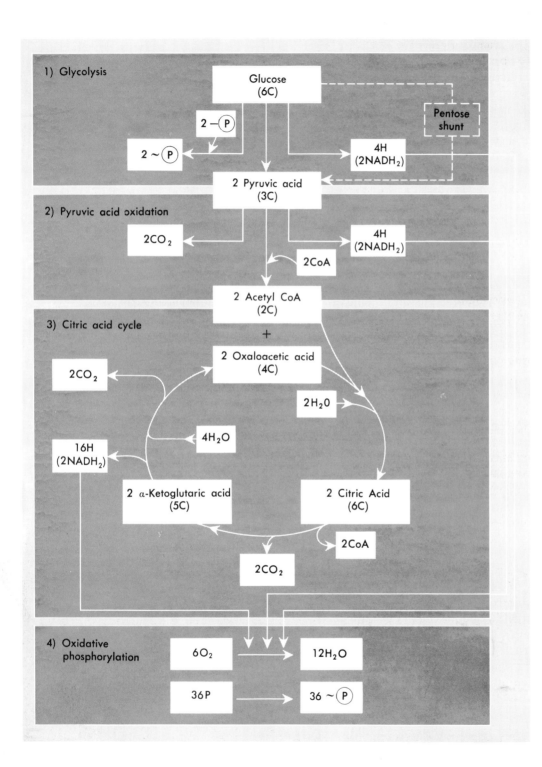

FIG. 4-6 The four stages of glucose metabolism. Carbon is released as CO_2, energy is released as $\sim$(P) groups, hydrogen is transferred in oxidative reactions, and molecular oxygen is consumed. Note that many intermediary compounds are omitted in this scheme.

In the second stage of sugar metabolism, each of the three-carbon pyruvic acid molecules is converted to a two-carbon derivative of acetic acid called *acetyl coenzyme A* (or acetyl CoA). Coenzyme A (abbreviated CoA) is essential in a large number of group-transfer reactions, in which the group transferred is an *acyl* radical, that is, the R— CO— portion of an organic acid, R—COOH. The CoA molecule, like most coenzymes, contains a vitamin—in this instance, pantothenic acid. Other coenzymes participating in the reactions at this stage are NAD from the vitamin niacin, thiamine pyrophosphate from vitamin B_1, and lipoic acid. For each pyruvic acid molecule, the reaction sequence liberates one carbon atom as CO_2, produces one molecule each of acetyl CoA and $NADH_2$, and oxidatively removes two hydrogen atoms per pyruvic acid molecule (meaning that four hydrogens are removed per original glucose molecule). As in the first stage, no oxygen is utilized, and relatively little energy is generated. In sum, stage two involves the following net transformations:

2 Pyruvic acid + 2CoA → 2 Acetyl CoA + 2CO_2 + 4H

Acetyl CoA is a "crossroads compound" of formidable versatility. Indeed, as shown in Figure 4-7, it occupies the central position in intermediary metabolism. It is also produced in the breakdown of fatty acids and certain amino acids. We shall later see that some molecules of acetyl CoA—those that escape further oxidative metabolism—serve as key building blocks in biosynthetic reactions.

In the third stage of glucose metabolism, the two two-carbon molecules of acetyl CoA enter into a remarkable metabolic cycle in which their four carbons are ingeniously converted to CO_2 (Figure 4-6). First, acetyl CoA combines with a four-carbon molecule, *oxaloacetic acid,* to produce a new six-carbon molecule, *citric acid* (and free coenzyme A). Citric acid is then systematically oxidized, first to a five-carbon and then to a four-carbon molecule. In the course of these reactions, two molecules of CO_2 are released, and four pairs of hydrogens are removed as $NADH_2$, for each molecule of acetyl CoA entering the cycle. The four-carbon molecule emerging from this sequence is oxaloacetic acid, which is free to combine with more acetyl CoA, so that the cycle begins again. The net transformations of stage three are as follows:

2 Acetyl CoA + 6H_2O + 2ADP + 2P + 16NAD →
4CO_2 + 2ATP + 16NADH + 2CoA

This stage has been variously termed the *citric acid cycle, tricarboxylic acid cycle,* and *Krebs cycle* (in recognition of Sir Hans Krebs, who first postulated its existence in 1937).

The reactions of the citric acid cycle convert all the available carbon of acetyl CoA to CO_2. But they produce no ATP directly. Instead, there is an accumu-

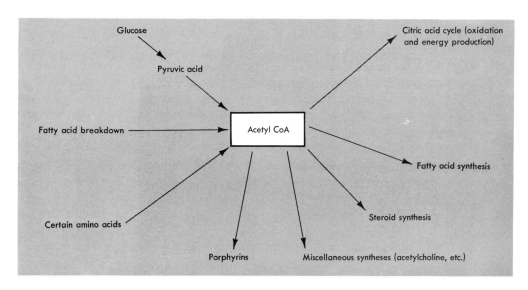

FIG. 4-7 The central position of acetyl CoA in intermediary metabolism.

lation of hydrogens, or electrons, that have arisen in the oxidations (that is, dehydrogenations) of the first three stages—the hydrogens being in the form of $NADH_2$. It is in the fourth stage that all these hydrogens are transferred through a complex chain of coenzymatic hydrogen donor-acceptors (including pyridine nucleotides, flavoproteins, and cytochromes) to oxygen, the final hydrogen acceptor, converting it to water and incidentally freeing the coenzymes to function again as hydrogen acceptors. Thus, oxygen is utilized at last, and thus the fourth reaction sequence is appropriately designated as the *respiratory chain,* or *cytochrome system.* In the course of this final hydrogen transfer, the bulk of the ATP is generated. The net transformations of stage four are as follows:

$$12NADH_2 + 6O_2 + 34ADP + 34P \rightarrow$$
$$12NAD + 12H_2O + 34ATP$$

If one adds up the equations describing the over-all changes in each of the four stages of glucose metabolism, the net result is identical to the summary equation on p. 78.

OXIDATIVE PHOSPHORYLATION.   Let us examine the fourth stage more closely. At the completion of two turns of the citric acid cycle, the six original glucose carbons have been converted to CO_2. Six molecules of H_2O have been utilized, and 12 pairs of hydrogens have been transferred to NAD. Only two molecules of ATP have been produced, however, and the major remaining task is that of stage four, oxidative phosphorylation: (1) transferring the 24 accumulated coenzyme-bound hydrogens to 12 atoms of oxygen so that NAD can be regenerated for another cycle; (2) establishing a couple, or connection, between these oxidative hydrogen transfers and the conversion of inorganic phosphate to $\sim$ⓟ; and (3) then transferring $\sim$ⓟ to ADP to make new ATP.

Exactly how this takes place is an unsolved biochemical problem. It is well established that NAD-borne hydrogens (or electrons) are transferred from one molecular electron carrier to another along the reaction sequence shown in Figure 4-8. This respiratory chain is a series of interlocking cyclic processes. Each carrier molecule is reduced when it accepts an electron and becomes reoxidized by passing an electron to the next link in the chain. In three of the cycles there occurs an intermediate step in which the oxidation causes the synthesis of a $\sim$ⓟ group, which is then transferred to ADP to form ATP.

What molecules serve as electron carriers and phosphate carriers in the respiratory chain? The electron carrier next in line after NAD is FAD (flavin adenine dinucleotide), a nucleotide containing the vitamin riboflavin. FAD transfers its electron to coenzyme Q, which passes the electron to the acceptors called *cytochromes.* Cytochromes are chromoproteins (Chapter 2), found in all oxygen-utilizing cells. The colored prosthetic groups of these proteins are complex porphyrin structures similar to those that we have already encountered in chlorophyll and heme (see Figure 4-3). The metal of the cytochromes is iron. The various cytochromes (known as cytochrome *b,* cytochrome *c,* cytochrome *a,* and cytochrome a_3) differ from one another in the fine structures of their proteins. But the iron-porphyrin groups of all four function similarly as electron carriers, the central iron atom undergoing reversible reduction and oxidation.

$$Fe^{+++} + e^- \rightleftharpoons Fe^{++}$$

As the electron moves from molecule to molecule in the cytochrome system, some energy is lost at each step. At three steps in the sequence, energy is transferred to ADP and phosphate to produce ATP (Figure 4-8). Thus, we can say that the transfer of electrons in the cytochrome system and ATP formation are coupled. Unfortunately, we do not understand the molecular events involved in this coupling mechanism.

In summary, oxidative phosphorylation involves the transport of energy in the form of the 24 hydrogens (or electrons) derived from one molecule of glucose to oxygen via the following route: NAD to FAD to cytochromes to 12 oxygens. Simultaneously, 36 molecules of inorganic phosphate are converted to the $\sim$ⓟ groups of ATP.

We can now answer a question raised at the start of this discussion. In the photosynthetic trapping of solar energy much of that energy is transferred to the structure of organic molecules, including glucose. We inquired how the energy trapped in this process could be harnessed for the cell's purposes. The answer is: by being converted into $\sim$ⓟ groups. Although

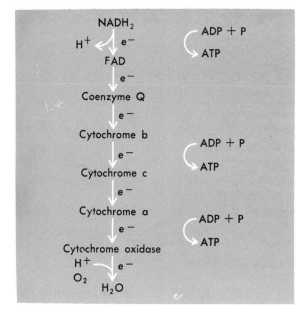

FIG. 4-8 Oxidative phosphorylation in the respiratory chain. Respiratory enzymes transfer energy by a series of reactions, each set in motion by the one preceding it. The known coenzymatic carriers in the chain are nicotinamide-adenine nucleotide (NAD), flavin adenine dinucleotide (FAD), and four cytochromes. Coupled with the reduction-oxidation cycles of three carriers (NAD), cytochrome b, and cytochrome a, are reactions with unidentified enzymes that transfer energy released in the cycles to ATP. As noted in the text, the transfer is not fully understood. When two electrons are passed down the whole chain, they give rise to three molecules of ATP.

plant and animal cells alike depend upon the process of oxidative phosphorylation just described as a principal source of ATP, plant cells also derive some ATP from the reactions associated with photosynthesis. Consequently, it is possible for green plants to produce ATP without having to oxidize stored carbohydrates. Hence, they can manufacture more carbohydrates than they use, and the stored excess can be utilized by other organisms to supply their energy requirements.

ROLE OF THE MITOCHONDRIA. The enzymatic apparatus of the citric acid cycle and the respiratory chain is of such complexity that it could scarcely function efficiently if the individual participating enzymes were distributed randomly in the fluids of the cell. The precision of the bookkeeping is astonishing and is in fact the result of a highly ordered

physical arrangement of the enzymes of the citric acid cycle and respiratory chain within the mitochondria. Since only the mitochondria are fully capable of converting pyruvic acid to CO_2 and H_2O when isolated from the cell, they are truly the power plants of the cell.

Investigators now are attempting to determine the exact locations of the enzymes within the mitochondrial membrane, whose structure we saw in Figure 3-12. When a mitochondrial membrane is broken by intense sound waves or detergents, the internal matrix escapes, and insoluble membrane fragments can be separated by centrifugation. The matrix is found to contain the enzymes of the citric acid cycle; the enzymes of the respiratory sequence are exclusively in the membrane fragments. Recent theoretical estimates suggest that the respiratory-chain enzymes are organized in assemblies, or sets, each containing one molecule of each enzyme. A complete assembly would contain 15 or more active protein molecules close together in a precise geometrical array, a sort of molecular bucket brigade. These assemblies are now thought to comprise 30 to 40 per cent of the mitochondrial substance. Significantly, the prediction that such assemblies exist is supported by recent electron-microscopic studies using new high-resolution techniques. They show that the membranes of the internal cristae of a mitochondrion are built from small particles (Figure 4-9). These so-called *electron transport particles* appear as regular subunits, 100 Ångstrom units in diameter, within the lipoprotein framework of the mitochondrial membrane. That each of these minute mitochondrial subunits contains all of the enzymes of the respiratory chain now seems likely. This means that the mitochondrial membrane is far more than an inert wall or container. Rather, it is a functioning metabolic machine, whose highly ordered pattern of enzyme molecules determines the organization and programing of the enzymatic activity of the living cell.

Mitochondria have been observed to swell and shrink, and the mitochondrial membrane itself changes its dimensions in the course of its activity. Like a sheet of muscle tissue, it can relax or contract,

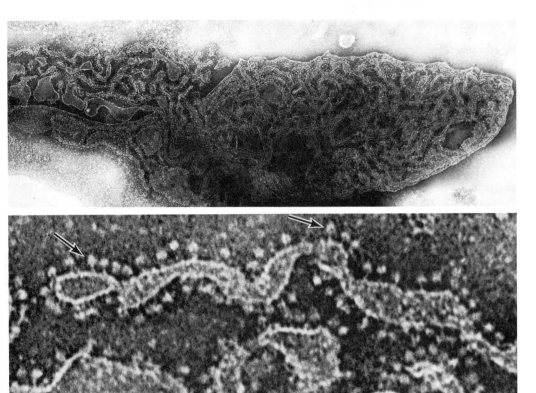

FIG. 4-9 Demonstration of the elementary particles of the mitochondrion. Top, longitudinal cross section of a mitochondrion as seen by electron micrography ($\times 42,000$). Bottom, enlargement of a small area at the upper photograph ($\times 280,000$). Note the electron transport particles attached to the membrane of the crista. (Photo, H. Fernández-Morán)

its behavior apparently being related to the local ATP concentration. The membrane contracts when the ATP concentration is high and relaxes when it is low. This suggests that the rate of oxidative metabolism is somehow regulated by shifts in the internal structure of the mitochondrion, which keep the rate of power production in accord with the needs of the cell. Clearly, the integration of chemical behavior and physical structure in the mitochondrion provides a fine and important example of the ultimate convergence of structure and function in biological systems.

ENERGY UTILIZATION: SYNTHESIS OF CELL COMPONENTS

We have now learned how remarkably intricate and efficient is the cell's machinery for deriving usable energy from the molecular fuel glucose. In essence, the cell achieves this efficiency by not liberating more energy from glucose at any one time than can be picked up and stored as $\sim \text{\textcircled{P}}$. Second, the stepwise breakdown of sugar yields fragments with four-, three-, and two-carbon skeletons

intermediate between the six-carbon glucose and the one-carbon CO_2. These intermediates play leading roles in the rest of the cell's economy, for they are the raw materials used in the manufacture of all lipids, proteins, and nucleic acids. Let us turn now to this aspect of cellular work.

Principles of Biosynthesis

So far we have treated the cell's economy as though it were all a matter of energy—wealth and its expenditure. But an economy needs more than energy to do its work; it needs raw materials. The four main constituents in the cell's raw materials are carbon, oxygen, hydrogen, and nitrogen. The *ultimate* source of all the carbon is atmospheric CO_2, which is fixed (reduced) in photosynthesis (and to an extent insignificant in most cells by nonphotosynthetic processes). Oxygen enters the cell in gaseous form from the air and also in water. Hydrogen and nitrogen never enter as gases despite their abundance in the atmosphere. Hydrogen enters ultimately in water. Nitrogen enters plants ultimately as nitrates (for example, potassium nitrate, KNO_3) absorbed from the soil by roots; and animals are ultimately dependent on plants for nitrogen. The point to be noted is that three of these four elements—carbon, oxygen, and hydrogen—enter the life of the cell by way of the glucose crossroads. We are back at the crossroads again in discussing materials, just as we were in discussing energy.

We shall try here to clarify only the basic outline of the cell's economy. Therefore, we shall deal with just the bare essentials of synthetic processes, as follows: (1) all synthetic steps are enzyme-controlled; (2) all syntheses consume energy; (3) generally speaking, all cells build complex molecules from the same relatively small group of molecular building blocks; (4) in the macromolecules formed from simpler organic molecules, the simpler units are frequently linked together chemically by *ester* linkages (that is, bonds formed by the removal of water)—however, the metabolic pathways that ultimately create these linkages may be very complicated, involv-

ing many separate reactions, enzymes, and coenzymes; and (5) all syntheses obtain their energy and materials (or both) from the catabolic processes described earlier (Figure 4-10).

Let us now consider briefly and selectively the methods by which the cell converts its small building blocks into recognizable cell components.

Ribose and the Nucleotide Precursors of RNA and DNA

As we have seen, a major function of the sugars is energy production. Another is the production of the versatile building block acetyl CoA. In addition, intact monosaccharide molecules themselves can serve as building blocks for a number of critically important

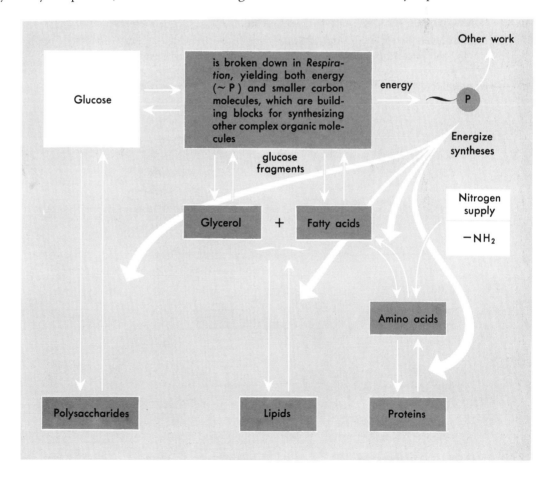

FIG. 4-10 Synthetic pathways.

cell constituents. For example, they join together to form the polysaccharides—glycogen in animals and starch in plants (Chapter 2); and in certain cells, unusual polysaccharides, such as heparin and hyaluronic acid, are synthesized from various carbohydrate derivatives, such as acetylglucosamine and glucuronic acid.

One of the most significant functions of the sugars is the synthesis of ribose, the five-carbon sugar of RNA, and its ribonucleotides. Ribose synthesis begins with glucose 6-phosphate. As indicated in Figure 4-6, this compound has an alternative route open to it. It can enter the main pathway of glycolysis, or it can enter a series of reactions that eventually produce ribose and thus are known as the *oxidative,* or *pentose, shunt.*

Ribose may react with ATP to produce ribose polyphosphate. The ribose polyphosphate is then enzymatically joined to a purine or pyrimidine to form a nucleotide (Chapter 2). Ribonucleotides must undergo several modifications to become nucleic acid precursors. To serve as RNA precursors, they must first be converted to the corresponding nucleotide triphosphates. For instance, the monophosphate of the ribonucleotide of guanine must be converted to the triphosphate before the enzyme RNA polymerase can incorporate it into new RNA. We now know that ribonucleotides are converted to deoxyribonucleotides, the precursors of DNA. Since deoxyribose is ribose minus one oxygen atom, this conversion is a reduction. The steps leading to RNA and DNA synthesis are summarized in Figure 4-11.

Nucleic Acids and Proteins

We shall defer to Chapter 7 further discussion of the means by which the cell polymerizes the triphosphates of the ribonucleotides and deoxyribonucleotides into RNA and DNA. For these are much more than mere enzymatic reactions of the conventional type. We shall learn in the following chapters that the genetic pattern of the cell is coded in a specific sequence of nucleotides in DNA and RNA. Hence these unique molecules must be capable of somehow being "stamped" with genetic information. The same is true of proteins, whose synthesis will also be described in Chapter 7. It is one thing to speak of the biochemical arrangements in which amino acids are strung together as proteins. But we must also recognize that the specificity of each protein molecule depends upon the precision of amino acid sequence and that amino acid sequence is in turn the final expression of a specific nucleotide sequence in DNA. This is the stuff of genetics, and we shall save it for the section on reproduction.

Despite this reservation, it is possible to remark briefly on proteins in the nongenetic context of cell metabolism. Protein synthesis requires a constant supply of amino acids. Many of these are present ready-made in the animal diet, and indeed some are essential in the diet since the animal cannot make them for itself. Others can be synthesized in the body cells.

FIG. 4-11 Outline summary of RNA and DNA synthesis.

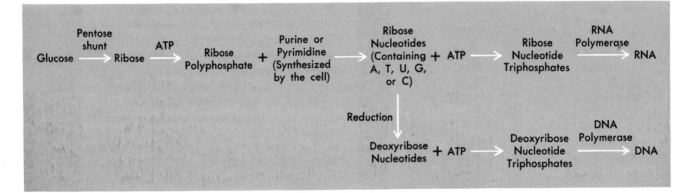

Amino groups can be incorporated into many of the carbon skeletons arising in glycolysis and the citric acid cycle (see Figure 4-6). Thus, amino acid biosynthesis is largely dependent upon active carbohydrate metabolism.

Lipids and Fatty Acids

Like carbohydrates, lipids (as well as other organic components of the cell) may contribute to the production of pyruvic acid and acetyl CoA (see Figure 4-6). Indeed, they make up a most important storage form of substances capable of yielding large amounts of metabolic energy. As in the case of carbohydrates, the breakdown of lipids involves a long sequence of enzymatic reactions. We shall not attempt to review this pathway in detail. However, several of its interesting features must be noted.

We saw earlier (Chapter 2) that a simple lipid or fat is formed when the acidic —COOH groups of three fatty acids react with the three —OH groups of glycerol. When the resulting triglyceride is later used by the cell as a fuel, it is first split into fatty acids and glycerol. The glycerol is eventually converted into 3-phosphoglyceraldehyde which then follows the usual glycolytic route to pyruvic acid and acetyl CoA (see Figure 4-6). The remaining fatty acids have an equally interesting fate. A naturally occurring fatty acid always contains an even number of carbon atoms. Through ingenious biochemical investigations, it was found that a long-chain fatty acid is degraded entirely by successive removals of carbon atoms *in pairs*. This elegant series of reactions can occur only if the fatty acid is first attached to coenzyme A. The resulting two-carbon units then become two-carbon acetyl CoA molecules. Since carbohydrates (and many amino acids) also break down to acetyl CoA, it is evident that many independent lines of metabolic breakdown converge in a common compound. Thus lipids, carbohydrates, and proteins all are degraded along their own catabolic pathways, but all arrive in the end at a remarkable focal point of cell metabolism, acetyl CoA.

It was long believed necessary merely to reverse the pathway of degradation in order to synthesize a fatty acid. However, recently a major synthetic pathway has been discovered that begins with malonyl CoA, a three-carbon compound produced on the addition of CO_2 to acetyl CoA.

$$\begin{matrix} CH_3 \\ | \\ CO{-}SCoA \end{matrix} + CO_2 + ATP \rightarrow \begin{matrix} CH_2{-}COOH \\ | \\ CO{-}SCoA \end{matrix} + ADP$$

Acetyl CoA   Malonyl CoA

Malonyl CoA condenses with acetyl CoA or the CoA derivative of a longer acid, and the CO_2 is again liberated so that the chain becomes lengthened by two carbons in a sequence of reactions involving NADP and ATP. For the cell there is a distinct safety factor in having synthesis follow a pathway differing from that for degradation (thus the reactions synthesizing glycogen are also different from those breaking it down). Among other things, this situation permits rate-controlling agencies, such as hormones, to speed up one of the two processes without affecting the other. For example, the hormone epinephrine (adrenalin) stimulates one specific enzyme (phosphorylase) in the pathway of glycogen breakdown. Thus, epinephrine acts by supplying the body with needed glucose in emergencies. If the enzyme were also in the pathway of glycogen synthesis, epinephrine might simultaneously stimulate breakdown and synthesis, yielding no benefit to the organism.

Fatty acids are involved at some stage in the syntheses of all three main kinds of molecules—carbohydrates, lipids, and proteins. In the world of life as a whole, solar energy is first made available through the respiration of sugars. But much of the energy one expends each day may derive more immediately from a beefsteak. Lipids and proteins, initially synthesized at the expense of sugar energy (via ATP), may in their turn be broken down to release energy. Their breakdown products include fatty acids, which may enter the citric acid cycle and be oxidized just as though they had arisen directly from sugar. Thus the three major groups of compounds (carbohydrates, lipids, and proteins) are interchangeable as energy resources and also as raw-material reservoirs. The carbon-chain skeleton of a fatty acid today may be part of a protein, lipid, or carbohydrate tomorrow. Organisms synthesize many other compounds, such as pigments, alkaloids, essential oils, and steroids, that do not fall into the three major classes we have covered. It is not possible to discuss them here.

Control of Cell Metabolism

Even the briefest survey of the cell's metabolic pathways must convince us of the necessity for regulatory systems capable of coordinating them. Complex traffic-controlling mechanisms must exist to allow cells to channel energy into the performance of specific tasks, to function uninterruptedly during periods of nutritional deprivation, and to adapt to adverse or injurious conditions.

Although the study of control systems—cellular and otherwise—is still in its infancy, it is evident that control of any activity in the cell can be effected only by the acceleration or deceleration of some particular metabolic process. Thus the maintenance of the so-called *steady state* within the cell becomes an exercise in the integrated control of metabolic rates.

When the nature of control systems is examined in abstract terms, it is seen that *all* operate in the same way; *effect acts back upon cause,* informing it of the consequences of its previous action and thereby permitting it to determine its future action. The most familiar example of such a system is the ordinary room thermostat, which turns the heat off when the rising air temperature exceeds the thermostat setting. Or consider the steersman of a boat: when he sees his vessel moving too far to leeward, he swings the rudder to windward. The function of the steersman (or the thermostat) consists in holding the course (or the temperature) by swinging the rudder (or the heater) in a direction that will offset any deviation from that course (or temperature). This general mechanism is called *negative feedback,* since the response is opposite to the initiating stimulus, or negative with respect to it (for example, rising temperature decreases heat production). Negative feedback systems demonstrate *oscillation* when for any reason there is a delay in response. The response then continues longer than it should to reach equilibrium, and the system overshoots. Feedback then occurs in the opposite direction. This accounts for the zig-zag course of the rudder-controlled boat. Oscillation of this type accounts for much normal physiological behavior, such as breathing and the heartbeat.

During the several decades that ended in the mid-1950's, biochemists were engaged chiefly in defining the individual steps of the metabolic pathways. Now that most of the principal pathways are known, it is possible to analyze the factors controlling the rates of their reactions. In general, these can be divided into two groups: (1) those that regulate traffic along a pathway by controlling the *level of activity* of individual enzymes; and (2) those that regulate traffic by controlling the *rate of formation* of individual enzymes.

FACTORS AFFECTING THE LEVEL OF ENZYME ACTIVITY

Although a specific reaction along a metabolic pathway depends upon the functioning of a specific enzyme, the activity level of that enzyme is a critical determinant of the rate of the entire pathway only when the reaction in question is the rate-limiting step, or bottleneck, of the whole sequence.

Substrate and Coenzyme Availability

Up to a certain point, the rate of an enzyme reaction rises as the concentration of its substrate rises. Beyond that point, the enzyme is considered saturated with substrate molecules, and reaction velocity can be increased further only if the amount of enzyme present is increased.

It follows that the rate of a metabolic pathway varies with variations in the concentration of the initial substrate of the pathway. If the glucose supply were limited by starvation, glycolysis would be depressed (see Figure 4-6). Conversely, an excess of glucose would accelerate the pathway to the point at which the rate-limiting enzyme would be saturated with substrate. Reactions requiring the participation of a coenzyme are similarly affected by the availability of the coenzyme. Since most coenzymes are derivatives of vitamins, vitamin deficiency decreases coenzyme concentration and thereby depresses enzyme function.

The local availability of coenzyme and substrate is of particular regulatory significance in the case of substrates that stand at metabolic crossroads. A compound such as glucose 6-phosphate has at least four pathways open to it.

Coupling

This rate-regulating mechanism, inherent in the design of a pathway, is best explained by the example of the controlled oxidation in the respiratory chain (see Figure 4-8). The transfer of hydrogen (or electrons) along the carrier chain is possible only when ADP and P are simultaneously being converted into ATP within the mitochondrial structure. Thus, demand controls supply in a simple interlocking manner. When ATP is utilized in the cell in the performance of work, ADP is produced, making possible the synthesis of new ATP. As a result, ATP is synthesized only when it is required, and glucose is oxidized only when it is necessary to make ATP.

Many other such couplings exist between metabolic systems.

Hormone Action

Hormones are agents that are secreted into the body fluids by special glands, called *endocrine* glands, and are transported to distant locations where they affect the metabolic rates of certain cells or groups of cells. In other words, hormones arise in special cells that are remote from the cells whose enzymes they control—and their chief importance is in the functioning of multicellular organisms. It may therefore be inappropriate to mention them in connection with the means by which a cell regulates its own metabolism. Nevertheless, hormonal control appears to involve intracellular control systems.

Hormones were the first rate-determinants recognized. It was early found that epinephrine (adrenalin), the hormone secreted by the adrenal medulla (Chapter 11), stimulates the breakdown of glycogen. We now know that epinephrine activates phosphorylase, the enzyme that cleaves glycogen. Epinephrine functions by converting a catalytically inert enzyme precursor (dephosphorylase) to its active form. Other hormones have recently been shown to change the physical

structures of specific enzyme proteins. Although it is likely that all hormones act by controlling the behavior of specific enzymes, we are only now beginning to understand the details of these relationships in molecular terms.

Feedback Inhibition

In *feedback inhibition* an enzyme appearing early in a biosynthetic pathway is inhibited by the final product of the pathway. Let us picture a pathway the contains a branching point, thus:

$$A \to B \to C \to D \begin{array}{c} \nearrow E \to F \to G \to H \to I \\ \\ \searrow J \to K \to L \to M \to N \end{array}$$

In many pathways of this type, a final product (for example, compound N) is directly inhibitory to the first enzyme in the sequence that is unambiguously committed to the synthesis of that product (here the enzyme converting compound D to compound J). The inhibition can be demonstrated in a test tube with purified preparations of the enzyme and the inhibitory end product (and in such experiments the inhibitory effect is a powerful and instantaneous one). Obviously, with such an arrangement, the final product of the pathway will be fabricated only in the requisite amounts—and only when its concentration falls below the value at which it is inhibitory to a key biosynthetic enzyme.

In general, feedback inhibition serves the important purpose of preventing the wasteful synthesis of unneeded end products. It performs this function rapidly and with precision. If, for example, a cell capable of synthesizing an essential amino acid suddenly receives an outside supply of the amino acid, feedback inhibition instantaneously shuts off synthesis within the cell, thus promoting economy within the cell and avoiding possibly toxic accumulations of biosynthetic intermediates. Feedback inhibition usually involves a binding of the inhibitory product to the inhibited enzyme. This binding produces a change in the tertiary structure of the enzyme which results in inactivation of the enzyme. This inhibitory phenomenon is called an *allosteric* effect.

The occurrence of this phenomenon implies that an enzyme may have two kinds of specificity—the usual specificity with respect to substrate and an additional specificity with respect to inhibitor. There need be little chemical similarity between the inhibitory end product and the substrate for which the enzyme has affinity.

REGULATION OF THE RATE OF ENZYME FORMATION

Induced Enzyme Synthesis

Induced enzyme synthesis is defined as the increase in the rate of synthesis of a single enzyme relative to the rates of synthesis of other cell proteins resulting from exposure of the cell to compounds (*inducers*) identical or closely related to the substrates of the enzyme. For instance, a culture of the bacterium *Escherichia coli* growing in a medium with a carbon source such as succinic acid contains only trace amounts of the enzyme β-galactosidase, which splits galactosides. The addition of a suitable galactoside—for example, lactose, a disaccharide of glucose-galactose (Chapter 2)—is immediately followed by a sharp increase of over 10,000-fold in the rate of synthesis of β-galactosidase (Figure 4-12). The high rate of synthesis is maintained as long as the bacteria grow in the presence of the inducing galactoside. When it is removed, the rate of synthesis drops to its original low level. No compounds other than galactosides induce the synthesis of β-galactosidase.

Enzymes such as β-galactosidase have been called *inducible enzymes* in contrast to the *constitutive enzymes* normally within the cell. It should be noted that only certain enzymes are inducible. Moreover, enzymes that are inducible in one cell strain may be constitutive in another.

Repression of Enzyme Synthesis

Repression of enzyme synthesis has one feature in common with feedback inhibition. Both depend upon

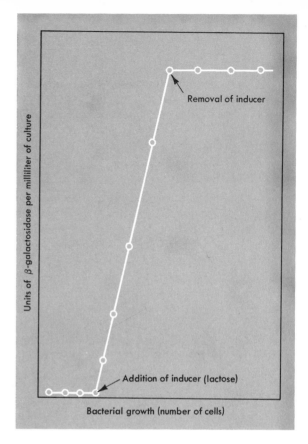

FIG. 4-12   Induction of β-galactosidase in a culture of *Escherichia coli*.

the concentration of the final product of a reaction sequence—that is, they are both feedback mechanisms. In repression of enzyme synthesis, however, the end product does not inhibit the activity of a biosynthetic enzyme; it represses its *synthesis*. Conversely, when the concentration of end product is low, synthesis of the enzyme is accelerated as a result of derepression.

Although the mechanisms of enzyme induction and repression are still under study, it is evident that the two are closely related. We shall consider a promising hypothesis explaining their relationship when we discuss gene action in Chapter 7. Suffice it to say here that repression is exhibited in most of the major biosynthetic pathways. Functionally, it resembles feedback inhibition in that both prevent the wasteful synthesis of an end product within the cell in the presence of an adequate supply from outside the cell. Feedback inhibition, however, is by far the more rapid and sensitive of the two mechanisms. It appears, therefore, that inhibition is the chief regulator of small-molecule production, whereas induction and repression aim mainly at programing or orchestrating the processes of protein synthesis so as to provide an optimal combination of essential enzyme proteins with a maximum of economy. Induction and repression represent the coarse adjustment of a metabolic machine, and inhibition represents the fine adjustment.

By harmonizing competing protein syntheses in the cell, repression prevents what otherwise would surely be a lethal overactivity of the mechanisms of protein synthesis. It has been shown, for example, that when the synthesis of an enzyme such as β-galactosidase or alkaline phosphatase is fully active, the enzyme alone may constitute 8 per cent of the total cell protein. Obviously, even a few such non-repressed syntheses would wreck the economy of the cell. If the gene for each of the cell's several thousand enzymes were to attempt a synthesis of this magnitude, universal repressibility would be essential to survival.

Enzyme Activation and Molecular Conversion

We have already seen that epinephrine converts an inactive dephosphorylase to active phosphorylase (p. 85). Other instances of enzyme activation have been observed, though they are few in number. The zymogens of the digestive tract are inactive precursors of the digestive enzymes that are secreted into the stomach and intestine. For example, we shall later learn (Chapter 10) that the pancreas produces a strong proteolytic enzyme, trypsin. In fact, the material secreted by the pancreas is the catalytically inert substance, trypsinogen, which is chemically converted in the intestine to the active protease trypsin. In the case of the powerful hydrolytic digestive enzymes, the existence of control mechanisms that delay "turning on" the activity until the enzymes are in the proper physical locations is of obvious value to the cell.

Summary

Concept of homeostasis; the apparent purposiveness of organismic behavior.

Cell metabolism: anabolism and catabolism; the universality of fundamental metabolic processes; cellular environment and nutrition; autotrophism and heterotrophism; how cells obtain their materials; relations of cell structure and metabolism.

Review of the concepts of energy and work: energy as the capacity to accomplish work; the diverse forms of energy and their interchangeability—potential and kinetic energy; the cell's energy exchanges—sugar as the focal point of the economy, energy income and expenditure, energy storage and transport.

Photosynthesis: energy income leading to the formation of glucose; the capture of light energy by chlorophyll; chloroplasts; dissociation of water and transfer of energy from chlorophyll, producing O_2 and H; the reduction of CO_2 to glucose by the released H.

Energy release and expenditure: analogy with a business economy; the use of phosphate as a convenient form of energy currency; the conversion of the released energy into the energy-rich phosphate bonds of ATP; the utilization of ATP energy in the coupling of exergonic reactions; coupled exergonic reactions as a substitute for endergonic reactions.

Four stages of glucose metabolism: (1) glycolysis, the cleavage of glucose to pyruvic or lactic acid; (2) the conversion of pyruvic acid to acetyl CoA plus CO_2; (3) the citric acid cycle; and (4) oxidative phosphorylation in the mitochondria.

Energy utilization and the synthesis of cell components: ribonucleotides and deoxyribonucleotides; nucleic acids and proteins; lipids and fatty acids. ·

Control of cell metabolism: principle of negative feedback; factors influencing the level of enzyme activity—substrate and coenzyme availability, coupling, hormone action, feedback inhibition; the regulation of the rate of the enzyme synthesis—induced enzyme synthesis, feedback repression, enzyme activation, and molecular conversion.

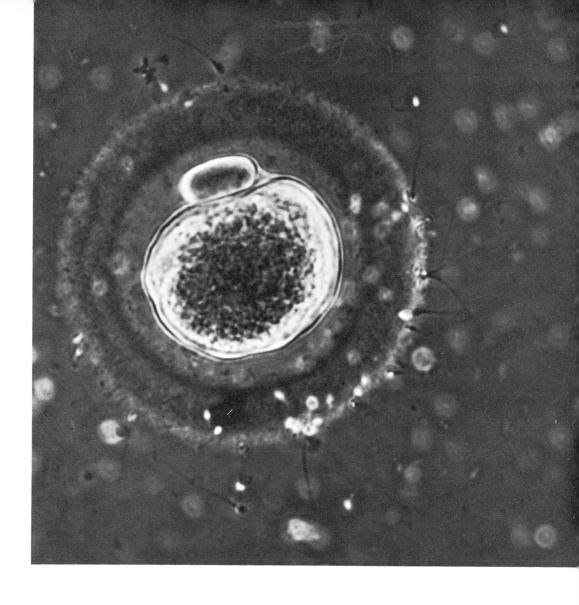

PART THREE

REPRODUCTION:
THE CONTINUITY OF LIFE

Self-reproduction, the most characteristic feature of all living systems, is the subject of Part 3. It is introduced by a remarkable photograph of a human egg cell with sperm cells attached. One of the sperms will fertilize the egg; in other words, its nucleus will migrate into the egg and there fuse with the egg nucleus. The fertilized egg cell—or zygote—contains nuclear material from both parents. It marks the beginning of the life of a new human being and is a useful focal point for presenting all the diverse aspects of organic reproduction.

In the first place, the nature of the zygote—a single cell—points up the fact that organic reproduction is basically a cellular process. Second, the origin of the zygote through fertilization illustrates the fact that organic reproduction nearly always involves the added complication of sex; the new individual organism originates with the union of two different cells, frequently, as in this example, from different kinds of parents, male and female, specialized for their roles in reproduction. Third, a zygote produced by human parents develops into a human being, not into a mouse or other species; thus one generalization about organic reproduction is that it involves heredity, the production of like by like. Fourth, an essential property of virtually all reproduction is elaborate development, whereby the parents' complex organization is created afresh in the offspring out of the simple beginnings afforded by a single cell. Several of these aspects are to be considered in Part 3.

Chapter 5 shows that the inherited information is in the nucleus and mainly in the chromosomes. It describes how identical sets of chromosomes are transmitted to new cells in mitosis and meiosis.

Chapter 6 traces the growth of the major tenets of genetics, including the rigorous demonstration that the genes containing the inherited information are arranged in linear order as parts of chromosomes.

Chapter 7 discusses the chemical nature of the genes; it details the exciting recent discoveries illustrating in part how genes act to achieve their control over the life of the cell—in other words, how the inherited information is translated into the cellular machinery that determines how the cell is to be built and how it is to function.

REPRODUCTION:

CELLULAR ASPECTS

The individual organism—bacterium, rosebush, mouse, or man—is an elaborate and complex system whose structure and activities are highly organized. It can maintain its organization and its activities for varying lengths of time by capturing energy and expending it appropriately. The organism can adjust its structure and behavior, within limits, in such a way as to remain adapted to changing environmental conditions. Again within limits, it can repair damage due to accident and the inescapable ravages of wear and aging. We do not understand precisely how the machinery of the body deteriorates with age, but clearly it does; and ultimately the damage is beyond the organism's capactiy to repair. Death comes to all living things—indeed, there is no surer or wider generalization that we can make in biology.

The persistence of life on earth in the face of death's certainty points up the universal ability of organisms to reproduce themselves as their most characteristic, and most defining, feature. The long-term edurance of life is not due to the capacity of the individual organism to repair and adjust itself. It is due to the fact that, in a sense, it can throw off its worn-out machinery and start again in the form of its offspring. These in turn can repair and adjust for only so long; ultimately they face the same fate as their parents. They live into posterity only insofar as they leave offspring. What survives on earth over the millennia is not the individual organism but the species, and its endurance depends on the act of reproduction as a vital bridge that spans successive mortal generations.

Major Features of Organic Reproduction

HUMAN REPRODUCTION: PROBLEMS AND PRINCIPLES

The phenomenon of reproduction is many-sided. It involves several different kinds of problems and several different features of the organism's structure and activities. We shall begin by sorting out the major features of reproduction as they are more or less familiar to us in humans, and in doing this we shall define the general problems to be given detailed attention in later sections.

In man, as in the vast majority of other species, the individual organisms fall into two categories, male and female, with respect to their roles in reproduction. The new human begins its life inside the body of its mother, and the role of the male is restricted to the act of copulation, during which he introduces into the female a fluid known as *semen*. It has been realized in Western culture for well over 2000 years that the act of copulation in man is causally related to pregnancy and the production of offspring. The thick seminal fluid ejaculated by the male in copulation is a heavy suspension of single cells called *sperm* cells, or *spermatozoa*. Introduced from the penis of the male into the female vagina, these cells swim upward in special ducts, down one of which migrates a cell or cells contributed by the female. These are egg cells, or *ova*. The ultimate sexual event is the union of one egg cell with one sperm cell, an event known as *fertilization*. The product of fertilization is the *zygote*, or fertilized egg cell.

The zygote marks the real beginning of the new organism's life. In humans it lodges on the wall of the mother's uterus, where it remains for 9 months, undergoing growth and the initial development of the adult human's complex structure. From this single-celled zygote, which to the eye appears simple and unspecialized, the entire staggering complexity of an adult human is developed afresh in each generation.

The photograph used to open Part 3 is of the human egg cell as it normally exists in the mother during fertilization. The egg proper is the large cell (bright in the photograph) in the center of the mass. At its side lies a smaller cell (a polar body, p. 270), which will play no further role in development. The egg is surrounded by a wide membrane, which many spermatozoa are entering. Only one of these ultimately invades the egg proper to fertilize it. The single cell resulting from fertilization proceeds to divide into two replicas of itself. Each of these in turn divides, so that the embryo becomes four-celled. The multiplication of cells continues and is one of the basic elements in the increase in bulk of the embryo as a whole. Increase in bulk through cell reproduction is clearly not the whole story of development, however. Figure 5-1 shows that the cell mass of the embryo soon takes on a definite form, although not, to begin with, a form that is recognizably human. The cell mass becomes elongate, corresponding with the future long axis (head to tail) of the body. At the side of the future spinal column, one can see regularly repeated bulges, which are destined to develop into the musculature of the adult. Only after about 5 weeks can the grotesque outline of a head be identified as such by the uninitiated; it is a head grossly out of proportion (by adult standards) with the rest of the embryo. Later the heart and limbs become evident, but each is only a rough expression of the fine structure of the adult, which is developed gradually in successive stages of embryonic life.

We are not here concerned with the details of human development. It is our purpose only to emphasize the cardinal point that each reproductive cycle involves the fresh creation of adult form and that the development concerned is not a simple unfolding of detail present in the egg from the outset. The development of adult complexity in each generation is an integral part of the problem of reproduction as a whole.

Sexuality, development, and its cellular foundations are not the only major features of reproduction illustrated by humans. The simple fact that new

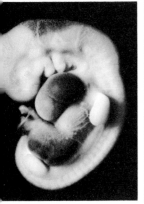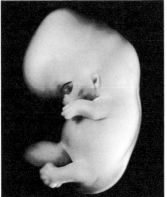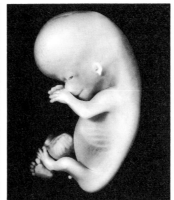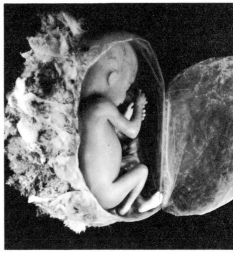

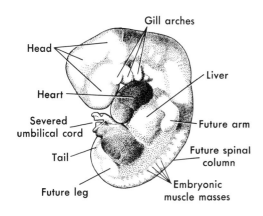

Gill arches

Head

Heart

Severed
umbilical cord

Tail

Future leg

Liver

Future arm

Future spinal
column

Embryonic
muscle masses

FIG. 5-1 **Human embryos.** Left to right, a human embryo in its fourth week of development. (Bottom left, the same embryo with some parts labeled.) Embryo in its sixth week of development. The eye and ear are now recognizable, as well as the fore- and hind limbs. Note how, in the hind limb, the five toes are only roughly sketched out. Embryo in its eighth week of development. The mouth is clearly evident, and the digits (fingers and toes) on the limbs are fully formed. Note also the ribs. Fetus, in about the sixteenth week, lying in the fetal membranes. (Photos, Chester F. Reather, except right, Richard D. Grill)

humans arise only as offspring of preexisting humans implies two more generalizations. First, living things arise from other living things and do not appear spontaneously (without the intervention of life) from nonliving materials; this is the principle of biogenesis. Second, humans have human babies; flies reproduce flies; bacteria reproduce bacteria. This is the phenomenon of heredity—like begets like.

There are thus five general features of reproduction: *sexuality, development, cellularity, biogenesis,* and *heredity.* Of these, sexuality is the least general. Sexual processes occur in the great majority of organisms, but many reproduce themselves without sex. Asexual reproduction is common and familiar in horticulture, where many plants are propagated by cuttings, suckers, or bulbs; and bacteria reproduce asexually much of the time. Sexual and asexual reproduction will be discussed further in Chapter 9.

We have learned that reproduction is basically a matter of cells rather than of whole, adult organisms.

Therefore, biogenesis, development, and heredity are best approached as problems in cellular reproduction. Let us briefly examine these three great principles to see how they are related to each other.

BIOGENESIS:
ARGUMENT FROM EXPERIMENT

In Chapter 3 we mentioned the old belief in the spontaneous generation of organisms from the nonliving and outlined the experiments of Redi and Pasteur to test that belief. As a matter of fact, their experiments did not disprove the possibility of spontaneous generation, or abiogenesis, but they did indicate that it is extremely improbable. All subsequent experimental results have supported their conclusion, and there is no serious doubt that biogenesis is the rule, that life comes only from other life, that a cell, the unit of life, is always and exclusively the product or offspring of another cell.

We take biogenesis as a fundamental principle of reproduction from the experimental evidence and also from theoretical considerations. It must, however, be remembered that life had to start sometime. Almost all biologists now think that the very earliest life originated from nonliving matter by natural processes (Chapter 22). It must have appeared at a very remote time, on the order of at least $3\frac{1}{2}$ billion years ago, when conditions on the earth were very different from what they are today. For most of the time since then, the origin of new organisms has not been spontaneous but has been a matter of living cells producing other living cells. This fact accounts for the continuity of life as we know it.

BIOGENESIS:
ARGUMENT FROM THEORY

Quite apart from the strong argument that experiment raises against the idea of the spontaneous generation of life under present world conditions, there are convincing theoretical reasons for rejecting the whole notion. An attempt to understand these theoretical reasons is worthwhile because the argument forces us to frame the problems of organic reproduction in terms of concepts that are most useful for further study.

We have previously referred to the tendency of the physical world toward a state of disorder—a tendency expressed technically in the second law of thermodynamics. The most probable state for any system of matter—the state it tends ultimately to assume—is one of simplicity and disorder. The idea of complexity embodies within it the idea of improbability; the more complex a thing is, the less probable it becomes that it arose by chance. This is also true of the ideas of order and organization. A complex organization is in itself improbable, and if left alone, it will decay. If no work is put into the system to maintain its organization, it will tend to assume its most probable state—simple disorder.

We first introduced these notions about simplicity and disorder versus complex organization in relation to the universal demand in organisms for an energy supply. In the face of the universal tendency for order to be lost, the complex organization of the living organism can be maintained only if work—involving the expenditure of energy—is performed to conserve the order. The organism is constantly adjusting, repairing, and replacing; this requires energy.

But the preservation of the complex, improbable organization of the living creature needs more than energy for the work. It calls for *information,* or instructions *on how the energy should be expended,* to maintain the improbable organization. The idea of information necessary for the maintenance and, as we shall see, creation of living systems is of great utility in approaching the biological problems of reproduction. Information, in the sense in which it can be treated as a useful scientific concept, is the idea of how much specification is essential to exclude all but one defined possibility out of an array of many possibilities. The more possibilities that exist, the more information that must be given to specify one in particular. That anything requiring as much specification as a living organism could arise by chance is out of the question. Theory and experiment together refute the ancient myth of spontaneous generation; and the theoretical argument helps us recognize what we must learn about reproduction as a whole.

That a complex organism cannot develop by chance but must proceed according to some set program raises the question as to how the information for the program is acquired. This is the fundamental problem of evolution, and it will be discussed in Part 5. Our present concern is with the fact that information does exist, with its location and nature, and with the way in which it acts.

HEREDITY AS INFORMATION
FOR THE CONTROL
OF DEVELOPMENT

The hallmark of living systems is their complexity and their organization, and the focal point of the reproduction problem is how complexity and organization can be reproduced. Simple cleavage of a living system like man into two parts does not lead to reproduction; it leads only to destruction. The reproduction of man, as of all other living systems, involves the development or building from a simple beginning of the complexity that is to be duplicated. The phenomena of embryonic development are an integral part of the process of reproduction. The redevelopment of complexity in each successive act of reproduction demands information for its control. Embryologically, you and I were constructed in much the same fashion, and so were our parents and grandparents before us. In each generation there is a supply of information that regulates development, and in each generation the "blueprint" containing this information is essentially similar. What we inherited from our parents at the outset of our lives as single cells was the information that controlled our development and that delimits our functioning even today.

In its immediate aspect, heredity is the phenomenon of like begetting like in successive acts of reproduction. Like begets like because parent and

offspring both develop by processes controlled by the same kind of information. Clearly, there must be a sense in which it is true to say that what is reproduced and transmitted from generation to generation of living organisms is the information needed for their creation. We shall direct our study of development and heredity along these lines.

We must discover (1) the nature of the information that controls the development of an organism; (2) how the information is reproduced; (3) how copies of it are transmitted from generation to generation; and (4) how the information achieves control.

Cellular Basis of Reproduction

VIRCHOW'S DOCTRINE: "ALL CELLS FROM CELLS"

We learned in Chapter 3 that the cell theory in its explicit form, the doctrine that all living systems are built of cells, was announced in 1838–1839 by Matthias Schleiden and by Theodor Schwann but that it was not until about 1860 that its full implications began to be evident. The decade from 1850 to 1860 still saw much discussion about what was called "free cell formation," or the "spontaneous origin" of cells from noncellular materials. As the whole concept of spontaneous generation began to fall, it became increasingly clear that the aphorism, "All life from life," could be translated, as it was by the German physiologist Virchow in 1855, into a more precise formulation, *"Omnis cellula e cellula"*—"All cells from cells."

Cells are the elementary structural units of living systems; if new life arises from old, it must take the form of new cells from old. In most organisms, life begins, as we have seen in man, as a single cell, the zygote. The growth and development of one cell to the massive complexity of adult man is, in one major respect, a result of the activity of the original cell

and its progeny of cells in reproducing themselves. When the multicellular organism is mature and reproduces itself, the fundamental event is again one of producing a new cell.

Obviously the single-celled zygote from which the adult develops contains within its minute structure the controlling information we have argued must be present—the real inheritance of the child from its parents. We shall now proceed to determine where in the cell the control center must be and how copies of it are transmitted to new cells as they are produced.

THE NUCLEUS AS CONTROL CENTER

Several kinds of observation indicate that the nucleus is the control center for the whole cell's activities. In the first place, nuclei can be removed from some cells that are sufficiently big to permit operation on them with micromanipulating equipment. A cell devoid of its nucleus soon dies, and so we know at least that the nucleus is indispensable for the enduring welfare of the cell. In other experiments, it has been possible to transplant nucleii from cells of one species to denucleated cells of another related species. Some characteristics of the host cells are modified toward those of the species of the transplanted nucleus. Hence, the transplanted nucleus has exerted a control over the recipient cytoplasm. Thus, we are probably on the right track in our search for the controlling information in the organism if we pursue our study of the nucleus. To do so, we must consider the mechanisms of cell reproduction.

MITOSIS

Cells multiply by dividing. This arithmetic oddity means that the number of cells increases by the splitting in two of single cells. This splitting of a cell is preceded by complex events involved in the division of the nucleus, a process called *mitosis* (Figures 5-2, 5-3, and 5-4).

When it is not reproducing, the nucleus gives little evidence of its intimate structure. It lies in the cytoplasm, revealing only its *nucleolus* and a fine granular appearance. Outside the nucleus in animal cells (although not in most plants) lies the *centrosome,* or aster, which is a star-shaped body, and at the very center of the centrosome is the minute *centriole.* Details of nuclear structure become abundantly apparent, however, as soon as the cell begins to reproduce.

The onset of reproductive activity is marked by the division of the aster and its centriole into two parts and the separation of these toward opposite sides of the nucleus. Within the nuclear membrane, visible changes begin as elongate threads replace the previous fine granules. These threadlike structures are the *chromosomes.* As we shall see, they are the carriers of the cell's inherited controls, and, consequently, the details of their structure and behavior are what we want to understand.

The diagrams in Figure 5-4 represent the successive events that occur during the mitotic division of a cell into two new daughter cells. The word "mitosis" derives from the Greek root *mitos* (thread) and refers to the threadlike nature of the chromosomes at mitosis. The nucleus in the figure belongs to a purely hypothetical organism in which the number of chromosomes is kept small for diagrammatic purposes. The duration of mitosis varies in different cell types; it may last for minutes or for several hours. It is convenient to treat the long and continuous process of mitosis by recognizing in it a sequence of more or less distinct stages or phases. The stages are *interphase, prophase, metaphase, anaphase,* and *telophase.*

Interphase

The period during which the cell is not visibly dividing or preparing for division is termed *interphase.* Thus cells spend most of their lifetimes in interphase. During interphase the cell is metabolically active,

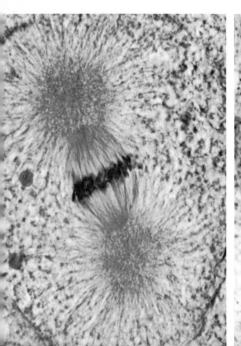
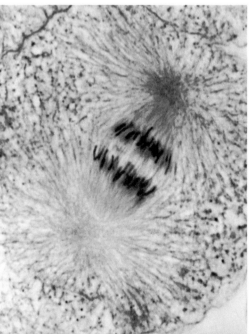

FIG. 5-2 Mitosis in cells of the white-fish. The spindle lying between the two star-shaped centrosomes is very clear. The chromosomes lie on the central part, or equator, of the spindle. In the right-hand figure the two duplicate sets of chromosomes can be seen on their way to opposite ends of the spindle. (Photos, General Biological Supply House, Inc., Chicago)

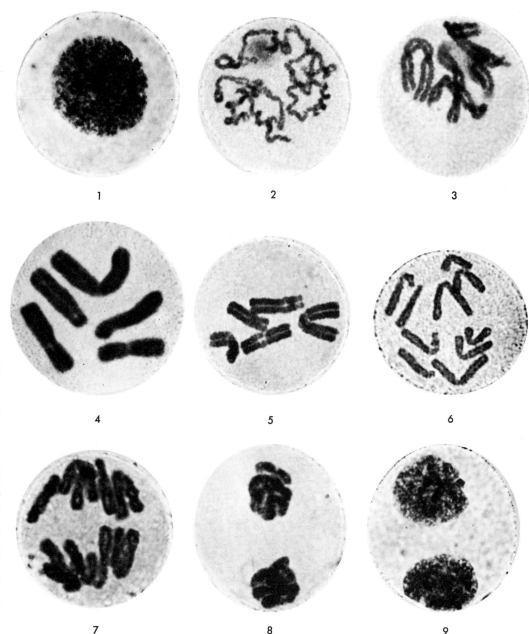

FIG. 5-3 Mitosis in *Trillium* microspores (developing pollen). The centrosome is missing in plant cells, and the spindle, which is so clear in animal cells (see Figure 5-2), is not easily stained and seen, although it is present. In 1 the nucleus has not yet entered mitosis; the chromosomal material appears diffuse and structureless. In 2, 3, and 4 the chromosomes are progressively clearer as they shorten and thicken. There are five chromosomes, and each is present in duplicate. In 5 they are lying on the equator of the spindle, which is unstained and therefore invisible in this preparation. In 6 and 7 the duplicate sets of chromosomes move to opposite ends of the spindle. In 8 and 9 new nuclei are formed from the two sets of chromosomes, and the process of mitosis is completed. A wall eventually develops between the nuclei, and two new cells are thus established. (Photo, A. H. Sparrow)

carrying out the biochemistry of catabolism and anabolism (covered in Chapter 4) as well as specialized activities. The initial events of mitosis actually occur during interphase; these are the synthesis and duplication of the genetic material, DNA. This replication of DNA is very difficult to detect in the laboratory, and it passed unnoticed until recent years. We now subdivide interphase into three stages: (1) G_1—the first "gap" or nonmitotic stage, which may last for hours or years, depending on the function of a specific cell. This stage is that of normal metabolic activity (2) S—the synthetic stage of DNA duplication. The total DNA content of the nucleus is doubled. (3) G_2—the second "gap" stage, just preceding the visible stages of mitosis. The second gap stage usually lasts only a few hours.

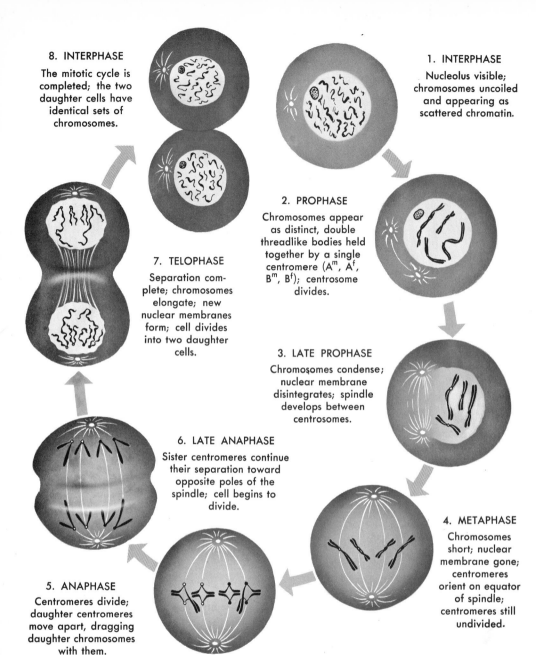

8. INTERPHASE
The mitotic cycle is completed; the two daughter cells have identical sets of chromosomes.

1. INTERPHASE
Nucleolus visible; chromosomes uncoiled and appearing as scattered chromatin.

2. PROPHASE
Chromosomes appear as distinct, double threadlike bodies held together by a single centromere (A^m, A^f, B^m, B^f); centrosome divides.

7. TELOPHASE
Separation complete; chromosomes elongate; new nuclear membranes form; cell divides into two daughter cells.

3. LATE PROPHASE
Chromosomes condense; nuclear membrane disintegrates; spindle develops between centrosomes.

6. LATE ANAPHASE
Sister centromeres continue their separation toward opposite poles of the spindle; cell begins to divide.

5. ANAPHASE
Centromeres divide; daughter centromeres move apart, dragging daughter chromosomes with them.

4. METAPHASE
Chromosomes short; nuclear membrane gone; centromeres orient on equator of spindle; centromeres still undivided.

FIG. 5-4 The behavior of the nucleus during its mitotic cycle.

At the beginning of each prophase, each chromosome is already duplicated, and the duplicates are tied together by a single centromere. Mitosis involves only the orderly separation of the two duplicate sets and their transmission to different cells. Obviously, the duplication of a chromosome is a real reproduction of a copy of the already existing one, and not simply a splitting in two of the existing one. In the next chapter we shall return to the problem of how the chromosome is reproduced.

Prophase

In *prophase* the chromosome threads are elongate to begin with and progressively shorten, becoming at the same time apparently thicker and more heavily stainable when treated with dyes in laboratory prep-

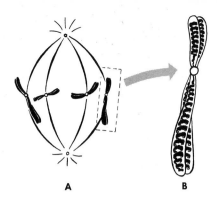

FIG. 5-5 The helical structure of the metaphase chromosomes. A. The four chromosomes of Figure 5-4 seen on the metaphase spindle. B. One of the chromosomes enlarged to show how its thread is thrown into a helix and embedded in a matrix.

arations. The shortened and thickened appearance is due to the fact that the elongate thread of the earliest prophase is thrown into a helix (Figure 5-5).

Even from the earliest prophase, we can recognize two characteristics of the chromosomes that are fundamental and shared by almost all organisms: (1) They occur in pairs. In our hypothetical form there are two pairs (A^f and A^m, B^f and B^m). The members of each pair are similar and are said to be *homologous*. (2) Each chromosome is itself double-stranded due to the previous duplication of DNA in the S stage of interphase. The two strands of each chromosome are held together by a small body called the *centromere*. Each chromosome has one centromere.

As the prophase of mitosis progresses, the two strands of each chromosome coil into helixes independently of each other; when prophase is complete, each chromosome has the appearance shown in Figure 5-5.

Metaphase

Metaphase is the stage of mitosis that follows prophase. At the end of prophase the nuclear membrane breaks down and in the space between the two centrioles there develops a remarkable structure called a *spindle* (see Figure 5-2). The spindle consists of microtubular fibers that radiate from the two centrioles, producing a biconical structure. Some of the spindle fibers run from pole to pole (centriole to centriole); others run from the centromere of a chromosome to a pole. At metaphase, the chromosomes are pulled to the central or equatorial portion of the spindle by the spindle fibers. The arms of the chromosomes may lie loosely off the equator of the spindle itself, but the centromeres lie precisely on it. The centromeres then split in two in a definite plane (see Figure 5-4), as the anaphase of mitosis commences.

Anaphase

Each of the two daughter centromeres of a chromosome is attached to a spindle fiber. The centromeres begin to move apart. As they move, they carry with them the daughter chromosomes. Thus at each of the two ends, or poles, of the spindle there accumulates a complete set of chromosomes: A^m, A^f, B^m, and B^f.

Telophase

Telophase, which follows anaphase, is in a way the reverse of prophase. A new nuclear membrane develops around the chromosomes, which uncoil and resume their original appearance as elongate, poorly stainable threads. The nucleolus re-forms, and the daughter cells reassume the G_1 configuration of interphase.

Movements of the Chromosomes

The highly organized movements of the chromosomes, first in their orientation on the spindle equator at metaphase and later in their separation and progression to the spindle poles, are among the great wonders of biology. We still do not understand fully what causes these movements. Does the anaphase movement result from the spindle fibers' contracting, like muscles, so that they drag the daughter centromeres to the poles? Or does the middle region of the spindle expand and push the centromeres toward the poles? Perhaps the movement of the chromosomes is in part autonomous; that is, the forces responsible for their movement may be internal, so that they *go* to the poles rather than being *forced* to the poles.

The problem of explaining the chromosomes' movements during mitosis has attracted and baffled many biologists. The most widely held view at present is that the spindle fibers do exert a pulling effect on the centromeres to which they are attached, so that the chromosomes are drawn to the poles rather than moving there independently. One thing is certain. Both the centromere and the spindle fibers are essential for the movement. Chromosomes without centromeres do not proceed poleward; and chromosomes that have centromeres but fail to attach to fibers also fail to reach the poles. The centromere and the spindle fiber are therefore indispensable for orderly chromosome movement, and are in some way responsible for it.

In animals an additional element is necessary for this movement—the centriole. Centrioles are not known to exist in higher plants, and so they are not universally necessary.

Ordered Separation of Duplicates

We digressed briefly to the subject of the chromosome movements not only because it is one of the main biological problems studied today but for the more general reason that the organized and controlled movements of the chromosomes at mitosis merit emphasis as a focal point in organic reproduction in general.

If we survey mitosis throughout the plant and animal kingdoms, we can discover fascinating differences in detail, but we study these largely because they are so rare. It is the other side of the picture that we want to stress: mitosis is virtually coextensive with life, and its major features are amazingly constant. The universality and constancy of mitosis bespeak something fundamental, and what is fundamental is clear enough in the light of our earlier discussion of heredity as information. The mitotic mechanism is the basic mechanism of hereditary transmission. As a result of mitosis, two cells are developed from one, and to each of the daughter cells is transmitted—by virtue of the orderly movements of the chromosomes on the spindle—a copy of all the chromosomes.

DIPLOIDY: ITS ORIGIN IN FERTILIZATION

One important point that demands explanation is that the chromosomes in the nucleus occur in pairs. Biologists usually represent the number of pairs as n. In our simplified hypothetical organism in Figure 5-4, there are 2 pairs (A^m and A^f, B^m and B^f); therefore, $n = 2$. In man there are 23 pairs (46 chromosomes) (Figure 5-6). In some relatives of the lobster, there are 100 pairs. In the fruit fly *Drosophila*,

FIG. 5-6 Chromosomes from a human male cell and their karyotype. Cells to be studied are cultivated briefly in a tissue culture. Then a drug (e.g., colchicine) is added to stop mitosis in metaphase. The cells are then literally squashed. This procedure disperses the chromosomes so that they can be photographed. Such a presentation reveals the general morphology of the chromosomes, or their karyotype. (Photos, J. H. Tjio)

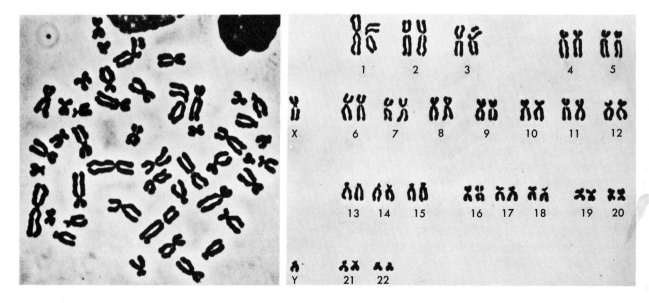

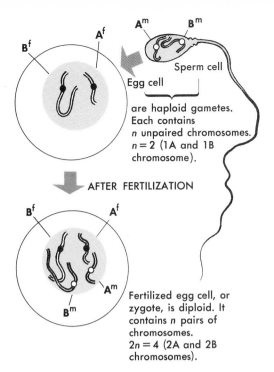

are haploid gametes.
Each contains
n unpaired chromosomes.
$n = 2$ (1A and 1B
chromosome).

AFTER FERTILIZATION

Fertilized egg cell, or
zygote, is diploid. It
contains *n* pairs of
chromosomes.
$2n = 4$ (2A and 2B
chromosomes).

FIG. 5-7   The origin of diploidy at fertilization.

to which we give much attention in the next chapter, there are 4 pairs. In some ferns there are over 500 pairs, the highest numbers known in any organisms, but even at this high level, the normal number is fixed for any given species. What is the significance of this regularity—the fact that the nucleus of each species contains a definite number, *n*, of chromosome pairs?

The answer is found in the nature of sexual reproduction. The sexual act leads to the union of two cells, one contributed by each parent. These cells (sperm and egg), called *gametes*, prove to be special with respect to their chromosome contents. Each contains half the number of chromosomes present in the nucleus of the zygote and in the nuclei of body cells in adult multicellular organisms. Thus, in the organism of Figure 5-4, with four chromosomes (two A's and two B's), each gamete contains only two (one A and one B); the union of the egg and sperm is followed by a pooling of their chromosomes so that the fertilized egg contains four (Figure 5-7).

The nucleus of a gamete is said to be *haploid*, or to have *n* chromosomes. The nucleus of a fertilized egg, with two sets of chromosomes, one from each

gamete, is said to be *diploid*, or to have 2*n* chromosomes. In each pair of chromosomes (such as the A pair) within the diploid nucleus, one chromosome is derived from the male parent through the sperm (A^m), and the other from the female parent through the egg (A^f). The two A chromosomes are said to be a homologous pair, as are the two B chromosomes. A^m is homologous with A^f, and B^m is homologous with B^f; but neither A chromosome is homologous with either B chromosome.

The diploid nucleus of the fertilized egg contains two complete sets of information, one set from the egg and one set from the sperm. These two sets are copied in each S stage of interphase, and the duplicates are separated during mitosis into the two new daughter cells. Thus, from the single-celled zygote produced by fertilization, the multicellular adult arises as a result of repeated cell divisions, and every nucleus throughout the organism contains its own copy of the controlling instructions.

HAPLOIDY: ITS ORIGIN IN MEIOSIS

An obvious new problem now confronts us. In all organisms that reproduce sexually, a union of two cells takes place. The two gametes pool their chromosomes, and the zygote therefore has double the chromosome number of a gamete. Yet the number of chromosomes remains stable and characteristic of the species from generation to generation. Evidently a special form of mitosis must occur in the production of gametes, whereby the diploid number of chromosomes present in all other cells of the body is reduced to the haploid number found in the gametes. This special mitosis is called *meiosis*

Where Meiosis Takes Place

Let us suppose that the hypothetical organism of Figure 5-4 is some kind of fly whose adult form is outlined in Figure 5-8. This figure shows that, after the fusion of haploid gametes, the diploid zygote undergoes successive cell divisions during which the duplicated chromosomes are transmitted faithfully by

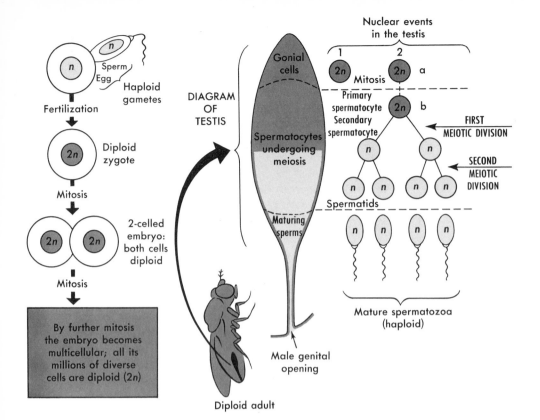

FIG. 5-8 The nuclear cycle in sexual reproduction.

mitosis to all new cells. All the tissues of the adult fly are composed of diploid cells, including those of the reproductive organ. Let us suppose further that this individual fly is male; the reproductive organ is therefore a testis. The sperms produced by this testis are, we know, haploid, and so meiosis—the special nuclear division yielding haploid cells—must occur in cells in the testis.

The cellular organization of the testis is represented in highly schematized fashion in Figure 5-8. At the head of the testis are *spermatogonia* (or *gonial* cells), which divide mitotically. One of the daughter cells (labeled 1) produced by a spermatogonial mitosis remains as a gonial cell, and the other (labeled 2) becomes a *spermatocyte*. A spermatocyte is a cell in which meiosis takes place. The entire meiotic process comprises two cell divisions, conveniently designated as meiosis I and meiosis II. The cell in which meiosis I takes place is diploid, being derived by mitosis from a gonial cell; it is the *primary* spermatocyte. Meiosis I produces two *secondary* spermatocytes, which then undergo meiosis II, thus yielding four cells, all of which are haploid and are gametes.

Here our task is to investigate the special chromosome movements in meiosis that are responsible for the transition from the diploid condition of the primary spermatocyte to the haploid condition of the four sperms derived from each primary spermatocyte. In meiosis, as in mitosis, DNA and chromosome replication also occur in the S phase of interphase.

Pairing, or Synapsis, at Prophase I

The complexities of meiosis are best understood if we focus our attention on the behavior of the centromeres and confine our discussion initially to one of the pairs of homologous centromeres with their attached chromosomes. We shall follow the A pair (A^m and A^f) in our hypothetical fly, although our description will apply equally well to the B pair or, for that matter, to any of the 23 pairs of chromosomes in man. Thus the problem in understanding the events of meiosis is essentially one of understanding how in meiosis *only one member of a homologous pair of centromeres* (with its chromosome) *is transmitted to each new nucleus* instead of both members, as in mitosis.

In mitosis, the two homologous A centromeres with their attached chromosomes behave absolutely independently of each other. They move onto the equator of the spindle at metaphase quite separately, and then each splits in two so that both A^m and A^f centromere move to each pole of the spindle.

The behavior of the centromeres during the first meiotic division is different in two respects. First, the homologous centromeres (A^m and A^f) do not behave independently of each other; and second, they do not split as they do in mitosis but move instead one to each pole. We shall examine these differences now in more detail.

In the prophase of meiosis I the chromosomes now begin to pair up; A^m pairs with A^f, and B^m with B^f. Strictly corresponding, or homologous, regions of the chromosome pairs are brought next to each

other. Only *after* this pairing, or *synapsis,* do the individual chromosomes undergo the normal process of duplication. As a result, the chromosome pair becomes four-stranded and includes two centromeres.

Separation, or Segregation, at Anaphase I

The pairing persists throughout prophase. When the spindle is formed, the chromosomes move onto its equator at metaphase, still in their paired condition. The homologous centromeres (A^m, A^f, etc.) do *not* now split. Instead, one intact centromere moves to

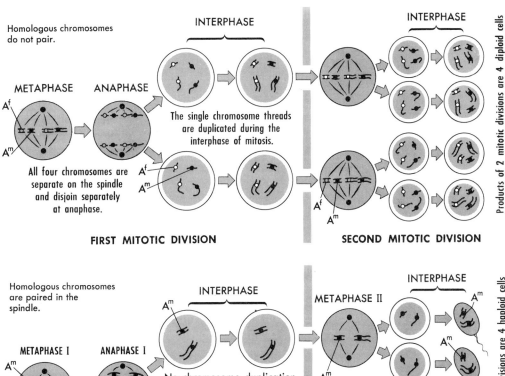

FIG. 5-9 **Mitosis and meiosis compared.** Note how A^m and A^f, for example, are paired at meiotic metaphase, whereas they are separate entities at mitotic metaphase. Trace the behavior of each chromosome in mitosis and meiosis with your finger.

each pole of the spindle at anaphase, and in doing so it carries its two chromosome strands with it.

Thus each nucleus that re-forms at the end of the spindle at telophase I contains only one A centromere and only one B centromere (see bottom of Figure 5-9).

Second Meiotic Division (Meiosis II)

In the interphase following meiosis I, the nucleus contains only one of each kind (A, B, etc.) of centromere. Each centromere already carries two chromosome strands with it, and accordingly no further duplication takes place. When the second division (meiosis II) commences, each centromere moves onto the spindle at metaphase and splits, so that one of the two strands goes to each pole.

Arithmetic of Meiosis

The four strands present in the paired chromosome at metaphase I finish up separated, one in each of four gametes. In the whole process of meiosis, there are two chromosome separations on a spindle—one at the first division and another at the second division. But chromosome duplication precedes only one of these divisions, the first; and the centromere divides only once, at the second division. The chromosome separation at the first division is based not on the *division* of individual centromeres but on the *separation* of paired homologous centromeres.

Random Assortment of Chromosomes

In our account of meiosis so far, we have stressed the sequence of chromosome movements responsible for separating the members of a single pair of homologous chromosomes. An additional item of great importance is necessary to make the picture complete. Figure 5-10 (1) shows that A^f, the A chromosome derived originally from the mother of the organism we are studying, goes to one pole of the spindle in meiosis I and A^m to the other. The figure also shows B^f going to the same pole as A^f. This is not the only possible way that the chromosomes could behave. The orientation of the B pair on the spindle is quite independent of that of the A pair. The metaphase

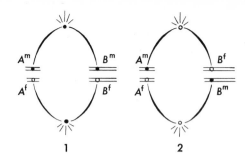

FIG. 5-10 Independent chromosome assortment. The orientations of the chromosomes shown in 1 and 2 are equally probable at metaphase 1.

arrangements shown on the spindles in Figure 5-10 (2) are equally frequent, since they are equally probable. B^m may go to the same spindle pole with A^f just as often as with A^m. The following combinations of chromosomes in the gametes are, therefore, all equally probable and frequent.

$$A^m \text{ and } B^m$$
$$A^f \text{ and } B^f$$
$$A^m \text{ and } B^f$$
$$A^f \text{ and } B^m$$

All that the mechanism of meiosis guarantees is that the gametes produced by an organism will contain one member of each pair of homologous chromosomes. It does not guarantee that the two groups of maternal and paternal representatives remain together in the gametes in the combinations in which they were inherited.

SIGNIFICANCE OF MITOSIS AND MEIOSIS

We began our discussion of cellular reproduction by noting that it must involve, somehow, the transmission, from one cell generation to the next, of the information controlling the maintenance of the cell's complexity and organization.

We have found that the nucleus contains a number of elongate threads, the chromosomes. The chromosomes prove to be the vehicles of the control mechanisms. We have found also that when the cell reproduces, it provides—in the mitotic process—for a highly ordered transmission to the new cell of the information (the chromosomes) it requires.

When mitosis begins, the information needed has already been copied. The two copies are held together by the centromere. The centromere does not divide until it is properly oriented on the spindle. The spindle's fibers guide the duplicates of each chromosome to two opposite poles. These poles are foci for the gathering together of all necessary information into two strictly equivalent packets promptly enclosed in new nuclear membranes at telophase. The significance of the spindle is apparent: it is a device for the orderly separation of the two copies, or blueprints, of the chromosomes.

Other features of the system need clarification, however. What is the meaning of the fact that the cell is usually diploid, carrying two basic and equivalent sets of information, one of which seems, in a sense, redundant? There is a simple and obvious answer to this question: diploidy is a consequence of sexual reproduction, since it results from the fusion of representative nuclei from two parents. Each parent contributes one complete copy of the total information necessary. To understand fully why diploidy is so nearly universal in organisms, we must answer a second question: "Why is sexual reproduction so nearly universal?" This is a question that we are not yet ready to treat, for the answer emerges only from an understanding of evolution, which will be taken up in Chapters 12 through 14.

Similar considerations apply to meiosis. There are simple features of meiosis that are easily explained in terms of sexual reproduction. Since this does involve nuclear fusion in each generation, the meiotic process must occur if the number of chromosomes is to be held constant. Again, however, we must emphasize that, like diploidy, meiosis can be understood in all its detail only in relation to evolution, and so we must return to it later.

Summary

Continuity of life dependent on the universal ability of organisms to reproduce themselves.

Major features of reproduction illustrated by reference to the familiar case of man: sexuality; embryonic development—preformationism versus epigenesis (the creation of adult complexity); biogenesis; and heredity.

Biogenesis: experimental evidence against spontaneous generation in the modern world; theoretical argument against modern spontaneous generation.

Complexity and information: heredity as information for the control of development.

What the study of reproduction must reveal: the nature of the information that controls the development of the organism; how the information is reproduced; how copies of it are transmitted from generation to generation; how the information acts to achieve control.

Cellular basis of reproduction: "all cells from cells"; the nucleus as the control center.

Mitosis: nuclear division; chromosomes at mitosis; the sequence of stages—prophase, metaphase, anaphase, telophase, interphase; chromosome movements; duplication of chromosomes; ordered separation of duplicates.

Diploidy: its origin in fertilization.

Haploidy: its origin in meiosis; where meiosis takes place; chromosome pairing at prophase I; separation at anaphase I; the second meiotic division; the arithmetic of meiosis; the random assortment of chromosomes; the significance of mitosis and meiosis.

CHAPTER SIX

THE CHROMOSOME THEORY OF HEREDITY

"We hold these truths to be self-evident: that all men are created equal.
. . ." All men are equal before the law, and all are equal in dignity as human beings:
that is what the writers of the Declaration of Independence meant. It is, however,
one of the profound lessons of genetics that only identical twins are born equal
biologically. Unless you are an identical twin (and only about 0.4 per cent of births
yield identical twins), you are not equal to anyone else on earth in the sense of
being biologically the same. No judgment is involved here as to who is better
and who is worse, or as to whether "better" and "worse" have valid meanings in
this connection. Nevertheless, the fact remains that the mechanisms of heredity make
it virtually impossible that any two nontwins ever have inherited just the same genes.

In the last chapter we showed that heredity involves the transmission of controlling
information, not only from generation to generation but also from cell to cell. We
showed that the controls are in the nucleus. Their physical basis is in linear "tapes"
of information (the chromosomes) that are accurately copied and transmitted to
new cells in orderly fashion like so many blueprints for the government of the cells'
activities. The logical sequence we followed was dictated by our present understanding
of the problem. We wish to emphasize now that the logical sequence bears little
or no relation to the historical sequence of discovery and development of understanding. Cell division and the details of mitosis were studied well before there was
rigorous proof that the nucleus was the cell's control center. Indeed, the facts of
cell and nuclear division were being studied at the same time that many able students
were still arguing for a kind of spontaneous generation called *free cell formation*.

Whenever a great advance is made in science, it is in the form of a theory—a
scheme of explanation in terms of which all the facts, previously scattered and
confusing, seem clearly and simply to fall into a pattern. T. H. Huxley is said to

have remarked after reading Charles Darwin's *The Origin of Species,* "Why didn't I think of it?" Until a theory is found, the meaning of the facts is obscure.

The historical development of a theory nearly always involves several distinct lines of investigation. In the development of the chromosome theory of heredity, there were two distinct lines that ultimately fused. One of these we have looked at already, although not in a historical way: the study of the cell's visible structures and their behavior in cell reproduction. The other line of inquiry was the study of differences and similarities between parents and offspring, with a view to defining general rules of inheritance. This direct study of the regularities of heredity is very much older than the study of the

cell. Democritus and Aristotle, among other ancients, had discussed the problems of heredity, and eighteenth- and nineteenth-century scientists were much preoccupied with the same problems before the cell theory gave biology its firm start about 1840. The theory that began to emerge from the fusion of these two lines of inquiry in 1902 was like the opening of a floodgate. It produced a flow of biological investigation and new insight that is still at its height more than two generations later. This is characteristic of the best theories; they not only explain old facts but also point ways to new knowledge.

Pre-Mendelian Ideas on Heredity

We may well ask, "If a theory, once discovered, is the main guide to inquiry and research after it is discovered, what guided inquiry before?" There are really two answers to this question.

First, much of the earliest inquiry was in effect random, helter-skelter, and unguided. Consequently, it produced relatively little except oddities such as notions about strange hybrids issuing from the mating of camels and leopards or myths concerning the lingering effect of a woman's first husband on her children by a later husband. Other erroneous ideas more important to the history of the subject will be treated later.

Second, the human tendency to seek order in the world leads men to find frameworks for discussion. It is not surprising that the most common source of analogies or models to which men have turned in the absence of exact theories is the realm best known to them: human nature and human society. Before the scientific development of the modern Western world, the universal tendency was for men to try to explain nature by talking about it in the familiar terms of human attributes; the forces of nature took on human will and motivations. The conscious effort to avoid such analogies and to depersonalize the explanation of the nonhuman world is a real hallmark of the Western scientific movement. But the influence of human models has nevertheless remained, often subcon-

sciously. For instance, the cytologist Virchow used a model from human experience when he sought to interpret how discrete cellular units work in subservience to the welfare of the whole organism; he called the organism a *cell-state.*

BLENDING OF INHERITANCE

The familiar idea of blending—of mixing and getting intermediates as we do with paints—must have been at the root of many of the quaint and amusing misconceptions about heredity. A giraffe was supposed to have issued from the mating of a camel and a leopard—blending the leopard's spots and the camel's long neck. Camels were indeed favorite and versatile hybridizers. One authority stated that an ostrich was a cross between a camel and a sparrow—a curious blend to say the least. Arabian scholars thought that sea cows were crosses between humans and fishes, and Greek mythology is full of half-human, half-animal hybrids. Many a visitor to the zoo still explains the queer animals as crosses between the most diverse parents.

Of course, only animals of the same or very closely related species can cross and produce offspring. Even when two closely related species cross, the offspring produced are usually not fertile; witness the mule. It is entirely impossible for animals as distinct as man and ape, cat and dog, or horse and cow (let alone camel and sparrow) to engender offspring.

INHERITANCE OF ACQUIRED CHARACTERISTICS

The persistence of other errors about heredity is as nothing compared with the persistence of the belief in inheritance of acquired characteristics. A man who exercised and developed large muscles would, it was thought, pass on his muscular development to his children. An animal that stretched its neck reaching for leaves would have offspring with longer necks than if he had been content to browse near the ground. Hence, in time, a giraffe would develop.

At one time this theory was especially in vogue in relation to problems of evolution. Although it has gone under the name of *Lamarckism,* after Jean Baptiste de Lamarck, the French evolutionist of the early 1800's, the idea is at least 2000 years older than Lamarck. It was discussed by many Greek scholars, and its origin was independent from evolutionary thought. In fact, the mechanism of biological heredity renders the inheritance of acquired characteristics impossible. The idea is historically important only because it was part and parcel of the first full and consistent theory of evolution—Lamarck's.

PANGENESIS

Pangenesis, like the idea of the inheritance of acquired characteristics, which demands it, was in vogue in the late nineteenth century before the development of the chromosome theory of heredity. Again, the Greeks, Democritus in particular, had discussed pangenesis in only slightly cruder form 2000 years earlier.

If a blacksmith's enlarged muscles, acquired by virtue of his work, are inherited by his son, there must be some mechanism whereby the condition of his muscles can be represented in what heredity transmits to his son. Democritus spoke of representative particles, *pangens,* coming from all parts of the bodily organization and entering the semen introduced into the female in copulation.

In his later years Darwin resorted to a theory of the inheritance of acquired characteristics and to a revived form of Democritus's pangenesis. He spoke of *gemmules,* representative particles again, entering the germinal material.

WEISMANN'S ONE-WAY RELATIONSHIP BETWEEN GERM CELLS AND SOMA

The advent of the cell theory in the mid-nineteenth century brought with it the seeds of many advances, including especially a clarification of ideas about heredity. We saw some detailed fruits of the cell theory in the last chapter. Once it became clear that all organisms were derived from single cells, it became difficult to subscribe to pangenesis and associated ideas.

All the diverse body cells (muscle, nerve, bone, etc.) are descendants of the single zygote cell. From which type of cell is the egg or sperm derived? August Weismann provided the solution to this problem by pointing out that the germ cells of each generation descend directly through a lineage of unspecialized cells from the germ cells of the previous generation. That is, the specialized body cells of each generation are related to germ cells in a one-way fashion: they are derived from germ cells but do not give rise to them. This insight dealt a death blow to pangenesis in all its forms.

The great clarification that Weismann's insight brings is due again to the study of the cell itself. We shall now turn to the study of heredity, of resemblances between parent and offspring, the other main line of investigation leading to the chromosome theory.

Mendel's Principles of Heredity

Gregor Mendel (1822–1884) was a monk in the Augustinian monastery of Brünn, Austria (now Brno, Czechoslovakia). He taught natural science in the monastery school and thus became interested in the problems of heredity. He devised ingenious and careful experimental techniques, and, by crossing different strains of peas, he discovered the fundamental principles of *genetics,* the science of heredity.

Mendel's results were published in 1866, but they were long neglected by other students. Mendel himself did not follow up his discoveries, and their importance was not recognized by other biologists for 35 years. Finally, about 1900, three other experimenters independently rediscovered the Mendelian principles: Karl Correns in Germany, Hugo De Vries in the Netherlands, and Erich von Tschermak in Austria. This situation is a striking example of the fact that a theory, even though it is correct, may not be accepted and bear fruit until the general progress of science creates an atmosphere receptive to it.

MENDEL'S FIRST EXPERIMENTAL RESULTS: A SINGLE CHARACTER DIFFERENCE

Most of Mendel's work was done with a sweet pea (*Lathyrus*). Among other advantages, this pea offers an abundance of variant types that can be crossed or hybridized. Many garden varieties differ in a clean-cut, either–or way. Some have colored flowers, others white; some have yellow seeds, others green; some are tall, others dwarf; some have flowers clustered at the apex of the stem, and others spread out. The most valuable feature is that these differences in character are clean-cut. Mendel seems to have been aware of this advantage; he sensed that he was correctly attempting to study and analyze the simplest possible kind of heredity. This was a major reason for the success of his work. The complexity involved in the inheritance of most commonly studied human characters had been a block to their successful analysis.

Mendel's first experiments were crosses between varieties that differed in only one visible respect. He crossed tall plants with dwarf plants, colored flowers with white flowers, and so on. He had seven pairs of alternative characters for study, and in all seven cases he found the same result as he did, for example, in the cross between red-flowered and white-flowered types. When red-flowered plants were crossed with white-flowered plants, the hybrid offspring were all red-flowered. This result was obtained whether the red form was used as the male (pollen) parent or as the female (ovule) parent. However, when two hybrid reds were crossed, the offspring surprisingly

comprised both reds and whites in a ratio of about three reds to every white (Figure 6-1). These results can be summarized schematically as follows:

P_1 plants Red-flowered $\times$ White-flowered
F_1 plants 100% Red-flowered $\times$ Red-flowered
$$\downarrow$$

F_2 plants	Red : White
Number	705 : 224
Per cent	75.9 : 24.1
Ratio	3.15 : 1.00

P_1 designates the initial parents; F_1 the first hybrid (or filial) generation; and F_2 the second hybrid generation, arising from the crossing of F_1 plants.

The two important results are these: (1) F_1 consists entirely of plants resembling only one of the parents; and (2) F_2 consists of plants resembling both parents in the P_1 generation. The parental character missing in F_1 appears in about one-fourth of the individuals in F_2. All Mendel's experiments yielded similar ratios. The generality of the result immediately suggests its significance. Mendel perceived this and proceeded to seek an explanation, which he found and then tested.

MENDEL'S HYPOTHESIS OF PAIRED FACTORS: SEGREGATION AND DOMINANCE

The most remarkable aspect of Mendel's results is the reappearance of the white-flowered plants in the F_2 generation. It is obvious that, although the F_1 plants do not show white flowers, they nevertheless must carry some hereditary factor for them, because when they are crossed among themselves, white flowers appear in approximately one-fourth of the offspring. Indeed, each F_1 plant has a factor for white flowers that it passes on to half of its offspring. This line of argument suggests two other conclusions: first, that each plant carries at least two hereditary factors for each flower color; and second, that the factor for white is completely dominated by the factor for color when both are present in the same plant.

Mendel saw that he could explain his results if he made the following assumptions: (1) there is in each plant a pair of hereditary factors controlling flower color; (2) the two factors in each pair are derived from the plant's parents—one member of the pair from each parent; (3) the two factors in each pair separate, or segregate, during the formation of germ cells, so that each germ cell receives only one factor; (4) the factors for red flowers and white flowers are alternative forms of the same factor, the red being dominant over the white.

For discussion and understanding of Mendel's scheme and the whole science of genetics that has developed from it, we need to define several terms.

1. The paired hereditary factors are now called *genes*.

2. The alternative forms of the same gene are called *alleles*. Thus the genes for red flowers and for white flowers are alleles of each other. Again, the gene for plant size occurs in two allelic forms; there is an allele for tallness and an allele for dwarfness. Tallness, however, is not an allele of redness.

3. One allele is *dominant* over the other, *recessive*, allele. The alleles of a gene are symbolized by the same single letters or brief combinations of letters. The dominant allele is often written as a capital letter (here C represents the red allele), and the recessive allele as a small letter (here c represents the white allele).

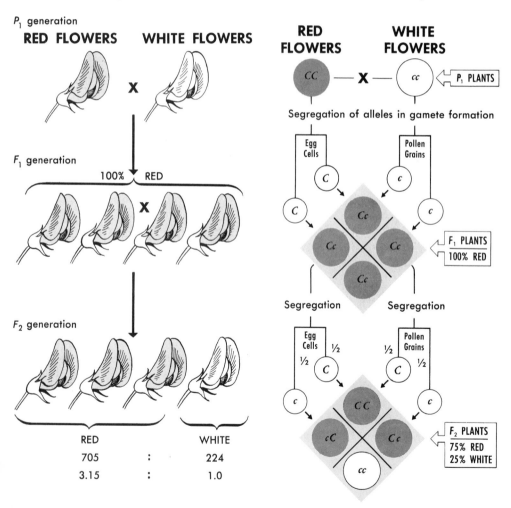

A OBSERVATIONS

B EXPLANATORY HYPOTHESIS

FIG. 6-1 **The results of Mendel's experiments in crossing red- and white-flowered peas and his interpretation of the results.** P_1 refers to the parental generation with which an experiment is started; F_1 refers to the offspring of that generation, or the first filial generation; F_2 refers to the next, or second, filial generation; and so on.

4. When both members of the pair of alleles in a plant are the same (for example, *cc* or *CC*), the plant is said to be *homozygous* ("like joined"). When the two alleles differ (for example, *Cc*), the plant is said to be *heterozygous* ("differently joined").

5. Although all the offspring in the first hybrid generation (F_1) are alike and indistinguishable in appearance from their parents (P_1), they nevertheless have different hereditary constitutions. We shall constantly have to make this distinction between appearance and hereditary constitution. In doing so, we shall speak of the *phenotype* ("visible type") and the *genotype* ("hereditary type") of the organism. The phenotype of the F_1 plants in our example has red flowers in every case, but each plant has a factor for white flowers in its genotype.

Now we can follow Mendel's interpretation, as given in Figure 6-1B. In the P_1 generation both the red-flowered plant and the white-flowered plant are homozygotes. The genotype of the red-flowered plant is *CC*, and the genotype of the white-flowered plant is *cc*. When they produce gametes, the genes segregate, so that the red-flowered plant produces only *C* gametes and the white-flowered plant produces only *c* gametes. Union of these gametes in the zygote at fertilization yields only a heterozygous F_1 plant with a *Cc* genotype (we can equally well write *cC*; the order of the symbols is meaningless). The phenotype of this plant is, however, red-flowered and indistinguishable from the red-flowered parent.

The F_2 arises from crossing two F_1 reds, each genotypically *Cc*. What gametes will these F_1 plants produce? In both parents the *Cc* pair segregates so that each parent produces two kinds of gametes, *C* and *c*. Mendel correctly assumed, moreover, that these two kinds of gametes (*C* and *c*) must be produced in equal numbers by each parent. Thus, if the F_1 plant used as male parent produces 1000 pollen grains, 500 will be *C*, and 500 will be *c*.

Only one kind of fertilization was possible in the formation of F_1 plants—the union of *C* and *c*, giving *Cc* as the F_1 genotype. However, in the mating of the two F_1 plants, more than one kind of fertilization is possible. In fact there are four types, and all four are equally probable or frequent.

Figure 6-1B shows a checkerboard system, making it easy to visualize the symbolic meioses (gameto-geneses) and fertilizations. Note that these fertilizations produce F_2 plants with the genotypes *Cc* and *cC:* these two heterozygotes are identical. Thus we conclude that, on the basis of the Mendelian scheme, the F_2 generation should contain three kinds of genotypes in the following proportion:

CC	:	Cc	:	cc	
$\frac{1}{4}$		$\frac{1}{2}$		$\frac{1}{4}$	genotypic ratios
$\frac{3}{4}$				$\frac{1}{4}$	phenotypic ratios
Red			White		

Because the *CC* homozygotes and *Cc* heterozygotes are phenotypically the same, only two classes of phenotypes will appear in F_2, and they will tend to appear in the ratio of $\frac{3}{4}$ red : $\frac{1}{4}$ white. The class of plants that are *cc* homozygotes are those with white flowers that Mendel had found were missing in F_1. They constitute about one-fourth of the F_2.

MENDEL'S TESTS OF THE HYPOTHESIS

Let us, in spite of our present greater knowledge, assume ourselves to be in Mendel's position for a moment. We have no knowledge of chromosomes and their role in heredity. Indeed, we have no knowledge at all of the real physical basis of heredity. We have just performed some crosses with garden plants differing in flower color and obtained quantitative results. Then to explain these results we have *created a hypothesis* that assumes the existence of hereditary factors which we will call genes, although at this stage we have no knowledge of what they are physically or how they are related to cell structure. We did not observe the hypothesis; it was a pure invention, as given in Figure 6-1B.

The fact that the hypothesis will explain the data is not in itself a sufficient basis to accept it as true; there may be other hypotheses that could explain the facts equally well. What we now seek, therefore, is some further basis in fact for the acceptance or rejection of our scheme: we must *test the hypothesis*.

In Chapter 1 we stated that a proper scientific hypothesis is testable; Mendel's hypothesis is scientific because it is testable. In this case and many others the test takes the form of finding out whether or not certain predictions arising out of the scheme hold good. We must look in the hypothesis for predictions as to the outcome of new crosses yet to be performed.

The most obvious tests of the scheme hinge around the fact that red-flowered plants are of two kinds genotypically. The red in the P_1 generation is, by hypothesis, homozygous CC and when crossed with a white-flowered plant (cc) can produce only red-flowered offspring that are Cc heterozygotes. But the superficially similar mating of F_1 red with white will have a different outcome. The prediction (Figure 6-2) is that the progeny will be one-half red and one-half white because, although the white parent produces only c gametes, the red parent produces one-half C and one-half $c,$ so that Cc and cc fertilizations will be equally frequent. Mendel performed such a cross and obtained 166 plants, of which 85 were red-flowered and 81 were white-flowered. The result is as near to equality as could be expected in an actual experiment with that many plants.

It is very important to notice that the prediction was not just a *qualitative* one. The scheme predicted not only that red-flowered plants would arise from this cross of F_1 red with white plants but also that the offspring would tend toward a particular *quantitative* relationship—$\frac{1}{2}$ red : $\frac{1}{2}$ white. When specific forecasts are thus fulfilled both qualitatively and quantitatively, we have that much more reason to believe in the validity of the hypothesis that produced them.

It is clear from these and other experiments that the Mendelian hypothesis is formally or mathematically valid. Mendel did not know at the time what the paired factors or genes were, but he recognized that they did exist, and in pairs that segregate when gametes are formed. His hypothesis became a sound theory that has since been supplemented but never supplanted.

TWO CHARACTER DIFFERENCES: INDEPENDENT SEGREGATION

Having discovered the rules governing the hereditary transmission of genes controlling one character difference (such as flower color), Mendel proceeded to a more complex situation. He traced

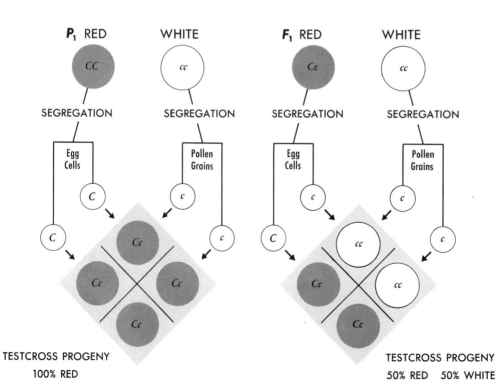

FIG. 6-2 A testcross that distinguished the genotypes of P_1 and F_1 red-flowered peas. P_1 red crossed with white gives a progeny that is 100 per cent red. F_1 red crossed with white gives a progeny that is 50 per cent red and 50 per cent white.

the inheritance of two distinct character differences simultaneously: seed shape and seed color in peas. Each of these character differences he had studied separately, finding them to obey the same rules as flower color.

In peas the seeds may be either yellow (controlled by the dominant gene Y) or green (y, recessive). Second, they may be fully swollen, making the whole pea seed round (controlled by the dominant gene R), or shrunken, making the seed wrinkled (r, recessive). For each pair of characters (yellow versus green, round versus wrinkled), there are, as with flower color, three possible genotypes.

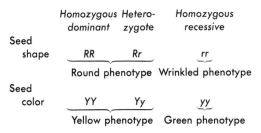

Mendel began by crossing plants raised from round, yellow seeds ($RRYY$) with plants raised from wrinkled, green seeds ($rryy$). In meiosis, when gametes are formed, each pair of alleles (for example, RR or YY) segregates independently of each other. Thus, the round yellow plants ($RRYY$) produce only RY gametes, never RR or YY. In other words, *each pair of alleles is always represented in the gametes by one of its members*. The wrinkled green plants ($rryy$) produce only ry gametes. The F_1 consists of seeds that are

FIG. 6-3 All F₁ plants from the cross round yellow × wrinkled green have the genotype RrYy.

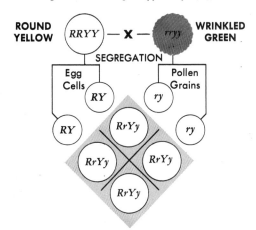

round and yellow, with the genotype $RrYy$ (Figure 6-3). The F_1 is heterozygous for both pairs of alleles and is called *dihybrid*. (Why?)

What are we to expect when two such dihybrid F_1 plants are crossed to produce the F_2 generation? We know from the study of each character separately that in the formation of gametes R will segregate from r, and Y will segregate from y. However, we are left with an uncertainty as to whether there will be two or four kinds of gametes. Thus

P_1 plants	$RRYY$	$rryy$
P_1 gametes	RY ×	ry
F_1 plants	$RrYy$	

What kinds of gametes?
There are two possibilities

	either (a) or	(b)
F_1 gametes	RY, ry	RY, ry, Ry, rY

When the F_1, $RrYy$, was formed, the gametes from the parental plants were of two types, RY and ry. The two dominant alleles were associated in one gamete, and the two recessives in the other. Are they necessarily always associated? If so, we expect only two classes of gametes to be produced by the F_1: RY and ry. These two types of gametes (*a* above) are said to contain *parental* combinations of alleles. (Why?) However, if the Rr pair of alleles segregates independently of the Yy pair, and the original combinations are not necessarily maintained, then (as in *b* above) two new kinds of gametes (Ry and rY), in addition to the two original ones, will be produced by F_1. Ry and rY are said to be *recombination* types of gametes. (Why?)

It is easy to find out which of the two possibilities (*a* or *b*) is in fact realized, because they will lead to different F_2 generations, as indicated in Figure 6-4. (1) If the only combinations produced by the gametes are the parental ones, RY and ry, there will be only three classes of genotypes in F_2 and two classes of phenotypes—round yellow $\frac{3}{4}$:wrinkled green $\frac{1}{4}$ (see Figure 6-4A). (2) If the two recombination types of gametes are produced in addition to the parental types,

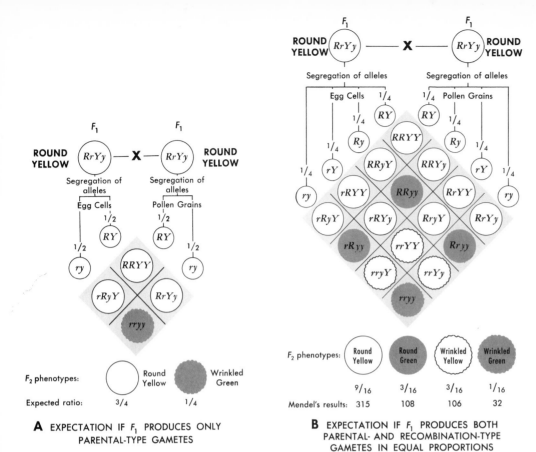

FIG. 6-4 Alternative expectations from the cross *RrYy × RrYy*, and the fit of Mendel's actual results to the second alternative.

and all four occur in equal frequencies, there will be nine classes of genotypes in F_2 and four classes of phenotypes. The four phenotypes and their expected frequencies are round yellow $\frac{9}{16}$: round green $\frac{3}{16}$: wrinkled yellow $\frac{3}{16}$: wrinkled green $\frac{1}{16}$ (see Figure 6-4B).

At the bottom of Figure 6-4 are the results from Mendel's own experiment. It is clear that the four kinds of genotypes are produced; the parental combination *RY* and *ry* can be recombined in the F_1 to yield gametes that are *Ry* and *rY*. Moreover, all four are produced with the same frequency, as shown

by the close agreement between expected and observed proportions.

Mendel's demonstration of the independence of the *Rr* and *Yy* pairs of alleles in their segregation is often referred to as the rule of *independent assortment.* We shall shortly see that it is not universal. Exceptions were found in the outburst of genetic work that followed the rediscovery of Mendel's principles in 1900, and it was by understanding the causes both of the rule and of its exceptions that still further advances were made. The explanation of these exceptions is discussed on p. 124.

Physical Basis of Heredity

THE CHROMOSOME THEORY

The reader, armed with the information from the last chapter, will long ago have perceived the significance of the main Mendelian results—proofs of the

paired nature of the genes, one derived from each parent, and their segregation in gamete formation. Clearly these characteristics of genes must be related to the like characteristics of chromosomes discussed in Chapter 5. We have deliberately avoided using what we know of chromosome behavior here to emphasize the brilliance and adequacy of Mendel's analysis, for Mendel was actually ignorant of chromosome behavior when he performed and analyzed his experiments in 1865.

The people who did pioneer research on chromosomes overlooked the importance of Mendel's work. It was not until after De Vries, Correns, and von Tschermak had rediscovered the Mendelian phenomena that biologists put the two lines of study together.

Sutton's Formulation of the Chromosome Theory

In 1902 an American cytologist, W. S. Sutton, saw the implications of Mendel's analysis in relation to chromosome behavior. Sutton maintained that the hereditary factors—or genes—are carried on the chromosomes or are parts of chromosomes. The theory that genes are chromosome parts explains (1) why they occur in pairs (because chromosomes do); (2) why the two members of a pair are derived one from each parent (because chromosomes are so derived); and (3) why genes segregate at meiosis (because

chromosomes do). Other features of Mendel's results are immediately explainable by the assumption that the genes are carried on the chromosomes.

Chromosomal Basis of Segregation: the 1:1 Segregation Ratio

Mendel assumed that the Cc genes in his F_1 (red-flowered) heterozygotes segregated to produce two types of gametes, C and c; and he further assumed that the two types were produced in equal numbers (see Figure 6-1B). The chromosome theory shows his assumption to be correct and explains it. The F_1 red-flowered plant must contain a pair of chromosomes carrying the alleles C and c. Figure 6-5A shows schematically the origin of the F_1 red and its chromosome constitution, with the same hypothetical nucleus that illustrated meiosis in Chapter 5. At metaphase of meiosis I in this F_1 plant, the chromosomes are at the equator of the spindle (Figure 6-5B). The larger pair of homologous chromosomes carries

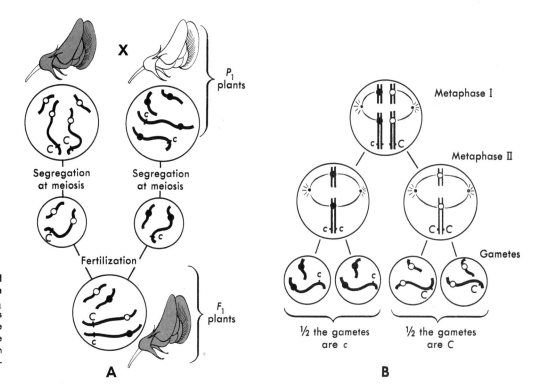

FIG. 6-5 The chromosomal basis of the 1:1 segregation ratio. A. The origin of the F_1 plant and its nucleus, which carries the genes C and c on its large chromosomes. B. Meiosis in the F_1 plant, leading to the production of c and C gametes in equal numbers.

Metaphase I

Metaphase II

Gametes

½ the gametes are c

½ the gametes are C

P_1 plants

Segregation at meiosis

Segregation at meiosis

Fertilization

F_1 plants

A

B

C and *c*. Each member of the chromosome pair has duplicated, and the two members are going to different poles. Each telophase I nucleus contains a large chromosome carrying either *C* or *c*. The two strands of each chromosome are separated at meiosis II, and so eventually each cell produces *precisely* two gametes with *C* and two gametes with *c*. If a pea plant produces 4000 pollen grains, these must have arisen from 1000 diploid cells in which meiosis occurred. Each of the 1000 cells yielded four gametes, two of which are *C* and two of which are *c*. No matter how many gametes are produced, the segregation ratio will always be 1:1.

Chromosomal Basis of Independent Segregation

Sutton pointed out that the chromosome theory could explain another feature of the Mendelian results—the independent segregation (or independent assortment) that Mendel had discovered in his experiment on the inheritance of two characters. Fig. 6-6 depicts independent segregation when the two pairs of genes (*Rr* and *Yy*) are carried on different chromosomes. Suppose that the *Yy* alleles are carried on the larger (B) pair of chromosomes and that the *Rr* alleles are carried on the smaller (A) pair of chromosomes. The orientation of the large pair of chromosomes on the equator of the spindle is independent of the orientation of the small pair. Thus the arrangements given in Figure 6-6A and Figure 6-6B are equally likely, and, accordingly, the allele *Y* is just as likely to enter the same nucleus with *r* as it is with *R*. Four types of gametes (*YR, yr, Yr,* and *rR*), then, are produced with equal frequency (check with Figure 6-4B).

Statistical Nature of Mendelian Heredity

The ratios of different genotypes and phenotypes in F_2 generations are often referred to as *Mendelian ratios*. For instance, when two F_1 red-flowered plants are crossed, the Mendelian ratios expected in F_2 are as follows: phenotypes, $\frac{3}{4}$ red : $\frac{1}{4}$ white; genotypes, $\frac{1}{4}CC : \frac{1}{2}Cc : \frac{1}{4}cc$. In actual experiments the ratios are

realized only as statistical approximations. Why is this so? Why, for example, did Mendel obtain 75.9 per cent red and 24.1 per cent white, not exactly 75 per cent and 25 per cent, respectively? The answer to this question emerges from the understanding that any *sample* is only an *approximate representation* of the population of events or things from which it is drawn.

Consider, first, what happens in tossing a coin. We expect heads half the time and tails half the time. If we were to throw a coin a million times, the ratio of heads to tails would be very close to 500,000 heads : 500,000 tails ($\frac{1}{2} : \frac{1}{2}$). But if we throw it only four times, there is a good chance (actually 1 in 16) that we may get four heads instead of the expected ratio of 2 heads : 2 tails. The more times we toss the coin, the less likely is the observed ratio of heads to tails to depart far from the expected ratio of $\frac{1}{2} : \frac{1}{2}$.

When a geneticist crosses two F_1 red-flowered pea plants, he obtains a relatively small number (say, 100) of F_2 plants. The 100 ovules and 100 pollen grains that gave rise to the F_2 plants were only a sample of the entire population of gametes produced by the F_1 plants. Like a small sample of coin throws, the sample of gametes only approximates the exact ratio of $\frac{1}{2}C : \frac{1}{2}c$ that applies to the gamete population as a whole. Consequently, the sample of zygotes obtained merely approximates the $\frac{1}{4}CC : \frac{1}{2}Cc : \frac{1}{4}cc$ ratio to be expected in an infinitely large progeny.

In any such situation we do not in fact expect our sample to have exactly the ratio inferred from the hypothesis being tested. By statistical methods, however, we can calculate how likely we are to find the observed ratio in our sample if the hypothesis is correct. If the observed ratio is unlikely, we suspect that the hypothesis is wrong, and perhaps we discard it altogether. If it is likely, the hypothesis is supported to some extent, although not proved. In Mendel's experiment summarized in Figure 6-4B, the theoretically expected and actually observed numbers compare as follows:

Expected from theory: 315.5	105.2	105.2	35.1
Observed by Mendel: 315	108	106	32

The agreement is remarkably close. The experiment gives us no reason to doubt the hypothesis. On the contrary, it greatly strengthens our confidence in it.

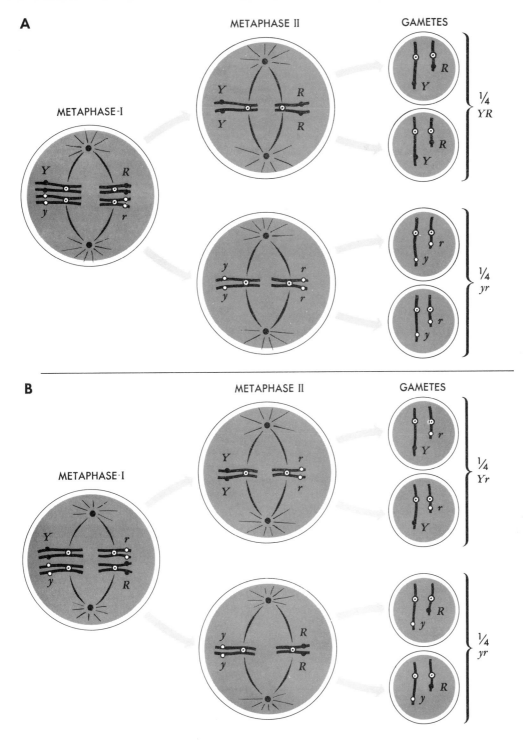

FIG. 6-6 The chromosomal basis of independent segregation. The chromosomes are shown at meiosis in the dihybrid plants *YyRr*, with the *Yy* genes on the larger pair of chromosomes and the *Rr* genes on the smaller pair. A and B are equally probable ways in which the chromosomes can orient themselves at metaphase I, as explained in Chapter 5. The consequence is that the four kinds of gametes—*YR*, *yr*, *Yr*, and *yR*—are produced in equal numbers.

TESTS OF THE CHROMOSOME THEORY

With the announcement of the chromosome theory of heredity in 1902, the science of genetics in its modern form was born. This theory, unlike earlier views on heredity, was precise and quantitative and had its foundations in cellular structures (chromosomes) whose behavior and properties were open to direct observation and interpretation. The earlier theory of pangens (which nobody could see) made virtually no specific predictions by which its merits could be judged. On the other hand, the chromosome theory offered abundant predictions, the testing of which led to the rapid growth of genetics as an exact science. From 1906 onward, much of the experimental work in genetics was carried out with the common fruit fly *Drosophila melanogaster,* the small yellowish fly that hovers around garbage cans and fruit in the late summer and fall.

Drosophila Melanogaster

Someone should erect a much-larger-than-life monument to this tiny (2 millimeter) insect. It is an ideal laboratory animal and has done more than any other to enlarge our knowledge of genetics. It is big enough to work with but small enough to raise by the hundreds in containers without crowding a laboratory. It breeds readily in captivity, it is prolific, and it has short generations (as little as 10 days). All these properties make experimentation with *Drosophila* relatively easy, quick, and cheap. The experiments that took Mendel 7 years with peas and required a large garden can be repeated with *Drosophila* in a few months in a dozen or so flasks tucked away on a shelf. *Drosophila* has two other advantages not realized when experiments with it were begun. It has a small number of chromosomes (four pairs in the most-used species), and its salivary glands contain chromosomes enormously larger than those of its other parts or of most other organisms. The small number of chromosomes simplifies the study of the grouping of genes in chromosomes. The giant chromosomes greatly aid in correlating heredity with the anatomy of the chromosomes.

Genetic experiments have been carried out with many organisms besides *Drosophila,* from bacteria and the viruses that infect them to corn, pine trees, chicks, and mice. Many interesting peculiarities of heredity occur in one species or another. Thousands of experiments on hundreds of species have, nevertheless, confirmed that the *principles* of heredity are basically the same in all organisms. Most of the principles learned from *Drosophila* apply in the widest way to all living things.

Sex Determination

Analysis of chromosome behavior was also significant in the discovery of the inheritance and determination of sexuality. There is a pair of special chromosomes in the nucleus of nearly every higher animal—the sex chromosomes. It is no coincidence that the attention of modern geneticists for a time focused strongly on the behavior of sex chromosomes in *Drosophila.*

Figure 6-7 is a simplified diagram of the chromosomes at metaphase of mitosis in a male and female *Drosophila.* There are only four pairs of chromosomes. One pair is dotlike and very small; it is called pair IV. Two larger V-shaped pairs, with the centromere in the middle of the chromosome, are called pairs II and III. These three chromosome pairs are collectively designated *autosomes,* to distinguish them from pair I, designated *sex chromosomes.* In organisms with other numbers of chromosomes, all except the sex chromosomes are called autosomes. The sex chromosomes are different in the two sexes. In the female they are both rod-shaped, with the centromere near the end. In the male one is rod-shaped, but its partner (unique to the male) is J-shaped, with the centromere at the bend. The two sex chromosomes in the female are known as X-chromosomes; in the male there is one X-chromosome and one special

FIG. 6-7 The chromosomes of *Drosophila melanogaster.*

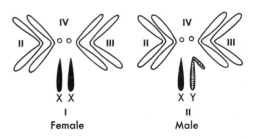

Female   Male

Y-chromosome, which is the J-shaped member. It is obvious that although the female will produce only one kind of gamete so far as the sex chromosomes are concerned, the male will produce two kinds. All the female's eggs will carry an X-chromosome, but of the sperms produced by the male, half will carry an X-chromosome, and the other half a Y-chromosome.

Figure 6-8 indicates the outcome of the gamete constitution at fertilization. One-half the fertilizations yield zygotes with two X-chromosomes; the other half yield zygotes with an X-chromosome and a Y-chromosome. The former become females, and the latter males. Thus, sex determination, which like other aspects of heredity had been discussed in vague and mythical terms for over 2000 years, is clarified by the chromosome theory. In most cases, sex in animals is determined at the moment of fertilization, and the decisive factor is whether the sperm carries an X-chromosome or a Y-chromosome.

Offhand, it looks as if X-chromosomes carry genes

TABLE 6-1   *Effect of X/A Ratio*

Number of X-chromosomes	Sets of autosomes (A) (three in a set)	Ratio X/A	Sex phenotype
3	2	1.5	Superfemale[a]
2	2	1.0	Normal female
2	3	0.67	Intersex
1	2	0.5	Normal male
1	3	0.33	Supermale[a]

[a] Both supermales and superfemales are weaker flies than their normal counterparts. Indeed, there is nothing "super" about them except that their chromosomal balance exceeds that characteristic of their sex.

for femaleness and Y-chromosomes those for maleness, but, as often happens in biology, things turn out to be not so simple. The Y-chromosome has little to do with sex determination. Its genetic effect is slight in man and apparently nil in some other animals. In some, indeed, there is no Y-chromosome (Figure 6-9). It has been established in some animals, and probably is a valid generalization, that the development of sex is determined by an interaction between genes on the X-chromosomes and genes on various autosomes. As usual, the best evidence comes from *Drosophila*.

In experiments with *Drosophila* it has been possible to obtain flies differing in the ratio of X-chromosomes to autosomes. Table 6-1 illustrates the different ratios obtained and shows how the scale of X/A ratios from 0.3 to 1.5 is a scale of increasing femaleness. The normal male has an X/A ratio of 0.5 (1 X-chromosome : 2 sets of autosomes); the normal female has an X/A ratio of 1.0 (2 X-chromosomes : 2 sets of autosomes). Evidently the genes of the autosomes tend to produce males, and genes concentrated on the X-chromosomes interact with those, producing females when they overbalance the autosomal genes.

Sex Linkage

Some characters, like white eye color or the trait known as *Bar* eye (in which the eye is abnormally small in size), show a markedly aberrant pattern of inheritance, suggesting that they are controlled by genes on the sex chromosomes.

FIG. 6-8   **Sex determination in *D. melanogaster*.**

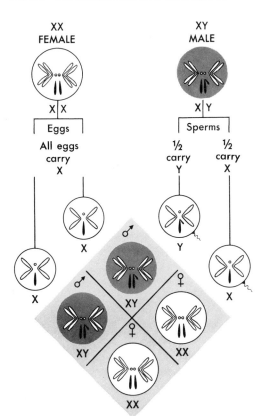

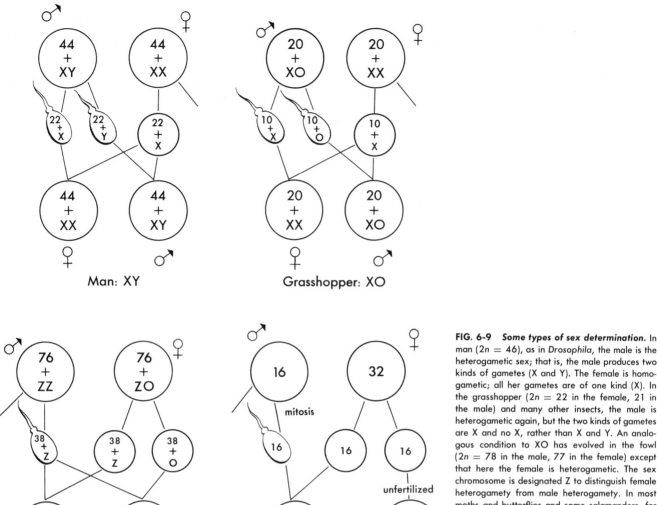

FIG. 6-9 *Some types of sex determination.* In man ($2n = 46$), as in *Drosophila*, the male is the heterogametic sex; that is, the male produces two kinds of gametes (X and Y). The female is homogametic; all her gametes are of one kind (X). In the grasshopper ($2n = 22$ in the female, 21 in the male) and many other insects, the male is heterogametic again, but the two kinds of gametes are X and no X, rather than X and Y. An analogous condition to XO has evolved in the fowl ($2n = 78$ in the male, 77 in the female) except that here the female is heterogametic. The sex chromosome is designated Z to distinguish female heterogamety from male heterogamety. In most moths and butterflies and some salamanders, for example, the female has a counterpart to the Y-chromosome, designated W, and sex determination is of the ZW type with the female being heterogametic. The honeybee ($2n = 32$) and many other members of the insect order Hymenoptera (bees, wasps, ants) have a remarkable sex-determining mechanism: unfertilized eggs develop into (haploid) males; fertilized eggs develop into (diploid) females.

First let us note the inheritance of vestigial versus normal wings in the fly. As in Mendel's pea experiments, it does not matter which parent—male or female—carries a particular character. Whether the vestigial-wing character is in the male or female parent, the F_1 is always all normal-winged, and the F_2 contains three normals to one vestigial. Moreover, the 3:1 ratio applies to both the male and female members of F_2.

The situation is very different in the case of white eye color versus red eye color. Figure 6-10 shows that the constitution of the F_1 depends on whether the white-eyed parent is father or mother. And the F_2 differs in the two cases. Hopelessly aberrant as this inheritance looks at first sight, it is exactly what we would expect if (1) the genes for white and red eye color were carried by the X-chromosome and (2) the Y-chromosome were an empty shell carrying no genes at all or at any rate not these genes. Note Figure 6-10A, which interprets the cross between a white female and a red male. All the male offspring are white-eyed because a male's X-chromosome is always derived from its mother; from its father it receives only the Y-chromosome, which evidently is empty of genes, at least as far as this character is concerned. On the other hand, a female always receives one X from its father and one from its mother. Since red (R) is dominant over white (r), all daughters in this cross must be red-eyed because the father was red-eyed; all sons must be white-eyed because both the mother's X-chromosomes carry the recessive gene r. Follow

the segregations and fertilizations involved in both parts of the figure to see how the assumption that the genes are on the X-chromosome and missing from the Y-chromosome explain all the results.

The conclusion that the Y-chromosome carries few or no genes fits in with some observations on other insects, such as the grasshopper, in which the Y-chromosome has been dispensed with altogether. Here again the female has two X-chromosomes, and the

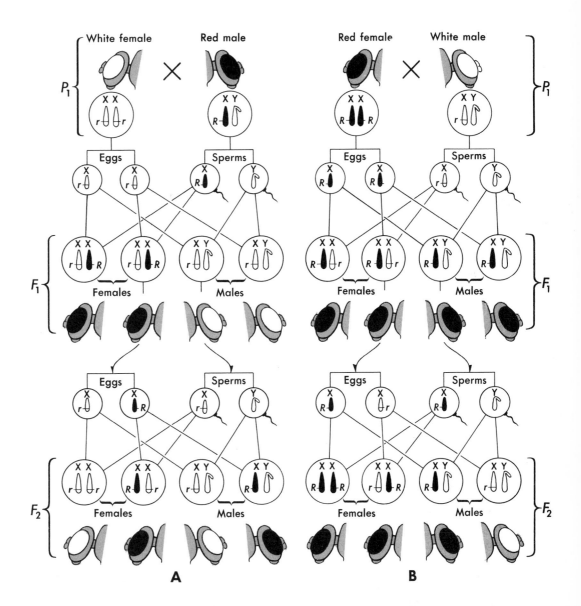

FIG. 6-10 Sex-linked heredity.

male has one. As in the XY system, the male produces two kinds of gametes, but they are X and no X rather than X and Y (see Figure 6-9). Notwithstanding these findings, there is now conclusive evidence that genes are present in the Y-chromosomes of some animals.

LINKAGE AND CROSSING OVER

There remains one striking aspect of the chromosome theory of heredity that may have occurred to the reader before now: the independent segregation that Mendel discovered when he followed the inheritance of two pairs of genes simultaneously must be the exception rather than the rule. Sutton explained independent segregation by assuming that the two gene pairs must be on separate chromosomes; the physical basis of gene segregation is chromosome segregation. In *Drosophila* there are only four pairs of chromosomes. It follows that the independent segregation of genes could only be a valid generalization for *Drosophila* if there were only four genes in its entire hereditary blueprint—one gene pair on each chromosome pair.

We must surely anticipate far more than four gene pairs in the hereditary blueprint of an organism as complex as *Drosophila*. And we must therefore anticipate that many gene pairs will not segregate independently at meiosis because they will be linked together, carried by the same chromosome. Such a linkage—or nonindependence—between genes was detected in the early growth of genetics after 1900. It was found, in fact, that in *Drosophila* all known genes (several hundred) fall into four groups called *linkage groups*. All the genes within a linkage group tend to segregate as a unit. The fact that there are four such groups in *Drosophila* is obviously significant, since there are four pairs of chromosomes. One of the four groups is very small and clearly belongs to the dotlike chromosome pair, IV. Another group is sex-linked and belongs, as we have seen, to the X-chromosomes. The other two groups are very large and are associated with the two big V-shaped pairs of chromosomes (II and III; see Figure 6-7).

Let us take an example of linkage between two

genes in corn, which is one of the plants best known genetically. In corn there are two genes, each with two alleles, that affect the color and texture of kernels as follows:

	Alleles	Effect on kernel
1st gene pair	C	Colored
	c	Colorless
2nd gene pair	S	Smooth (or full)
	s	Shrunken

We begin with the following cross:

P generation	CCSS	×	ccss
P gametes	CS	↓	cs
F₁ generation		CcSs	

If these two genes follow Mendel's rule of independent assortment, we should expect (1) that the F_1 would produce four types of gametes—*CS, cs, Cs, cS*— and (2) that it would produce them in equal numbers, with each type constituting one-fourth of the total pool of gametes produced. Furthermore, if all four classes of gametes were produced in these frequencies, we should expect the F_2 generation ($F_1 \times F_1 \rightarrow F_2$) to contain kernels in the ratio $\frac{9}{16}$ colored smooth: $\frac{3}{16}$ colored shrunken: $\frac{3}{16}$ colorless smooth: $\frac{1}{16}$ colorless shrunken. (Why? Cf. Figure 6-4B.) We would test whether or not the F_1 did produce all four kinds of gametes expected on the basis of independent segregation by making an F_2. There is, however, a more direct and generally useful way— known appropriately as a *testcross*—of finding out what kinds of gametes the F_1 produces. Compare this dihybrid testcross with the monohybrid testcross in Figure 6-2. It is performed by crossing the F_1 (*CcSs*) to a plant that is homozygous for both recessive alleles (*ccss*). The double recessive (*ccss*) plant is known as the *tester;* clearly it can produce only *cs* gametes.

Table 6-2 shows that the phenotypes of the testcross offspring indicate immediately what kinds of gametes came from the tested plant (*CcSs*) because it alone contributed dominant alleles. Scoring the frequencies of phenotypes in testcross progeny amounts to scoring the kinds and frequencies of gametes produced by the tested plant (*CcSs* in the present case). If the *Cc* and *Ss* gene pairs segregate independently, we can expect the four possible phenotypes in the testcross progeny to occur in equal numbers, $\frac{1}{4}$ colored smooth : $\frac{1}{4}$ colored shrunken : $\frac{1}{4}$ colorless smooth : $\frac{1}{4}$ colorless shrunken (row 4 in the table—no linkage). If, however, the two kinds of genes are on the same chromosome, and cannot segregate independently, we can expect the tested plant to produce only *CS* and *cs* gametes in equal numbers, leading to a testcross progeny of $\frac{1}{2}$ colored smooth : $\frac{1}{2}$ colorless shrunken (row 5 in the table—complete linkage).

Row 6 shows what kinds of testcross progeny were *actually* obtained in this experiment, which was carried out in 1922 at Cornell Agricultural Experiment Station by C. B. Hutchinson. It is apparent that the two genes are not independent in their segregation; the ratio among the *CS*, *cs*, *Cs*, and *cS* gametes is far from $\frac{1}{4} : \frac{1}{4} : \frac{1}{4} : \frac{1}{4}$. It is much closer to $\frac{1}{2}CS : \frac{1}{2}cs$, which is what we would expect if linkage were complete. Therefore, we must be on the right track in attributing the results to linkage. The most common allele combinations produced by the *CcSs* plant are the combinations (*CS* and *cs*) that existed in the gametes producing the plant. These combinations are appropriately called the "parental combinations"; the new types (*cS* and *Cs*) are called the "recombinations." It is clear that we cannot ignore the few recombination gametes. Yet our notions about linkage so far

demand that we anticipate progeny in the ratios given either by row 4 or by row 5. We cannot have our cake and eat it, so to speak; either the genes are linked, or they are not.

This is another excellent illustration of the importance of exceptions in scientific progress. By focusing attention on the exceptions in the present case—the recombination gametes—genetics made one of its most significant advances.

A close study of the behavior of chromosomes in the prophase of the first meiotic division reveals details that explain the appearance of a small number of recombination gametes. When the homologous chromosomes, such as those carrying *CS* and *cs* in our tested plant, pair up in meiosis, the two homologous partners often undergo an exchange of parts. This exchange of chromosome parts between homologous chromosomes at meiosis is called *crossing over*. The process is diagrammed in Figure 6-11, where the

TABLE 6-2   *A Testcross to Determine What Kinds and Proportions of Gametes the F₁ Corn Plant (CcSs) Produces*

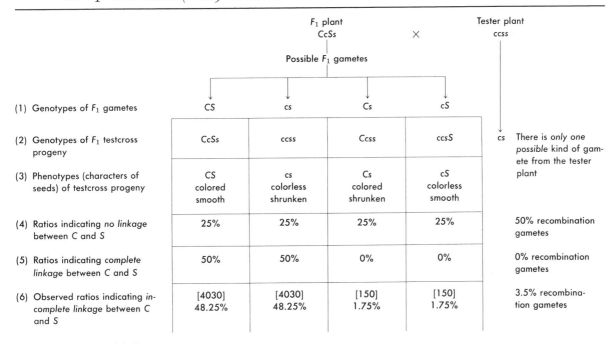

	CS	cs	Cs	cS	
(1) Genotypes of F₁ gametes	CS	cs	Cs	cS	
(2) Genotypes of F₁ testcross progeny	CcSs	ccss	Ccss	ccsS	cs There is *only one possible* kind of gamete from the tester plant
(3) Phenotypes (characters of seeds) of testcross progeny	CS colored smooth	cs colorless shrunken	Cs colored shrunken	cS colorless smooth	
(4) Ratios indicating *no linkage* between C and S	25%	25%	25%	25%	50% recombination gametes
(5) Ratios indicating *complete linkage* between C and S	50%	50%	0%	0%	0% recombination gametes
(6) Observed ratios indicating *incomplete linkage* between C and S	[4030] 48.25%	[4030] 48.25%	[150] 1.75%	[150] 1.75%	3.5% recombination gametes

(Top of table: F₁ plant CcSs × Tester plant ccss. Possible F₁ gametes)

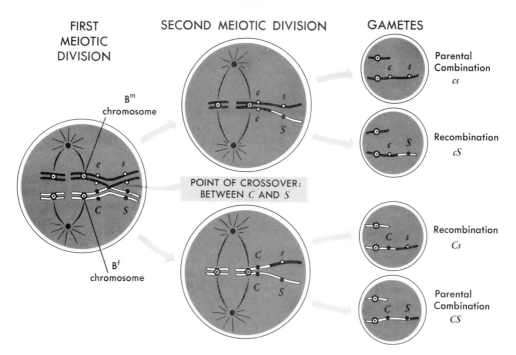

FIRST MEIOTIC DIVISION

SECOND MEIOTIC DIVISION

GAMETES

B^m chromosome

Parental Combination
cs

Recombination
cS

POINT OF CROSSOVER: BETWEEN *C* AND *S*

Recombination
Cs

Parental Combination
CS

B^f chromosome

A   CROSSING OVER OCCURS BETWEEN *C* AND *S*
AND PRODUCES RECOMBINATION GAMETES

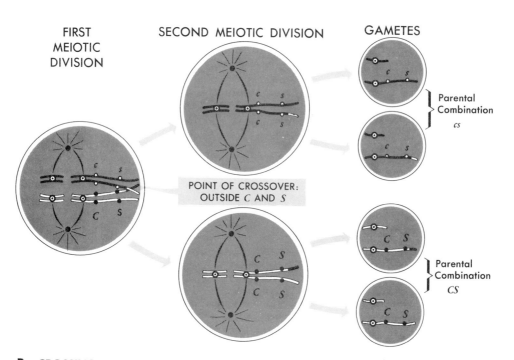

FIRST MEIOTIC DIVISION

SECOND MEIOTIC DIVISION

GAMETES

Parental Combination
cs

POINT OF CROSSOVER: OUTSIDE *C* AND *S*

Parental Combination
CS

B   CROSSING OVER OCCURS, BUT OUTSIDE THE REGION BOUNDED BY *C* AND *S;*
CONSEQUENTLY NO RECOMBINATIONS ARE PRODUCED

FIG. 6-11 The chromosomal events involved in crossing over.

C and *S* genes and their alleles *c* and *s* are situated on one pair of homologous chromosomes. We have used again, for the sake of simplicity, our nucleus with only two chromosome pairs. Actually in corn there are 10 pairs. The genes for seed color and texture are on the B-chromosomes. *C* and *S* are on the B^f-chromosome, which came from the female parent (*CCSS*). Both chromosomes from the male parent (A^m and B^m) are drawn in black to contrast with those (A^f and B^f) from the female parent.

In Figure 6-11A the exchange, or *crossover,* has taken place *between* the genes *C* and *S*. The diagram entails a discovery that was one of the great achievements of genetics; each gene (such as *C* or *S*) has a definite and fixed place, or *locus,* on the chromosome. The crossover involves only two of the four strands. It arises because the B^m and B^f strands broke at strictly homologous points. When the broken ends reunited, they did so in such a way that the B^f strand joined with the B^m strand. As a consequence, one-half of the four gametes produced contain B-chromosomes that are mixtures of B^m and B^f parts and are thus recombination types (*Cs* and *cS*).

In this particular meiosis the crossover occurred between *C* and *S,* but it does not always occur in this region of the chromosome. Sometimes it occurs outside the region bounded by *C* and *S,* and when this happens, no recombination gametes for these genes will be formed (Figure 6-11B). A moment's thought discloses that, once we have the data given in row 6 of Table 6-2, we actually know how often a crossover occurs between the genes *C* and *S.* Altogether, there were 8067 parental-combination gametes produced by the *CcSs* plant, and there were 301 recombination gametes. Let us round these numbers out to 8060 (96.5 per cent) and 300 (3.5 per cent). All told, we have 8360 gametes derived from 2090 cells by meiosis ($2090 \times 4 = 8360$). Remember that in every cell in which a crossover occurs between *C* and *S* half the gametes will be crossovers and half will not. It follows that a crossover occurred between *C* and *S* in only 7 per cent of all the cells undergoing meiosis.

What is the significance of the fact that a crossover occurred between *C* and *S* in only 7 per cent of all the cells that underwent meiosis in the corn plant? Why is it 7 per cent and not, for example, 20 per cent? The answer to this question was perceived by

Morgan and his collaborators, especially A. H. Sturtevant, at Columbia University between 1910 and 1915. It provided geneticists with a means of making maps of chromosomes and pinpointing on these maps the positions of individual genes.

Here is their answer: Each chromosome is a long thread on which the genes are located at fixed places in a definite sequence. The frequency of crossing over between two genes is approximately proportional to the distance between them. Thus, if genes are arranged in linear order on a chromosome,

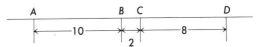

the frequency of crossing over between *A* and *B* (10 per cent) is greater than between *B* and *C* (2 per cent), which are closer together. By measuring crossover frequencies between genes, we can determine not only their relative spacing on the chromosome but also the sequence, or order, in which they are arranged. The procedure is as follows. Suppose that we study another gene, *E,* which is on the same chromosome as *A,B,C,* and *D.* First we measure the frequency of crossing over between *D* and *E.* It turns out to be 6 per cent. Where does *E* lie? It could be in either of two places.

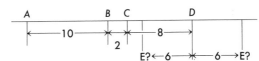

To settle the issue, we measure the frequency of crossing over between *C* and *E.* It proves to be 2 per cent. We now know that the following map is correct.

A ——10—— B C E D ——6——
        2 2

Where would *E* lie if the *C-E* value had been 14 per cent?

Many of the hundreds of genes so far discovered in *Drosophila* have been mapped (Figure 6-12). A start, although only the barest, has even been made in

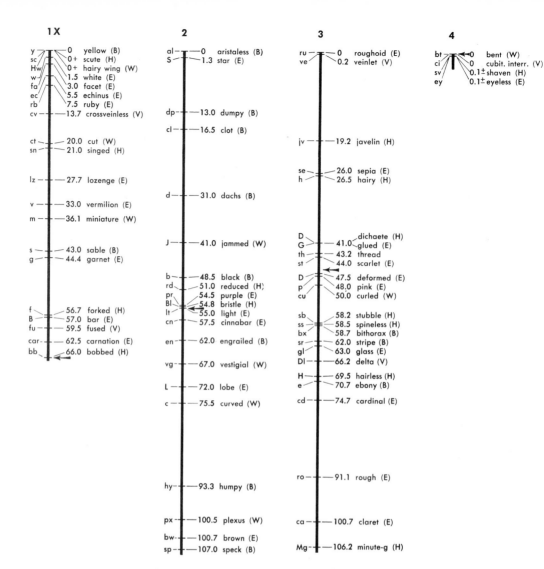

FIG. 6-12 **Linkage maps of _D. melanogaster_ chromosomes.** The chromosomes are numbered 1 through 4, corresponding with the usage in Fig. 6-7: chromosome 1 is the X-chromosome, 2 and 3 are the large V-shaped autosomes, and 4 is the small dot-shaped autosome. On the map of each chromosome given here, the centromere is marked by an arrow. The descriptive name of each gene (for example, "bent") is given to the right of its position, and the standard symbol for the gene (for example, "bt") is given to the left. The capital letters in parentheses following the name designate the part of the fly most affected by the gene: W = wing, V = veins of wing, H = hairs, E = eyes, B = body. On each map one gene is taken as an arbitrary starting point; its map distance is taken as zero. The positions of the other genes are then mapped in relation to this. The number given for each gene (for example, 13.0 for "dumpy" on the chromosome 2 map) is the standard map distance fro that gene; it is discovered experimentally through a study of crossing over. The map distance for "dumpy" implies that there is essentially 13 per cent crossing over between "aristaless" and "dumpy"; there is 3.5 per cent crossing over between "dumpy" and "clot."

mapping human genes. With his long generations and his aversion to controlled breeding, man is the worst of all animals for genetic experiments. Nevertheless, there are exceptionally full nonexperimental data on human pedigrees and on the distribution of many hereditary characters in large human populations. By applying to these data the principles learned from experiments in other species, we have gained a great deal of knowledge about human genetics, and this is a flourishing field of research at present.

Quantitative Inheritance

THE THEORY OF MULTIPLE FACTORS

The new science of genetics, which Mendel founded and later workers developed as the chromosome theory, is based on the assumption of distinct genes arranged in linear file on the chromosome. The early success of genetic analysis depended on the distinctness and recognizability of some individual genes. Their transmission from one generation to the next could now be followed as if it were the transmission of particles. Genetics, like physics and chemistry, became quantitative largely because of its particulate—or "atomic"—foundation, for, in a sense, the gene is an atom of heredity.

During the first decades of this century, an important aspect of genetic phenomena seemed inconsistent with the new theoretical scheme. Experimentation in the classic or Mendelian way centered almost entirely on characters with only a few easily distinguishable alternatives. A flower is red or white; a seed is full or shrunken; a chicken is black, blue, or spotty white. Most variations among organisms are not so simple. Instead of falling into a few sharply distinct groupings, they consist of numerous intergrading conditions. Men are not either tall or short, either black or white; cows do not produce either much or little milk; field mice are not either pale or dark; ears of corn are not either small or large. In all these characters, and indeed in a majority of the characters of plants and animals, there is a broad spectrum between extremes. Individuals cannot be classified merely as one thing or another but can only be placed somewhere along a scale.

The widespread occurrence of continuous, quantitative variation was a serious problem for genetics. It seemed at first that the Mendelian principles did not apply to it. If they did not, they would have decidedly limited value, and a significant part of heredity would remain unexplained. It was, however, possible to frame and test a hypothesis attributing continuous variation to genes inherited in accordance with the Mendelian principles. The hypothesis is that (apparently) continuous variation is controlled by numerous different genes, whose effects tend to add up *without distinct dominance*. This is a reasonable hypothesis, for it has been established that two or more genes can affect one character and that gene effects can add up without dominance. Let us see how the hypothesis interprets continuous variation.

Suppose that a character such as height in a plant depends on only two genes, A and B, each with two alleles, A_1 and A_2 and B_1 and B_2. Suppose that A_1 and B_1 make for tallness and A_2 and B_2 for lowness. Then the tallest plants would have the genotype $A_1A_1B_1B_1$, and the lowest would have the genotype $A_2A_2B_2B_2$. If these two were used as parents, all the offspring in F_1 would have the genotype $A_1A_2B_1B_2$. Since we have postulated that no dominance is involved, these offspring with half tall and half low alleles would be intermediate in height. Now suppose that the intermediate F_1 is interbred. The checkerboard (Figure 6-13) predicts that five height classes would appear in F_2 in the proportions indicated in Table 6-3.

If tallest and lowest were crossed as parents, and if, instead of just two genes, a great many were involved, the hypothesis would lead to these predictions:

1. F_1 would be intermediate between the parents, with few size classes, and no individuals as tall or as low as the extreme parents.

2. F_2 would have many size classes, so close together as to intergrade in practice.

3. The extreme-size classes of F_2 would be about equal to the tallest and lowest parents.

4. There would be very few individuals in the extreme-size classes of F_2 and increasing numbers of individuals in classes nearer intermediate size.

Do you see how these predictions follow by extension from the simple two-gene situation? They can be checked experimentally. The results in Table

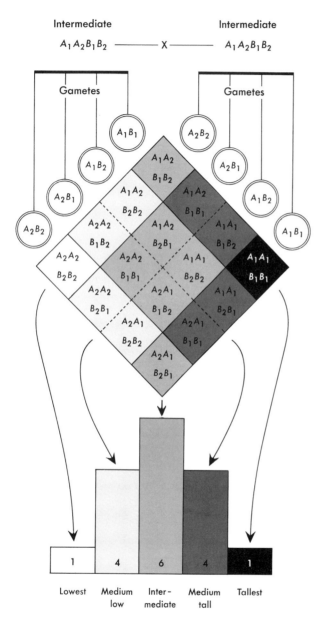

FIG. 6-13 **Multiple-factor inheritance.** For an explanation see the text and Table 6-3.

TABLE 6-3 *F_2 Progeny from the Cross $A_1A_2B_1B_2 \times A_1A_2B_1B_2$*

Genotypes	Expected ratio	Phenotypes	Expected ratio
$A_1A_1B_1B_1$	1	Tallest	1
$A_1A_1B_1B_2$	2	Medium tall	4
$A_1A_2B_1B_1$	2		
$A_1A_1B_2B_2$	1	Intermediate	6
$A_1A_2B_1B_2$	4		
$A_2A_2B_1B_1$	1		
$A_1A_2B_2B_2$	2	Medium low	4
$A_2A_2B_1B_2$	2		
$A_2A_2B_2B_2$	1	Lowest	1

6-4 and Figure 6-14 were obtained by E. M. East (1879–1938) in a now-classic experiment. Corn with short and long ears was used for the parents.

The predictions from the hypothesis are well confirmed. Many similar tests have been made, and other sorts of tests have been devised and carried out. They leave little doubt that the hypothesis is correct and that continuous variation is due to *multiple factors,* which are genes inherited according to Mendelian principles.

There is another interesting agreement with the theory of multiple factors. Continuous variation in

TABLE 6-4 *The Inheritance of Ear Size in Corn*

Length of ears in centimeters	Number of individuals		
	P_1	F_1	F_2
21	2		1
20	7		2
19	10		1
18	15		12
17	26		11
16	15		10
15	12	4	13
14	11	9	21
13	3	17	27
12		14	33
11		12	33
10		12	33
9		1	17
8	8		5
7	24		2
6	21		
5	4		

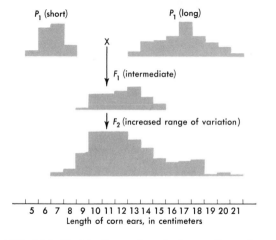

FIG. 6-14   The inheritance of ear size in corn. The results are based on the data of Table 6-4, from East's experiment.

natural populations almost always has the sort of distribution seen in F_2 of experiments like that of East. Most individuals are near the intermediate or average condition, and the number of individuals becomes smaller the greater the deviation from the average. This is one of the most important generalizations on variation in nature (Chapter 14). Although variation is also affected by nonhereditary, environmental factors, to the extent (usually large) that it is hereditary, it is explained by the theory of multiple factors.

Summary

The chromosome theory of heredity: two lines of investigation leading to it and fused by it; discovery of the theory opening up the flood of work that is modern genetics.

Pre-Mendelian ideas on heredity: their derivation from analogies with human nature and human affairs; the blending of inheritance; the inheritance of acquired characters; pangenesis, and its dismissal by Weismann, who showed the one-way relationship between germ line and soma.

Mendel's principles of heredity (1866): results of a single-character cross; Mendel's hypothesis of paired factors to explain his results; his tests of the hypothesis; the results and interpretation of a two-character cross; independent segregation (or assortment).

Physical basis of heredity: Sutton's (1902) formulation of the chromosome theory: genes as parts of chromosomes; the chromosomal basis of the $1:1$ segregation ratio, of independent assortment, and of the statistical nature of Mendelian heredity.

Tests of the chromosome theory: the role of *Drosophila melanogaster* in the history of genetics; sex linkage.

Linkage and crossing over: linkage groups—their number equal to the number of chromosome pairs; crossing over and its basis in chromosome behavior—crossover maps.

Quantitative inheritance: an early difficulty of the Mendelian theory, explained by the theory of multiple factors and illustrated by East's experiments with ear size in corn.

CHAPTER SEVEN

GENES
AND THEIR ACTIONS

The Inherited Message in Living Systems

Organisms are the most intricate systems that exist, far more complicated and elaborate than even the most advanced electronic computers, detection and control systems, or automated factories so far constructed by man. Organisms produce replicas of themselves, and we have already emphasized that the reproduction of such exceedingly complex systems must of necessity involve a transfer of information by devices comparable with the plans or blueprints used in organizing man-made systems. We have shown that these devices, which can be called "messages" in a metaphorical sense, are present in organisms, that they are passed from parents to offspring, and that they control the development of the offspring into the likeness of the parents. We have also shown that a major part of these hereditary specifications is located in the chromosomes. Further, we have noted how genetic experimentation led to the theoretical recognition of genes as operational units in the processes of heredity and revealed the basic facts about how genes are transmitted and reassorted in the usual circumstances of reproduction.

That something to which the name "gene" was given *does* exist in chromosomes and that a gene *does* produce specifiable results could be and was thoroughly established before anything was really known about the nature of the gene and its behavior. This latter knowledge, still incomplete, has been gained largely in the past few years. Recent investigations on the chemical nature and activity of genes have been especially productive and now constitute a brilliant chapter in the history of biology. In surveying it, we should not merely assimilate facts and conclusions. Here is an unusual opportunity to witness the vitality and pace of modern biological science and to observe how its various subdivisions can all shed light on fundamental problems.

The exploration of heredity must continue in two directions, corresponding with different aspects of scientific explanation (see Chapter 1). The direction just mentioned is concerned with physiological explanation, with how information, figuratively speaking, is coded in the genes and then put into effect. That is the subject of this chapter. It is, however, at least equally important to know what the message means, and why and how it arose in the first place. That

is the direction of historical explanation, to be discussed later. In the meantime, let us remember that the significance of the processes considered in this section will be fully appreciated only when they are brought into the broader evolutionary picture.

Nature of the Genetic Material

We shall begin with the question, "What are the physical and chemical characteristics of the genetic material?"

SMALL SIZE OF THE INHERITED MESSAGE

The number and the size of the chromosomes are fixed characteristics of any particular species. All normal humans have a diploid number of 46, and all normal *Drosophila melanogaster* flies have a diploid number of 8. The number and size of chromosomes differ considerably between species, as is illustrated by the comparison of fruit flies and men. The most common diploid number is 12 or thereabout, although the known range extends from 2 to hundreds. There is no correlation at all between the chromosome number and the degree of complexity of the organism. It is true that man (46) has more chromosomes than the fruit fly (8), but there are ferns and some crabs with chromosome numbers in the hundreds.

The most remarkable fact about the number and size of the chromosomes is the extremely small bulk of material that carries the inherited message. It is not more and probably much less than $\frac{1}{1000}$ of the material in the fertilized egg. Moreover, not *all* the material of the chromosomes is directly concerned with carrying hereditary information. We now know that chromosomes are complex chemically as well as structurally. They consist of several ingredients, some of which serve only as skeletal supports for the rest. There is some analogy between a chromosome and the cards or tape that feed information into a computer, but there is a radical difference in that a chromosome is part of a *living* system. As such, it

is metabolically active, containing enzymes and metabolic machinery that are not necessarily involved in message carrying.

WHAT IS A GENE?

We cannot see genes as distinct parts of the chromosome even with the most powerful electron microscopes. Most chromosomes give no visible evidence at all of linear differentiation. Some chromosomes, however, show a linear sequence of small swellings (*chromomeres*) at prophase of mitosis and

FIG. 7-1 Salivary-gland chromosomes in *Drosophila melanogaster*. In the salivary glands of many flies, including *Drosophila*, the chromosomes are enormously enlarged and clearly visible even during interphase. Moreover, they are strikingly crossbanded. The bands (local concentrations of nucleic acids) are constant in position from nucleus to nucleus. Thus it is possible to construct topographic maps of chromosomes. Particular genes have been localized in the region of some bands. (Photo, B. P. Kaufmann)

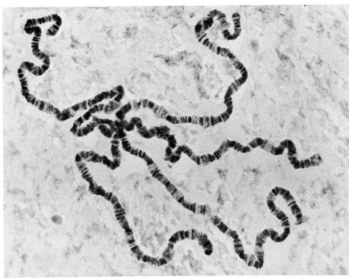

meiosis; others, in special tissues like the salivary glands of *Drosophila,* are enormously enlarged, with clearly defined crossbands (Figure 7-1). Some geneticists have suggested that these swellings and bands represent individual genes. However, this is unlikely to be true in general because it has been discovered that at least some chromomeres and bands contain more than one gene.

In Chapter 6 we defined genes as the units of heredity, located on the chromosomes, in linear order, and mapable according to the frequency of crossing over. Let us go on to ask "What is the chemical nature of the gene?"

CHEMISTRY OF THE GENETIC MATERIAL

Test-staining techniques have revealed that the chromosomes contain, principally, two classes of molecules: protein and nucleic acid. The two kinds of molecules occur in the chromosomes in a saltlike chemical combination, nucleoprotein.

We have already noted the special importance of the two forms of nucleic acid, ribonucleic acid, RNA, and deoxyribonucleic acid, DNA, (Chapter 2). It will be recalled that DNA is found mainly in the chromosomes of the nucleus, whereas RNA is found mainly in the cytoplasm, although, as we shall see, it is probably synthesized in the nucleus. Let us now consider the evidence that DNA is the primary message-bearing substance of the gene.

GENETIC SIGNIFICANCE OF DNA

The very presence of DNA in the chromosomes strongly suggests that it is the message-carrying fraction of the genetic material, and a recent series of important scientific discoveries greatly strengthened this presumption. All living nuclei contain DNA, and the amount of it in a nucleus is mathematically related to the number of chromosomes, the DNA level of haploid cells (for example, spermatozoa) being half that of diploid cells. The quantity of DNA doubles during mitotic interphase, just prior to cell division.

An early indication of the significance of DNA came in the 1930's from studies on the pneumonia-causing bacterium, *Pneumococcus.* In *Pneumococcus* there are many different hereditary cell types, and it was learned that a particular type (for example, type III) could be changed into one of the other known types (type II) by a chemical extract taken from type II. The chemical extracted from type II was called the *transforming principle;* it transformed the heredity of type III to that of type II.

The transforming principle was subjected to intensive chemical investigation and found to consist of DNA; the most careful scrutiny revealed only a minute trace of protein. This was a historic experiment in biology because for the first time part of the hereditary message of one genetic strain was extracted as an inert chemical and introduced into and accepted by another genetically different strain.

Equally strong evidence that DNA is the actual carrier of hereditary information has come from recent research on the heredity of viruses. Viruses are extremely small particles, many of them no bigger than some protein molecules (see Figure 3-3). We have seen that viruses are incapable of self-reproduction. Rather, they must enter a living host cell, which is then caused to start producing new viruses. The life cycle of a typical virus (bacteriophage) with bacteria as the host is outlined in Figure 7-2.

Note that the virus shown consists of little more than a small bit of DNA with a protein coat. Its reproduction, therefore, involves the synthesis of new virus DNA and new virus protein and their assembly into new virus particles. The new viruses are like the old ones, and virus reproduction has some of the basic characteristics of reproduction by living systems; we may therefore speak of *virus heredity.*

The particular virus in Figure 7-2 is a widely studied one that infects, and ultimately destroys, the common colon bacillus *Escherichia coli.* This bacterial virus attacks the host cell tail first. The tail penetrates the cell membrane. The contents of the main body of the virus then enter the cell as though squeezed from a syringe through the tail, which can be likened to a hypodermic needle. The empty shell of the virus is left outside. What has entered the bacterium is the carrier of virus heredity, and once inside the cell, it is copied again and again until the cell is destroyed and breaks open, yielding

One such bit of evidence on the mechanism of DNA replication is found in the enzymatic studies of Arthur Kornberg, who successfully synthesized DNA in a test tube. Soon after the discovery of the double-strandedness of DNA, Kornberg discovered DNA polymerase, the enzyme that catalyzes the formation of the DNA chain from its four component deoxyribonucleotides (in the form of their triphosphate derivatives). Interestingly, the synthesis requires not only the four nucleotides, magnesium ions, and DNA polymerase but also a small amount of single-stranded fully formed DNA to act as an information-containing and sequence-ordering primer or template for the reaction. The reaction can be formulated as follows.

$$
\begin{matrix}
x \text{ molecules of A} \cdot \text{dR} \cdot \text{PPP} \\
x \text{ molecules of T} \cdot \text{dR} \cdot \text{PPP} \\
y \text{ molecules of G} \cdot \text{dR} \cdot \text{PPP} \\
y \text{ molecules of C} \cdot \text{dR} \cdot \text{PPP}
\end{matrix}
+ \text{DNA (primer)} \rightleftharpoons
$$

$$
\begin{pmatrix}
x\text{A} \cdot \text{dR} \cdot \text{P} \\
x\text{T} \cdot \text{dR} \cdot \text{P} \\
y\text{G} \cdot \text{dR} \cdot \text{P} \\
y\text{C} \cdot \text{dR} \cdot \text{P}
\end{pmatrix}_x \cdot \text{DNA} + (2x + 2y)\text{PP}
$$

As noted in Table 2-4, the letters A, G, C, U, and T denote the purines and pyrimidines adenine,

GENES AND THEIR ACTIONS

guanine, cytosine, uracil, and thymine, respectively. The symbols R and dR refer to ribose and deoxyribose, so that $\text{A} \cdot \text{dR} \cdot \text{P}$ is deoxyadenosine *mono*phosphate and $\text{A} \cdot \text{dR} \cdot \text{PPP}$ the corresponding *tri*phosphate. Likewise, $\text{A} \cdot \text{R} \cdot \text{P}$ is adenosine monophosphate, and $\text{A} \cdot \text{R} \cdot \text{PPP}$ adenosine triphosphate. Note that DNA and RNA are polymers consisting of x molecules and that the true substrates of both DNA and RNA polymerase are nucleoside triphosphates. It is significant that polymerization does not occur unless single-stranded DNA is present. Single-stranded DNA is easily prepared in the laboratory from purified DNA heated to separate the strands and then quickly cooled to prevent reassociation. When the primer has a measurable biological property, such as transforming activity (p. 134), the newly synthesized DNA also has it. Biochemists have not yet devised a method for direct determination of long nucleotide sequences, and so the replication of genetic information leaves us with the presumption, if not the proof, that the base sequence of the primer is present in the new DNA strands.

Mechanism of Gene Action

We learned in Chapter 6 how genes are transmitted to the offspring, how they are recombined, and how certain regularities observed in breeding experiments can thereby be explained. We have also seen that the primary genetic material is DNA, a double-stranded structure that duplicates by separating its two strands, each of which then serves as a template in the formation of a new partner strand. In this way the unique nucleotide sequence of each DNA molecule is handed down to daughter cells. We must now inquire how genes determine the existence of given traits.

In recent years it has become apparent that genes act primarily by controlling the structures and rates of synthesis of specific proteins (notably enzymes). Discoveries have been made of the form in which the relevant information is coded in the nucleic acid

molecule, the method of communicating the coded message to the sites of protein synthesis, and the mechanisms governing the amino acid sequences upon which specificity depends. Let us consider some of the evidence underlying these new and epoch-making concepts of gene action.

THE ONE GENE–ONE PROTEIN THEORY

The preceding chapters have indicated that once the zygote of a future organism has been formed and its future traits determined, it becomes a self-regulating metabolic system engaged primarily in extracting energy from nutrient materials and converting them to building blocks for the compounds essential in tissue synthesis. Metabolism thus may be illustrated quite simply.

$$A \xrightarrow{e_1} B \xrightarrow{e_2} C \xrightarrow{e_3} D \xrightarrow{e_4} E \xrightarrow{e_5} F$$

A is a nutrient (or its derivative); *F* is a compound that the organism must have; *B, C, D,* and *E* are products and precursors in an orderly sequence of stepwise chemical reactions; and e_1, e_2, etc., are enzymes, each of which catalyzes one of the reactions.

We may regard the traits of an organism as visible consequences of sequences of enzyme reactions. For example, there are genes that cause hair to be black; but the direct cause of black hair is a black pigment synthesized from simpler materials by a sequence of enzyme reactions in skin cells. Other phenotypic traits may similarly be attributed to specific sequences of enzyme reactions, although the relationships may be much less direct than in the example.

The work of George Beadle and Edward Tatum, published in 1945, led to one of the first great simplifications in our ideas of gene action—the one gene–one protein theory. These investigators performed their experiments with a common red bread mold, *Neurospora crassa*. A typical experiment is diagrammed in Figure 7-3. When organisms that were fully capable of synthesizing the vitamin thiamine were exposed to x-irradiation, they produced offspring that would not grow unless thiamine was supplied. Radiation had apparently eliminated the capacity of the offspring to produce thiamine for themselves from ordinary dietary carbon sources such as glucose. It was found that this loss of synthetic ability was associated with the absence (or nonfunction) of a specific enzyme. If we represent this enzyme as e_3 in our sequence, assuming it to be the pathway of thiamine synthesis, the organism had lost the capacity to convert *C* to *D*. When growth was sustained with an artificial supply of thiamine, reproduction continued normally, and all subsequent generations

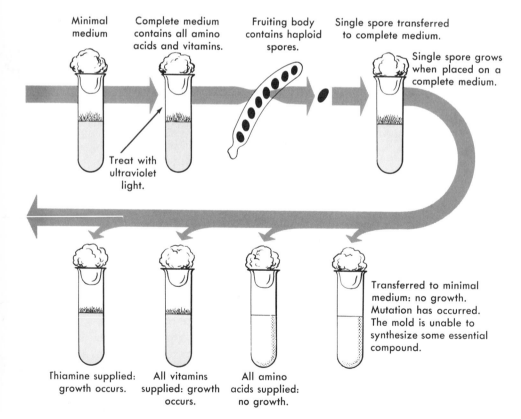

Minimal medium

Complete medium contains all amino acids and vitamins.

Fruiting body contains haploid spores.

Single spore transferred to complete medium.

Single spore grows when placed on a complete medium.

Treat with ultraviolet light.

Thiamine supplied: growth occurs.

All vitamins supplied: growth occurs.

All amino acids supplied: no growth.

Transferred to minimal medium: no growth. Mutation has occurred. The mold is unable to synthesize some essential compound.

FIG. 7-3 The production and isolation in *Neurospora* of mutations affecting single chemical reactions. The sequence of steps illustrated demonstrates that a mutation has been induced that affects the synthesis of the vitamin thiamine.

displayed the same enzyme deletion. Hence they were in perpetual need of the product of the missing enzyme.

The implications of this classic experiment are obvious. A mutation, induced by radiation, produced strains lacking one enzyme. As long as the environment provides an ample supply of the compound the organism can no longer make for itself, the heritable loss of an enzyme does not jeopardize survival. On the basis of many similar data, Beadle and Tatum postulated that a single gene governs the synthesis of a single specific enzyme.

This suggests an explanation for certain of the nutritional needs of man and other higher organisms. For example, thiamine is just as necessary in human metabolism as in *Neurospora* metabolism, but the normal (wild) *Neurospora* can make it from simpler compounds whereas man cannot. Hence human beings require thiamine in their food. Vitamins are essential substances that an organism cannot make for itself; thus thiamine is a vitamin for man and for the *Neurospora* mutant but not for wild *Neurospora*. We may reasonably speculate that our remote evolutionary ancestors could make thiamine but that, through mutation, the enzymatic machinery for its synthesis was lost. Had there been no organisms in the environment (for example, *Neurospora,* wheat plants, and other foods), that could make thiamine for the mutants, they would have been eliminated, and we should either retain the ability to synthesize thiamine—or be extinct.

HOW DNA CONTROLS PROTEIN SYNTHESIS

It is now evident that genes act by controlling amino acid sequences in the synthesis of proteins (including enzymes). Proteins contain 20 amino acids. DNA contains only four bases. How, then, can DNA be coded so that its genetic information can be read off as an amino acid sequence?

The answer to this question began to emerge in late 1961 and 1962. DNA was first found to direct the synthesis of RNA in much the same way that it directs its own replication. In 1960 an enzyme was discovered that catalyzes the synthesis of RNA—an RNA polymerase that, like DNA polymerase, demands the presence of a DNA primer. Moreover, the base ratio of the newly formed RNA was funda-

mentally identical to that of the DNA primer (if the U in RNA is taken as the equivalent of T in DNA).

a molecules of $A \cdot R \cdot PPP$
b molecules of $U \cdot R \cdot PPP$
c molecules of $G \cdot R \cdot PPP$ $+ DNA \text{ (primer)} \rightleftharpoons$
d molecules of $C \cdot R \cdot PPP$

$$\begin{pmatrix} aA \cdot R \cdot P \\ bU \cdot R \cdot P \\ cG \cdot R \cdot P \\ dC \cdot R \cdot P \end{pmatrix} + PP + DNA$$

The requirement for DNA in RNA synthesis suggested the following means for transmitting information from the nuclear gene to the cytoplasmic ribosome, the site of protein synthesis (Chapter 3): the coded instructions for protein synthesis contained in the DNA nucleotide sequence are duplicated in the arrangement of nucleotides in the DNA-determined RNA strand; the RNA then carries these instructions from the nucleus to the ribosome. The existence of this *messenger RNA* and its template function were postulated as a theoretical necessity in early 1961 and confirmed experimentally a few months later.

Protein synthesis begins only after another series of events has taken place (Figure 7-4). First the individual amino acids must be carried to the ribosome. It was learned in 1957 that another type of RNA, much smaller than messenger RNA, serves as an adaptor molecule and performs this transport function. Because of its role, it was termed *transfer RNA*. Special enzymes (plus ATP) activate the amino acids, and then a specific transfer-RNA molecule, a different one for each of the 20 amino acids, moves in, attaches itself to an amino acid, and carries it to the ribosome. Transfer RNA thus provides the mechanism by which the amino acids are brought into confrontation with the messenger RNA.

The Genetic Code

How is specificity stamped into the amino acid sequence? How is the amino acid chain faultlessly arranged in a given order? How can a four-letter

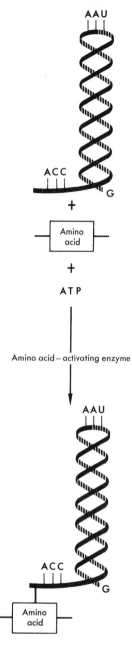

AAU

ACC
G

+

Amino
acid

+

ATP

Amino acid – activating enzyme

AAU

ACC
G

Amino
acid

FIG. 7-4 Activation of an amino acid with ATP and amino acid-activating enzyme and attachment of the activated amino acid to a molecule of transfer RNA specific for the amino acid. Note that transfer RNA contains one unpaired triplet. It is this triplet (AAU in the example) that provides the means by which transfer RNA "recognizes" the messenger RNA triplet specific for the amino acid. Transfer RNA carries ACC at the point where the amino acid attaches and G at the opposite end. The specific combination of each amino acid with its type of transfer RNA is made possible by very specific activating of "adaptor" enzymes, which "recognize" the appropriate amino acid and transfer RNA.

alphabet (the nucleotides) give a 20-word dictionary (the amino acid determinants)?

It was clear fairly early in 1961 that the amino acid sequence depended on the nucleotide sequence of the messenger RNA that has coated the ribosome surface (Figure 7-5). It seemed likely that the correct amino acid sequence could be achieved if a particular group of bases in each strand of transfer RNA would attach to a complementary group of bases in the messenger RNA on the ribosome. For example, the base sequence uracil-adenine-guanine (UAG) in the transfer RNA would attach to the complementary sequence adenine-uracil-cytosine (AUC) in the messenger RNA. (Bear in mind that A is always complementary to U (or T) and C to G.) The amino acid would be left dangling in a manner that would allow it to form peptide bonds with the amino acids dangling on either side of it, probably facilitated by enzymes associated with the ribosome. (The chemical mechanisms that link amino acids were discussed in Chapter 2.) As the chain of amino acids is joined in the sequence dictated by the gene's messenger, the resulting protein peels away from the ribosome and enters the cell sap to serve as an enzyme, hormone, or structural element.

The spectacular breakthrough in deciphering the amino acid-ordering code was made possible by the production of synthetic or unnatural messenger RNA's containing combinations of nucleotides chosen by the investigator. When a synthetic messenger RNA containing only uracil nucleotides was added to a cell-free protein-synthesizing system (complete with amino acids, ATP, isolated ribosomes, and transfer RNA's), it was discovered that the artificial protein synthesized contained only one amino acid, phenylalanine. It was apparent that the base uracil (U or some combination of U's, such as UU, UUU, or UUUU) was the code word that instructed the ribosome to insert phenylalanine in the chain.

When the synthetic messenger RNA contained one molecule of adenine for every two molecules of uracil, it was found that the artificial protein synthesized consisted mostly of phenylalanine with small amounts of isoleucine. The 2:1 proportion of uracil to adenine in the synthetic messenger RNA indicated that the code word for isoleucine must contain two U's for one A (that is, UUA, UAU, or AUU). The incorporation of phenylalanine into the protein presumably reflected the many stretches of UUU that would be expected in the messenger RNA. When the ratio of adenine to uracil was 2:1, asparagine was present in the artificial protein—in addition to phenylalanine and isoleucine. The three amino acids were incorporated in direct porportion to the statistical frequency with which 3U, 2U:1A, and 1U:2A would be expected in the messenger RNA. Thus the code designation for asparagine is 2A:1U (sequence unknown).

By such studies the code has been elucidated for all 20 amino acids (Table 7-1). Although some amino acids have more than one code word—the significance of this fact is debated—most if not all nucleotide triplets are specific for a particular amino acid. Therefore, if the sequence of bases in messenger RNA were UUU-UUA-AAU-UUU, the sequence of amino

acids would be phenylalanine-isoleucine-asparagine-phenylalanine—or, using amino acid symbols (see Table 2-3), PHE-ILEU-ASP (NH)$_2$-PHE. In summary, it appears that nonoverlapping nucleotide triplets make up the code that determines the sequence of amino acids in a protein.

Elegant indirect support for the genetic code is furnished by a number of recent experiments. For example, the genetically determined human disease called *sickle-cell anemia* is associated with the presence of an abnormal hemoglobin molecule. Vernon Ingram conclusively demonstrated that this abnormality is due entirely to the insertion of *one erroneous amino*

FIG. 7-5 **The mechanism of action of messenger RNA.** A. The DNA molecule is a series of nucleotide triplets. Note the A-T and G-C pairings in complementary strands. B. Messenger RNA is a series of triplets complementary to one of the two DNA strands. C. Messenger RNA finds its way to a ribosome, the site of protein synthesis. D. Amino acids are carried to the proper sites on messenger RNA by molecules of transfer RNA. The amino acids are then linked by peptide bonds, and the resulting protein "peels off."

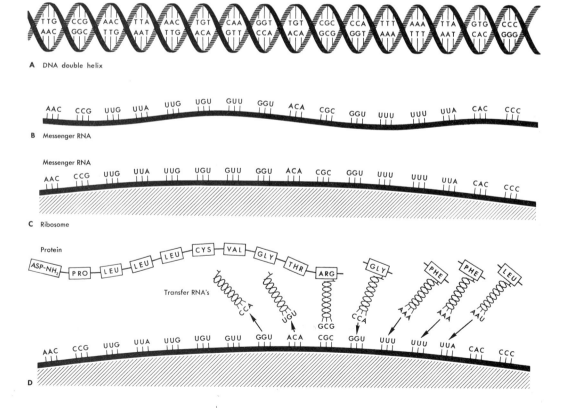

acid in the chain of over 300 amino acids that comprises the hemoglobin molecule. Instead of the sequence

-HIS-LEU-THR-PRO-GLU-GLU-LYS-

the abnormal molecule contains

-HIS-LEU-THR-PRO-VAL-GLU-LYS-

Through mutation, valine has replaced glutamic acid in the amino acid chain. Ingram's discovery, made before the elucidation of the genetic code, was significant because it showed a specific *biochemical* consequence of mutation and indicated the localized nature of the mutational event, for surely this localized error in the gene product must reflect an equally localized change in the messenger RNA and its parent DNA. When the genetic code was discovered, it was found that one code word for glutamic acid (UAG) differs from that for valine (UUG) by only *one* base.

Thus it may be concluded that the mutation causing the synthesis of an abnormal hemoglobin—possibly many hundreds of generations ago—in fact altered no more than one nucleotide in the DNA sequence.

Operator and Regulator Genes

Most genes act by producing messenger RNA (mRNA), which in turn determines the amino acid sequence of protein structure. Obviously, all genes cannot be actively producing RNA all the time. If they were, all cells of a multicellular organism would be functionally identical. Thus, the genes must be carefully controlled both during development and throughout the life of the cell. One type of control mechanism currently receiving much attention is the activation and repression of mRNA production by the action of other genes. The activity of these *operator* and *repressor* genes may be influenced in turn by chemical agents from outside the cell or by metabolic products of the cell itself. Our knowledge concerning genetic control is, however, still in its infancy, and many research biologists are attempting to work out an understanding of the processes involved.

TABLE 7-1   *The Genetic Code*[a]

Second base

First base		U	C	A	G	Third base
	U	UUU UUC } phe UUA UUG } leu	UCU UCC UCA UCG } ser	UAU UAC } try UAA non UAG non	UGU UGC } cys UGA ? UGG try	U C A G
	C	CUU CUC CUA CUG } leu	CCU CCC CCA CCG } pro	CAU CAC } his CAA CAG } gln	CGU CGC CGA CGG } arg	U C A G
	A	AUU AUC AUA } ileu AUG met	ACU ACC ACA ACG } thr	AAU AAC } asn AAA AAG } lys	AGU AGC } ser AGA AGG } arg	U C A G
	G	GUU GUC GUA GUG } val	GCU GCC GCA GCG } ala	GAU GAC } asp GAA GAG } glu	GGU GGC GGA GGG } gly	U C A G

[a] The nucleic acid code listed above (UUU, UUC, etc.) is probable for that of messenger-RNA. As you can see, the code is "degenerate," in that more than one messenger-RNA code word frequently specifies the same amino acid. Code words marked "non" are either "nonsense" words which are not translated to an amino acid or which may act as punctuation in the genetic message. The code words "gln" and "asn" refer to molecules which are amino derivatives of glutamic acid and aspartic acid, respectively.

MUTATIONS

We have now considered the gene from the viewpoint of the classical geneticists, whose methodology is the breeding experiment and the test of progeny in intact organisms, and from the viewpoint of biochemistry, which seeks to understand molecular mechanisms of replication and sequence coding. The problems of mutation—the alteration of the gene in an irreversible manner—may also be considered from these two viewpoints. Over the short period of human experience, the most obvious aspect of heredity is its highly conservative nature. It assures that each normal individual will develop just those characteristics that define its species. All members of *Homo sapiens,* or of any other species, resemble all other members in essential ways and, as a rule, tend to resemble their parents more than more distant relatives within the species. This conservativism is evidently explained by the replication of DNA and the distribution of chromosomes in mitosis and meiosis.

Nevertheless, heredity can and does change. If it did not, evolution could not occur, and man and all the other species of today would not exist. Therefore, change is just as normal, characteristic, and important in heredity as is conservatism. Initial changes take place as sudden, discrete events in individual cells. They are mutations in a broad sense.

Plant and animal breeders have long known that an individual sharply different from its parents may suddenly appear in the most uniform, carefully bred strain. Such "sports," as the early breeders called them, or *mutants,* as they are now called, have been a source of numerous distinctive true-breeding varieties. The ancon mutation (Figure 7-6), producing animals too short-legged to jump fences, has occurred at least twice in sheep. The bulldog-faced (locally called *ñata*) breed of Argentine cattle represents a mutation that has also occurred in swine and other animals including dogs. Mutations for hornlessness have occurred in many horned animals and have been used to develop hornless breeds. Horses that pace by heredity rather than by training have been bred from mutants. Many popular horticultural varieties—dwarf, double-flowered, variegated—have appeared spontaneously as mutants. Many mutations have also been observed in humans. The tragic hemophilia in Queen Victoria's

FIG. 7-6 Ancon, a dominant mutation in sheep. The short-legged ram on the right carries a mutant gene ("ancon") that causes a shortened leg. Bred to a normal ewe (*left*), it produces an ancon F_1. This particular mutant is agriculturally useful, for it cannot jump fences. (Photo, LIFE Magazine © TIME, Inc., 1947)

descendants arose as a mutation in the germ cells either of the queen or of her parents, although this was not known at the time.

Mutations result in heritable alterations in the genotype. They may have all sorts of visible effects, from barely perceptible to great and obvious. Mutations are, indeed, the ultimate sources of all *new* genetic materials, which then are endlessly shuffled in the processes of sexual reproduction. In the final analysis, all evolutionary change depends on mutations. Of course, not all mutations lead to evolutionary change. Most of them are disadvantageous and are eventually eliminated. What happens to mutations after they occur—whether they vanish, remain as rare variants, or spread and cause significant change—will be dealt with in Chapter 12.

Mutations have been seen in all organisms that have been carefully studied for any length of time, from bacteria to the highest plants and animals. That they appear in all organisms is a very fundamental generalization; a capacity for mutation is one of the universal and definitive characteristics of life, and all organic evolution is contingent on it.

Breeding experiments together with microscopic observations of chromosome sets and structures have shown that mutations may occur in several different ways, in fact, in as many ways as the copying and transmission mechanisms may vary. All mutations fall into one of the following categories:

> Chromosome mutations
> Change in chromosome number
> Change in chromosome structure
>
> Gene mutations
> Change in an individual gene

The gene mutations are believed to have the most far-reaching significance. Indeed, when the word "mutation" is used without specification as to whether gene or chromosome mutation is meant, gene mutation is generally implied. Chromosomal mutations do, however, play important roles in some phases of variation and evolution. Let us briefly consider them before we discuss gene mutation.

Changes in Chromosome Number: Polyploidy

We have learned that an organism normally has a basic set of chromosomes, the haploid (simple) set, in which the number of chromosomes may be symbolized as n. A biparental organism usually receives one full set from each parent and therefore has two sets, each with n chromosomes, for a total of $2n$ chromosomes; $2n$ is the diploid (double) number. Abnormalities in mitosis and meiosis can produce changes in the number of sets of chromosomes. Organisms which have additional chromosome sets

are called *polyploids* (see Figure 7-7). Examples of polyploids are

triploid	$3n$
tetraploid	$4n$
pentaploid	$5n$, etc.

Polyploids differ in various ways from their parents. Their cells, containing more chromosomes, are usually larger. Often the organisms themselves are larger. Polyploids derived from the crossing or hybridization of different races and species may be more or less intermediate but often also have some new characters of their own. Thus polyploidy results in the sudden appearance of new kinds of organisms. It is a form of mutation. Polyploidy has been important in the systematic improvement of agricultural crops—both by the uninformed selection of favorable strains that were later found to be polyploid and by scientifically planned hybridization programs.

Chromosome Rearrangements

Genes are arranged in single file along a chromosome. In any chromosome they have a definite sequence, so that if they are designated as A, B, C, D, E, F, and so on, a chromosome can be represented as A-B-C-D-E-F-. . . . (Actually, there are hundreds or thousands of genes in most chromosomes.) During meiosis, paired chromosomes often exchange segments in the normal process of crossing over (Chapter 6). This process does not disturb the gene sequences. Sometimes, however, crossing over, too, is irregular, and the gene sequences are altered. The following types of changes are possible:

1

2

3

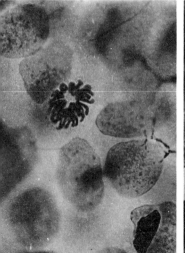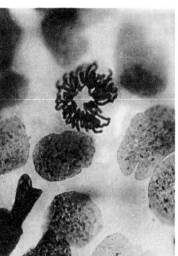

FIG. 7-7 Polyploid nuclei in salamanders. 1. A normal diploid nucleus ($2n = 22$). 2. A triploid nucleus ($3n = 33$). 3. A pentaploid nucleus ($5n = 55$). Interestingly, polyploid salamanders have been shown to be more intelligent than their diploid fellows. (Photos, G. Frankhauser)

1. A gene is dropped out. *A-B-C-D-E-F* becomes *A-B-D-E-F* (*deficiency*).

2. A gene is duplicated. *A-B-C-D-E-F* becomes *A-B-B-C-D-E-F* (*duplication*).

3. Part of the gene sequence is reversed. *A-B-C-D-E-F* becomes *A-B-E-D-C-F* (*inversion*).

4. A segment of one chromosome changes places with a segment belonging to a chromosome of another pair (not its own mate). Two nonpaired chromosomes, *A-B-C-D-E-F* and *G-H-I-J-K-L,* become *A-B-C-J-K-L* and *G-H-I-D-E-F* (*translocation*).

Since the genes control development, it is easy to see that a deficiency (the absence of a gene) or a duplication (a double dose of a gene) would be likely to affect development adversely. This probability is confirmed in *Drosophila,* where, for example, an apparent gene deficiency in a short X-chromosome produces a notch in the wings in the phenotype. One might suppose, however, that an inversion or a translocation would have no effect. The same genes are present; only their positions are changed. Sometimes, indeed, no difference in the phenotype is apparent even though inversion or translocation is visible by microscopic study of the chromosomes. Still, when chromosomes in only one parent have undergone inversion or translocation, the pairing of the chromosomes in meiosis may result in a decrease in fertility or various peculiarities in inheritance. Sometimes the action of a gene is modified simply because it has new neighbors. In *Drosophila* it has been found that the size of the eye is influenced by the identities of the genes adjacent to the gene specific for eye size. This *position effect* is evidence that genes interact.

Gene Mutations

We shall now consider mutations that are associated not with gross changes in the structure or number of the chromosomes but rather with changes in the DNA molecule. For many years it was entirely unclear how or why such genic alterations occurred, but that they did occur was manifested by their effects. Since mutation is the only known mechanism whereby new genes, the principal raw materials of evolution, can arise, we may assume that the various alleles of genes, such as those extensively treated in Chapter 6, have all arisen through mutation. This was certainly

true of the alleles used in Mendel's experiments, although the mutations occurred at some unknown time before he began his work.

The frequency of mutation varies greatly from gene to gene, but mutation is always an infrequent event. Tests for mutations with distinctly visible effects in corn have given frequencies for single genes of from 0 to about 500 mutations per 1,000,000 gametes. There are so many genes that the total frequency for all genes is much higher. The proportion of individuals with a mutation in some gene may be around 5 to 10 per cent in many organisms. Such figures are necessarily only estimates. They are probably underestimates because the most frequent mutations may be those with such slight effects that they are overlooked. With ingenious statistical procedures it is possible to estimate the rates of some mutations with strong effects in man. Mutations producing hemophilia are found in 1 to 5 X-chromosomes in every 100,000. Fortunately this is a small figure, but it is large enough to keep hemophilia present in human populations even if no one ever passed the gene on to descendants. It is possible that at least 1 per cent of the babies born have some mutation. Some students place the figure at 10 per cent or even higher.

The frequency of mutation is subject to a certain amount of control by mechanisms within the organism itself. For instance, it was found that a particular population of *Drosophila* in Florida possessed a gene that increased the mutation frequency of the other genes in the chromosomes to a value 10 times as high as that in an Ohio population of the same species.

Research on mutations (chiefly in *Drosophila*) proceeded very slowly when genticists had to wait for them to turn up spontaneously. The field was revolutionized in 1927, however, when H. J. Muller discovered that mutations could be induced by the application of x-rays. This method is illustrated in Figure 7-3. Since 1927, several other means of increasing the frequency of mutations have been found. These *mutagenic agents* have consisted mainly of various types of radiation and chemicals. For the most part they merely speed things up. The mutations produced are those that would occur naturally less often. Also, there is no way to predict what mutation will occur in any given experiment.

MOLECULAR MECHANISMS OF GENE MUTATIONS. Nitrous acid (HNO_2) is a chemical mutagenic agent which changes cytosine to uracil by direct chemical action. In the following diagram, this mutation is indicated by the box and is transmitted thus:

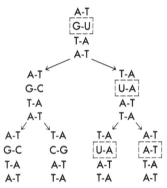

The change (or "error") in base pairing is now perpetuated, and the mutant DNA contains an A-T pair in place of a G-C pair.

. Some of the many mutagenic agents now utilized are chemical analogues of natural purines and pyrimidines that "trick" the DNA into making a pairing "error." Others, by some unknown means, cause the synthesis of DNA molecules containing one more or one less nucleotide. All, it appears, act by producing a localized alteration in the nucleotide sequence of DNA. In light of the ease with which experimental mutations can be induced, the rarity of natural mutations is astonishing.

DOMINANCE AND MULTIPLE ALLELES

When the one gene–one protein theory was first advanced, a simple interpretation was also given to the familiar genetic phenomenon of dominance. It was supposed that, although the dominant allele of a gene was capable of making its specific enzyme, the recessive allele was not. This situation was summed up as the *presence and absence theory* of dominance

and recessiveness. It is certainly attractive in its simplicity and nicely explains the similarity of the heterozygote (*Aa*) to the homozygous dominant (*AA*); both of them have the enzyme necessary for a particular reaction that fails in the homozygous recessive from complete lack of the enzyme. Unfortunately, the hypothesis has proved too simple.

Dominance has turned out to be relative and seldom complete. It is only sometimes true that the heterozygote (*Aa*) has precisely the same phenotype as the homozygous dominant (*AA*). Often the heterozygote is different from both homozygotes (*AA* and *aa*). This is obvious, for instance, in Andalusian chickens. When homozygous, one allele for feather color produces black, and another produces white with small spots. When both alleles are present in heterozygous combination, the feathers are blue. It is hardly accurate to say that either allele is dominant. Their effects blend. But note that the *genes* do not blend. They segregate as usual when gametes are formed. When blue fowls are interbred, the characteristic ratio appears: 1 black : 2 blues : 1 spotty white.

It is impossible to reconcile such cases with the presence and absence theory of the enzyme. Two distinct forms of the gene must be present, both of them active. This is even more clearly demonstrated in the inheritance of the human blood groups.

All people fall into one of four blood groups—A, B, AB, and O. Each blood group is characterized by a particular *antigen* on the surfaces of the red blood cells. Antigens are substances (usually proteins) that induce certain cells in the animal body to form *antibodies*. These are proteins that react specifically with antigen molecules, inactivating them. Most antigens are foreign substances. Thus antibody synthesis, the phenomenon called *immunity,* is an important defense mechanism. Group A people have antigen A on their red cells; group B people have antigen B on their red cells; group AB people have both antigens A and B; and group O people have neither antigen A nor antigen B. It is a remarkable fact that group A people also have an antibody in their blood *serum* (Chapter 10) that, given an opportunity, specifically combines with the red cell antigen of group B people. This causes clumping or *agglutination* of the red cells (Figures 7-8 and 7-9); thus the antibodies are known as *agglutinins.* For clarity, the anti-B antibody in the serum of group A people is

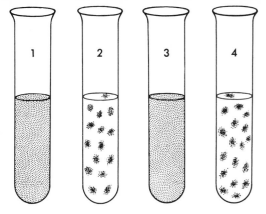

1. Serum of A, cells of A → No agglutination
2. Serum of A, cells of B → Agglutination
3. Serum of B, cells of B → No agglutination
4. Serum of B, cells of A → Agglutination

FIG. 7-8 Tests for human blood groups. When serum and cells from different blood groups are mixed, the cells agglutinate, or clump together.

I^A produces A antigen, I^B produces B antigen, and I^O produces neither. The genotypes I^AI^A and I^AI^O produce type A blood; I^BI^B and I^BI^O produce type B blood; I^AI^B produces type AB blood; and I^OI^O produces type O blood.

There are three noteworthy points about the heredity of the blood groups. First, the gene concerned acts directly, causing the synthesis of antigens with specific configurations. Second, no dominance is involved. Third, one gene can have more than two alleles. The situation illustrated by human blood groups, with three alleles, is by no means exceptional. Geneticists believe that most, if not all, genes can occur in many allelic forms. In *Drosophila* there are known to be at least 12 alleles of one gene controlling eye color.

The existence of multiple alleles and the common absence of dominance force us to reject the idea that the total range of possible actions for a particular gene is a simple pair of alternatives—such as making or not making the enzyme. The relations between

called the β antibody; the serum anti-A antibody in group B people is the α antibody.

Of immediate interest to us here is the inheritance of the blood groups. They are absolutely determined by three alleles at a single gene locus, I^A, I^B, and I^O.

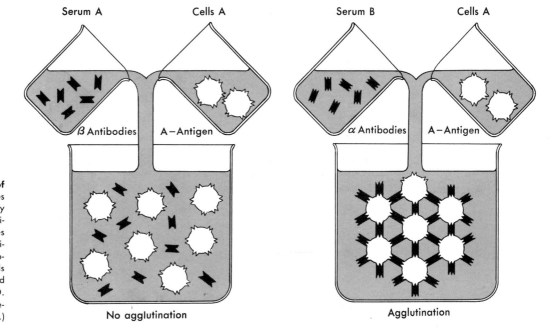

FIG. 7-9 The mechanism of agglutination. α antibodies have surfaces complementary to those of A antigens; β antibodies do not. α antibodies serve to bind together A antigens and hence to bind together those red blood cells that carry A antigens. (Adapted from A. M. Srb and R. D. Owen, *General Genetics*, Freeman, San Francisco, 1952.)

the gene and the reaction it normally controls can be far more varied than this. In a heterozygous organism, all gradations between complete homozygosity and complete heterozygosity are present. Thus allelic interaction is basic to all of diploid genetics.

ACTION OF THE GENOTYPE AS A WHOLE

Genes and Development

Our discussion of how an individual gene ultimately effects its control may seem remote from the more familiar aspects of an organism. Are not size, shape, pattern, and color the more obvious features whose development we want to understand? How does the molecular mechanism of gene action relate to them?

With respect to color the connection is clear enough. Red petals or white, the observable difference between fully developed organisms is a chemical difference in the pigments of their flowers. Indeed, in some cases the chemical difference is fully known, as well as the particular reaction that did or did not take place, leading to the development, or lack of development, of the pigment concerned.

With respect to size and shape the connection between cell chemistry and the final organism is less clear. But here too there is no need to alter our concept of gene action. There is less difficulty in envisaging the connection between the primary biochemical effect of a gene and its eventual morphological (size, shape) effects when we realize that *all* the genes in the total inherited message tend to act together as an integrated whole in the regulation of development. We speak of a single gene for red flowers in peas, for wrinkled seeds in corn, or for baldness in man. This practice reflects a scientific truth, for in each case—redness, wrinkledness, baldness—the development of the character is dependent on the presence of one particular gene allele that we have been able to study. But it is also dependent on many other genes. We should not fall into the habit of thinking that an organism has a set number of characters with one gene governing each character. The experimental evidence indicates that genes never work altogether separately. Organisms are not patchworks with one gene in charge of each of the patches. They are integrated wholes, whose development is controlled by the entire set of genes acting cooperatively. The rules are (1) that *each character is affected by many genes* and (2) that *a single gene may affect many characters.*

Many Genes Affect One Character

In the blue Andalusian fowl, two different alleles of the same gene work together, and the result is a phenotype distinct from that produced by either allele alone (that is, when homozygous). It is also common for different genes to interact, so that phenotypic characters depend on two, three, or many genes and not on one alone. In mice there is a gene that tends to produce white spotting, but its effect is modified by a whole series of other genes, called *modifiers* in genetic terminology. If numerous modifiers are present, the animal is almost pure white. Practically all intermediate conditions also occur, with various numbers of modifiers (Figure 7-10). Another example is a Norwegian family in which for over

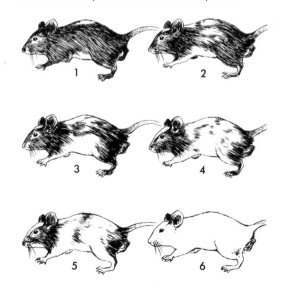

FIG. 7-10 The action of modifying genes in mice. All six mice are heterozygous (Ww) for a gene producing white spots, but they differ in the number of modifying genes they carry for bolstering the effect of the primary (white-spotting) gene. 1. Fewest modifiers present. 6. Most modifiers present.

four generations about half the children had short index fingers. In some children the finger was very short, and in others it was just barely shorter than usual. Study of the pedigree strongly suggests that two genes are involved, one determining that the finger will be short and the other determining the degree of shortness.

When multiple-factor effects can be traced to a few genes, the genes sometimes can be identified and counted. More often, as in corn size, so many genes are involved that their separate identification is a practical impossibility. When a single gene has an obvious effect on a mature organism, we can recognize Mendelian inheritance, but even then we are merely picking out one element from an integrated system.

One Gene Affects Many Characters: Pleiotropy

In the development of an organism, a single constructional step has trivial or far-reaching effects depending on when it occurs and how basic it is. The majority of clean-cut inherited differences involve trivial and terminal steps in development; the formation of a pigment in a particular organ, eye, or petal may fail, but little else is affected. But failure or abnormal execution of earlier or more basic single steps has far-reaching, ramifying results. In mice a particular gene mutation is known that improperly specifies a single step in bone formation. Its consequences are seen everywhere in the body where bone formation takes place. In *Drosophila* the gene "vestigial" is so called because its most obvious effect is to reduce the single pair of wings to mere vestiges of the normal (Figure 7-11). Careful observation shows that it also affects the balancers behind the wings, certain of the bristles, the reproductive organs, and other parts. More significantly, it also shortens life and lowers egg-producing capacity. Clearly, the gene directly or indirectly influences the development of a wide range of the organism's characters.

In man there is a recessive mutant allele that, when homozygous, produces imbeciles of pale skin coloring. They excrete phenylpyruvic acid, a compound absent from the urine of normal people, who possess the nonmutant form of the gene. The disorder, known as *phenylketonuria*, has widely diverse symptoms—abnormal skin color, abnormal urine composition, and brain damage—and all are effects of one gene. It is now known that individuals with phenylke-

tonuria lack the enzyme that normally converts phenylalanine to tyrosine (a precursor of the skin pigment melanin). Phenylalanine is alternatively converted to phenylpyruvic acid, which is excreted.

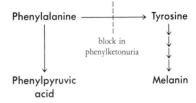

The missing enzyme normally controls one step in

FIG. 7-11 The action of the gene "vestigal" in *Drosophila*. A. An adult female fly homozygous (vg-vg) for the gene "vestigial." Note the rudimentary nature of the wings. B. The normal (*upper*) and vestigial (*lower*) wings and balancers compared. C. The wings of vgvg flies reared at different temperatures. The action of the gene is dependent on the temperature: at lower temperatures its effect (in causing departure from the normal) is greatest; at 33°C the wing is nearly normal.

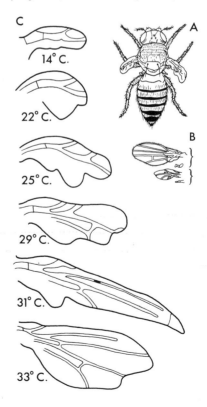

a complex metabolic cycle—involving phenyl compounds and producing at various points in the organism not only pigments but also substances necessary for proper brain development.

The phenomenon of genes affecting many characters is called *pleiotropy* ("more changing") and is a genetic generalization of great importance.

Environment Affects Gene Action: Nature and Nurture

We have just shown that the action of a gene may be influenced by other genes. We could say that a gene's action is affected by its *genetic* environment. And it is similarly affected by the *physical* environment in which it acts. A fly homozygous for the recessive gene "vestigial" (*vgvg*) served earlier for illustration; the gene *vg* affects many characters besides the wings, and its action is affected by many other genes. Its action is also strongly dependent on the temperature at which the fly develops. At high temperatures (30 to 31°C) the wings grow nearly as long as in a fly carrying the normal gene (see Figure 7-11).

A tendency to develop *diabetes mellitus* (manifested as an elevation of the blood sugar level) is hereditary in man. The manner of gene control is unknown, but the facts are consistent with the belief that an enzyme or other compound essential for the formation of insulin is produced by one allele of a gene and not by another allele. Insulin, in turn, affects the metabolism of carbohydrates, and hence the level of sugar in the blood; high levels are reflected by the presence of sugar in the urine. It has been found that persons who have the genotype for diabetes do not necessarily have the disease; that is, it does not always appear phenotypically. An investigator who studied 63 pairs of identical twins, one or the other of whom had diabetes, found that in 10 of the pairs only one twin was afflicted. Identical twins are so called because they have identical genotypes (Chapter 8). Therefore, in these 10 pairs, the twin who did not have overt diabetes nevertheless had a diabetic genotype. It was learned that in some instances the twin who developed diabetes had a different diet, one that made larger demands for carbohydrate metabolism. Thus the appearance of diabetes does not depend on the genotype alone but on the genotype plus the diet.

We may then ask "Is diabetes mellitus caused by inheritance or by environment?" The disease is caused neither by inheritance alone nor by environment alone but by the interaction of the two. This is true of the great majority of the characters of organisms. It is one of the most important principles of biology that development is an *interaction* between heredity and environment.

There is every gradation between characters that are not (as far as we know) modifiable by the environment and those that are greatly modifiable. Height is strongly affected by heredity, but it may be equally influenced by diet and even more strongly influenced by glandular disease or by the administration of hormones. Skin color is primarily determined by heredity, but it is also much modified by exposure to sunlight, as well as by some diseases and chemicals. It is common knowledge that plants of the same varieties and races (hence closely similar in genotypes) have different sizes and shapes (different phenotypes) when grown on different soils, with different fertilizers, with different water supplies, or in different climates.

In summary, what is inherited is a developmental mechanism. The mechanism determines how the organism will develop under given environmental conditions. It sets narrower or wider limits to the developing organism's reactions to different environments. This is the principle of the reaction range. All phenotypes that actually occur, including those that we consider abnormal or pathological, are necessarily within the reaction ranges of the underlying genotypes. The meaningful question about any trait is not "Is it hereditary or environmental—due to nature or to nurture?" but "What is the reaction range of its genotype, and what are the environmental factors correlated with this particular position in the range?" The processes of development will be treated in more detail in the next chapter.

Summary

The inherited message in living systems: information; chromosomes compared to the information tape that controls the work of automatic machines; the study of gene action.

Nature of the genetic material: the small size of the inherited message; the difficulty in defining a gene.

Chemistry of the genetic material: proteins and nucleic acids; evidence that DNA is the message-carrying molecule; transforming activity in *Pneumococci* and other organisms; the demonstration that bacteriophage DNA alone carries the instructions for bacteriophage replication.

Reproduction of the genetic material: the significance of the double-strandedness of the DNA molecule and of complementary base pairing; proof that one strand orders the nucleotide sequence of its new partner strand, thus serving as a template that preserves the sequence from generation to generation.

Mechanism of gene action: the "one gene–one protein" theory; mutation as the ultimate cause of loss or alteration of an enzyme; the control of protein synthesis by DNA; evidence that DNA orders the sequence of "messenger RNA," which then travels to the ribosome and orders the amino acid sequence during protein synthesis; the genetic code; regulator and operator genes.

Mutations as changes in gene reproduction: meanings of "mutation"; chromosome and gene mutations; the experimental production of mutations by radiation and chemicals; the molecular mechanism of gene mutation.

Dominance and multiple alleles: the argument against the simple presence-absence hypothesis of dominance-recessiveness.

Action of the genotype as a whole: genes and the control of development; many genes affecting one character—modifier genes; one gene affecting many characters—pleiotropy; the environment affecting gene action.

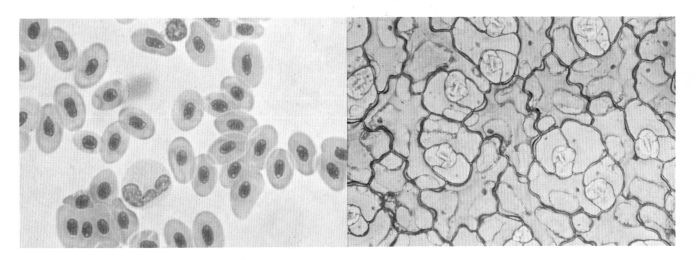

Animal and plant cells. Left, frog blood cells; right, plant leaf epithelial cells. (Harbrace photos)

Top, nerve cell; bottom, epithelial cheek cells.

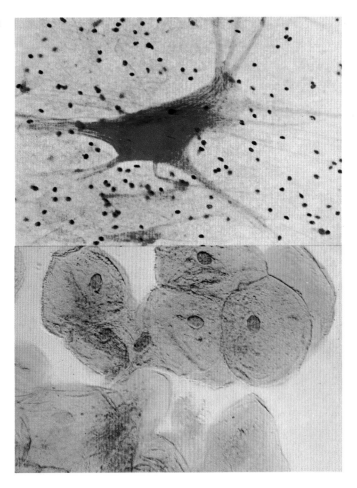

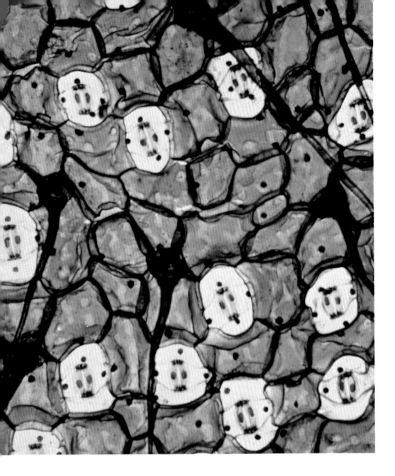

Left, leaf epidermis of *Tradescantia virginiana* (spiderwort) showing stomata and leaf hairs (trichomes). Right, striated muscle cells. (All photos, courtesy Carolina Biological Supply Company)

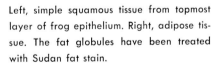

Left, primary root of Zea, somewhat oblique section showing meristem and region of elongation. Right, stem tip of *Anacharis (Elodea)* showing apical meristem and leaf and lateral bud primordia.

Left, simple squamous tissue from topmost layer of frog epithelium. Right, adipose tissue. The fat globules have been treated with Sudan fat stain.

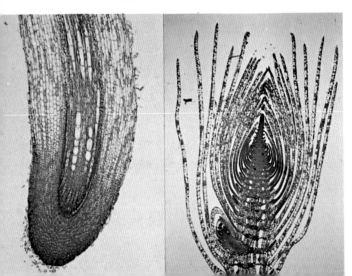

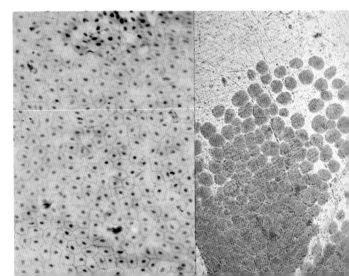

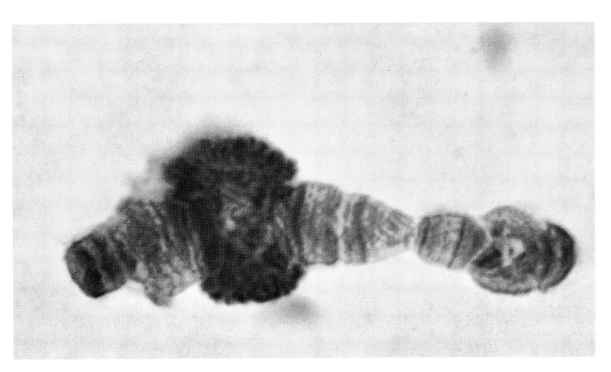

In this photomicrograph chromosome puffs are shown on the giant chromosome IV from the salivary gland of the midge *Chironomus tentans*. Ribonucleic acid (RNA), the product of the puffs, is reddish-violet when dyed with toluidine blue. The deoxyribonucleic acid (DNA) of the chromosome has been stained blue. (Magnification, 2500 diameters.) Opposite, giant salivary gland chromosomes of *Drosophila melanogaster* with clearly perceptible banding. (Top, Dr. Ulrich Clever; right, Carolina Biological Supply Company)

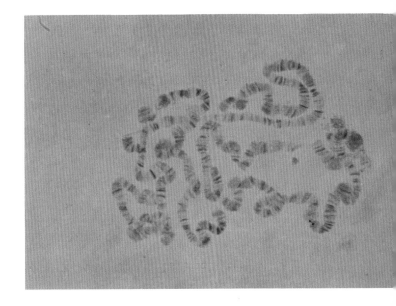

Drosophila melanogaster with variation in eye color caused by gene mutation. (Edmund B. Gerard)

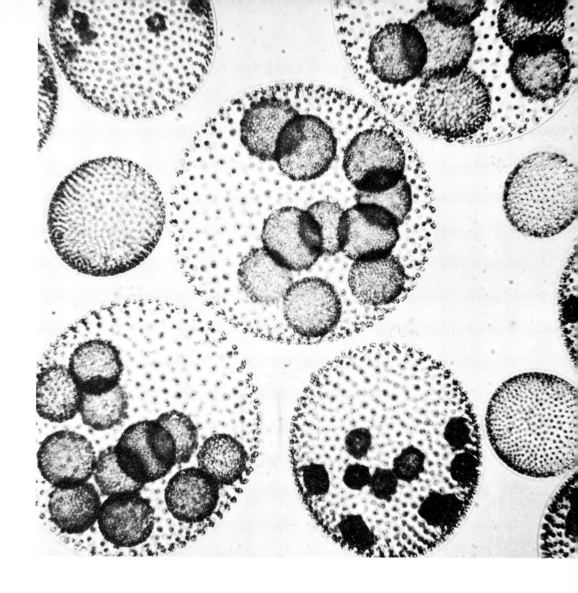

PART FOUR

THE ORGANISM: DEVELOPMENT, REPRODUCTION, MAINTENANCE, AND INTEGRATION

Whatever complexity of organization we may infer from electron micrographs or genetic studies or metabolic data of a single cell becomes insignificant when we consider the whole multicellular organism.

The photograph introducing Part 4 shows an enlargement of a few Volvox cells. Volvox, a plantlike protist, is believed to resemble the organisms which first became multicellular. It forms a colony of cells which probably evolved by the tendency of recently divided cells of unicellular organisms to remain associated after cell division. Volvox shows a specialization increased over a simple aggregation of similar cells. It has differentiated reproductive cells and protoplasmic connections between cells. To the trained eye these specializations of cells are apparent and can be related to the roles played in the integrated activity of the entire organism. It is from the study of multicellular organisms that we have gained much of our present knowledge of how living systems develop, reproduce, maintain, and integrate their organization. Part 4 is devoted to these topics.

We emphasize that the processes of development, which is essentially creative construction, cannot take their orderly course leading to a particular kind of an adult without a set of specifications or instructions to guide and control them. Such specifications must be present in the zygote. What an organism inherits from its parents—its heredity—is a body of information with specifications for proper development; and since the organism in turn transmits a copy of this same information to its own offspring, it is clear that reproduction is ultimately concerned with duplicating inherited information. The cellular and biochemical details of this phenomenon were considered in Part 3. In Part 4, we will look at the results and implications of this phenomenon in multicellular organisms.

Chapter 8 is concerned with the cellular structure of multicellular organisms and outlines the processes of development. It suggests how those processes may be controlled by the inherited information in the chromosomes.

Chapter 9 discusses adaptive specializations related to the sexuality of organisms.

Chapter 10 focuses upon maintenance, which involves the procurement and processing of materials and energy. One theme running through this discussion is the size of a multicellular organism. Although a large size has certain advantages, it also creates difficulties that are overcome only by special features in the organism. One such feature is a rapid-transport system, like that of blood.

Chapter 11 includes consideration of both respiratory gas exchange and integration. The integration of constituent parts and processes into an ordered whole via intraorganismal communication will be considered. This section describes the system of chemical messengers—hormones—and the nervous systems of animals.

CHAPTER EIGHT

THE ORGANISM: CELLULAR STRUCTURE AND DEVELOPMENT

When a protist reproduces, it does so like any other single cell. The nucleus undergoes *mitosis* (see Chapter 5), and the cell mass constricts into two halves, each carrying a daughter nucleus. Sometimes, however, several or many organisms formed by division from what was originally one protist remain clumped together for a while. They may stick together at their outer surfaces or be caught in a gelatinous envelope that they have secreted. In a clump each cell (or protist) continues to be essentially independent in form and in activity. The clump is merely an aggregate in space, with no particular biological interaction among its units.

Some protists, especially certain of the green *flagellates,* carry the process of aggregation several steps further. The individual cells resulting from repeated divisions remain together not incidentally and in chance clumps but in *colonies* of definite shape and characteristic size when mature. A common arrangement is for the cells to be held in the outer part of a gelatinous envelope forming a hollow sphere. The number of cells, usually a power of 2 (why?), may vary from a few to about 50,000. Reproduction occurs when one or more cells divide and form smaller daugher colonies inside the sphere. Eventually these colonies break out of the parental sphere and grow into separate, new, mature colonies.

In some colonial forms (Figure 8-1) the cells are not connected with each other and are all exactly alike. Each can give rise to a daughter colony (although all do not necessarily do so). In such cases the cells are still essentially distinct individuals, protists that live together. Other forms, of which some species of *Volvox* are examples, are more complex and of peculiar interest: the cells are connected to each other by strands of protoplasm running through the gelatinous envelope (see Figure 8-1). Thus the cells are not fully independent; happenings in one cell may affect its neighbors. Moreover, the cells are not quite alike. The number of cells may run

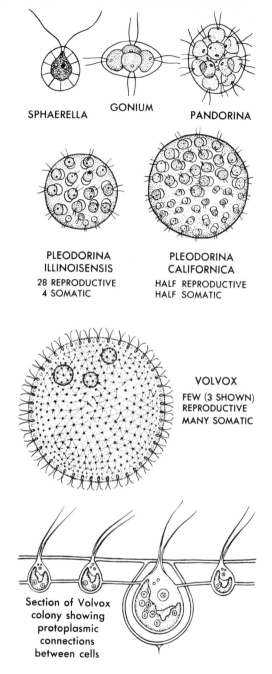

SPHAERELLA   GONIUM   PANDORINA

PLEODORINA
ILLINOISENSIS

28 REPRODUCTIVE
4 SOMATIC

PLEODORINA
CALIFORNICA

HALF REPRODUCTIVE
HALF SOMATIC

VOLVOX

FEW (3 SHOWN)
REPRODUCTIVE
MANY SOMATIC

Section of Volvox
colony showing
protoplasmic
connections
between cells

FIG. 8-1 Colonial green flagellates.

sensitive organelles, which influence the orientation and movement of the colony.

Is this a colony of protists, or is it a multicellular organism? On the one hand, it is made up of similar cells and quite surely evolved from a unicellular or acellular protistan individual. On the other hand, the cells display some differences in form and activity and a certain amount of coordination throughout the whole colony, as do the cells of unquestionably multicellular organisms.

The colonies of *Volvox* and its relatives reveal a puzzling biological phenomenon that will appear repeatedly in our study of living organisms. Like the cells of multicellular organisms, although to a much lesser degree, the cells of a *Volvox* colony differ in size, shape, potentialities, and other characteristics. In a word, they *differentiate* as they mature; each specializes in a division of the colony's total labor. And yet their heredity is exactly the same. They all arose from one cell, and at each mitosis the new nuclei were endowed with identical sets of chromosomal controls. Finding an explanation for cellular differentiation in spite of identical heredity is one of biology's greatest and most interesting problems.

CELLULAR DIFFERENTIATION: CELLS, TISSUES, ORGANS, AND SYSTEMS

If one examines a complex multicellular organism such as a tree or a man, it is plain, first of all, that the organism has its own individuality. It is a unit and acts as such. Yet the unit is made up of visibly different parts. The basic units, the cells, which we have discussed earlier, have many forms and functions within the individual. They are differentiated, and through differentiation they have become functionally *specialized*. A cell in a root tip is quite different from one in the surface of a leaf, and the leaf surface cell in turn differs from a cell within the leaf. In the human body a nerve cell, a muscle cell, and a blood cell are decisively different.

Each cell type usually occurs with many others of its kind and shares the same life processes. The whole leaf surface is covered with similar cells. A muscle is made up not of one cell but of thousands, all much the same in appearance and properties. An aggregation of cells is called a *tissue*. In *simple tissues* all cells are of the same type. *Composite tissues* contain

into the thousands, but only 4 to 20 larger cells in the back part of the colony are capable of reproducing, giving rise to daughter colonies. The cells in the front part of the colony cannot reproduce. They are smaller and have relatively larger light-

two or more cell types in characteristic relationship with one another.

Tissues of several or many different kinds usually make up the complex parts of organisms. The hand, for instance, is a functionally distinct part, or *organ,* of the body, composed of skin, bones, muscles, nerves, and other tissues. Leaves and flowers or eyes and ears are other organs that are complexes of different tissues. Organs may, in turn, be cooperating and interacting parts of a larger complex, an anatomical and physiological *system.* The human digestive system, for example, is a sequence of organs from the mouth through the esophagus (the passageway from the mouth to the stomach), the stomach, the small intestine, and the large intestine to the anus. Each part or organ is different, but all interact one after the other in the processes of digestion. Each organ in the system is composed of tissues, and each tissue is composed of cells.

The striking differences that exist among tissues are related to the different functions that they perform; the structure of muscle is related to its function of movement, and the structure of nerve to its function of communication. This is in fact but one illustration, at the level of the cell itself, of a paramount principle that pervades all biology: *the structure of a living thing is intimately related to its functions.* Plants and animals are distinguished by great differences in their modes of life. Plants, nearly always sedentary, feed directly upon the materials of soil and air in a manner that requires a minimum of movement. Their immobile existence is clearly reflected in their tissue organization. Animals, on the other hand, are dependent upon living food, which they must actively ingest in solid form and which, moreover, most animals must actively pursue. Their constant movements and their searching activities are possible only because they possess certain organs and tissues—sensory, muscular, nervous, and connective—of which plants have no need. These basic differences between plants and animals should be borne in mind as we survey their characteristic tissues.

PLANT CELLS AND TISSUES

The bodies of the more highly evolved plants consist of two organ systems. The *root system* occurs below ground; and the *shoot system,* including *stem*

and *leaves,* occurs above ground (Figure 8-2). In these two organ systems four classes of tissue can be recognized. These are described briefly in the following paragraphs.

Meristematic Tissues

The two main aspects of plant growth are *primary* growth, the growth in length of shoots and roots, and *secondary* growth, the subsequent growth in thickness. Each kind of growth is accomplished by

FIG. 8-2 Plant organ systems.

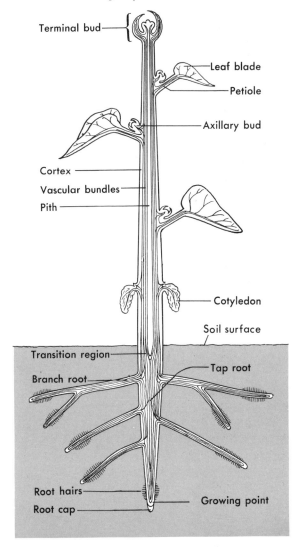

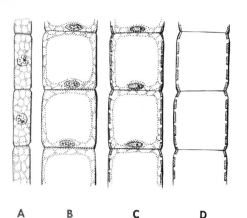

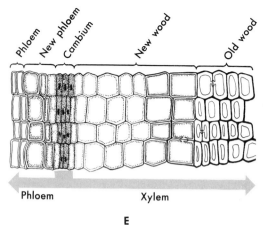

A   B   C   D

E

FIG. 8-3 Meristematic tissue in plants. A, B, C, and D are successive stages in the differentiation of a xylem vessel (D) from a sheet of cambial cells (A). Note how the cells enlarge, vacuolate, acquire thickened walls, and eventually lose their cytoplasm and nuclei. E is a cross section through part of a stem. Division of the cambial cells (stippled) produces new cells, which on the right differentiate into xylem and on the left differentiate into phloem.

meristematic tissue. This tissue, called *meristem* for short, consists of thin-walled, unvacuolated, and unspecialized, dividing cells. When growth is active, cell divisions occur throughout a meristem, producing new cells, each of which differentiates into one of the three other classes of specialized (protective, fundamental, or conductive) tissue. Apical meristems, at the tips of roots and shoots, are responsible for primary growth. Meristematic tissue elsewhere causes secondary growth (Figure 8-3).

Protective Tissue

Protective tissue (*epidermis* or *cork*) comprises the outermost layers of cells that cover and protect underlying tissue in both organ systems.

Fundamental Tissue

Various types of cells are rather loosely categorized collectively as *fundamental tissue.* Some of them (*sclerenchyma* and *collenchyma*) have thick walls, which add greatly to the mechanical strength of an organ— root, stem, or leaf (Figure 8-4). Others (*parenchyma*) are thin-walled and highly vacuolated; some of them contain the green chloroplasts, which are the sites of photosynthesis.

Conductive Tissue

Conductive (or *vascular*) *tissue* is concerned with transport in a plant, as the name implies. There are two kinds of conductive tissue. The *xylem* carries water and dissolved minerals upward from the roots, where they are absorbed from the soil, to all other parts of the plant. Xylem cells, like all other specialized types, begin life as unspecialized cells, derived from

FIG. 8-4 Some plant fundamental tissue. Two types (sclerenchyma and collenchyma) of fundamental tissue are supportive. Their cell walls are especially thick, conferring strength and rigidity on the whole tissue. In sclerenchyma the wall is uniformly and heavily thickened at all points. In collenchyma the thickening is heaviest at the corners of the cell.

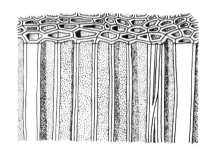

Sclerenchyma fibers (*Agave*)

A

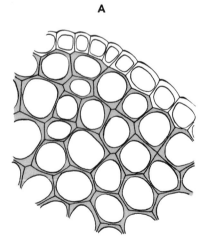

Collenchyma fibers (*Coleus*)

B

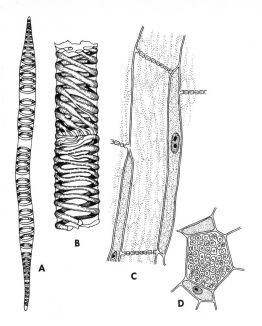

FIG. 8-5 Conductive tissue cells in plants. A and B are xylem cells. Note the thickening of the cell walls. C and D are phloem cells. C shows one complete phloem cell whose end walls are sieve plates. The nucleated cell lying to the right of the phloem cell is a companion cell, a characteristic constituent of phloem tissue. D is an end view of a sieve plate; two companion cells lie beside it.

the plant. They also lose their cytoplasm and nuclei, but though they are dead, their function as conducting vessels is unimpaired. As we shall see, each plant organ is supplied with an abundance of xylem vessels.

The second kind of conductive tissue is *phloem*. It carries the food materials manufactured in the leaves to all parts of the plant, both above and below the leaves. Mature phloem cells are elongate cylinders whose walls are not so heavily thickened as those of xylem cells. Nor do the end walls of the phloem cells break down. Instead, connection between phloem cells is effected through a series of pores in their end walls, which are appropriately called *sieve plates*. The nuclei of phloem cells disintegrate, but their cytoplasmic contents remain, fusing through the sieve-plate pores and forming a protoplasmic highway along which food is carried (Figure 8-5).

Tissue Organization in the Leaf

Each leaf bud arises during the growing season from a small mound of meristematic tissue. Later on each opens, and, as the leaf grows to maturity, its constituent cells differentiate into specialized tissues. A simple leaf, as on a willow or lilac, has a flattened blade and a cylindrical piece (the *petiole*) by which

a meristem. As they mature, their walls become heavily thickened. In the more highly evolved plants, adjacent xylem cells, one above the other, eventually lose their end walls and fuse with each other to form a continuously open vessel running up the axis of

FIG. 8-6 Tissue organization in a leaf. The upper and lower surfaces of the leaf are bounded by an epidermis (protective tissue), which is one cell in thickness. Stomata are present in the lower epidermis. The bulk of the internal tissue is parenchyma (fundamental tissue), whose cells contain chloroplasts. The parenchyma cells are loosely packed and are therefore surrounded by intercellular spaces, which, via the stomata, are continuous with the external atmosphere. The mass of parenchyma is penetrated by veins (or vascular bundles) that consist mainly of conductive tissue (xylem and phloem) and some supportive fibers (fundamental tissue).

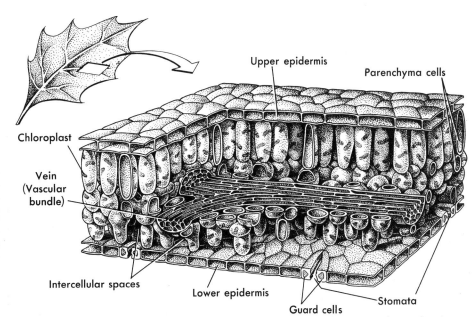

Upper epidermis

Parenchyma cells

Chloroplast

Vein (Vascular bundle)

Intercellular spaces

Lower epidermis

Guard cells

Stomata

it is joined to the stem of the plant. To examine the tissues, one may cut a thin slice across the blade and view it with a microscope. The tissues are shown in Figure 8-6.

Protective tissue is present in the form of a single layer of cells, tightly fitted together and looking like a jigsaw puzzle in surface view. This is the epidermis. Its cells, especially on the leaf's upper surface, are glossy and waterproof because of a heavy deposit of a fatlike substance (*cutin*). Between the upper and lower epidermis there are parenchyma cells containing chloroplasts. The parenchyma cells, which are pulled apart during the growth of the leaf, have open, gas-filled spaces between them.

In the epidermis, especially on the lower side of the leaf, are numerous small openings (*stomata; singular stoma*) between adjacent specialized cells; these usually open in the light and close in the dark. The mechanism by which the stomata open and close exemplifies the biological importance of osmosis.

As illustrated in Figure 8-7, *guard cells* (usually a pair) surround the opening of a stoma. Light falling on the guard cells start a series of enzymatic reactions that convert the osmotically inactive insoluble starch to a large number of soluble sugar molecules. These increase the osmotic pressure and thereby cause water to enter from adjacent cells. The guard cells swell, and the swelling pulls apart the walls of the stoma and opens it. In the dark the reactions are reversed, and the stoma closes. The stomata open into the intercellular spaces of the parenchyma; gases involved in photosynthesis and other reactions in the parenchyma cells diffuse through them to the outer air.

The parenchyma cells contain large numbers of chloroplasts, in which is found the green pigment chlorophyll. Photosynthesis occurs in the chloroplasts, and it is now believed that the effective participation of chlorophyll in this process depends in part upon the way it is physically organized within the chloroplasts.

The conductive tissue in the leaf appears in the form of distinct veins, or *vascular bundles,* each of which contains both xylem and phloem cells. The vascular bundles in the leaf blade are, of course,

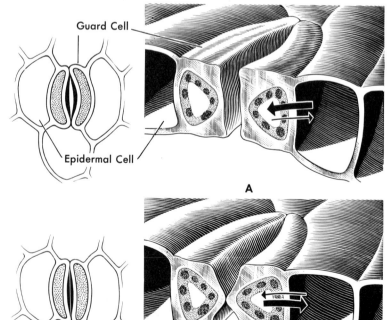

Guard Cell

Epidermal Cell

A

IN SUNLIGHT

Water moves into the guard cells, expanding them and opening the stomate.

B

IN DARKNESS

Water moves out of the guard cells, collapsing them and closing the stomate.

FIG. 8-7   The mechanism by which a stoma opens and closes.

continuous with those in the petiole and, ultimately, with the conductive tissue throughout the main axis of the root and shoot. The leaf is constantly supplied through the xylem with water and minerals. In turn, it supplies to the rest of the plant through its phloem the sugars it manufactures in its parenchyma cells.

Tissue Organization in the Stem

The word "stem" applies to all parts of the shoot system other than leaves—trunks and main branches as well as what are more commonly called "stems" in popular language. All these structures have similarities in their tissues and in their relationships to the life of the plant. In general, the differentiated stem tissues are involved in the support, growth, and protection of the plant and in the movement of solutions. In addition, some stems contain cells with chloroplasts and consequently manufacture sugars, but this is predominantly a leaf function. Stems also are often places of storage for food and water.

The tissues of the stem of a woody plant, such as ash or box elder (Figure 8-8), are best studied in a section cut transversely across the stem. All the tissues are organized in a series of concentric cylinders surrounding a central mass of loose parenchyma cells, the *pith*. The first cylinder of tissue around the pith is the *wood*, composed of xylem cells. This is followed, in order, by cylinders of meristematic tissue (the *cambium*), phloem, parenchyma, meristematic tissue (the *cork cambium*), and finally cork.

The two cylinders of meristematic tissue permit the stem to grow in thickness as it gets older. The protective tissue of the cork consists of cells whose walls are all impregnated with a waterproofing substance (*suberin*). This effectively protects underlying tissues from water loss but prevents the cork cells themselves from obtaining water, so that they die. As they are sloughed off, they are replaced by new cells from the cork cambium.

The principal layer of meristematic tissue is the cambium, between the xylem and the phloem. In each growing season the new cells on its inner surface differentiate into new xylem, and those on its outer surface into new phloem. Thus, in each growing season a new layer of xylem is added inside the cambium, and a new layer of phloem is added outside it. The cells laid down during the most favorable part (spring) of the growing season are usually larger

FIG. 8-8 Tissue organization of a woody stem (box elder). The two lower figures show diagrammatically how the tissues are organized as concentric cylinders. In the left-hand figure there is only 1 year's growth of wood; in the right-hand figure a second year's growth forms a distinct annual ring in the wood. The upper figure shows the cellular detail of the various tissue layers in a segment of a 2-year-old stem.

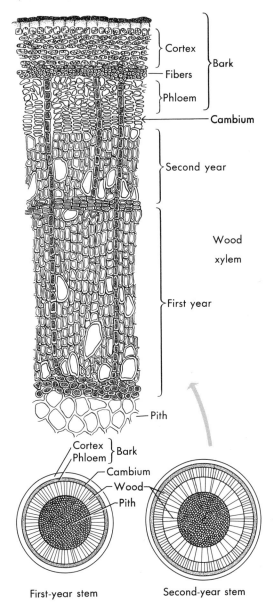

First-year stem   Second-year stem

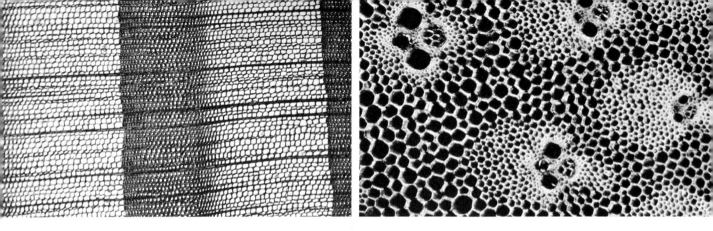

FIG. 8-9 Annual rings in pine wood ($\times$23). (Photo, Carl Strüwe)

FIG. 8-10 Scattered vascular bundles in the stem of bamboo, a monocotyledonous plant ($\times$75). (Photo, Carl Strüwe)

than the later cells, with the result that the phloem and especially the xylem show, in cross section, annual growth rings (Figure 8-9). In climates without well-marked seasons, these rings are faint or absent.

The great masses of xylem cells in the wood of a tree like the oak are dead vessel elements. The oak, symbol of sturdy life, is in one sense, therefore, more dead than alive. However, the presence of the actively growing cambium between the xylem and the phloem guarantees a continual supply of living cells, whose number remains nearly constant throughout the life of the tree. A tree's increasing bulk with age signifies an increase in dead wood tissue, whose function is a combination of conduction and mechanical support.

There is much less wood (xylem cells) in the stems of herbaceous plants, which usually have large amounts of pith. Their protective tissues commonly are green, containing chloroplasts and carrying on photosynthesis.

The organization of tissues we have outlined here applies generally to the plants in one (the *dicotyledons*)

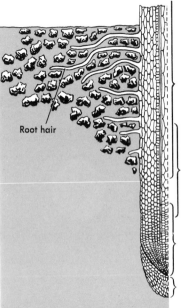

Region of maturation

Root hair

Region of elongation

Region of cell multiplication

Root cap

FIG. 8-11 **Plant root.** Longitudinal section of a root, showing epidermal cells extending as root hairs into the soil between soil particles. The growing tip (region of cell multiplication) is protected by a root cap. The cells of the root cap are continuously abraded away by friction on the soil particles, as growth forces the tip downward; they are continuously regenerated by cell divisions in the growing tip. Immediately behind the region of cell multiplication, new cells elongate under the pressure of osmosis. These cells eventually mature (region of maturation) into specialized types such as xylem and phloem. The inset photograph shows root hairs on the young root of a radish plant germinating from its seed. (Photo, Hugh Spencer)

of two principal groups of higher plants. In the other group (the *monocotyledons*), which includes plants like the lily, bamboo, palm, corn, and other grasses, the same kinds of tissues are present, but they are not arranged in the series of concentric cylinders characteristic of the dicotyledons. The vascular bundles of xylem and phloem are scattered throughout the pith (Figure 8-10). Nor do the monocotyledons have continuous cambium layers; consequently, most of these plants cannot maintain continuous growth in thickness.

Tissue Organization in the Root

Roots anchor plants, but their main role is the gathering in of water and dissolved salts from the soil. Among other specialized activities, they may also store materials, especially starch. Their tissues are quite similar to those of stems, but they have no pith, and the vascular bundles are arranged in a somewhat different way. The surface cells just back of root tips usually have elongated extensions of their walls, forming root hairs (Figure 8-11). The root hairs worm their way in among fine particles of soil. The development of root hairs is of functional significance, for they increase the surface through which water and dissolved minerals can be absorbed.

ANIMAL CELLS AND TISSUES

Many tissues and tissue products are peculiar to certain groups of animals—for instance, bones to vertebrates and feathers to birds. There are, however, broad classes of tissues that occur in virtually all multicellular animals, differing only in detailed structure and origin. Among these are *surface* or *epithelial tissue, muscle tissue, nerve tissue,* and *connective tissue.* As we review these classes, bear in mind that their diversity and specialization are often related to the mobility that characterizes animals.

Surface Tissue

Every organism is enclosed. It has a boundary between itself and the environment. In a protist this may be simply the cell membrane. In a multicellular form, either plant or animal, it is one or more layers of epithelial cells. *Epithelium* is a tissue that covers a surface, and the external surface is only one of many

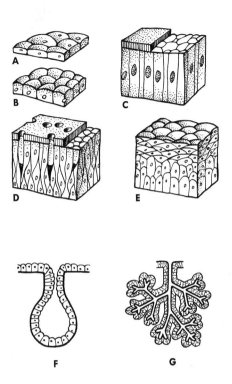

FIG. 8-12 Animal epithelium. A. Simple squamous epithelium consists of flattened, tile-like cells; it lines cavities such as the mouth. B. Cuboidal epithelium occurs, for example, in kidney tubules. C. Columnar epithelium occurs, for example, in the lining of the stomach. D. Ciliated columnar epithelium lines the breathing duct (trachea) of a land vertebrate. E. Stratified epithelium occurs on surfaces subject to heavy wear, such as human skin. The lowest (germinative) layer of cells in the epithelium continually supplies, by mitosis, new cells to replace those worn away from the external layers. F and G. Simple and more complex glands, with the epithelium specialized to produce and secrete a particular substance or substances.

in the animal body. Some internal surfaces are actually continuous with the outside; for example, the surfaces of the mouth, throat, stomach, intestines, and lungs are covered with epithelium. Other internal surfaces, like the linings of blood vessels and body cavities, have no connections with the outside but are nevertheless, since they are surfaces, covered with epithelium. The several types of epithelial cells are shown in Figure 8-12. Note that *glands* are made of epithelial cells.

The functions of epithelium are determined by its surface position. They are to *protect* and to *repair*. In its exposed location, epithelium is subject to wear and tear, but there is continual replacement of its dead cells. The epithelial cells are lost either cell by cell or—as in human skin—in many-celled flakes, so small that we are hardly aware that we are always shedding our skins. In some other animals—as in most snakes—the whole surface comes off in one piece from time to time.

As the organism's limiting boundary, the epithelium also controls what enters and leaves the body, just as a cell membrane controls traffic into and out of the individual cell. Thus the epithelial linings of the stomach and intestine absorb foodstuffs; oxygen enters the body through lung epithelium; urine is excreted by kidney epithelium; and so on. And many sense stimuli enter the body via epithelium, which, for this reason, is an important constituent of such sense organs as the eye and nose.

The word "skin" is often used synonymously with epithelium, but in man, as in many other animals, it refers not to a single tissue but to a very complex organ. Human skin (Figure 8-13) consists of many layers of cells, only the outermost of which are epithelial. Below are muscle cells, blood vessels, nerves, and much of the loose fibrous connective tissue described later.

Muscle Tissue

Probably the protoplasm of all types of cells is capable of contraction to some extent. In muscle

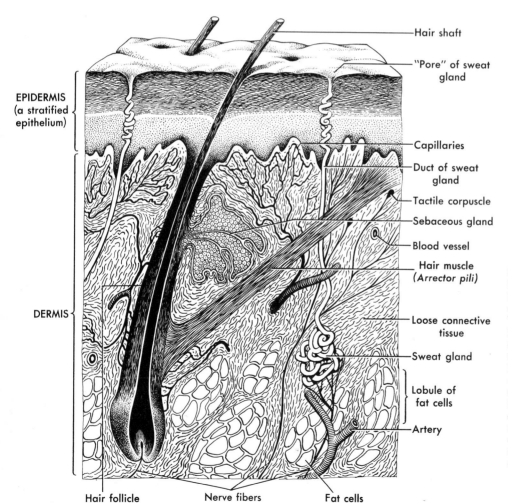

EPIDERMIS (a stratified epithelium)

DERMIS

Hair shaft

"Pore" of sweat gland

Capillaries

Duct of sweat gland

Tactile corpuscle

Sebaceous gland

Blood vessel

Hair muscle (Arrector pili)

Loose connective tissue

Sweat gland

Lobule of fat cells

Artery

Hair follicle   Nerve fibers   Fat cells

FIG. 8-13 Tissue organization of human skin. On the outside is a many-layered epithelium, the outermost cells of which are continously worn away. The tissue is maintained by the production of new cells from a generative layer (stippled in the figure) at the base of the epithelium. Below the epithelium lies the dermis, in which the following can be seen: capillary networks, arteries, and veins; nerve fibers and sense organs (tactile corpuscles); sweat glands; lobules of fat cells; hair follicles bearing hairs; muscles capable of raising the hairs; and loose connective tissue that serves to bind together the whole complex of other tissues.

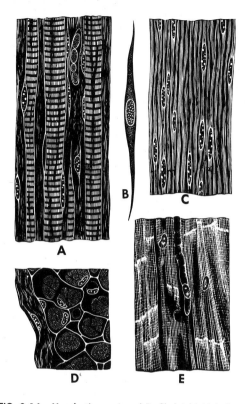

FIG. 8-14   Muscle tissue. A and D. Skeletal (striated) muscle in longitudinal (A) and cross (D) sections. The nuclei can be seen lying at the periphery of the muscle fibers. The individual muscle fibers are packed together in bundles embedded in loose connective tissue. B. An individual smooth-muscle cell. C. A sheet of smooth muscle from the intestine of a cat. E. Heart, or cardiac, muscle.

tal muscle, which is conspicuously crossbanded when viewed under the microscope, brings about the movement of the whole animal by moving its skeleton; legs move because their bones are moved by muscles. The response of skeletal muscle to stimulation is rapid; and so is its relaxation, readying it for new messages. Smooth muscle, unstraited, is responsible for much of the movement of internal organs such as the stomach and intestines. Smooth muscle is slow to contract and capable of more prolonged contraction than skeletal muscle. Heart muscle exists only in the walls of the heart, as its name suggests. It is striated in much the same manner as skeletal tissue but is unique in other ways. For example, extensive branching of the muscle fibers is seen only in heart muscle.

Nerve Tissue

A small boy stubs his toe and cries out. Unknown to him, he has demonstrated one of the most complex and extraordinary of all the phenomena of life—the transmission of impulses by nerve tissue. This tissue is as widespread among animals as is muscle tissue. The association is significant, for nerves are involved in the stimulation and coordination of muscular contraction.

In spite of the expected variety in details, nerve tissue is even more uniform throughout the animal kingdom than is muscle tissue. Its basis is the nerve cell, or *neuron,* which, perhaps more clearly than any other cell, illustrates the relation of cellular structure to function (Figure 8-15). The function of the nerve cell is the transmission of nerve impulses—or messages—often over long distances within the body. The nerve cell has a central cell body containing the nucleus and is drawn out into two or more long protoplasmic processes termed *nerve fibers.* These fibers are integral parts of the cell. (The fibers in connective tissue are *outside* the cells.) Some are simple, and others are greatly branched; some end very near the cell body, whereas others extend for some distance. In large animals this distance may be 3 to 4 feet. A group of nerve fibers bound together by connective tissue constitutes a nerve.

cells this capacity is fully developed; the muscle cell is a specialist in this protoplasmic function. Multicellular animals as a whole, and the parts within them, are generally moved by muscular tissue. Muscles occur in all but the lowest animals, and muscle tissue is remarkably uniform throughout the animal kingdom.

In higher vertebrates, like man, three different sorts of muscle tissue are distinguished: *skeletal* (or *striated*) *muscle; smooth muscle;* and *heart muscle* (Figure 8-14). Muscle cells generally are elongate, their contraction taking place along the long axes. The contraction of muscles is usually initiated by stimuli coming to them through *nerves.* Rapid transmission of nerve *impulses* (messages) and rapid response to them by muscle form the basis of the quick and beautifully coordinated movements of the higher animals. Skele-

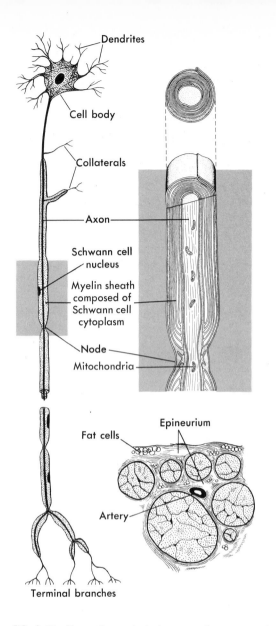

FIG. 8-15 Nerve tissue. A single nerve cell, or neuron, is diagramed at the left. Dendrites are incoming fibers that carry impulses to the cell body, in which the nucleus can be seen. The axon, which may branch, is the outgoing fiber along which the nerve impulse is transmitted. In some nerve cells the axon is surrounded by sheaths. In the one illustrated at left, there is a sheath partly composed of the fatty substance myelin. As shown in the upper right-hand figure, myelin is laid down in concentric lamellae. These arise from layers of Schwann-cell cytoplasm that repeatedly wrap themselves around a new grow-ing axon. In places the sheaths may be constricted, forming distinct nodes. Note the mitochondria in the axon cytoplasm. The lower right-hand figure is a partial cross section of a nerve. A nerve consists of many nerve fibers packed together by connective tissue (epineurium) into bundles. Blood vessels penetrate the nerve, supplying it with food and oxygen.

All the complexities of perception, behavior, and conscious thought that we find in ourselves and see, in varying degrees, in other animals are founded on a relatively simple basis. This is the nerve cell's capacity to transmit electrical impulses and join with other nerve cells in an intricately organized associa-tion—the nervous system. The importance of this system for understanding ourselves and other living things is obvious.

Connective Tissue

A wide variety of tissue types is included under the heading of connective tissue; and they have a wide variety of functions (Figure 8-16). All the tissues have one feature in common: the constituent cells lie in an extensive *matrix,* or bed, of extracellular material containing fibers. Both matrix and fibers are manufactured by the cells. The specialization of connective tissue is reflected in a characteristic special-ization of the intercellular matrix and fibers. We shall distinguish two broad functional classes: supportive connective tissue and binding connective tissue.

SUPPORTIVE CONNECTIVE TISSUE. Most kinds of animals are built around or within a hard supporting *skeleton* that not only helps to hold them together but also serves as a mechanical framework for loco-motion. It may also protect against attack by other animals and assist in waterproofing, among other roles. In most animals without backbones, like clams and insects, the skeleton is external to the body, secreted by—and lying on top of—an epithelial tissue. In vertebrates—animals with backbones—the skeleton consists of one or both of two supportive tissues, *cartilage* and *bone,* which we must treat more fully.

In cartilage (gristle) the intercellular matrix is extensive, consisting of organic compounds with a rubbery texture. This matrix gives the tissue an elasticity that resists compression. The fibers embed-ded in the matrix give cartilage added strength against pulling and stretching. Cartilage can be likened to the wall of a rubber tire; the rubber resists compres-sion, and the internal nylon cords resist stretching. Most cartilage, like that in the nose and ear, is subject to stresses from all directions, and the fibers appro-priately course in all directions within the matrix.

In some fishes (sharks and their relatives) cartilage forms the whole skeleton. In most vertebrates, how-ever, the skeleton consists almost entirely of bone, cartilage being restricted largely to joints, where it forms resilient caps over the bone surfaces involved in the joint.

Bone, like other connective tissues, contains innumerable living cells. It owes its rigidity to the dense intercellular matrix secreted by the bone cells. The rigidity, lacking in cartilage, is what makes bone such excellent supportive tissue for large and heavy animals. Bone is rigid because the bone matrix is impregnated with mineral salts (mainly a complex phosphate of calcium), which commonly make up about two-thirds of the weight of fresh bone. The matrix is maintained in proper condition by the bone cells that lie within it. These, in turn, remain alive only because the dense matrix is perforated by a system of canals carrying blood vessels that supply the cells with their needs.

BINDING CONNECTIVE TISSUE. The active movement characteristic of animals makes structural demands that are satisfied by many special tissues, including binding connective tissue. It includes *tendons, ligaments,* and loose connective tissue. In tendons and ligaments the intercellular matrix is packed with fibers that, unlike those of cartilage, are all oriented in one direction. Tendons bind muscles to bones and are subjected to strong stresses—always in one direction—when the muscles contract and the bones are moved. Tendons are appropriately inelastic—were they not, some muscle contraction would be wasted on their stretch. On the other hand, ligaments, which envelop bones at a joint, are appropriately elastic. They have the same resilient "give" characteristic of the knee bandage sometimes used to supplement them in supporting a weak joint.

Loose connective tissue serves many functions. It binds constituent muscle cells together into the mass of individual muscles (see Figure 8-14) and, similarly, nerve fibers into individual nerves. Indeed, it binds

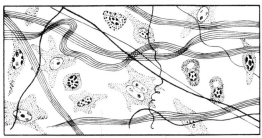

Loose connective tissue

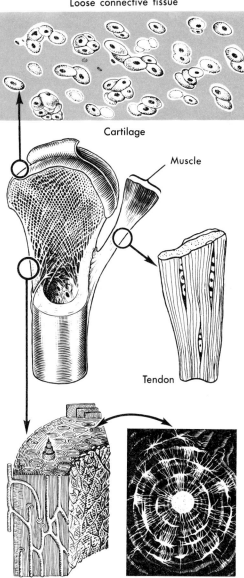

Cartilage

Muscle

Tendon

Bone

Fig. 8-16 Connective tissue. The lower figure illustrates diagrammatically the structure and components of a long bone like the humerus of man. The head of the bone is capped by cartilage. Muscle is attached to the bone by a tendon whose cells (black in the figure) lie surrounded by inelastic fibers oriented along the axis of the tendon. The bone itself is essentially a cylinder. Within, the bone tissue has a spongy texture. A piece of the wall of the bone cylinder is shown at the lower left. It is perforated by blood vessels that supply food and oxygen to the living bone cells embedded in the hard ground substance. The bone (*lower right*) cells are organized in concentric cylinders at the center of which lies a blood vessel.

all kinds of organs together in a loose but strong fashion that keeps them in proper place but allows them to move on each other as the organism moves. Again, between and within organs it serves as a loose

elastic highway on which blood vessels and nerves are carried. Internal fluids of the animal body, such as blood and lymph, contain cells and may be regarded as special connective tissues whose intercellular matrix is fluid. Lymph occurs in body cavities and between cells, although in many forms it also moves through special vessels. Blood is pumped through a partly or completely closed system of vessels.

Development

Now that we have some understanding of the cellular composition of a multicellular organism, we will focus upon the development of these various types of cells from a single cell to form an adult multicellular organism.

In the whole realm of biology there is nothing more remarkable or more baffling than the development of a mature organism from a zygote. Here is a single cell, often of microscopic size and always very small in comparison with the developed organism. It divides; the two cells divide again; and the resulting cells divide again and again. Unerringly from this process there emerge all the tissues and organs of a rosebush or a man, an immensely complex,

patterned organism whose essential characteristics were somehow determined from the start by the specifications in the zygote's chromosomes (Chapters 6 and 7). These specifications involve molecular contents and structures, and the primary action is chemical. This knowledge is a substantial step toward the goal of understanding heredity in general, but it is only a beginning. We still cannot explain precisely how one egg becomes a rosebush and another a man. Now we shall turn directly to the processes of development. By knowing in more detail what has to be controlled, we may get hints as to how it is controlled, although we must admit that many unsolved problems remain in this realm of biology.

Processes of Development

In a study of the development of a multicellular organism from a zygote, it is useful, for purposes of description and analysis, to distinguish the three constituent processes: (1) growth, with cell division; (2) morphogenesis; (3) differentiation. These processes are neither successive nor independent. At various times in development one or the other may predominate, but as a rule all proceed together, and each may influence the others.

GROWTH AND CELL DIVISION

At first, offspring are always smaller than their parents. When a protist divides, the two offspring are necessarily about half the size of the parent. In higher plants and animals parents are commonly thousands or millions of times as large as the zygote

that begins a new generation. The process of development, then, always involves growth. Cell division and a consequent increase in the number of cells is one aspect of the over-all growth process. But, of course, growth also necessarily means that some individual cells increase in size.

MORPHOGENESIS: THE CREATION OF PATTERN AND SHAPE

Compare yourself with the tiny, spherical zygote from which you developed. You are enormously larger than the zygote and contain a trillion times as many cells, or more. In a word, you have grown a great deal. But there is clearly more to your development than growth alone. You differ from the zygote even more strikingly in having, as a whole organism, a definite, complex structure and functional pattern and shape created by the foldings and mass movements of groups of cells.

DIFFERENTIATION: CELL SPECIALIZATION

You also differ strikingly from the zygote in that your constituent parts (cells and tissues) are visibly differentiated into several highly specialized types. Cellular differentiation is a distinct developmental process to which we shall pay detailed attention later; but it is also inextricably a part of morphogenesis. Much of the characteristic pattern of the adult organism derives from the intricate interrelationships that develop between specialized tissues.

It is characteristic for differentiation to affect most of the cells and to be irreversible. Specific kinds and arrangements of tissues arise; after the cells are well differentiated, they cannot revert to an undifferentiated form. By the time a human infant is born, its organic pattern is fully established. Subsequent changes are almost entirely in size and shape. Such development is called *closed* development. The least differentiated cells in animals, and those that longest retain the embryonic capacity for repeated division, are the *germ cells*. Concentrated in the primary sexual organs, these continue to divide and to produce gametes through most of the life of the organism.

In plants differentiation may also be irreversible once a plant is fully developed. However, even the higher plants, in which differentiation is most elaborate and complete, retain throughout life extensive tracts of undifferentiated cells. These constitute the meristematic tissue. From it specialized tissues, such as those of wood and bark, and organs, such as leaves and flowers, continue to be differentiated periodically throughout life. Such development is called *open* development.

The actual continuity between generations is not established through the differentiated cells that comprise most of the developed organism. Continuity passes by way of embryonic tissues and the germ cells derived from them. The following mode of continuity applies to the majority of multicellular organisms, both animals and plants:

$$\underbrace{\text{Embryonic tissue} \rightarrow \text{Germ cells} \nearrow \overset{\text{Differentiated cells, P}}{} \rightarrow}_{\text{P generation}}$$

$$\underbrace{\text{Embryonic tissue} \rightarrow \text{Germ cells} \nearrow \overset{\text{Differentiated cells, } F_1}{} \rightarrow \text{to } F_2, \text{ etc.}}_{F_1 \text{ generation}}$$

Patterns of Morphogenesis and Differentiation in Animals

MATURATION OF THE EGG CELL

The process of meiosis is the same in both sexes as far as chromosome behavior is concerned. The chromosome number is reduced from the diploid to the haploid number. In the female, however, nonchromosomal aspects of gamete formation are modified in a way directly bearing on the general problem of development (Figure 8-17).

In sperm production, or *spermatogenesis,* the cells that give rise to spermatozoa divide equally twice in the course of meiosis. Each original diploid cell (spermatogonium) thus becomes four haploid cells (spermatocytes), which in turn mature into four spermatozoa. The size of the cells decreases during these processes, and the cytoplasm is greatly reduced, so that a spermatozoan consists of little more than a small nucleus, essentially just a set of chromosomes, and a motile tail. In egg production, or *oögenesis,* on the other hand, each original diploid cell (oögonium) gives rise to only one mature haploid ovum, which is larger than the original cell. The other nuclei produced in the course of meiosis form small separate

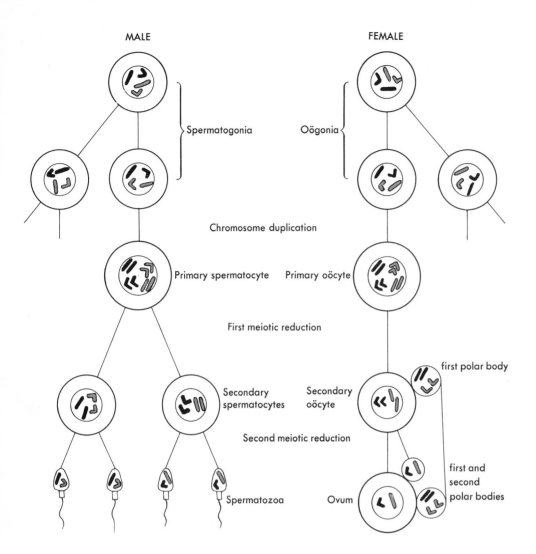

MALE

FEMALE

Spermatogonia

Oögonia

Chromosome duplication

Primary spermatocyte   Primary oöcyte

First meiotic reduction

Secondary
spermatocytes

Secondary
oöcyte

first polar body

Second meiotic reduction

first and
second
polar bodies

Spermatozoa   Ovum

FIG. 8-17 Maturation of gametes in male and female animals. For simplicity, the organism
is represented as having four
chromosomes. The ovum is actually
relatively much larger than indicated in the diagram. The polar
bodies degenerate after the ovum
is fertilized and have no part in
subsequent development.

bodies (called *polar bodies*), which simply degenerate.
The cell that matures into an ovum, called an *oöcyte*
during its meiotic development, is enclosed and
nourished by a *follicle* of other cells in the ovary. There
it grows substantially, partly by the addition of food
materials, or yolk. The result is that a mature egg
is a relatively large cell, much larger than a sperm,
with much cytoplasm and generally also food that
provides energy and material for the growth of the
embryo.

The large cytoplasmic content of the egg is not
uniform throughout. It has a high degree of organization, such as we have found in other active, living
cells. It also has a characteristic spatial arrangement

and other properties which can profoundly influence
development, morphogenesis, and differentiation.

FERTILIZATION

Cytoplasmic organization is complete by the
time meiosis occurs in the egg. Meiosis commonly
is arrested at the metaphase of the second meiotic
division and is completed only when the entry of
the fertilizing sperm cell acts as a signal to proceed.
Indeed the response of the egg cell to the sperm's
entry is not only to complete meiosis but also to
proceed with the rest of development.

In some species artificial stimuli, such as the prick

of a fine needle, can cause the egg to complete meiosis and to start development. This shows that the sperm's nucleus is not always essential for development. A haploid egg cell can go ahead in some instances and complete all or nearly all of its development. Even eggs without nuclei may begin development. To be sure, such eggs do not develop far along the normal path, and they soon die, but the fact that they develop at all tells us that the cytoplasm itself carries some information on how to proceed. This reflects the early differentiation of the egg cytoplasm that took place during the egg's maturation (which was nuclear-controlled) before fertilization.

CLEAVAGE

In normal development the fertilized egg proceeds to divide immediately following the formation of a diploid nucleus by union of egg and sperm chromosomes. Cell division continues for some time in the absence of any protoplasmic growth. Thus the cleaving embryo remains constant in over-all size, and cell dimensions steadily decrease with successive divisions until the growth accomplished by the egg's maturation is canceled out (Figure 8-18). A usual result of egg cleavage is a raspberry- or mulberrylike cluster of cells called a *morula* (Latin for "mulberry"). With further divisions the number of cells continues to increase, and a cavity may develop in among them.

In this stage, which does not occur in all animals, the whole embryo has the form of a hollow sphere and is called a *blastula*.

Experiments with cleavage-stage embryos are very instructive. With many species it is possible to shake apart the individual cells and observe their subsequent behavior. In some animals, these separate cells are able to start all over again and complete development; in other animals this is not possible.

When renewed development is possible, as with sea urchins and frogs, we must conclude that the cells were not irreversibly differentiated; that is, they all were still essentially alike, and each was capable of complete development, just like the original egg. Lack of differentiation in the cells of young embryos is surprising, for we noted earlier that the mature egg cell is regionally differentiated. The explanation lies in the plane of cleavage in the egg. The first divisions of the zygote cleave the egg *along* the axis of differentiation (Figure 8-19A). If, however, another egg cell is experimentally cleaved *across* the axis of visible differentiation, the separated halves fail to develop into normal embryos (Figure 8-19B). In those animals like snails and worms, in which cell differentiation starts with the first cleavage, the first cleavage plane cuts across the field of differentiation in the egg cytoplasm.

Embryos that develop from separate cells derived from the same morula do, of course, possess exactly the same heredity. Their nuclei were produced by the mitotic division of a single zygote nucleus. This is the way in which identical twins arise. The potentiality for separate development may persist later than the two-cell stage. Identical quadruplets can arise by separation of cells in the four-cell stage, after two cleavages. (How could identical triplets arise?) In man this potentiality for total development persists even after three cleavages. This is one way the Dionne quintuplets may have arisen. There are other possible ways in which identical twins, triplets, and so on, can arise from one zygote, but all depend on the absence of irreversible differentiation among cells in the young embryo.

FIG. 8-18 Cleavage of a fertilized egg. Note that successive cell divisions proceed without cell growth; at the end of cleavage, the embryo, though many-celled, is no larger than the zygote after the first cleavage division (A). (Although some animals, such as the starfishes, follow this simple sequence rather closely, in others it may be greatly altered.)

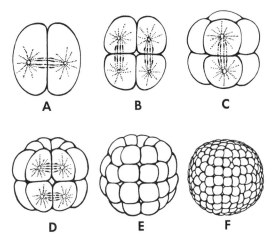

A   B   C

D   E   F

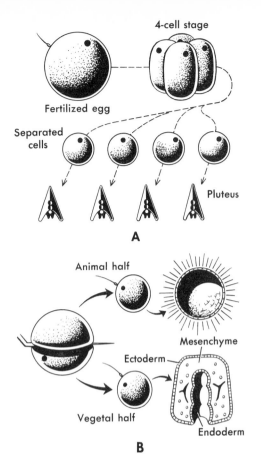

A

B

FIG. 8-19 **Experimental evidence of differentiation in the zygote's cytoplasm.** A. The fertilized egg of a sea urchin cleaves along the axis of differentiation, producing four cells, all of which are the same and contain a complete sample of the field of differentiation; shaken apart, each of the four cells can produce a complete embryo. B. When the fertilized egg is cleaved with a needle across the axis of differentiation, a different result is obtained. Neither of the two halves ("animal" and "vegetal") contains a complete sample of the field of differentiation; consequently, neither develops into a complete embryo. The vegetal half of the egg reaches only an advanced gastrula stage, and the animal half stops development while a blastula.

Sooner or later there is some differentiation of cells within the developing embryo. Thereafter a single cell removed from the rest will not develop into a whole organism, and development of the remaining cells does not produce a normal organism. Parts that would have developed from the removed cell are missing.

The cleavage of the zygote is often profoundly modified by the amount of food materials (yolk) and other factors in the embryo. Figure 8-20 compares cleavages in Amphioxus, frog, and bird—a series of embryos with increasing amounts of yolk material. In the hen's egg the zygote cell is the whole yellow mass we designate as yolk. The nucleus and cytoplasm from which the embryo develops are localized on a part of the surface of the yolk. Much of the original zygote cell is never involved in cleavage. Cleavage of the cytoplasm occurs first in a platelike area on one side, and the growing embryo gradually consumes the yolk proper, finally occupying the whole available space.

GASTRULATION: A PRINCIPAL MORPHOGENETIC PHASE

Even in the earliest stages, development follows different lines in various groups of animals. As the process goes further, there is tremendous

FIG. 8-20 **The effect of yolk on the cleavage of an egg.** In the Amphioxus egg, which contains virtually no yolk, cleavage is complete. In the frog's egg there is considerable yolk on one side (unstippled). The cleavage plane is displaced above it. The hen's egg is almost entirely yolk, and consequently cleavage is restricted to a small area. B, C, and D are corresponding stages in all three animals.

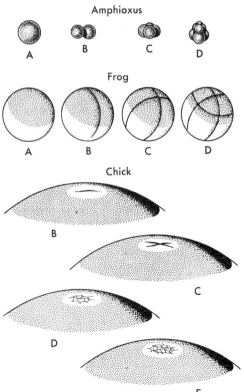

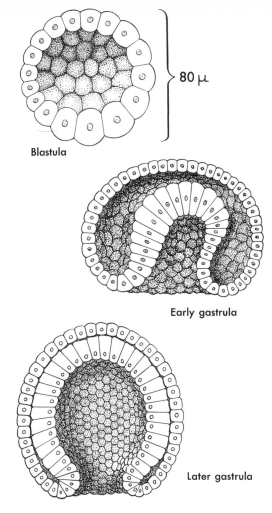

80 μ

Blastula

Early gastrula

Later gastrula

FIG. 8-21 **The gastrula of Amphioxus and its formation by invagination.** The endoderm of the gastrula has larger cells than the ectoderm.

gastrula we can recognize the gross outlines of the adult's future pattern. Gastrulation is indeed principally a morphogenetic phase of development, producing the main outlines of organic pattern rather than differentiation of cells into special types.

In most animals a more complex third layer of cells (the *mesoderm*) develops between the ectoderm and endoderm. The mesoderm may arise by pouchlike foldings from the endoderm region or as individual cells that migrate into the space between ectoderm and endoderm and proliferate there. In either case the mesoderm soon becomes quite complex and loses whatever clear resemblance to a layer it may have had. Usually at a rather early stage a cavity, the *coelom*, appears in it, lined with mesodermal layers or masses.

DIFFERENTIATION AND ORGAN FORMATION

The three germ layers represent an early sorting out and arrangement of cells as they increase in number in the embryo. The cells in the layers still are not strongly differentiated. When the cells do later form distinct tissues and organs, the layer arrangement is no longer evident. Many of the tissues can, however, be traced back more or less clearly to derivation from one layer or another (Table 8-1).

Gastrulation and germ-layer formation are processes of morphogenesis rather than differentiation; they are the processes whereby adult form is roughly

diversity in detail. However, some features can be seen in more or less modified form in most animals.

The process of *gastrulation*, whereby the embryo becomes a two-layered structure, follows the morula and blastula stages. The simplest, though not the most common, form of gastrulation is for one side of the blastula to cave in, much as does the side of a soft rubber ball that is poked with a finger. The result is a cup- or bowl-shaped *gastrula* with two layers of cells forming its walls (Figure 8-21). The outer layer is the *ectoderm* ("outside skin"); the layer lining the cavity of the gastrula is the *endoderm* ("inside skin"). The cavity inside the double-walled gastrula becomes the alimentary canal of the adult animal. Here in the

TABLE 8-1 *Tissues Derived from Germ Layers*

Ectoderm

Epidermis of the skin, nails, and hair; sweat glands in the skin; all nervous tissue; receptor cells in the sense organs; epidermis of the mouth, nostrils, and anus.

Endoderm

Epidermis lining the gut, trachea, bronchi, lungs, urinary bladder, and uretha; liver; pancreas; thyroid gland.

Mesoderm

All muscles; blood; connective tissue (including bone); kidneys; testes and ovaries; epithelia lining the body cavities.

sketched out and masses of potentially multipurpose cells are stockpiled ready for later cell differentiation and development of detailed organs. The later differentiation of a cell depends not so much on whether it is broadly ecto-, meso-, or endoderm, as on precisely *where* it is in the over-all pattern of the embryo. Muscles and bones usually develop from mesoderm only because mesoderm normally happens to occur in those parts of the embryo where muscle and bone are differentiated. But if by some variation of development in a particular species ectoderm happens to come into a region of muscle or bone development, muscle and bone develop from ectoderm. In other words, final and definitive differentiation depends on regional relationships and on later anatomical controls, not basically on the germ layers.

INDUCTION AND ORGANIZERS

Discussion of the germ layers emphasized the fact that later differentiation of a cell depends not only on what but especially on where it is—that is, on interactions among adjacent cells and tissues as well as on processes within single cells. Experiments have revealed something of the nature of the interactions among developing cells, although as a whole they are not yet understood. In typical experiments, bits of tissue removed from a living organism are kept in a solution of suitable temperature, osmotic pressure, and composition such that they continue to develop. If kidney cells from a mouse are so cultured, they grow in a formless way, like undifferentiated embryonic cells. If, however, kidney connective tissue is added to the culture, the cells differentiate and tend to form kidney tubules. The connective tissue somehow *induces* differentiation in the kidney cells.

Experiments on embryos show that *induction* likewise, and even more elaborately, occurs in normal development. The German experimental embryologist Hans Spemann (1869–1941) first showed that there is a special inducing region at the upper edge of the infolding lip of the gastrula in frogs and salamanders. He called this region the *organizer.* Its removal

prevents normal differentiation. Transplantation of the organizer into another embryo at a similar stage of development causes double differentiation and development of a sort of Siamese twins (Figure 8-22).

The organizer of frogs and salamanders is ultimately responsible for much of their differentiation. Specifically, the tissue just inside the organizer lip induces formation of the nervous system in the overlying ectoderm. In these animals, as in all vertebrates, the nervous system arises first as a plate or thickening (the *neural plate*) in the ectoderm along what is to become the back of the animal. Later the sides of the neural plate are elevated, forming the *neural folds,* which fuse together to form a tube that eventually becomes the brain and spinal cord. Experiments prove that this process is induced by the organizer tissue, which nevertheless does not itself form any of the nervous system. If the organizer tissue is removed just before the neural plate would have been formed in the ectoderm, no neural plate develops.

FIG. 8-22 Experimental demonstration of induction by the organizer. A. The piece of the organizer (dorsal lip of blastopore) that induces the formation of neural plate is presumptive notochord; it will become notochord eventually. **B.** The presumptive notochord is removed from one embryo and transplanted into the blastocoele of another, where it attaches at a point corresponding with the future left side of the embryo. **C.** It here induces a secondary neural plate. **D.** The result is a two-headed monster.

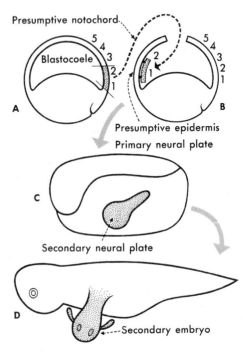

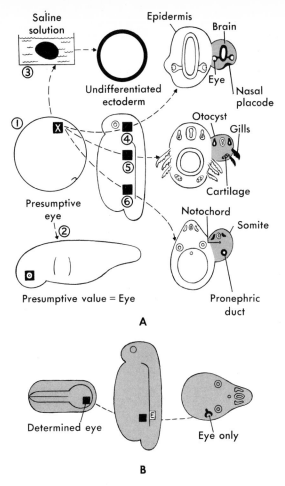

FIG. 8-23 Determination versus presumptive fate in embryonic development. A. 1, 2, A piece of embryonic tissue (marked X) in the amphibian gastrula normally develops into an eye; its presumptive fate is eye. 3. If, however, it is removed from the gastrula and allowed to develop in saline solution, it does not differentiate into an eye. 4, 5, 6. If it is transplanted to unusual locations in older embryos, it differentiates, not into an eye, but into a structure characteristic of the location to which it has been moved. In the gastrula the fate of X as an eye is only presumptive and is contingent on its embryonic location. B. If the same tissue is transplanted from a much older embryo than a gastrula, its fate is found to have become determined; no matter where it is transplanted, it differentiates into an eye.

If the organizer is transplanted and placed beneath another area of ectoderm, a neural plate will develop there instead of in the normal position.

Further experiments indicate that the induction of the neural plate, at least, is due to a chemical diffused from the inducing organizer tissue into the differentiating ectoderm.

Other experiments involving the transplantation of pieces of the embryo to new locations elucidate further aspects of the process of normal development. In the gastrula stage of the amphibian embryo, careful observation and experiment have enabled embryologists to draw a map showing what organs various parts of the gastrula will eventually produce. Figure 8-23A shows the location of a mass of cells that in normal development would give rise to an eye. These gastrula cells can be transplanted to various locations on an older embryo. When this is done, their future development is again controlled by the particular environment of cells into which they have been transplanted.

All the embryo's cells, arising by mitosis from the single-celled zygote, arrange themselves into a definite form and differentiate in a gradual process. What they differentiate into is initially controlled by their location in the embryo. Their differentiation cannot be primarily controlled by differences in heredity because all the cells receive one and the same set of chromosomes from the zygote by the process of mitosis. However, their differentiation, initially guided by embryonic location, eventually does reach a point of no return. In the normal embryo a stage of differentiation is ultimately reached by the cells we have discussed when their ultimate fate to be eye cells is no longer *presumptive* but *determined*. After differentiation has reached this state of determination, the cells can be transplanted and will go ahead and become an eye independent of their new location (Figure 8-23B).

THE PROBLEM OF GENETIC CONTROL

After a brief survey of the kinds of processes that go on in the normal development of organisms, we must now return to an earlier problem. How does the inherited set of chromosome specifications control these processes? To begin with, how can we reconcile the two following facts?

1. Development involves the organization of a multitude of cells into a complex but definite pattern and the differentiation of these cells into many diversified and specialized cell types.

2. All these cells with their widely different fates in the organism have identical heredity. They arose by mitosis from the single-celled zygote and have the same chromosomes.

There is no evidence that, in successive cell divisions in the growth of the embryo, neatly packaged fractions of the total blueprint are partitioned out—one set to presumptive leg tissue, one set to presumptive eye tissue, and so on. Indeed, there is evidence that this is not the case. The chromosome set remains visibly complete in different tissues. And, as we have seen, cells can proceed along one path of differentiation for some time and still retain their ability to differentiate into something entirely different if they are transplanted.

In plants many somatic cells can give rise to whole new plants without requiring the participation of the normally reproductive cells—hence the possibility of propagation by cuttings and vegetative reproduction in general. The cells involved are usually poorly differentiated (especially meristematic cells, as previously noted), but it has recently been found that even differentiated cells, notably almost any in a carrot, may act in this manner. Vegetative reproduction also occurs in a few lowly animals, and all animals retain some capacity for the regeneration of cells and organs, that is, for newly differentiating lost specialized cells and structures. Even animals as complex as salamanders readily regenerate whole legs.

These phenomena testify that the genetic endowment is usually the same in all cells. They thus make still more profound the mystery of how different cells assume such radically different forms and functions, chemically and otherwise, in spite of having the same nuclear controls.

Our earlier survey of gene action provides some leads toward the eventual solution of this problem. A gene apparently acts through its control of unitary chemical processes. This control, at least in most cases, is effected through the intermediary of an enzyme. But, as we have noted, the gene's action is not an absolutely fixed affair. There is not even a flat alternative of producing or not producing an enzyme—of

a reaction's taking place or not. There are instances in which a reaction (for example, the synthesis of pantothenic acid in some bacteria) fails to occur even when the necessary enzyme is present. Any reaction, such as the conversion of a substance A to a substance B, depends on many conditions, only one of which is the presence of the enzyme. For one thing, it depends on the rate at which A is supplied and the rate at which B is removed by being converted into other substances in other reactions (and the supply of A and the removal of B are influenced by the actions of other genes). It is also sensitive to physical conditions, such as acidity and temperature. A gene's action is, in short, subject to both the genetic and physical environment in which it finds itself. Consequently, the diverse effects of the same genotype must be due to the different cellular environments existing in the embryo.

We studied in the preceding chapter the mechanisms of action of genes which control the structures or amino acid sequences of proteins (that is, enzymes). We mentioned also that there are regulator and operator genes that control the rate at which other genes instruct the cell to synthesize messenger RNA and certain proteins. Those genes provide a reasonable explanation for the remarkable phenomena whereby enzyme synthesis is *induced* by the presence of substrate molecules and *repressed* by the presence of metabolic end products. These important discoveries may also lead to a more acceptable explanation for differentiation, a process that involves the systematic acquisition of capacities for the synthesis of new proteins. It is likely that differentiation depends upon intricate sequences of enzyme inductions and repressions, the basic information for which resides in the genes of the fertilized egg cell. Thus, when a product of one metabolic pathway serves as the substrate for an enzyme of another pathway, one could predict an increase in the amount of new enzyme. Many such schemes could be imagined and interconnected into regulatory circuits endowed with virtually any property.

These explanations support the conviction that the genes do in fact control development, and they hold out hope that the control processes will eventually be explained in physical and chemical terms. At present, however, there are still gaps in our knowledge of, on the one hand, the DNA-segment gene and its determination of an enzyme and, on the other hand, the systematic, structural development of an embryo. How and why should one collection of proteins produce the structure and function of a human brain and another set, different only in amino acid sequences, those of a rose bloom? We know enough to have faith that such questions are answer-

able, but as of now we do not have the final answers. Here, in all probability, is the greatest opportunity for research in biology.

Evolution of Development

In some respects the development of embryos may be singularly indirect. Human embryos develop tails, which later disappear. They also develop gill-like pouches in the neck region, which disappear as such and are in part transformed into quite nongill-like structures, including the ear canal. At this stage the embryo looks a little like a fish, although the resemblance is not so close as is sometimes suggested. Still, it seems very roundabout for a developing human to go through a stage even remotely fishlike and to have structures so little related to adult anatomy. Until the reality of evolution was recognized, such facts were inexplicable. Then it was realized that they have a historical, evolutionary basis.

SUPPOSED RECAPITULATION

The fact is that the tailed, gill-pouched stage of the human embryo is not much like an adult fish but is very like an *embryonic* fish. K. E. von Baer (1792–1876) noted this fact even before the fact of evolution was recognized. He considered it an example of the so-called biogenetic law, which is not really a law but a descriptive generalization with many exceptions. According to this generalization the earlier stages of embryos resemble those of other animals lower in the scale of nature, or, as we would now say, more like those of related or ancestral groups. As development proceeds, the embryos of different animals become more and more dissimilar. In its very earliest cleavage stages, a human embryo is rather like that of a starfish. In somewhat later stages it is still very similar to that of a (true) fish, amphibian, or reptile. Even later, it is quite like the embryos of other mammals. Finally, well before birth, it becomes clearly human and unmistakably distinct from any other species.

Early evolutionists, especially E. H. Haeckel (1834–1919), rephrased that generalization as the *principle of recapitulation:* "ontogeny repeats phylogeny," that is, successive stages of individual development correspond with successive adult ancestors of the line of evolutionary descent. *Ontogeny* is the "development of being" (the individual organism), and *phylogeny* the "development (or descent) of races." The vaguely fishlike stage of the human embryo was believed to represent the stage when our adult ancestors were fishes. Von Baer had more correctly generalized the facts, but at a time when the principles underlying those facts could not be understood. Haeckel correctly pointed out that the observed facts must result from evolution, as Darwin had already noted, but Haeckel misstated the evolutionary principle involved.

It is now firmly established that ontogeny does *not* repeat phylogeny. Ontogeny repeats ontogeny, with variations. Phylogeny is a series of ontogenies. Evolution is not manifested by a sequence of adults giving rise to later, modified adults. An individual organism has a time dimension. It is the same organism from zygote to death and is to be understood only as a dynamically developing living system. What is passed on from one generation to the next is a developmental mechanism. It is also the developmental mechanism that evolves. Heritable change in the adult can occur only on the basis of change in that developmental mechanism.

The developmental mechanism that produced a fish in our ancestors of about 300 million years ago has been inherited by us. In the meantime, however, it has undergone many and profound evolutionary changes and it produces quite a different kind of adult organism. The changes are more evident in later than in earlier developmental stages, and that is why an early human embryo is still rather like a correspondingly early fish embryo. There have, however, been some important evolutionary changes even in the earliest stages.

CHANGES IN ONTOGENY

In some instances, which are exceptions to von Baer's generalization, the young of related species differ more than the adults. This is especially likely among animals that have feeding larvae quite different in form from the reproducing adults; caterpillars and butterflies are a familiar example.

Even in forms without larvae, there are usually special adaptations to embryonic life that never occurred in any adult form and that may be quite different in different groups. In man and other high mammals, the umbilical cord, the placenta, and the membranes surrounding the fetus are embryonic adaptations of essential evolutionary importance. They differ in several respects from adaptations in marsupial mammals and are profoundly different from the embryonic adaptations of, for instance, fishes or birds.

Summary

Protistan colonies compared with multicellular organisms.

Tissues as aggregates of similar cells specialized in structure and function; organs as integrated aggregates of diverse tissues; systems as integrated aggregates of organs.

Plant cells and tissues: their organization into leaf, stem, and root.

Animal cells and tissues: their greater number and complexity; functional specializations related to the mobility of animals.

Developmental processes controlled by the inherited message in the chromosomes: growth and cell division; morphogenesis, the creation of pattern and shape; differentiation, the specialization of cell types; closed development in animals; open development in plants; continuity of germ cells; phases of development in which one or another of the developmental processes predominates.

Patterns of morphogenesis and differentiation in animals: maturation of the egg cell includes differentiation of egg cytoplasm; cleavage—cell division without growth; the blastula; twinning in relation to the plane of cleavage and the axis of the egg's differentiation; the effect of yolk in cleavage.

Gastrulation and morphogenesis: ectoderm and endoderm; origin of mesoderm and of coelom; differentiation of tissue types; their derivation from germ layers; organ formation.

Induction and organizers; the organizer in frogs; experimental demonstration of its inducing action; presumptive fate, dependent on embryonic environment; determination.

The problem of genetic control of development—in essence the problem of how the same inherited message (identical chromosome sets) is consistent with the differentiation of diverse tissue types: its solution to be sought in knowledge of how gene action is affected by the chemical and physical environment; known to be different in different cells after cleavage of the egg.

Evolution of development: similarity of human fish embryos; the biogenetic principle; Haeckel's misstatement of the principle; changes in ontogeny.

REPRODUCTION:

ORGANISMIC ASPECTS

If Mars had intelligent inhabitants, and if one of them should happen to land in the northern United States in winter, his first impression would be that most of the life on earth had become extinct. Many of the plants would be plainly dead. Most of the others, especially among the larger woody plants, would stand skeletonlike, gaunt and bare. The visitor might find a few insects, all dead or seemingly so. If wider investigation revealed some rodents or a bear, these, too, might be so profoundly quiescent as to seem dead at first sight.

What amazement the Martian would experience if he stayed until spring! Everywhere he would see a resurrection of life. Plants would burst forth from germinating spores and seeds. Trees would break out into vividly living greenery. From tiny eggs and mummy cases millions of insects would emerge. Birds would appear, seemingly from nowhere, and bustle about the business of nesting and reproducing. The hibernators would awaken, among them the she-bear, trailed by her cubs. The visitor would thus conclude that life on earth is cyclic. Each longer life has a recurrent pattern through the cycle of the seasons. All lives, long or short, are links in reproductive cycles in which one life follows another, each life repeating the pattern of its forebears within its species.

The seasonal cycle is not everywhere so apparent as in the so-called Temperate Zone, with its intemperate alternation of summer and winter. Yet the reproductive cycle is completely universal. It exists for all living things wherever they may be on earth and whether their life spans be measured in minutes or in centuries. All kinds of organisms are born and differ only in the manner of their origin. "Birth" may be the fission of a parent, the germination of a seed, the emergence from an egg or from the womb; but the resemblances are more fundamental than the differences. In every kind of organism, an individual in its turn gives birth in its own fashion to others, and so begins another cycle of life.

The Generalized Reproductive Cycle

The individual life cycle begins with reproduction from a parent or two parents. Development of the individual follows (Chapter 8) and then reproduction again, starting another cycle. There has thus been in all organisms a continuous sequence: reproduction–development–developed organism–reproduction–development–developed organism– . . . and so on through the centuries and millennia, ever since life began. It would be foolish to say that one phase is more important than another in a process that is continuous, with each phase dependent on the others. However, in some sorts of studies (for example, those of transfers of energy and materials in communities) attention is naturally focused on the developed organism. Then reproduction may be viewed merely as part of the background, as the process that keeps up a continuous supply of organisms. In consideration of the life cycle, on the other hand, reproduction is a particularly crucial phase. It begins the individual cycle and is the connection between the generations that are links in the long chain. From this point of view, the developing and developed individual is the medium of reproduction, or what intervenes between the crucial episodes of reproduction. The subject of life cycles may, then, be considered first of all in terms of reproductive cycles.

ASEXUAL AND SEXUAL REPRODUCTION

In Chapter 5 the subject of cellular reproduction introduced us to the study of heredity, and the distinction was there made between sexual and asexual reproduction. In *sexual reproduction* there is a fusion of two nuclei from different cells (gametes) into one cell (zygote); and in *asexual reproduction* there is not. One of the two usual forms of asexual reproduction (Figure 9-1) is *vegetative reproduction,* which occurs in both animals and plants but is much more common among plants.

In many plants and a few animals, almost any reasonably large part will grow into a new organism under proper conditions. Thus *cuttings* are often used to propagate cultivated plants; thus a planarian develops from a portion of its parent. Quite a few animals, of which *Hydra* is an example (Figure 9-2), reproduce vegetatively by *budding.* Many plants develop special *organs of vegetative reproduction.* Some of these are surely familiar to you: the tubers of

FIG. 9-1   Vegetative reproduction. A. Tuberous swellings of the stems in the potato plant serve to propagate the species vegetatively. The bulk of tissue is a food reserve (starch), but embryonic tissue is present in the "eyes" of the potato and can develop from these new shoot and root systems. B. In the strawberry the shoot system effects vegetative reproduction. Stolons, shoots growing along the surface of the ground, may develop new root systems and establish a new plant.

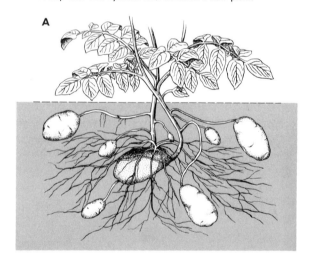

A

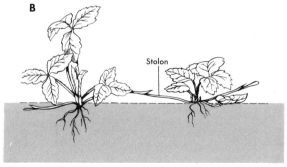

B

Stolon

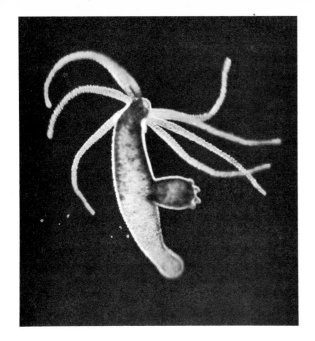

FIG. 9-2 Vegetative reproduction in *Hydra*, an animal. A bud in *Hydra* is an evagination of the polyp wall containing both ectoderm and endoderm tissue layers. It develops tentacles (barely visible in the photo) and a mouth. Eventually, severing itself completely from the parent, it becomes a new individual. (Photo, Hugh Spencer)

potatoes, the bulbs of onions or tulips, the bulblike organs of gladioli, the runners of strawberries, and the runnerlike underground structures of many grasses. The other usual form of asexual reproduction is by *spores,* plant reproductive cells each of which develops into a separate organism without fertilization.

The essential feature of sexual reproduction is the fusion of two nuclei within a single cell, which develops into a separate organism. You will recall from Chapter 5 that the specialized sexual reproductive cells of plants and animals are gametes and that they usually are of two kinds: smaller, more mobile male gametes, or sperms, and larger, more passive female gametes, or eggs. The union of male and female gametes is fertilization, and the resulting single cell is a zygote. Sexual reproduction is essentially the same and has the same evolutionary and biological significance whether it occurs in paramecia, roses, or humans. The basic phenomenon is that half the chromosomes from each of two individuals have been united in a single new individual.

DISTRIBUTION AND SIGNIFICANCE OF SEX IN ORGANISMS

It seems probable that the first organisms, perhaps 3 billion years ago, when life was young, had simple, asexual reproductive cycles. Even today, simple, asexual cell division and the mitotic transmission of identical nuclear controls to each new daughter cell is the fundamental mode of cellular reproduction.

The significance of sex in organisms is that it is a device for promoting genetic variability and adaptation. We saw in Chapter 6 that the gametes produced in meiosis contain a recombination, or reshuffling, of gene combinations present in the parents' gametes. Consider two organisms that are homozygous for two gene pairs as follows: *AABB* and *aabb*. As long as each reproduces only by asexual means, the offspring can be only *AABB* and *aabb,* respectively, generation after generation until the comparatively rare process of mutation changes one of the alleles. But were these organisms to reproduce sexually—were they to mate—producing hybrids (*AaBb*), the very next generation of sexually produced offspring would contain the following recombination genotypes: *AABB, AABb, AAbb, AaBB, AaBb, Aabb, aaBB, aaBb,* and *aabb.* Of course, normal sexual reproduction yields an even richer array of variants than this. Since an organism contains thousands of gene pairs, not just two, as we noted in Chapter 7, the number of genotypes possible with recombination among offspring is enormous.

The basis for evolution is genetic variation in a population (see Chapter 12). Asexual reproduction keeps such variation at a minimum, whereas sexual reproduction maximizes it. There is, therefore, no mystery attached to the nearly universal occurrence of sex in organisms. Those populations of organisms most able to vary have been those most able to survive changing conditions in the environment and those most able to evolve new ways of life as the opportunities arose. Sex is widespread because, like any other adaptation, it has promoted the long-term survival of the populations having it.

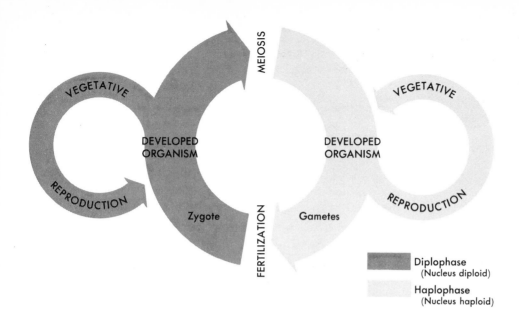

MEIOSIS

VEGETATIVE

DEVELOPED
ORGANISM

REPRODUCTION

Zygote

FERTILIZATION

Gametes

DEVELOPED
ORGANISM

VEGETATIVE

REPRODUCTION

Diplophase
(Nucleus diploid)

Haplophase
(Nucleus haploid)

FIG. 9-3 The generalized reproductive cycle.

THE HAPLOPHASE–DIPLOPHASE REPRODUCTIVE CYCLE

Most protists, a great many plants, and quite a number of animals have both asexual and sexual reproduction. In simplest form, possible combinations of reproductive cycles are generalized in Figure 9-3. The numbers and sequences of asexual and sexual cycles vary greatly. Most protists go through an asexual cycle repeatedly and then once in a while go through a single sexual cycle, followed by more asexual cycles. In animals and plants the sequences may be quite irregular. Not infrequently asexual and sexual cycles are simultaneous (in different offspring). For instance, *Hydra* often reproduces sexually and by budding at the same time.

Fertilization, which is nuclear fusion at the cellular level, is the definitive process of sexual reproduction. You have seen that fertilization must be preceded by meiosis, cell division with halving of chromosome number. Therefore the sexual cycle must include both of two key processes: meiosis and fertilization.

Meiosis and fertilization divide the whole life cycle of sexual organisms into two parts. After meiosis and before fertilization cells and organisms have a reduced number of chromosomes; they usually have n chromosomes and are haploid; this phase of the reproductive cycle is the *haplophase.* After fertilization and before meiosis they have the full complement of chromosomes: the number is usually $2n$, and they are diploid; this is the *diplophase* of the reproductive cycle.

There are three possibilities for the occurrence of developed organisms in the sexual cycle. (1) They may occur in the diplophase only. This is usual in animals, as has been noted, and common in protists. (2) They may occur in *both* the diplophase and the haplophase. This is a rare, unusual modification in animals, but it is almost universal in lower plants. There is some development of both phases in all higher plants, too, but the haplophase ordinarily consists only of a few cells. (3) Finally, they may occur only in the haplophase. This is the rarest of the three possibilities, but it does characterize some protists and lower plants, and it may be the primitive condition from which the others evolved. Note also that, wherever they occur in the sexual cycle, whether diplophase or haplophase, many developed organisms can reproduce vegetatively as well as sexually. The descriptive facts reviewed up to this point are summarized in Figure 9-3. No one organism is known to go through *all* the specific processes indicated. However, all the reproductive cycles occurring in organisms are shown in the diagram.

The valuable thing about the diagram is that it shows the biological relationships between the numerous kinds of reproductive cycles that occur among organisms. For instance, the reproductive cycles of most animals may seem to be fundamentally different from those of most plants, and they are usually so represented. Yet if, as we go along, the special cycles in plants and animals are compared with the generalized cycle, they will be seen to be fundamentally similar. The only essential difference is that in animals the cells (the haplophase) resulting from meiosis usually develop no further before fertilization

(they are simply gametes), while in plants the haplophase usually does develop somewhat further, becoming multicellular and, in some cases, may even develop into an independent organism.

Reproductive Cycles in Plants

GAMETOPHYTE AND SPOROPHYTE

The occurrence of development in the haplophase of the reproductive cycle is so nearly universal in plants and so rare in animals that this difference is even more definitive than the fact that most plants are photosynthetic. Since developed organisms commonly occur in both the haplophase and diplophase of plants (both to the right and to the left in our diagram), it is convenient to distinguish these by their technical names. The developed haplophase organism (between meiosis and fertilization and therefore haploid, or with reduced chromosome number) is called the *gametophyte* ("gamete plant") because it produces gametes. The developed diplophase organism (between fertilization and meiosis and therefore diploid) is called the *sporophyte* ("spore plant") because it produces spores. One of the striking things about reproductive cycles in plants is their great diversity in relative development of gametophyte and sporophyte.

The following examples will introduce you to this great diversity in reproductive cycles in plants.

PLANTLIKE PROTISTS

Chlamydomonas (Figure 9-4) is a single-celled photosynthetic organism. The cell, which swims around actively photosynthesizing for most of the life cycle, is haploid. It is capable of asexual reproduction in the haplophase.

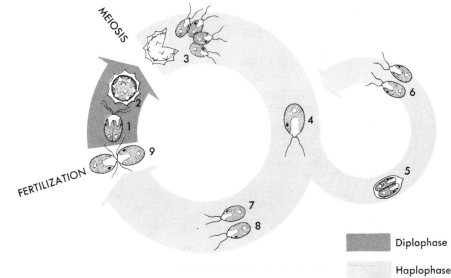

FIG. 9-4 The reproductive cycle in the protist Chlamydomonas. The diplophase is of minor significance; most of the life cycle is passed in the haplophase, which alone undergoes vegetative reproduction. 1. Young zygote. 2. Mature zygote, in which meiosis occurs. 3. Liberation of four haploid cells (products of meiosis) from the old zygote case. 4. Mature haplophase cell. 5, 6. Vegetative reproduction. 7, 8. Two haplophase cells acting as gametes. 9. Fertilization by union of the gametes.

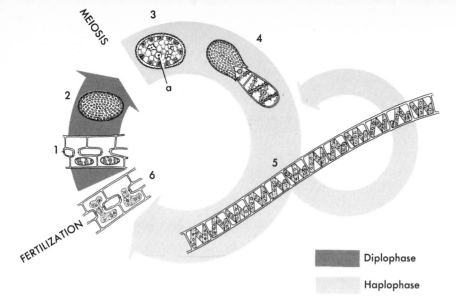

FIG. 9-5   The reproductive cycle in the green alga _Spirogyra_. As in _Chlamydomonas_, the diplophase is of minor significance; most of the life cycle is passed in the haplophase, which alone undergoes vegetative reproduction. 1. Two young zygotes in the cells of a former haplophase filament. 2. Mature zygote, which has developed its own cell wall (or case). 3. Four haploid nuclei (products of meiosis) within the old zygote case. Three of these disintegrate; one (a) develops further. 4. Young haploid filament, developed from the surviving cell in 3, germinating from the old zygote case. 5. Mature haplophase filament, which can vegetatively reproduce. 6. Conjugation of two haplophase filaments. The cytoplasm and nuclei of the cells in one conjugating filament migrate through specially developed conjugation tubes to the cells of the other conjugating filament; zygotes are formed in each cell of the latter filament.

Diplophase

Haplophase

ALGAE

Algae is a name applied to numerous plants, relatively simple in structure, almost all aquatic. Various groups of algae probably arose independently from protists; indeed, algae are classified by some as protists rather than as plants. The following examples deomonstrate diversity in reproduction in the algae.

1. In _Spirogyra_ (Figure 9-5), there is no sporophyte; the actively growing and dividing plant is a gametophyte.

2. _Ectocarpus_ (Figure 9-6) like _Ulva,_ the sea lettuce, possesses a definite sporophyte, evidencing an evolutionary trend present in all plants—a switch from the haplophase to the diplophase part of the cycle.

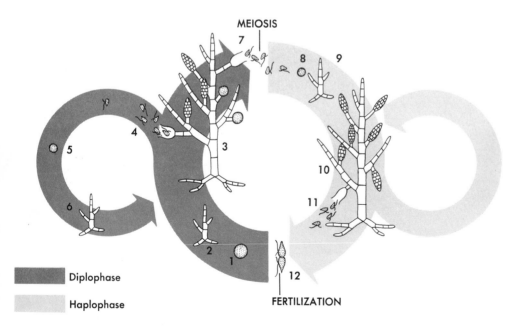

FIG. 9-6   The reproductive cycle in the brown alga _Ectocarpus_. Haplophase (gametophyte) and diplophase (sporophyte) are equally prominent and very similar. Vegetative reproduction occurs in both. 1. Zygote. 2. Young sporophyte. 3. Mature sporophyte. 4, 5. Diploid zoospores liberated from a sporangium. 6. Young sporophyte. 7, 8. Haploid zoospores (products of meiosis) liberated from a sporangium. 9. Young gametophyte. 10. Mature gametophyte. 11. Gametes being liberated from a gametophyte. 12. Fertilization.

Diplophase

Haplophase

FIG. 9-7 The reproductive cycle in the brown alga Laminaria. The diplophase is the dominant part of the cycle; a large sporophyte is developed. The gametophyte generation is a small filament of cells and occurs as two distinct sexes. 1. Fertilization: a sperm approaching a female gametophyte on which there are two egg cells, one of which has extruded from its cell wall and is ready for fertilization. 2. Female gametophyte carrying two fertilized eggs or zygotes, each of which marks the beginning of the diplophase. 3. Young sporophytes, each still consisting of only a few cells, attached to the old female gametophyte. 4. Older sporophyte. 5. Mature sporophyte, about 6 feet long. 6. Meiosis, in some surface cells of the sporophyte, liberating haploid motile spores (7) that mark the beginning of the haplophase. 8, 9. Male and female gametophytes, respectively, that have developed from the haploid spores.

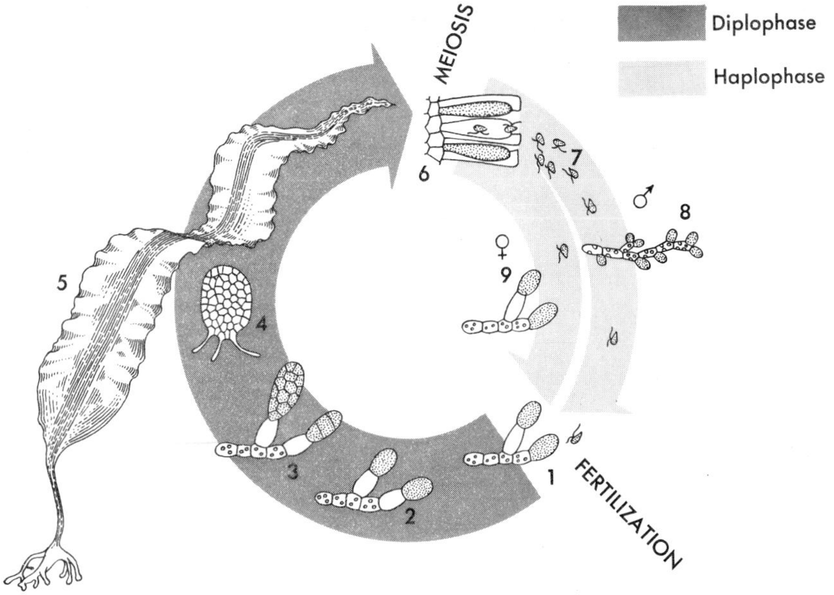

3. In *Laminaria* (Figure 9-7), the sporophyte has become more conspicuous than the gametophyte. In addition, this alga produces two different gametophytes, a male (♂) and a female (♀).

MOSSES

In mosses (Figure 9-8), the conspicuous developed organism, the one that has leaflike organs and that carries on most of the vital syntheses for the whole cycle, occurs in the haplophase; it is a gametophyte. This tendency for a conspicuous gametophyte is contrary to the trend of higher plants. Note in Figure 9-8 that mosses possess flagellated sperm. Mosses also have remarkable powers of vegetative reproduction, which occurs only in the haploid phase.

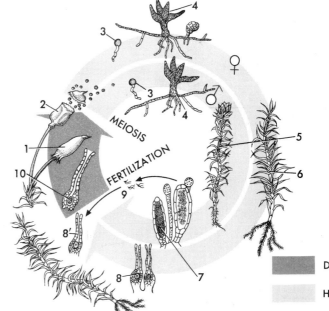

FIG. 9-8 The reproductive cycle in a moss. The haplophase (gametophyte) dominates the cycle; the sporophyte is a small structure, consisting of only a stalk and a sporangium and completely parasitic on the gametophyte. 1. Sporangium (capsule) of the sporophyte generation. 2. Liberation of haploid spores that have been produced (through meiosis) in the sporangium. 3. Germination of the spores to produce young gametophytes, which are of two distinct sexes. 4. Older gametophytes. 5. Mature male gametophyte. 6. Mature female gametophyte. 7. Male sex organ, or antheridium, which produces motile sperm (9). 8. Female sex organ, or archegonium, containing a single egg cell. 8'. Fertilization of the egg cell at the base of the flask-shaped archegonium, by the sperm (9), which swims over the surface of the female plant and eventually down the neck of the archegonium to reach the egg. 10. Zygote, marking the beginning of the diplophase, at the base of the archegonium.

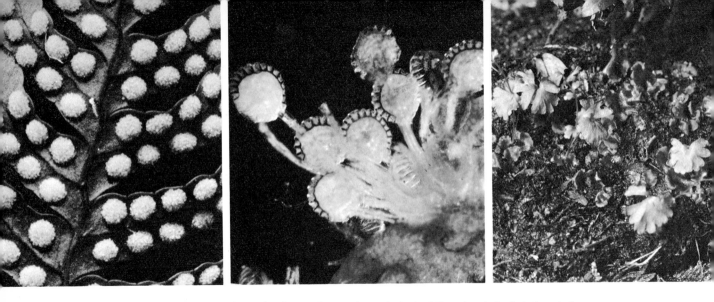

FIG. 9-9 Ferns. Left to right, clusters of sporangia on the back of the polypody fern's leaf; a single cluster of (about 10) sporangia from the Christmas fern; gametophytes. (Photos, Hugh Spencer and American Museum of Natural History)

FERNS

In ferns (Figures 9-9 and 9-10), the conspicuous leafy organism is the sporophyte. The gametophytes are seldom more than 5–6 millimeters in diameter. Like those of the mosses, the sperms are flagellated, and the sporophyte embryo starts developing on the gametophyte and is at first parasitic. But, unlike the mosses, the sporophyte soon develops its own true roots, stems, and leaves and grows as an independent plant.

SEED PLANTS

The highest plants, that is to say, those most complex and belonging to groups of most recent evolutionary origin, were derived from fernlike ancestors. In them, as in ferns, the conspicuous, vegetative plants are the sporophytes. The gametophytes

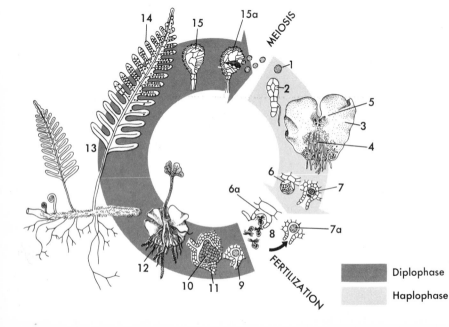

FIG. 9-10 The reproductive cycle in a fern. The diplophase (sporophyte) dominates the life cycle; the gametophyte is a small, short-lived structure bearing male and female organs. 1. Haploid spore (meiotic product) shed by the sporophyte. 2. Young gametophyte. 3. Mature gametophyte, or prothallus. 4. Antheridia (male sex organs) among rootlike structures on the underside of the gametophyte. 5. Archegonia (female sex organs). 6. Individual antheridium, liberating sperms (6a). 7. Individual archegonium with an egg cell (7a) at its base being fertilized (8) by sperm. 9. Diploid zygote at the base of the archegonium. 10. Embryo sporophyte still in the archegonium (11). 12. Young sporophyte still attached to the parent gametophyte. 13. Mature sporophyte. 14. Clusters of sporangia, on the back of the sporophyte leaf. 15. Individual sporangium bursting (15a) to yield haploid spores produced by meiosis in the sporangial cells.

Diplophase

Haplophase

are greatly reduced in number in comparison with the ferns and are microscopic in size. The female gametophyte is nutritionally dependent in the tissues of its parent sporophyte, and the free existence of the male gametophyte is only during the period when it is being transported as pollen and when little or no development occurs. These characteristics are associated with the production of seeds, in which the sporophyte embryo is enclosed with nutritive material inside a protective coat. Seeds are an adaptation to plant life in the open air and have made possible the great diversity and abundance of land plants.

FLOWERING PLANTS

The sporophyte in flowering plants, like that of ferns, bears special spore-producing organs, or sporangia. They are of two kinds, male and female. The male sporangia are *anthers,* and the female sporangia are *ovules.* These sporangia are not distributed over leaf surfaces, as they are in ferns; they are clustered together in a *flower.* Thus, the familiar flower is essentially an aggregate of sporangia surrounded by modified, often colored, leaves called *petals* and *sepals.* The significance of the (often) colored petals is something we will return to later; it is related to the problem of getting the male gametophyte from one flower to the female gametophyte of another. The reproductive cycle of a flowering plant is considered in Figure 9-11.

THE PROBLEM OF PLANT IMMOBILITY

Plants are usually anchored or rooted in place. This is one of their striking differences from most animals (although there are anchored animals, too). Their immobility is related, through the processes of evolution, to many special developments in the reproductive structures and cycles in plants.

Getting the Sexes Together

In the first place, there is the problem of sexual reproduction, which has been a condition of most progressive evolution throughout the history of life. Two immobile plants cannot get together to reproduce, as can any two mobile animals. In lower plants the immobility of the developed organisms is counteracted by the mobility of gametes. In seed plants

it is the pollen grains, partly developed male gametophytes, that are mobile. In most nonflowering seed plants pollen is produced in enormous quantities, and the grains are so light that they are spread far and wide, even for hundreds and thousands of miles, by winds and air currents. This was undoubtedly the primitive condition for the first plants that were able to rise well into the air, dispensing with a requirement for water in which gametes could be dispersed.

It is probably significant that so many plants, including the vast majority of seed plants are *hermaphroditic,* or in more strictly botanical parlance *monoecious;* that is, both sexes are present in the same individual plant. In spite of devices (reviewed below) to promote safe transmission of pollen from one plant to another, there is always a chance that this transmission will fail. Many plants can fertilize themselves; this may be viewed in broad perspective as a last resort, assuring some seed production. But self-pollination, if sustained over several generations, is effectively an abandonment of true sexuality, the essence of which is the reshuffling of different genotypes. Many plants, accordingly, have evolved quite elaborate mechanisms to assure *cross-pollination* between different individual plants. In some species the anthers of an individual plant mature before its stigma, thus minimizing the amount of (last-resort) self-pollination. The pollen is available to fertilize only other plants that are slightly ahead in their development and therefore possessed of ripe stigmas. In other species the order may be reversed; the stigma may ripen first. The effect is the same in either case.

It is especially characteristic of flowering plants that so many of them have the pollen carried by animals, usually insects but often birds or bats and occasionally other animals. It is clear that many features in the evolution of flowers are related to this complex process of pollen dissemination. Here is the biological significance of color, scent, and nectar in flowers. Nectar is a rich sugary secretion much prized as food by a host of insects—flies, butterflies, moths, bees, and so on—and also by hummingbirds and some bats. Many flower structures have evolved as guarantees that the visiting nectar-seeker will pick up and

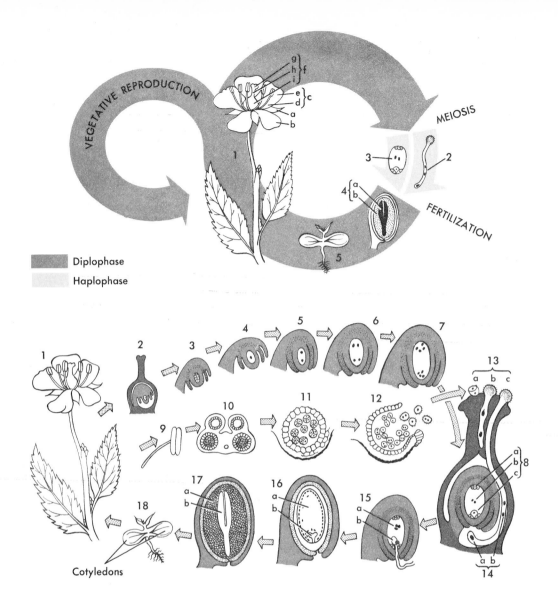

Diplophase

Haplophase

Cotyledons

transmit pollen from one flower to another in the same species. When Smyrna fig trees were first grown outside the regions where they had long been cultivated, the trees failed to produce any fruit. Eventually it was found that the reason for the failure was the absence of a particular kind of small wasp. The female wasp lays her eggs in fig flowers, which are the only places where the larval wasps develop normally, and in turn the wasp is the only means of pollinating the figs so that they bear fruit. The figs have separate male (staminate) and female (pistillate) flowers. Wasps can develop only in the male flowers. When the female wasps emerge from the flowers in which they are born, they are dusted with pollen. They then enter some other flower, lay their eggs, and die. The greatest peculiarity is this: if the female lays her eggs in a male flower, her eggs develop but no pollination occurs; if she lays them in a female flower, her eggs do not develop, but pollination occurs and fig seeds and fruit are produced. If all the wasps laid eggs in male flowers, there would soon be no more figs, and then no more wasps. But if all eggs were laid in female flowers, there would soon be no more wasps—and then no more figs.

FIG. 9-11 The reproductive cycle of a flowering plant. *Top*, broad features of the cycle. The diplophase (sporophyte) is the dominant part of the cycle. The male and female gametophytes are minute structures with a transient existence associated with fertilization. 1. Mature sporophyte with a flower: a, sepal; b, petal; c, stamen, consisting of filament (d) and anther (e); f, pistil, consisting of stigma (g), style (h), and ovary (i). 2. Pollen tube (male gametophyte) growing out of the pollen grain. 3. Embryo sac (female gametophyte). 4. Seed, containing an embryo sporophyte (a) and nutritive endosperm (b). 5. Seedling sporophyte. *Bottom*, detail of the gametophytes and fertilization. 1. Mature sporophyte with flower. 2. Young pistil. The ovary (black in the figure) is, historically speaking, a modified leaf (or leaves) folded over to enclose the sporangium (or sporangia) that it bears. This female sporangium is the ovule (gray in the figure); within the ovule is a single cell, which will undergo meiosis, producing four megaspores. 4. Ovule with the one surviving megaspore, which marks the beginning of the female gametophyte (embryo sac). 5–7. Successive mitotic divisions in the development of the female gametophyte, leading to its eight-nucleate state. 8. Mature embryo sac with eight nuclei. Three of these (a) are the antipodal nuclei; two others (b) are the future fusion nucleus; of the other three (c), the largest is the female gamete (egg cell), and the other two are sometimes thought to represent the vestigal remains of an archegonium. 9. Stamen. 10. Cross section through the anther (sporangium), which has four separate chambers; in two of these can be seen cells that will undergo meiosis, yielding microspores (pollen grains). 11. Section through a single anther chamber containing cells in which meiosis has occurred. 12. Same anther chamber at a later stage, bursting and yielding pollen grains that have already developed into young male gametophytes; their nuclei have divided. 13. Development of a pollen grain on the stigma (a), with germination of the pollen grain and growth of the male gametophyte (pollen tube) down the style to the embryo sac (female gametophyte) in the ovule (b, c). Nuclear constitution of the male gametophyte: a, tube nucleus, which is not a gamete; b, two male gametes. 15. Fertilization: a, one of the male gametes fuses with the diploid fusion nucleus of the embryo sac, producing a triploid nucleus that will later develop into the endosperm of the seed (16a); b, the other male gamete nucleus fuses with the egg cell, producing a diploid zygote that marks the beginning of the new sporophyte. 16, 17. Younger and older seeds including endosperm (a) and embryo sporophyte (b). 18. Seedling sporophyte still showing its embryonic leaves (cotyledons), of which there are two in this particular (dicotyledonous) flowering plant.

A final noteworthy point relates further to the problem of getting the sexes together. If fertilization is to occur (and therefore if the species is to persist), it is necessary that availability of pollen and access to a mature stigma be simultaneous. This would be impossible if liberation of pollen and opening of flowers with stigmas occurred at different times of the year or, in some cases, even at different hours of the day. Plants have evolved the necessary means to synchronize flowering time among individual plants in the same species population. It is commonly known that all crocuses bloom at the same time early in spring, and chrysanthemums only in the fall. But how is this timing accomplished? Many factors seem to be involved, like temperature and light intensity, but probably the most important of all is the relative length of day and night. No matter how fickle other conditions may be, the relative length of day to night is a rigorously constant signal of the season. It is the signal that usually synchronizes flowering, although in some instances flowering is affected or may be primarily controlled by temperature or, in arid regions, rainfall.

Many plants control flowering time not only as to season but also as to time of day. Their flowers

open and close rhythmically with a 24-hour frequency controlled by some internal timing device that establishes opening time at a fixed hour relative to dawn. Bees make use of the fact and economize on time and effort by visiting the right flowers at the right time of day.

Dispersal

So much for the problem of getting sexes together in biparental reproduction. There is the further question of how plants spread geographically. In lower plants dispersal usually occurs in the spore phase of the cycle, and in those plants spores can develop into independent organisms. Like their motile gametes, the spores of algae are water-borne and are often motile, having flagella. Fungi and ferns produce clouds of light spores that are carried by air currents far and wide, a few of them even for thousands of miles. The air you breathe is seldom free of spores. In seed plants the spores as such do not leave the parent organism (only pollen, which cannot by itself produce a new plant as spores can). For them dispersal is by means of seeds. The great success of the seed plants is clearly related to two characteristics of seeds: they protect the embryo through a dormant period and during times of drought or cold, and they are readily dispersed.

Adaptations for dispersal in seeds are as varied as those for pollination in flowers. Dandelions and many other plants have parachute seeds scattered by winds. Burrs stick to passing animals. Tempting fruits have hard-coated seeds that pass unharmed through the digestive systems of fruit-eaters. Coconuts and man-groves have floating seeds, resistant to long voyages in the currents of the sea. Vetches and a number of other plants have pods that open suddenly and scatter seeds like the fragments of a grenade. In Russian thistles—the tumbleweeds of Western song—the globular plant breaks off from its roots and rolls across the countryside, scattering seeds as it goes. Can you think of other ways in which seeds are dispersed?

Most individual plants are immobile as developed organisms, but seed dispersal is so effective that *populations* of plants may spread more widely and rapidly than populations of mobile animals.

Reproductive Cycles in Animals

DOMINANCE OF THE DIPLOPHASE

We have seen that both within the algae (most lowly of plants) and in the plant kingdom as a whole, there has been a strong evolutionary tendency to emphasize the diplophase (sporophyte). In the seed plants the haplophase has been greatly reduced. What is the significance of this trend? The answer is not entirely clear, but it probably involves two factors. First, an organism with a double set of chromosomes has a more complex and probably as a rule a more adaptively flexible biochemical system. Duplication of genes may not only be a sort of "fail safe" provision but may also, when there are different alleles, provide alternative means of maintaining homeostasis under fluctuating conditions. Second, populations of diploid organisms can store more genetic variability than populations of haploid organisms. Diploid organisms have therefore probably been favored for the same general reasons that sex itself was favored.

The usual reproductive cycle in animals is that familiar to you in man; there is no analogue of a gametophyte. Modifications of that cycle relate mainly to secondary regression in sexuality and to addition of vegetative (asexual) reproduction in the diplophase of the basic cycle (Figure 9-12). Both of these proc-esses are less common in animals than in plants, but they also occur rather widely in animals. Other

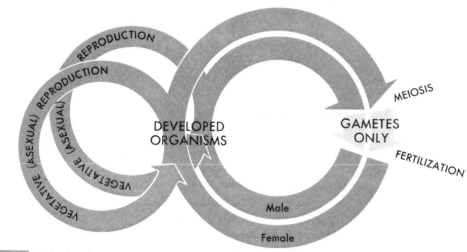

FIG. 9-12 **Generalized animal re-productive cycle.** No analogue of the gametophyte generation in plants exists in animals; the haplophase is represented by the gametes only. (There is one re-markable exception to the generaliza-tion in this figure; male bees and other Hymenoptera are haploid.)

Diplophase

Haplophase

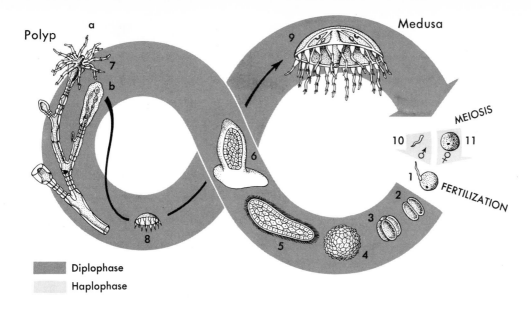

Polyp
Medusa

MEIOSIS

FERTILIZATION

■ Diplophase
□ Haplophase

FIG. 9-13 The reproductive cycle in coelenterates like Obelia. There is a so-called ''alternation of generations'' (medusa–polyp–medusa–polyp, etc.) in certain coelenterates like *Obelia*. However, this is not at all comparable to the alternation of sporophyte and gametophyte in plants; in coelenterates both polyp and medusa are diplophase. As in other animals, the haplophase is represented by the gametes only. 1. Fertilization—union of egg and sperm. 2–4. Successive stages in the cleavage of the egg and growth of the embryo. 5. Ciliated swimming larva. 6. Larva metamorphosing into a polyp adult. 7. Adult colony of polyps: a, feeding polyp; b, reproductive polyp, which asexually buds off medusas. 8. Young, free-swimming medusa. 9. Adult medusa, which produces sperms (10) and eggs (11).

evolutionary changes in reproduction and life histories in animals have involved not so much the over-all reproductive *cycle* as the structures and processes of reproduction and development. In these respects animals are extremely diverse.

SEXUAL PLUS VEGETATIVE REPRODUCTION

Vegetative reproduction is lacking in human beings and in the animals most familiar to us, the other vertebrates, but some animals do reproduce vegetatively. Such reproduction is not the rule for animals, and there are few—perhaps no—animal species in which it is the *sole* means of reproduction. Nevertheless, it does occur in many different kinds of invertebrates and even in tunicates, animals related to the vertebrates. Vegetative reproduction in animals is usually by budding (as in *Hydra*) or by fission (as in planarians), processes not always clearly distinguishable. In some insects a mass of cells formed early in embryonic development may bud off into many smaller clumps, each of which develops into a separate organism.

In many coelenterates, relatives of the jellyfishes, sexual and vegetative reproduction alternate regularly. In *Obelia* (Figure 9-13), a classic example, the zygote develops through a larval stage into an attached individual that grows into a branched colony of polyps by budding without separation. Parts of the colony then produce further buds that do become detached and that swim off as medusas, which look like small jellyfishes.

FERTILIZATION

Almost all animals produce specialized and sharply distinct female and male gametes: relatively large, approximately spherical eggs, immobile except as they may be passively moved by surrounding fluids, and relatively small, tailed or flagellated sperms, actively motile. The egg may remain attached within the maternal tissues until it is fertilized and starts to develop, as is usual in plants and, among animals, in sponges. Much more often in animals the egg is detached from the maternal tissues before fertilization, although it may remain in cavities or passages in the maternal body and the developing organism may even, as in man, become reattached.

In the majority of aquatic invertebrates—American oysters will serve as a concrete example—both eggs and sperm are simply shed into the water. There some of the swimming sperms, so enormously numerous that the water may be milky with them, eventually encounter eggs. Fertilization and development follow, with no special relationship to the parents. There are, however, innumerable modifications and complications of this simple process. In European oysters, for example, the eggs are retained in cavities in the mother, and are there fertilized and develop into larvae. In some fresh-water clams the eggs, after leaving the ovary in which they are formed, are retained under the gills. Water currents passed through the gills draw in sperms, which fertilize the eggs. Development of small larvae proceeds, still within the interior of the gills. After being expelled, the larvae die unless they encounter a fish on the fins or gills of which they live as parasites until they have developed far enough to take up independent life.

In many fishes also—indeed, in an extremely wide range of aquatic animals—eggs and sperms are shed into the surrounding water, where fertilization occurs. This seems, and sometimes is, an extremely haphazard process (Figure 9-14). A small pond, not to mention an ocean, is a vast volume in which a sperm can wander and never contact an egg. Animals have evolved, as have plants, a variety of devices that synchronize their sexual activity and so reduce the chance of wasting gametes. Most have seasonal periods of sexual acitivty, just as flowers are seasonal. And as in the flowering plants, many animals achieve synchronized seasonal reproductive activity by responding to day-night length as a reliable season marker. Of course, this is not a conscious recognition; the relative lengths of day and night act as purely physiological triggers to initiate sexual activity. Many animals, again like plants, also use internal timing devices—they have been metaphorically called "clocks"—to synchronize activity more finely to time of month and day. Thus many marine animals release their gametes on a 28-day cycle in relation to a particular moon phase. The palolo worm in Pacific coral reefs makes the sea milky with eggs and sperm, but only at full moon.

FIG. 9-14 A frog: life cycle involving external fertilization. 1. Fertilized egg. 2-4. Early cleavage of the egg. 5, 6. Later embryonic stages. 7. Young larva (tadpole). 8, 9. Older larvae with legs. 10. Young frog metamorphosing from larva, still with a vestige of tail. 11. Fully metamorphosed frog. 12. Adults spawning in water: eggs are shed by the female; the male, clasping the female from above, ejects sperm onto the eggs outside the female and free in the water. Thus begins another life cycle.

In addition to these broad physiological processes which tend to synchronize sexual activity, motile animals have evolved elaborate behavioral adaptations that synchronize their release of gametes. Males and females may be stimulated to expel gametes only in the presence of each other. There may even be a more or less elaborate *courtship* that has the result that eggs and sperms are discharged at the same time and place.

Fertilization is possible only in watery surroundings and with eggs that do not have a complete tough coating. Such a coating excludes sperms. An egg without a coating, a shell of some kind, must be surrounded by fluid or it dries and dies. Fluid is also a necessary medium through which sperms may swim and reach eggs. Fertilization cannot take place in the open air, where an egg without a shell rapidly dies and where a living sperm cannot reach the egg. The same limitations apply for the same reasons to fertilization in plants, and the limitations are really overcome in the same way in land plants and land animals, even though the organs and acitvities are so different in the two: in both, fertilization takes place within the maternal organism. In the immobile higher plants, as you know, the male gamete is brought to the egg (somewhat indirectly) by the mobility of the pollen. Land animals are mobile and, in simpler fashion, the male takes the sperms to the female and injects them into her: copulation occurs. In all animals fully adapted to life on dry land, notably insects, reptiles, birds, and mammals, fertilization is internal following copulation. In insects the shell is formed before fertilization, but there is a small hole in the shell through which a sperm enters. In reptiles and birds the shell forms after fertilization. In (true) mammals no shell forms, the zygote and resulting embryo being retained within the mother.

Copulation entails anatomical specializations. The male must have an organ (a penis) that can be inserted into the female and through which sperms are ejected. The female must have a receptacle from which the sperms can move to the eggs through a fluid internal medium. In insects but not in vertebrates there is an additional specialization. The females have sacs within which sperms are retained and kept alive for considerable periods of time. Copulation occurs only once, and thereafter sperms are released from the sacs whenever fertilized eggs are to be laid. The queen bee is an extreme case; she copulates only once

and stores the sperms received for the rest of her life, sometimes as long as 17 years.

EVOLUTION OF VERTEBRATE REPRODUCTION

There have been many different lines of evolution, and they have led to many and highly diverse specialized kinds of reproductive structures and processes. Even among the vertebrates there are myriad different lines of descent, leading to markedly different reproductive systems among recent animals. Of course, too, no species now living are in the lines ancestral to man, nor are they likely to have retained precisely the conditions that did occur in the human ancestry. Nevertheless, comparison of them in the light of phylogeny as revealed by fossils permits highly probable inference as to the course followed in the evolution of human reproduction. In this history there has been a trend toward greater protection and care of the embryo and young, and a major transformation connected with the change from water to land life.

Transition to completely terrestrial life in early reptiles involved many changes. Fertilization became internal, following copulation. The fertilized egg (a zygote soon becoming an embryo) was enclosed in a protective shell before being laid. Within the shell a membrane developed from the embryonic tissues and formed a fluid-filled sac enclosing the embryo proper, which thus continued to develop in a self-contained aquatic environment. Other membranes formed sacs and surfaces aiding in respiration, in absorption of food within the egg, in storage of waste materials, and in further protection of the whole complex inside of the shell. That is the reptilian condition, retained with variations in the reptiles still living.

In the gradual transition from early reptiles to advanced mammals, the eggs were retained during development in the lower (or posterior) parts of the tubes leading from the ovaries to the exterior. These parts of the tubes became enlarged and thickened to form *uteri* (singular, uterus). (In man and some other mammals the two paired uteri have fused into one medial uterus.) The egg shell was reduced and eventually lost. Then the membranes of the embryo came in direct contact with the wall of the uterus and began to exchange substances with that wall by diffusion. Oxygen and dissolved foodstuffs were absorbed from the uterus, and carbon dioxide and wastes such as urea were given off to it. Finally, this exchange was made most effective by a complex intergrowth of tissues from the embryo and those in the wall of the uterus, forming a *placenta*. In the placenta, capillaries from the maternal and the embryonic circulatory system come into close contact,

although normally there is no exchange of blood but only of dissolved substances by diffusion. Special vessels, which become inoperative at birth, connect the embryo with the placenta.

In the meantime, special provision for the young after birth was also evolving. Even before the eggs were retained in the uterus, *mammary glands* yielding milk arose in females and provided a rich, balanced liquid diet for the newborn. Finally, in man, even after the child is weaned, there is a long period of mental and social training by the parents.

Parental care is an extremely useful adaptation because it promotes survival of the next generation at the most dangerous period in life. It is therefore not surprising that parental care, extreme in man, is by no means confined to man but has evolved over and over again. The meticulous care given to larvae in the hives of bees and the nests of ants is well known. Although parental care cannot be considered characteristic of lower vertebrates, it does occur among numerous fishes, amphibians, and reptiles. In some form or other, it is characteristic and indeed universal among birds and mammals.

Mammalian Reproduction

Man is a fairly typical higher mammal as regards reproduction and may be used as our example. The organs involved are shown in Figure 9-15. Sperms develop in large numbers in the testicles and are stored in the coiled tubes of the epididymis and the connecting ducts. The seminal vesicles and prostate gland secrete fluid in which the sperms are transported. Prior to copulation, the penis becomes stiff and erect by the pressure of blood temporarily trapped in its internal tissues. It is then inserted into the female vagina. Frictional stimulation leads to a sudden reflex ejaculation of semen (sperms and fluid) through the urethra in the penis and out into the vagina. The sperms are motile and tend to move from the vagina through the uterus and thence up the uterine tubes. If an egg is encountered in one of the tubes, fertilization is likely to occur.

Eggs develop and ripen, usually one at a time in humans, in small, bubble-like structures, follicles (Figure 9-16), in the ovaries. When an egg is mature, the follicle bursts, releasing the egg, which normally passes into the funnel-like end of the uterine tube. If there are no live sperms there at the time, the egg disintegrates or passes on down the tube, through

FIG. 9-15 Human reproduction: I. Genitalia. A. Female. B. Male. These are drawn in longitudinal section, with the anterior to the left.

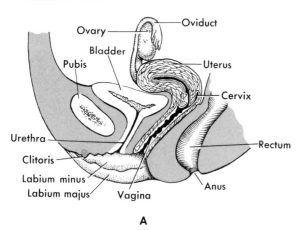

Ovary
Oviduct
Bladder
Pubis
Uterus
Cervix
Urethra
Rectum
Clitoris
Labium minus
Anus
Labium majus
Vagina

A

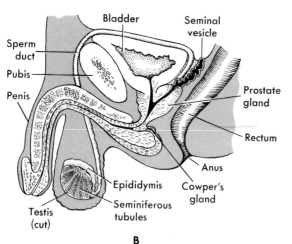

Bladder
Seminal vesicle
Sperm duct
Pubis
Penis
Prostate gland
Rectum
Anus
Epididymis
Cowper's gland
Testis (cut)
Seminiferous tubules

B

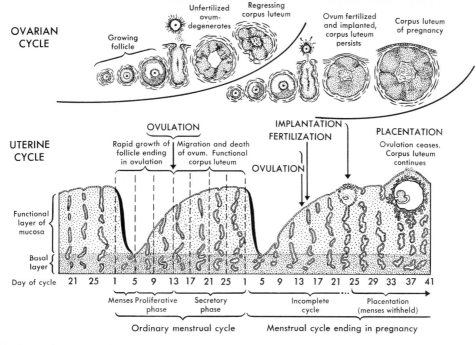

OVARIAN CYCLE

Growing follicle

Unfertilized ovum-degenerates

Regressing corpus luteum

Ovum fertilized and implanted, corpus luteum persists

Corpus luteum of pregnancy

UTERINE CYCLE

OVULATION

Rapid growth of follicle ending in ovulation

Migration and death of ovum. Functional corpus luteum

IMPLANTATION
FERTILIZATION

OVULATION

PLACENTATION

Ovulation ceases. Corpus luteum continues

Functional layer of mucosa

Basal layer

Day of cycle   21 25 1   5   9 13 17 21 25 1   5   9 13 17 21 25 29 33 37 41

Menses Proliferative phase   Secretory phase

Incomplete cycle

Placentation (menses withheld)

Ordinary menstrual cycle

Menstrual cycle ending in pregnancy

FIG. 9-16 Human reproduction: II. The ovarian and uterine cycle. The figure outlines the changes that occur in the ovary and in the wall of the uterus (1) during an ordinary menstrual cycle and (2) during a menstrual cycle that includes fertilization and ends in pregnancy. 1. The ordinary cycle in the ovary involves the growth of a follicle with its contained egg cell or ovum. When its growth is complete, the follicle bursts, discharging the ovum from the ovary; this event of ovulation occurs, on the average, on the fourteenth day of the cycle. If the ovum fails to be fertilized in the oviduct, it degenerates. After ovulation the old follicle undergoes a special development into a corpus luteum (yellow body). There is a parallel cycle of change in the wall of the uterus. The uterine cycle is indeed controlled, through hormones, by the ovarian cycle. While the follicle is growing in the ovary, the female sex hormone estrogen is secreted into the blood stream; it stimulates development of a special functional layer (the endometrium) of the uterine wall. This layer is richly supplied with blood vessels and built, so to speak, in anticipation of fertilization and the implantation on it of an embryo to be nourished. After ovulation the corpus luteum that develops from the old follicle secretes another hormone, progesterone, which maintains the growth of the endometrium. In the ordinary menstrual cycle (no fertilization), the corpus luteum eventually degenerates, and the endometrium is shed with a loss of blood during a 4- or 5-day period, the menses. The whole cycle is renewed as another follicle develops in the ovary and estrogen is again secreted, causing the endometrium to regrow. 2. If ovulation is followed by fertilization, the sequence of events is different. The fertilized egg becomes implanted in the endometrial layer of the uterus, and a placenta develops (Fig. 9-17). Following placentation, ovulation ceases because the high progesterone level in the blood (maintained by the corpus luteum, which does not, this time, degenerate) causes the pituitary to stop secreting the gonadotropic hormone that stimulates follicle growth. Menstruation does not occur, owing to the high progesterone level, and the endometrium is retained as a functional part of the placenta.

uterus and vagina to the exterior. The egg is so small that its passage is usually wholly unnoticeable. If the egg encounters live sperms in the uterine tube, fertilization is likely to occur (Figure 9-17). Development begins in the tube and continues as the embryo slowly passes on down the tube into the uterus. There the embryo becomes embedded in the wall of the uterus, in due course a placenta is formed, and development of the young (gestation) proceeds. After some time (21 days in mice, 9 months in humans) intra-uterine development is complete; then the muscular walls of the uterus contract rhythmically, expelling the young through the vagina and then tearing the placenta loose and expelling it.

The Estrus Cycle

In most male mammals mature sperms are produced and sex hormone secretion is intense only at certain times during the year. Sexual desire and behavior are strongly influenced by hormone concentration, and it is only during these periods that the male is ready and willing to copulate. Similarly in

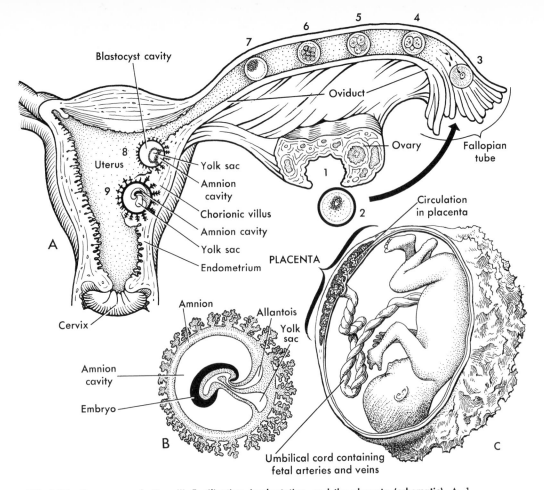

FIG. 9-17 Human reproduction: III. Fertilization, implantation, and the placenta (schematic). A. 1, 2. Liberation of an egg from a follicle in the ovary, which shows corpora lutea. 3. Fertilization of the egg in the oviduct shortly after it has entered (during ovulation the ovary is pressed closely to the mouth of the oviduct). 4–7. Cleavage stages. 8, 9. Embryo, with its amnion cavity already clear, implanting on the endometrium of the uterine wall. The chorion of the embryo has developed fingerlike villi that burrow deep into the endometrium and serve as the embryo's agents of exchange of nutrients and wastes with the maternal tissues of the placenta. B. The implanted embryo. C. An advanced fetus in the uterus, with the umbilical cord leading to and from the placenta and carrying the fetal circulation.

most female mammals, eggs mature in ripening follicles once or a few times a year. Simultaneously sex hormone secretion increases and is greatest at about the time when eggs are released from the ovary, the only time when most female mammals are willing, or anxious, to copulate. They are then said to be in *heat*. The whole process of buildup and drop in hormone concentration, ripening of follicles and release of eggs, and simultaneous changes in the uterus is called the *estrus cycle*.

As regards that cycle humans are aberrant mammals. In men maturation of sperms and secretion of sex hormones is approximately continuous from early adolescence with decreasing vigor into old age. Women have an estrus cycle, as do other female mammals, but this cycle is unusual in that it has constant periods of about 28 days instead of occurring a limited number of times at definite seasons. The cycle in women is continuous from early adolescence until the late forties or early fifties except during pregnancies. The main features of the human female cycle are summarized in Figure 9-16. Fertilization can occur only shortly after release of an egg from its follicle and, although highly variable, that usually happens in women about midway between menstruations.

Summary

The generalized reproductive cycle: asexual reproduction—vegetative propogation and spore production; sexual reproduction—the production and union (fertilization) of haploid gametes, forming a diploid zygote that initiates a new generation.

Distribution and significance of sex in organisms: sex as a phenomenon distinct from and added to the basic (asexual) process of reproduction; its evolutionary function in producing adaptive flexibility and genetic recombination.

The haplophase–diplophase reproductive cycle: haplophase initiated by meiosis and concluded by fertilization; diplophase initiated by fertilization and concluded by meiosis; major variations on the haplophase–diplophase reproductive cycle.

Reproductive cycles in plants generally: gametophyte and sporophyte as the developed organisms of the haplophase and diplophase, respectively; the reproductive cycles of green protists, algae, mosses, and ferns, showing an increasing evolutionary emphasis on the sporophyte (diplophase).

Reproduction of seed plants: the flower as a reproductive organ; sepals and petals, modified leaves, functionally related to effecting pollination; anthers, male sporangia; ovules, female sporangia; the ovary, formed by leaflike structures bearing the ovules; the embryo sac and the pollen tube as much reduced (vestigial) female and male gametophytes; seeds as ovules containing the embryonic sporophytes and food reserves (endosperm and embryonic leaves); fruits as modified ovaries or other flower parts containing seeds.

Reproductive problems inherent in the immobility of plants: (1) getting the sexes together; insects as agents for carrying pollen; devices that ensure cross-pollination; (2) the dispersal of seeds; adaptations with wind, animals, and insects as dispersal agents.

Reproductive cycles in animals: the dominance of the diplophase, asexual reproduction in the diplophase of animals; the alternation of generations in coelenterates entirely *within* the diplophase.

Fertilization in animals: external fertilization in aquatic animals; devices that ensure the simultaneous release of male and female gametes; synchronization with the moon; synchronization by mutual stimulation in courtship; internal fertilization as mainly an adaptation to land life.

Evolution of vertebrate reproduction: the reptilian evolution of internal fertilization and egg adaptations (membranes, shell) suited to land life; the reproductive specialization of mammals—live birth.

Mammalian reproduction: gametes; copulation; fertilization in the oviduct; implantation of the embryo in the uterine wall; formation of a placenta—its function in nourishing the fetus; the estrus cycle in women and other female mammals.

CHAPTER TEN

THE ORGANISM: MAINTENANCE AND INTEGRATION: I

The metabolism of energy and materials surveyed in Chapter 4 is the economy not only of cells but also of whole organisms and communities of organisms. It is the economy of life. Living systems differ only in their methods of fulfilling the fundamental energetic and synthetic requirements that they have in common. There are two broad, and never completely separate, categories of differences. The first, most fully exemplified by the difference between a green plant and an animal (that is, between an autotroph and a heterotroph), has to do with the degree of dependence on prefabricated sources of energy and materials. The second is related to the size of the living system. In the individual cell the procurement, transportation, and processing of raw materials is manifestly a different problem from that in a large multicellular organism like a man or an oak tree. The total economy—the living system—is confronted with new technical problems as it grows in size. For example, the internal distances to be traversed become so great that transportation can no longer be entrusted to simple diffusion and protoplasmic streaming. Specialized systems for the mass movement of products, parts, and raw materials play a novel and major role in the economy of the multicellular organism.

These differences among living systems—plant or animal, large or small—do not obscure a fundamental similarity in their ultimate material needs. In this chapter, and the next, on the maintenance of the whole organism, you will recognize that, when we discuss diverse modes of digestion, assimilation, respiration, transportation, and excretion, we are discussing diverse ways of achieving ends already familiar from our study of the individual cell.

You also noted from your study of the cell that processes within the cell were orderly and worked together toward a common end: preservation of the cell. This same principle applies at the organismal level, and in the next chapter we will consider various mechanisms of coordination and control.

Procurement Processes

INTAKE

The passage of materials through an organic metabolic system begins when they are taken into the organism. The most widespread method of intake of animals is the one we have ourselves: solids and liquids are taken into a tube, the *alimentary canal,* running through the body. Figure 10-1 outlines the alimentary canal in man and identifies its parts. Within the alimentary canal, parts of the solids go into solution, and liquids and substances in solution are absorbed through the wall of the tube.

Among the animals that take solid food into an alimentary canal there are many different systems for the actual acquisition of the food. Without attempting to consider all the details at this point, we can distinguish three main groups. (1) Some eat sizable plants and animals or chunks of them (Figure 10-1). (2) Many animals, however, eat food in particles very small in comparison with the animals themselves. These animals have filters to catch food, which is then swallowed whole in filtered masses (Figure 10-2). (3) There are some animals, fewer than those with other feeding habits, that simply take in samples of their whole environment, digest any food in it, and

FIG. 10-1   The alimentary canal in man. A–C. Stages in the passage of food through the mouth cavity and pharynx; the epiglottis prevents the passage of food into the larynx and, hence, into the lungs. D. The alimentary canal in relation to other internal organs in man. E. Part of the alimentary canal. (From *Biology: Its Human Implications*, 2nd ed., by Garrett Hardin. W. H. Freeman and Company. Copyright © 1952; after Sturtevant and Beadle)

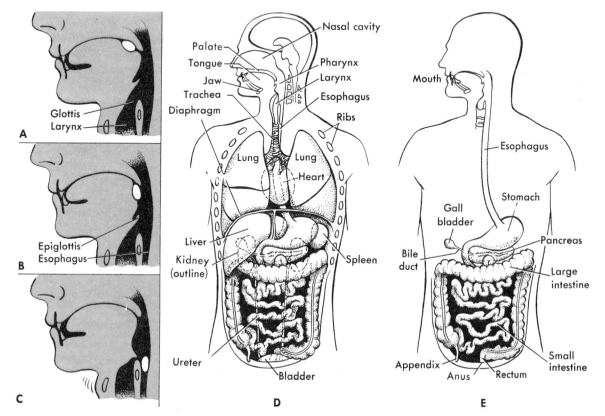

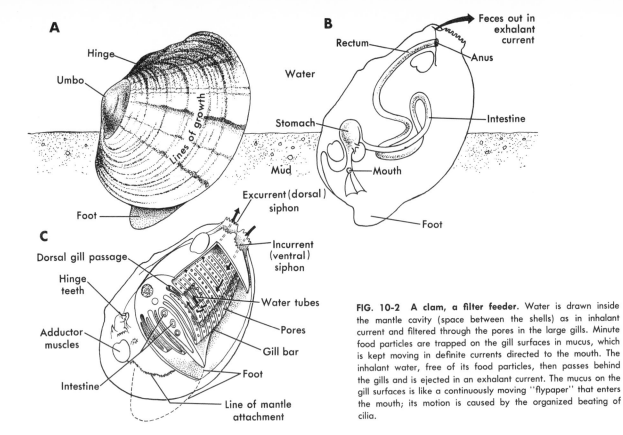

A

Hinge

Umbo

Lines of growth

Foot

Water

Mud

B

Rectum

Feces out in exhalant current

Anus

Stomach

Intestine

Mouth

Foot

C

Dorsal gill passage

Hinge teeth

Adductor muscles

Intestine

Excurrent (dorsal) siphon

Incurrent (ventral) siphon

Water tubes

Pores

Gill bar

Foot

Line of mantle attachment

FIG. 10-2 A clam, a filter feeder. Water is drawn inside the mantle cavity (space between the shells) as in inhalant current and filtered through the pores in the large gills. Minute food particles are trapped on the gill surfaces in mucus, which is kept moving in definite currents directed to the mouth. The inhalant water, free of its food particles, then passes behind the gills and is ejected in an exhalant current. The mucus on the gill surfaces is like a continuously moving "flypaper" that enters the mouth; its motion is caused by the organized beating of cilia.

evacuate the rest. Earthworms, for example, pass bits of whole earth through the alimentary canal.

Protists absorb water and dissolved materials directly through the body membrane. The body membrane is analogous to a cell membrane, if not exactly the same thing, and of course the absorption involves diffusion, active transport, and osmosis. It is really the same sort of process as absorption by cells lining the tube or sac—the alimentary canal—in multicellular animals. Many protists, especially some of those

that are often called animals, also take in solid food. They eat other protists and even small multicellular organisms, just as man eats plants and animals—although they often do not bother to kill their food before eating it. The solid food of protists is simply surrounded or captured by various devices. Some protists utilize solid food without actually taking it into the body for digestion. They secrete digestive fluid onto food outside the body wall and then absorb the dissolved products. Many starfishes and some other

FIG. 10-3 Carnivorous plants. Left to right, Venus' flytrap, Dionaea (natural size). Pitcher plant, Sarracenia (one-third natural size). Sundew, Drosera (slightly reduced in size). (Photos, Hugh Spencer)

multicellular animals do essentially the same thing. A few plants take in solid food in a way quite similar to that of carnivorous animals. These plants, including the pitcher plant, sundew, and Venus's flytrap, have modified leaves that trap insects (Figure 10-3).

The overwhelming majority of plants take in materials in only one way: by diffusion through the cell walls and membranes. In aquatic plants all materials, including water itself, are acquired from the water solution surrounding them. In terrestrial plants water and dissolved salts are acquired mainly by diffusion into root hairs and other cells on the surface of the roots. The other needed materials, oxygen and carbon dioxide, diffuse from their gaseous condition in the atmosphere into solution within cells of aerial parts, especially leaves. The intake of oxygen is part of the process of respiration, which will be discussed as a separate topic. Carbon dioxide, however, is a raw material for food.

Separate problems are involved in the diffusion into plant roots of water and its dissolved inorganic materials (mineral salts). Water is pulled into the roots by osmosis. Figure 10-4 is a schematic section across a plant root from its hair cells to its xylem vessels. Suppose, first, that all the cells along the path from hair to xylem have the same osmotic pressure (Chapter 3). The pressure in the cells is much higher than that of the soil water because of the high concentration of sugars and salts in the cell. Water is consequently drawn by osmotic pressure into the root hair cell, slightly lowering its osmotic value. The hair cell then yields water to the adjacent cell inside the root which has a higher osmotic value. This continues across the whole cortex (outer layer) of the plant to the xylem, into which the soil's water is pumped by the gradient of osmotic pressure. The pressure developed by this gradient of osmotic values across the root is often very great.

The movement into root hairs of dissolved substances in the soil water raises quite different problems. Where the incoming salt is immediately consumed in some synthesis or is bound to protein colloids in the cytoplasm, its concentration as a free molecule (or ion) in the cell may be kept very low. The cell is then assured of continued simple diffusion of the salt from higher concentrations in the soil to the lower concentrations in the cytoplasm. In some plants, however, the cell requires concentrations of salts above

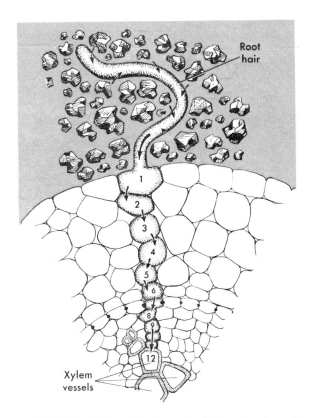

Root hair

Xylem vessels

FIG. 10-4 Water uptake by roots. Water enters the root hair by osmosis from the soil and then follows an osmotic gradient through successive cells (1–11) until it reaches a vessel (12).

those found in soil water. It has then to expend energy—in a manner still unknown—to pull salts into the cell against a concentration gradient.

In general, then, the ultimate, most common method of intake is absorption from aqueous solution.

DIGESTION

The principal feature of digestion is that it transforms foods into forms that can readily be absorbed. Substances insoluble in water or with very large molecules or in large globules cannot as a rule be absorbed; they usually cannot pass through the membranes that surround cells and vacuoles. Most foods fall into these classes of substances difficult or impossible to absorb. Simple carbohydrates (sugars) are generally soluble in water and are readily absorbed, but polysaccharides such as starch are water insoluble. So are lipids. Proteins are large molecules to which cell membranes are ordinarily impermeable. It appears, therefore, that most of the more complex compounds built up in cells cannot be passed on to other cells unless they are torn down again.

Most of the chemical reactions of digestion have the net effect of reversing the synthetic processes described in Chapter 4. All of the syntheses ultimately involve a linking together of molecules with the elimination of water. Digestion in general is the opposite process—a hydrolysis, or separation of molecules through the addition of the elements of water to them.

We normally think of digestion as the first operation after food is taken into the organism from outside. Exactly the same reactions, however, occur within almost all body cells whenever insoluble or colloidal materials pass into them from other cells. In biological terms, the reactions are digestion whether they occur at the first intake of food or later on. For example, the first digestion of a polysaccharide (usually starch) converts it to simple sugars, which

are carried to the liver and there resynthesized into another polysaccharide (glycogen), which in turn is later digested in the liver cells to simple sugars and passed on to other parts of the body.

Digestive Enzymes

Enzymes catalyze all the hydrolytic reactions of digestion. Usually they are not the same enzymes as those involved in the corresponding synthesis. Since digestion actually proceeds as a series of small steps, what is summarized as a single reaction may require a number of different enzymes. Unlike ordinary enzymes, which are found only within cells in minute quantities, the digestive enzymes of the animal alimentary canal are poured into the gut from surrounding cells in relatively large amounts—and in fairly simple mixtures. Thus they have been extraordinarily well studied. Table 10-1 lists some of the enzymes participating in human digestion.

Two solutions important in human digestion are *not* enzymes. First, the gastric juice in the stomach is a strong solution of *hydrochloric acid*. Pepsin, the principal enzyme of the stomach, is not effective unless it is in acid solution. (Some other enzymes, such as trypsin, require an alkaline environment; acid from the stomach is neutralized by alkaline secretions when the food passes into the duodenum.) Second, bile from the liver is, in part, a solution of *bile salts*. These are poured into the small intestine, where they help

TABLE 10-1   *Some Digestive Enzymes in Man*

Source of enzyme	Enzyme	Substances acted upon	Products of digestion
Salivary glands	Salivary amylase	Polysaccharides (cooked starch and glycogen)	Disaccharide (maltose)
Stomach glands	Pepsin	Proteins	Peptides
	Rennin	Milk casein	Clotted casein (curds)
Pancreas	Trypsin Chymotrypsin Carboxypeptidase	Proteins and peptides	Amino acids
	Pancreatic amylase	Starch	Maltose
	Lipase	Triglycerides	Fatty acids, glycerol, and monoglycerides
Small intestine	Peptidase	Peptides	Amino acids
	Sucrase Maltase Lactase	Disaccharides	Monosaccharides

to break up fats into small globules, forming an emulsion. This action does not change the fats chemically, but it puts them in a condition in which chemical reaction (catalyzed by lipase) occurs more readily.

Since the alimentary canal digests meat in the stomach and in the upper part of the small intestine (the duodenum), one might ask why it does not digest itself. Obviously it must have a lining that is not normally susceptible to the action of the digestive juices, but just why it is not susceptible is far from clear. In fact the juices of the stomach and duodenum do sometimes digest parts of their walls: the result is an ulcer. That ulcers and, more commonly, indigestion may be brought on by anxiety or nervousness illustrates the great complexity of interactions in an integrated organism.

Enzymes like those in the human digestive system occur widely among other animals. Similar, though not necessarily identical, enzymes, catalyzing the digestion of similar substrates, occur in both plants and animals.

Digestive Systems

Since green plants are autotrophs—that is, they do not take in complex organic foods but make their own—they have no special systems or organs for digestion, save for carnivorous plants. Nevertheless, digestion does occur in green plants. It is necessary if food manufactured or stored in one cell is to be passed along to another cell, and it may occur in any plant cell when food, enzymes, and the other necessary conditions exist. Such digestion within a cell, also common in animals, is called *intracellular* digestion.

In nongreen plants, which obtain food from the outside, the actual reactions and processes of digestion are essentially the same, but the procedure is different. For example, *Rhizopus nigricans,* the common bread mold (Figure 10-5), is a fungus that grows on bread, cake, and other foods at room temperature. Digestion in *Rhizopus nigricans* is similar to the way in which humans and other animals digest solid food: it is *extracellular,* or outside the cells. Indeed, it is outside the organism, strictly speaking. Some protists have permanent mouths, and a few have permanent anuses, but most have no special digestive organs at all (Figure 10-6A). In the group of animals to which

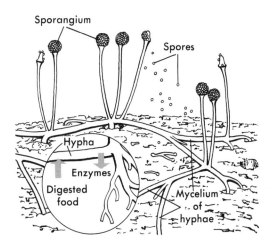

FIG. 10-5 Extracellular digestion by the bread mold *Rhizopus.* The body of the mold consists of a branching system (or mycelium) of threadlike structures, the hyphae. Enzymes produced by the hyphal protoplasm are secreted to the outside, where they digest the complex carbohydrates in the bread. The sugars resulting from this extracellular digestion are then absorbed by the hyphae.

the corals and jellyfishes belong, and also in the flatworms, there is a cavity surrounded by the body and freely open to the outside through a single opening (Figure 10-6B and C). With innumerable modifications of form and of the organs into which it is subdivided, an alimentary canal occurs in practically all the animals above the level of a coral or a flatworm. It is present and is even quite complex in an earthworm (see Figure 10-6D), which is much more advanced than a flatworm and belongs to a different branch of evolution.

With such supplementary information as you now have about the processes of digestion, the human digestive system (see Figure 10-1) will serve as an example of the system in higher animals. It should be understood that this or any other example is not typical. Every variety of animal has its own peculiarities of structure, enzymes, and so on that are adapted to its particular way of life (Figure 10-7). In this, as in so many respects, the diversity of life seems almost endless. And yet, once more, there is unity in basic principles.

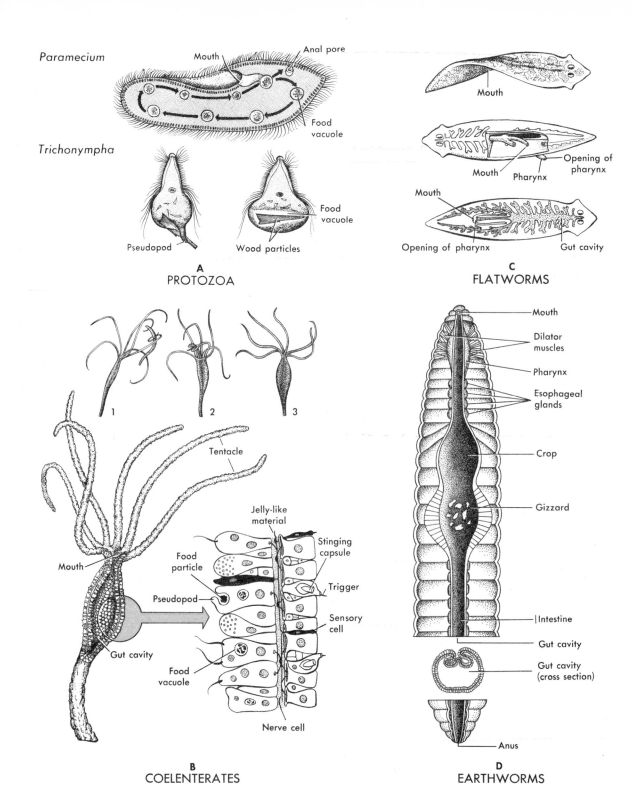

Paramecium

Mouth

Anal pore

Food vacuole

Trichonympha

Pseudopod

Food vacuole

Wood particles

A
PROTOZOA

Mouth

Mouth

Pharynx

Opening of pharynx

Mouth

Opening of pharynx

Gut cavity

C
FLATWORMS

1

2

3

Tentacle

Jelly-like material

Stinging capsule

Food particle

Trigger

Mouth

Pseudopod

Sensory cell

Gut cavity

Food vacuole

Nerve cell

B
COELENTERATES

Mouth

Dilator muscles

Pharynx

Esophageal glands

Crop

Gizzard

Intestine

Gut cavity

Gut cavity (cross section)

Anus

D
EARTHWORMS

FIG. 10-6 Digestive systems in animals, at left. A. Intracellular digestion occurs in protists. *Trichonympha*, which inhabits the alimentary canal of termites, engulfs solid wood particles eaten by the termite. Digestion of the wood takes place in a food vacuole inside the cell. In *Paramecium* a food vacuole forms under pressure of the water driven down the gullet by the beating of cilia. Bacteria and other microorganisma are engulfed in the food vacuole, which moves along a fixed path through the cytoplasm. B, C. Digestion in *Hydra* (and other coelenterates as well as in flatworms) is partly extracellular and partly intracellular. The alimentary canal is a blind sac (one opening only) and lacks any specialization of parts. Partly digested (but still solid) food in the gut cavity is engulfed by cells into food vacuoles, as in protists. Digestion is completed as an intracellular process. D. Extracellular digestion occurs in an earthworm (*Lumbricus*) and all higher animals. Here the alimentary canal has two openings, and food moves in one direction (mouth to anus). This situation permits specialization of the alimentary canal along its length.

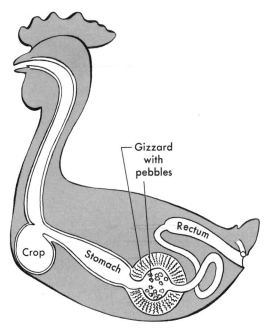

FIG. 10-7 The gizzard in birds. Pebbles in the gizzard functionally replace teeth by grinding up food (cf. earthworms, Fig. 10-6 D).

ASSIMILATION

Digestion changes food into soluble molecules able to enter cells and thus become incorporated into the body of the organism. The next event is the movement of these molecules from the regions where they are formed or absorbed to other parts of the organism.

An organism may be as small as a bacterium or as large as a whale or a sequoia. Whatever its size and structure, substances have to move about in it. Each cell requires material from outside, and these materials must move to where they are needed within the cell. The cells produce wastes that must move out. In a multicellular organism substances formed in one cell are required by other cells. Products of digestion have to be distributed through the body. In aerobic respiration O_2 must be delivered and CO_2 removed. Transportation within organisms is as important for their maintenance as any other process we have discussed.

Transportation And Circulation

TRANSPORTATION IN PROTISTS AND PLANTS

In protists and within single cells the movement of materials is largely by diffusion, atom by atom and molecule by molecule. In many of these organisms there is also some movement of the cytoplasm that helps to distribute materials around the cell. In the plants that have no transport vessels and for this reason are called *nonvascular*, movement of materials is also almost entirely by diffusion and cytoplasmic motion. There is some specialization of roles among the cells of such plants—particularly for reproduction—but the majority of cells may still be relatively independent, making their foods with materials diffused directly from the environment. Such transportation of materials as must occur between one cell and another is across the cell walls and membranes or along cytoplasmic threads joining the cells, not in distinct transport vessels. With more differentiation of parts and processes, however, and with development of organisms more complex and more fully integrated, more effective methods of transportation are necessary and have evolved. They did not evolve because they are necessary; the point is that if they had not happened to evolve no such complex organisms would exist.

The more advanced systems of transportation all involve the movement of fluids *outside* the living cells but *inside* the organism. In plants this fluid is sap. In animals it is often blood, although other animal fluids are involved in internal transportation. Such fluids necessarily are contained in and move

FIG. 10-8 Direction of transportation in the xylem and phloem of a tree.

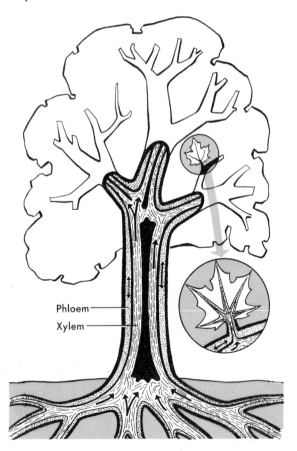

Phloem
Xylem

through otherwise open spaces within the organism. Frequently the spaces develop as long tubes, blood vessels in animals and various tubular structures or ducts in plants, in which there is a definite and directional flow of fluid.

The ducts of the vascular plants are of two sorts, xylem and phloem; they occur in bundles in roots, stems, and leaves. We have already seen examples of them (Chapter 8). Flow in the xylem is mainly upward from roots to stem and leaves, whereas products from leaves and other organs can move in both directions and commonly move downward through the phloem (Figure 10-8). An enormous amount of water enters the roots of a plant, moves through the vessels, and eventually leaves the plant by evaporation. Of the 2000 tons of water absorbed by corn roots during one growing season on 1 acre in Illinois, all but 5 tons were lost by evaporation, or *transpiration,* as this type of water loss by plants is called.

An important question that arises from these considerations is: what is the relationship between transpiration and the rise of sap in plants? The theory currently favored by most plant physiologists is the *transpiration–cohesion–tension theory.* According to this theory, the transpiration of water is not a "loss" but a functionally valuable process. Visualize columns of water extending through the xylem from roots to leaves. Now water has a high degree of *cohesion;* adjacent molecules tend to stick together and strongly resist separation. In the leaves especially, water molecules diffuse outward from the cells and evaporate into the air. As they go, other molecules move in behind them and exert a pull that affects the whole column of water. This *transpiration pull* is a principal factor in the supply of sap to the upper parts of vascular plants (Figure 10-9). The energy expended comes mainly from the heat necessary to produce evaporation. The heat comes directly or indirectly from the sun, and so in this process, as in photosynthesis, plants use solar energy. The total upward movement is effected by the combined power of a solar engine and an osmotic pump.

Most of the liquid in plants moves in one direction only, from soil into roots, up through the vessels, and out into the air through the leaves and other surfaces. Solutions also frequently move in the opposite direction (in the phloem), but generally with

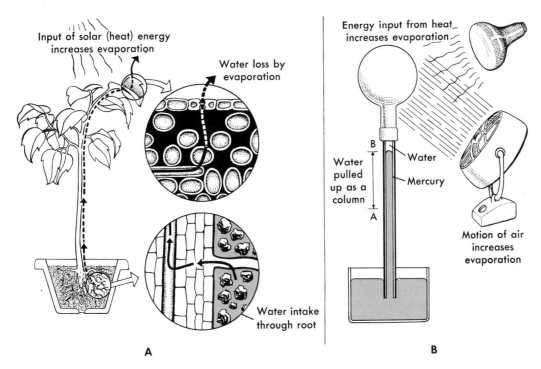

FIG. 10-9 Transpiration pull. A. An unbroken column of water extends from the soil through the root hair and root cortex (cf. Fig 10-4) into the xylem and thence to the leaves and leaf surfaces. The water column is maintained in an upward movement because its apex is drawn off as transpired water vapor. B. The efficiency of evaporation in raising a continuous water column can be demonstrated experimentally with a porous bulb at the head of a water and mercury column. As heat and wind from the lamp and fan increase evaporation from the bulb, the upward movement of the liquid column can be watched. (Adapted from *Principles of Plant Physiology*, by James Bonner and Arthur W. Galston. W. H. Freeman and Company. Copyright © 1952)

less regularity. There is no directed *circular* movement of liquids, and to this extent plants do not have circulation or circulatory systems.

TRANSPORTATION IN ANIMALS

The simpler multicellular animals—sponges, corals, jellyfishes, and their relatives—resemble the nonvascular plants in the absence of vessels or other special anatomical arrangements for the movement of internal fluids (Figure 10-10). They do, however, have passages or cavities in which there is movement of *external* fluids—the sea or fresh water of their environment.

Most other multicellular animals do have *internal* spaces or cavities between the outer body wall and the alimentary canal, and some of these spaces are devoted to transport systems. Internal-transport cavi-

ties usually take the form of definite vessels through which body fluids move. Local regions of these vessels are enlarged and have strongly muscular walls that contract rhythmically. The contractions force fluid through the vessels, and a system of valves keeps the motion always in the same direction. These organs may properly be called *hearts* in all animals, although they have evolved independently in different groups and differ markedly in number, arrangement, and structure (Figure 10-11).

In most animals one or more hearts constantly pump blood in the same direction, and there is no steady loss of body fluid analogous to transpiration in plants. There is a continuous water loss from the lungs—the breath is moist—but this makes no important contribution to the movement of body fluids. Nor does the more occasional or sporadic loss of water in perspiration effect any significant internal move-

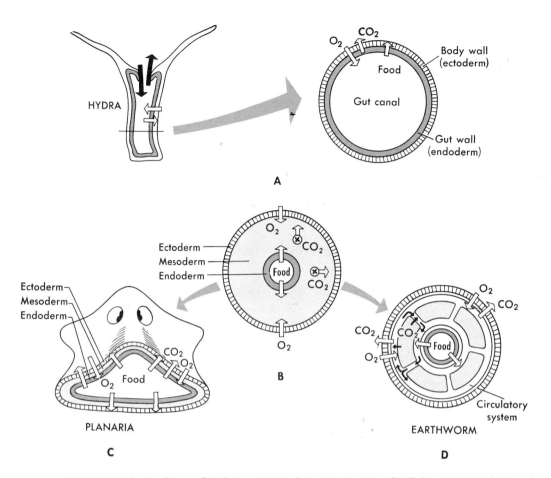

FIG. 10-10   The significance of fluid-transport (circulatory) systems in multicellular animals. A. Left, in a coelenterate, such as *Hydra*, the body wall is essentially only two cells thick. Water circulates in and out of the body cavity (black arrows), and diffusion is sufficient for the transport of food substances, O_2, and CO_2 to and from all cells (white arrows). Right, a cross section through a coelenterate. B. A cross section through a hypothetical animal with extensive mesoderm tissues between the gut and the body wall. The cells (marked X) in the middle of these tissues are too far removed from the gut and from the outside to rely on diffusion for transport of their food, O_2, and CO_2. C. In a flatworm, natural selection has produced a flattened body so that no cell is too far from the gut or the body wall to be served efficiently by diffusion. D. All animals higher than flatworms have evolved a more effective solution to the problem: a circulatory system that overcomes the limitations imposed by diffusion and permits animals to attain relatively enormous sizes. Food, O_2, and CO_2 are transported by the circulating blood over far greater distances than diffusion could cover.

ment of body water. It follows that the blood must eventually return to the heart: it must somehow make a circuit of the body. There is, in short, true *circulation*. In some animals, including some worms and many mollusks (snails, clams, and their relatives) and insects, vessels from the heart pour blood into irregular spaces or channels, *sinuses,* among the tissues. Here the blood moves rather sluggishly, exchanging materials with the cells in the various tissues and eventually seeping back into collecting vessels that return it to the heart. This is an *open* circularory system, because the blood is not retained in distinct vessels through the whole circuit. In most worms, all vertebrates (fishes, amphibians, reptiles, birds, and mammals), and a few other animals the circulatory system is *closed*. The blood does not normally leave the vessels. Its exchanges with cells are accomplished in networks of very tiny, thin-walled vessels called *capillaries.*

Even in animals with closed circulation there are

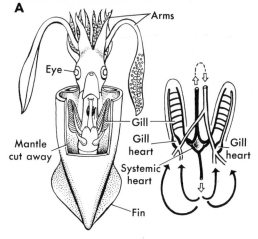

A

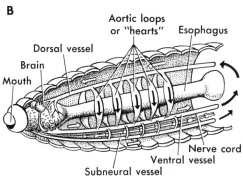

B

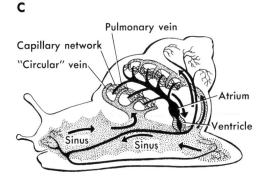

C

FIG. 10-11 **Circulatory systems.** A. A squid: a closed circulatory system with three hearts. B. An earthworm: a closed circulatory system with 10 hearts. C. A snail: an open circulatory system with a single heart. Blood from the heart reaches the muscular foot via a distinct artery; in the foot the blood enters an open sinus, from which it then drains once again into a distinct vessel (the circular vein) in the surface of the lung. Capillaries connect this vessel to other veins that return the blood to the heart.

in addition sinuses and other internal spaces among the cells and tissues, and these spaces are normally filled with fluids. Thus two (or more) body fluids

—blood and lymph—although separately contained in vessels or spaces, freely exchange many substances. In the most complex types of animal transport systems, there are two separate systems of vessels, one transporting blood and the other transporting lymph. There may even be a separate heart for the lymphatic system, as in frogs. Man has no lymph heart, but his circulatory system is otherwise one of the most complex. We shall consider the mechanism of man's circulation in a moment, but first it is advisable to learn a little more about blood, the fluid that is the main means of transportation in the animal body.

Blood Plasma

An examination of human blood under a microscope reveals cell-like objects floating in a colorless fluid. Since some of these objects lack nuclei, there is a question as to whether or not they should be called cells. Therefore, they are collectively referred to by the evasive term *formed elements.* The clear liquid is *plasma,* a solution, partly colloidal, of an extraordinarily large number of different substances. Some of the formed elements and the substances dissolved in plasma are related to the maintenance of the blood itself, and to its several activities. Others are merely in the process of being transported, transportation being one of the main functions of blood.

Blood donation and the use of serum and other blood derivatives in transfusions have become so commonplace that it is of interest to know the following relationships:

Whole blood = formed elements plus plasma (including fibrinogen and other clotting factors)
Plasma = whole blood minus formed elements
Serum = plasma minus fibrinogen and other clotting factors
Defibrinated blood = whole blood minus fibrinogen and other clotting factors, or
= serum plus formed elements

Except for the respiratory gases, most of the blood's substances are transported in the plasma. The distinction between materials being transported and substances involved in properties and processes of the plasma itself is not an absolute one. Nevertheless,

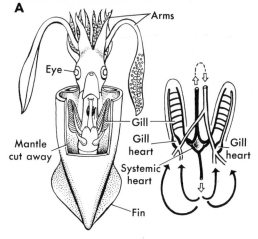

A

Arms
Eye
Mantle cut away
Gill
Gill heart
Gill heart
Systemic heart
Fin

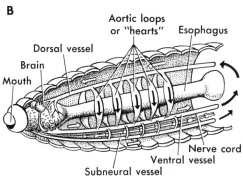

B

Aortic loops or "hearts"
Esophagus
Dorsal vessel
Brain
Mouth
Nerve cord
Ventral vessel
Subneural vessel

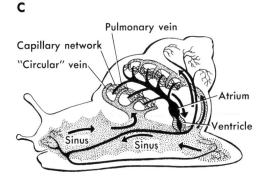

C

Pulmonary vein
Capillary network
"Circular" vein
Atrium
Ventricle
Sinus
Sinus

FIG. 10-11 **Circulatory systems.** A. A squid: a closed circulatory system with three hearts. B. An earthworm: a closed circulatory system with 10 hearts. C. A snail: an open circulatory system with a single heart. Blood from the heart reaches the muscular foot via a distinct artery; in the foot the blood enters an open sinus, from which it then drains once again into a distinct vessel (the circular vein) in the surface of the lung. Capillaries connect this vessel to other veins that return the blood to the heart.

in addition sinuses and other internal spaces among the cells and tissues, and these spaces are normally filled with fluids. Thus two (or more) body fluids

we can make a useful rough division. First, we note that virtually every substance used by cells is found dissolved in plasma at one time or another. With few exceptions, every substance secreted or discarded by cells is also present in plasma. We shall not try to list all these substances, but some of the more important ones are listed in Table 10-2. These substances are dissolved or suspended in water, which makes up about 90 per cent of the plasma.

Plasma (minus its proteins that are too large to pass through the capillary walls) is in contact with most of the cells inside the body. It is, in effect, the environment in which the internal cells live. It is

an environment that provides all necessary materials—this is the function of transportation—and that also maintains the chemical and physical conditions most favorable for the cells. Plasma and whole blood are pumped under pressure through a closed system of vessels. Even a small opening in this system as a consequence of injury or disease would lead to the loss of most of the blood and rapid death if it were not for a defensive activity of plasma, *clotting*. The reactions involved in clotting are complex, but in summary the process is approximately as follows. When an injury occurs, the injured cells and certain of the formed elements in the blood (the *platelets*) release substances that react together to produce *thromboplastin*, which catalyzes the conversion of a plasma protein called *prothrombin* to *thrombin*. Thrombin in turn reacts with *fibrinogen*, another protein

TABLE 10-2   *Some Materials in the Plasma of Human Blood*

Materials being transported	From	To	Significance
Sugars (chiefly glucose)	Intestine, liver	Whole body	Food for cells, especially energy source. Also transported to liver for storage.
Lipids and related compounds	Intestine, storage deposits in body	Whole body	Food for cells, energy source. Includes cholesterol (essential to nerve cells) and other special compounds. Fats are also transported to storage deposits.
Amino acids	Intestine	Whole body	Food, precursors for synthesis of proteins.
Inorganic salts	Intestine, storage many tissues	Whole body	Essential in building protoplasm, enzymes, and other compounds and hard tissues such as bones and teeth.
Hormones	Endocrine glands	Whole body and special "target" tissues	Regulate and coordinate organic activity
Urea, other nitrogenous compounds, acids, and salts	Whole body	Kidneys	Waste products being removed.
Gases			
Oxygen	(Mainly in red cells rather than plasma)		
Nitrogen	Lungs	Lungs	Inert. Taken in and given out incidentally in gas exchange in lungs.
Carbon dioxide	Whole body	Lungs	Waste product being removed.

Materials active in plasma	From	Activity
Blood proteins		
Fibrinogen	Liver	Clotting of blood.
Albumin and others	Liver	Metabolism, viscosity, and osmotic pressure of blood; also, indirectly, CO_2 transportation.
Antibody globulins	Lymphoid tissues	Act against antigenic bacteria, toxins, foreign proteins.
Inorganic salts	Intestine, storage, other tissues	Maintain osmotic level, degree of acidity, internal environment favorable for cells. Calcium necessary for clotting of blood.

dissolved in the plasma, to produce *fibrin*. Fibrin comes out of solution as a tangled network of fibers, which shrink and form a hard clot that plugs the opening in the circulatory system.

Formed Elements of the Blood

The formed elements (Figure 10-12) include red blood cells (*erythrocytes*), white blood cells (*leucoctyes*), and platelets (*thrombocytes*). Of these, the red blood cells are the principal vehicles of transportation. The white blood cells, of which five different types are commonly distinguished, are active mainly in combating bacterial infections. The platelets break down in the vicinity of an injury and liberate substances involved in the early stages of the clotting reaction. Let us now look at the red blood cells and the white blood cells in more detail.

RED BLOOD CELLS. In mammals, the mature red blood cells are biconcave discs with no nuclei; thus they cannot divide or reproduce. They form in connective tissue in the marrow of bones and lose their nuclei as they mature and pass into the blood stream, where they live and function for about 120 days (in man). Eventually they are devoured and digested by cells in the spleen and liver. In the average adult human approximately 27 million million—27,000,000,000,000—mature red cells are present in the blood at one time. *Anemia* results when there is either a deficiency of red blood cells or a deficiency of hemoblobin per red blood cell.

The red substance in a red blood cell is *hemoglobin*, a conjugated protein, globin, with heme as a prosthetic group (Chapter 4). This compound has the important property of combining loosely and reversibly with oxygen. When it is in an oxygen-rich environment, as in the capillaries of the lungs, it combines with oxygen. In an oxygen-poor environment, as in capillaries among cells in need of oxygen, it gives up the oxygen again. This is how oxygen is transferred from the lungs to the cells. Hemoglobin has another property, one that happens to be dangerous in our civilization. It combines with carbon monoxide, CO, even more readily than with oxygen, and when it has done so, it is incapable of picking up oxygen. Carbon monoxide is produced in large quantities in gasoline motors and in fumes from gas ranges and heaters or charcoal grills.

Some carbon dioxide, CO_2, is transported in the plasma, as we have already noted, but most of it is

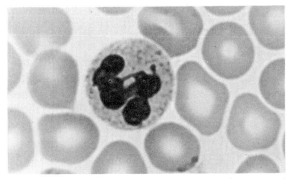

A

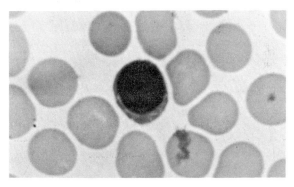

B

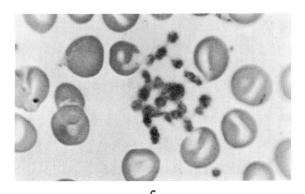

C

FIG. 10-12 Photomicrographs of a stained film of human blood showing the major formed elements. A. ($\times 1600$) The large nucleated cell is a neutrophilic polymorphonuclear leukocyte. The little "drumstick" extending upward from the right side of the nucleus is the sex chromatin that indicates that the cell comes from a female. The non-nucleated cells are erythrocytes or red cells. B. ($\times 1600$) The nucleated cell is a lymphocyte. C. ($\times 1700$) A clump of platelets surrounded by red cells.

FIG. 10-13 Vertebrate hearts. A. In the shark and other fishes, the heart consists of a single atrium and a single ventricle. It drives blood forward through a ventral aorta to the gills. The blood enters the gills through afferent branchial arteries and leaves them via efferent branchial arteries. It then passes to the rest of the body through a dorsal aorta. Thus in fishes there is only a single stream of blood (deoxygenated) passing through the heart. In terrestrial vertebrates, however, there are two steams of blood surging through the heart—deoxygenated blood and blood freshly oxygenated in the lungs, which returns to the heart to be pumped to the rest of the body. B. In the frog and other amphibians, the freshly oxygenated blood enters the heart through a distinct atrium (the left) but becomes partly mixed with deoxygenated blood when it passes on into the single ventricle. This system is clearly inefficient because some of the blood pumped to the body through the dorsal aorta is already exhausted of its oxygen. C. In reptiles the inefficiency is largely overcome by an imcomplete partition in the ventricle. D. In mammals the partition is complete; two distinct ventricles are present. Freshly oxygenated blood returning from the lungs via the left atrium is pumped by the left ventricle to the rest of the body without any contamination with deoxygenated blood.

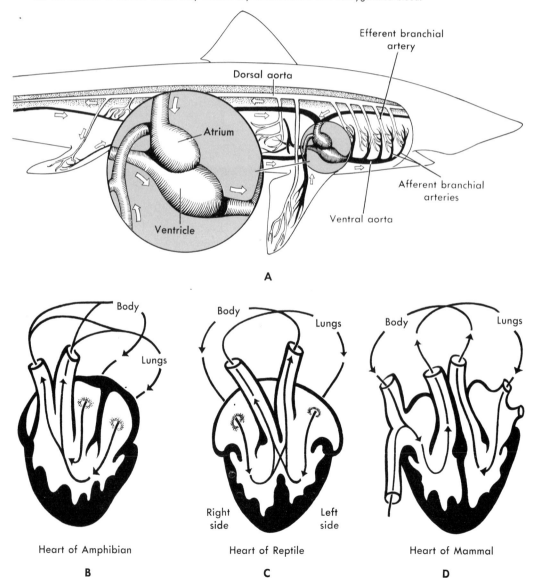

Efferent branchial artery

Dorsal aorta

Atrium

Afferent branchial arteries

Ventricle

Ventral aorta

A

Body

Lungs

Heart of Amphibian

B

Body

Lungs

Right side

Left side

Heart of Reptile

C

Body

Lungs

Heart of Mammal

D

carried in the red cells (erythrocytes). About a fifth of the total CO_2 combines chemically with amino acids in the hemoglobin, but the bulk is carried within the red cells as carbonic acid formed from CO_2 and water by a specific enzyme in the erythrocytes. The resulting acidity in the cell, which would rapidly become harmful if not counteracted, is neutralized by the buffering action of hemoglobin (Chapter 2).

WHITE BLOOD CELLS. White blood cells are nucleated cells that live in blood like separate, parasitic protists and, in fact, look and act like amebas. Their main role is in combating bacterial infections. When an infection occurs, white cells move out from the blood vessels in great numbers and surround and digest bacteria. Soon the area is strewn with living and dead bacteria, white blood cells, digestive enzymes, cell fluids, and cell fragments, all of which is called *pus*. Marked increase of white cells in the blood is nearly always a sign of infection somewhere in the body.

Occasionally, for unknown reasons, the production of white cells becomes uncontrolled, and their numbers tremendously increase, even though there is no infection. This abnormal condition, known as *leukemia,* is usually fatal.

The Mechansim of Circulation

We shall use man to illustrate the circulatory mechanism. The arrangement is practically the same in all mammals, and the principles involved are similar in most animals having a definite circulation, even though the differences in details are legion. Examples of some differences have already been mentioned (Figure 10-11).

The center of the mechanism is the heart. Maintenance of a constant flow of blood through the whole system requires the application of pumping pressure at some point, and this is the function of the heart. In man (and other mammals) the heart is really two separate organs (Figure 10-13), existing side by side, beating in unison, and yet quite distinct. The reason for this oddity, as might be anticipated, is historical. Our two hearts evolved by the gradual separation of a single heart. The heart is still single in fishes. Our right heart, or the right half of our double heart, pumps blood to the lungs, and the left heart pumps it to the body tissues as a whole. The functioning of the heart is described in Figure 10-14, and the

complete circulatory system is described in Figure 10-15.

There is just one complication in the arrangement of the blood circulation that we must mention briefly because it is an unusually interesting example of effective correlation of mechanism and process. When digestion occurs, large amounts of sugar are absorbed by the capillaries of the intestines. If this sugar went into the general circulation, it would cause a sharp rise in blood sugar. On the other hand, when digestion is not occurring, the sugar level drops. Body cells, especially nerve cells, are very sensitive to the sugar concentration in the blood. Sustained high sugar content produces the symptoms of diabetes, and low sugar content produces convulsions and unconsciousness. The sugar-rich blood from the intestinal capillaries does not go into the general circulation but into the *portal vein.* This vein carries it to another capillary network in the liver, where sugar is removed and stored. When sugar is not being absorbed from the intestines, the liver feeds a steady supply of sugar from storage through its capillaries into the general circulation.

Pulse and Blood Pressure

Every time the left ventricle contracts, it sends a column of blood surging through the arteries under strong pressure. As the ventricle relaxes, the pressure drops. It is these alternations of pressure that we feel as the pulse. There is, of course, a pulse in all arteries and not only in the wrist, where it is usually taken for convenience. Feeling the pulse is simply a way of checking how fast and regularly the heart is working. Even when the ventricle is relaxing, in diastole (Figure 10-14), there is some pressure in the arteries because they are elastic. When the systolic surge reaches them they expand. Then they contract again, and the contraction keeps the blood under some, but less, pressure when the systolic wave has passed.

The familiar procedure used to measure blood pressure involves compression of the arteries in the arm until the top of the systolic wave can no longer force blood through them. The pressure is then relaxed until even the low pressure of diastole forces blood through. Thus the highest (systolic) and lowest (diastolic) pressures of the whole pulse sequence are determined. As with many physical variables, each individual has his own average blood pressure, which is healthy and normal for him even though it may not be average for all people of his age. The blood pressure also can, and indeed should, vary considerably under the influence of emotional or physical factors. Extremes of high or low pressure may, of course, be danger signals.

William Harvey (1578–1657), the discoverer of the circulation, rather desparingly concluded that "The motion of the heart was to be comprehended only by God." Biologists cannot yet say that they have answered the last "why" about this or anything

FIG. 10-14   **The human heart and its pumping cycle.** The upper figure shows the detail of the heart's four chambers and its valves. Note that the wall is thicker in the left ventricle than elsewhere. What is the significance of this? A, B, C, and D are successive stages in the pumping cycle. A. The atria fill with blood as their walls relax (atrial diastole). B. The relaxation (diastole) of the ventricles causes blood to flow into them from the atria. C. Contraction (systole) of the atria completes the filling of the ventricles. D. Contraction of the ventricles (ventricular systole) drives blood from the ventricles into the aorta and pulmonary artery. The blood is prevented from returning to the atria by the bicuspid and tricuspid valves. During diastole it is prevented from returning to the ventricles from the arteries by the semilunar valves.

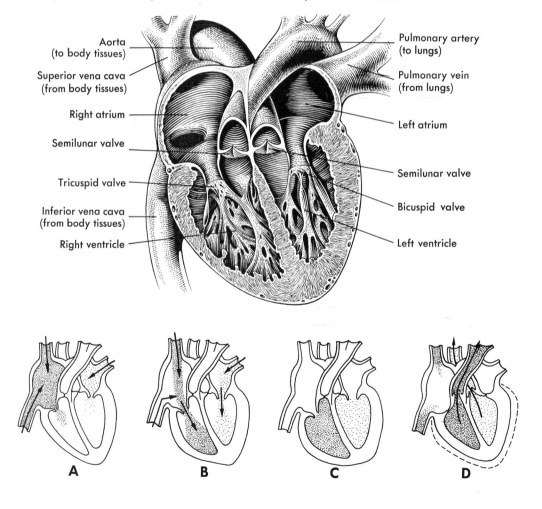

Aorta
(to body tissues)

Superior vena cava
(from body tissues)

Right atrium

Semilunar valve

Tricuspid valve

Inferior vena cava
(from body tissues)

Right ventricle

Pulmonary artery
(to lungs)

Pulmonary vein
(from lungs)

Left atrium

Semilunar valve

Bicuspid valve

Left ventricle

A   B   C   D

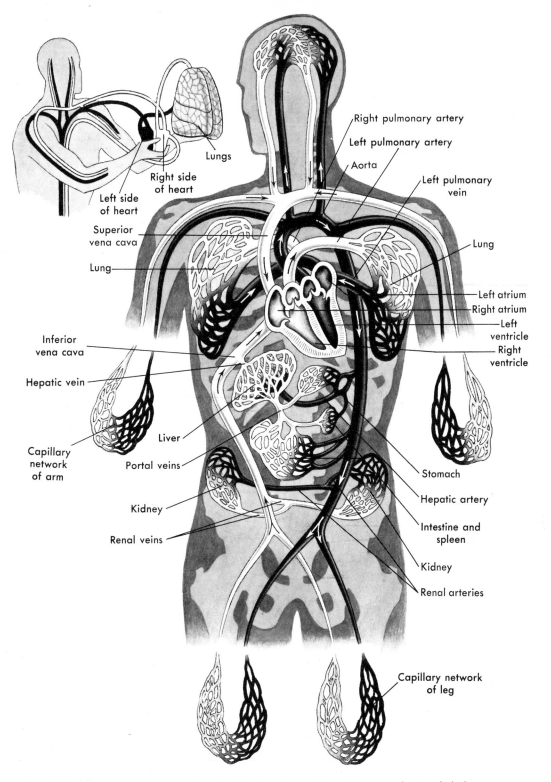

Right pulmonary artery

Left pulmonary artery

Aorta

Left pulmonary vein

Lungs

Right side of heart

Left side of heart

Superior vena cava

Lung

Lung

Left atrium

Right atrium

Left ventricle

Right ventricle

Inferior vena cava

Hepatic vein

Liver

Capillary network of arm

Portal veins

Stomach

Hepatic artery

Kidney

Intestine and spleen

Renal veins

Kidney

Renal arteries

Capillary network of leg

FIG. 10-15   The human circulatory system. (Top left adapted from *Biology: Its Human Implications*, 2nd ed., by Garrett Hardin. W. H. Freeman and Company. Copyright © 1952)

else, but the motion of the heart has now been described in fullest detail and a great deal is known about its causes and controls. In man and other vertebrates, the motion is inherent in the heart itself. A turtle's heart, for instance, entirely removed from the body of the turtle, can keep on beating for a long time. Even small bits of heart tissue, kept alive in solutions resembling lymph, may continue to contract rhythmically. The property of contracting, then relaxing, then contracting again, and so on, is,

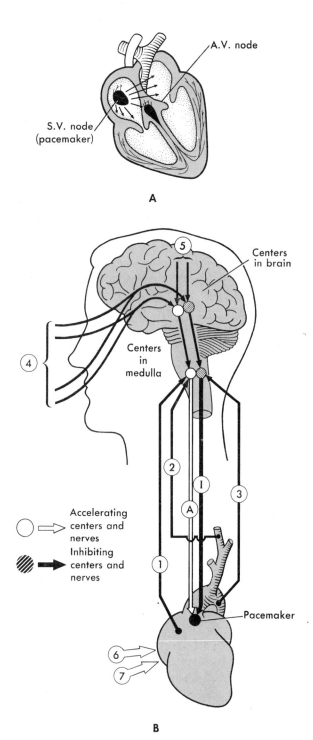

FIG. 10-16   **The control of the heartbeat.** A. The rhythmic beating of the heart is basically controlled by the pacemaker, or sinoatrial (S.A.) node, in the right atrium. Its impulses spread to the left atrium, which contracts a little later than the right atrium. The impulses from the pacemaker later stimulate the atrioventricular (A.V.) node, which in turn initiate's impulses that travel through the ventricle walls, causing them to contract. The impulses from the pacemaker thus underlie the rhythmic contraction of the heart's four chambers. B. The pacemaker's activity is, however, subject to modification. Centers in the medulla of the brain can transmit nerve impulses to it. Impulses from one of these centers inhibit (I), or slow down, the pacemaker; impulses from the other center accelerate (A), or speed up, the pacemaker. These inhibiting or accelerating impulses have several causes. 1. The increase of muscle movement during exercise forces more blood than usual through the veins and thence into the right atrium, which is stretched by the resulting high pressure. The stretching of the right atrium's wall initiates nerve impulses that are transmitted through channel 1 to the accelerating center in the medulla; this then sends further impulses back through channel A to the pacemaker, with a resulting increase in the rate of heartbeat. (Channel A is part of the sympathetic nervous system.) 2. The increase of respiration during exercise causes an increase in the CO_2 concentration in the blood stream. This is detected by special sense organs located at one site in the carotid artery. Nerve impulses initiated in the carotid artery by the high CO_2 concentration are transmitted through channel 2 to the accelerating center in the medulla, thus ultimately causing the increase in pacemaker activity appropriate to exercise 3. The heart is protected against beating at too fast a rate by the presence of pressure-sensitive nerve endings in the dorsal aorta. As the rate of the heartbeat increases, blood pressure in the aorta builds up and stimulates these nerves, which transmit impulses through channel 3 to the inhibitory (or decelerating) center in the medulla. This in turn initiates impulses that pass back through channel I and slow down the pacemaker. 4. Wholly external stimuli, received through the olfactory, auditory, or visual sense organs, can affect the rate of the heartbeat; these stimuli are relayed through higher centers in the brain to the centers in the medulla, finally accelerating or decelerating the pacemaker. What perceptions will stimulate the accelerating centers? What perceptions will stimulate the inhibitory centers? 5. Purely internal stimuli in the form of ideas arising in the cerebral cortex can be similarly relayed to the centers in the medulla. Can you think of examples of ideas that affect your heartbeat? 6, 7. The pacemaker's activity can also be influenced through non-nervous channels. An increase of body heat during exercise or fever increases pacemaker activity, as does an increase in the flow of the hormone epinephrine into the blood.

so to speak, built into vertebrate heart muscle, which is visibly different in structure from muscles that contract only when stimulated through nerves.

The heartbeat starts in a small region in the wall of the right atrium, picturesquely called the *pacemaker.* From this point, an impulse spreads to the left atrium, which thus starts to contract a little later, and then to both ventricles, which then contract together. Thus the contractions of the four chambers of the heart are kept in effective rhythm and sequence (Figure 10-16).

In a man at rest the heart rate or pulse is usually about 70 beats per minute. In a hummingbird the rate may be as much as 1000, and in an adult elephant it is only about 30. Considerably slower rates occur in some lower animals. Pulse rate, like other activities, depends on the size and other characteristics of each particular sort of organism. Your own heart beats much faster, as much as twice as fast, at some times than at others. The tissues need more supplies from the blood, especially oxygen, at certain times. It is important to organic maintenance that the blood flow be variable to meet these varying needs (Figure 10-16). The amount of blood pumped by the heart can be increased in two ways: by increase in the volume pumped at each stroke, and by increase in the number of strokes per minute.

The volume of blood per stroke depends largely on the amount of blood reaching the heart between contractions. Flow of blood through the veins to the heart is greatly increased by muscular action. These relationships automatically ensure that the heart will pump more blood per stroke during periods of muscular activity.

The whole mechanism by which blood flow and heart rate are controlled is remarkably intricate and complex, as evidenced in recent heart-transplant surgery. We have by no means gone into all the known complications, and there are still unknown factors involved. Even in summary, however, this is a good example of "the wisdom of the body," of how internal conditions are kept nearly constant under normal conditions but also respond to varying activities and needs.

The Lymphatic System

We have noted that there is fluid in various internal spaces of the body and, indeed, around almost all the cells. Much of this fluid, with the materials dissolved in it, has diffused from the blood in the capillaries and may diffuse back into it. It is, in fact, blood plasma minus the proteins held back by the capillary walls. Other materials have diffused from the cells bathed by the fluid, and these materials, too, may diffuse into the blood in the capillaries. The fluid is thus intimately involved in the delivery and pickup activities of the transport system of the blood. However, not all the fluid finds its way back into the blood directly.

In most parts of the body there is another set of capillaries quite separate from those through which the blood flows. These are the *lymphatic capillaries.* Much of the fluid outside the blood vessels and tissue cells finds its way by diffusion into the lymphatic capillaries (Figure 10-17). From them lymph passes into successively larger vessels, much as blood collects in veins after passing through the blood capillaries. The lymphatic system of vessels, however, runs in one direction only. Its capillaries end blindly and pick up materials only by diffusion through their walls. There is no delivery to them corresponding with the arterial part of the blood circulation.

The lymph vessels have internal valves, and flow through them depends on pressure and motion of surrounding tissues, as in veins, with no pressure from the heart. Eventually all the lymph in vessels reaches the upper part of the trunk and is emptied into veins near the shoulders (most of it on the left side). Thus the lymph, too, does finally enter the blood.

As would be expected from its relationship to the blood, the composition of lymph is similar to that of plasma, but it contains much less of the blood proteins. Since it flows only from and not to the body tissues, it also contains less dissolved food materials in transit, but it does transport waste products from the tissues. There is one important exception to the statement that lymph is not involved in food transportation: it picks up small globules of fat from the intestines and delivers them to the blood (Figures 10-17B and 10-18).

At points along the lymph vessels are lumpy enlargements, the *lymph nodes* (see Figure 10-17). *Lymphocytes,* one form of leukocyte (see Figure 10-12B), originate in lymph nodes and other lymph-

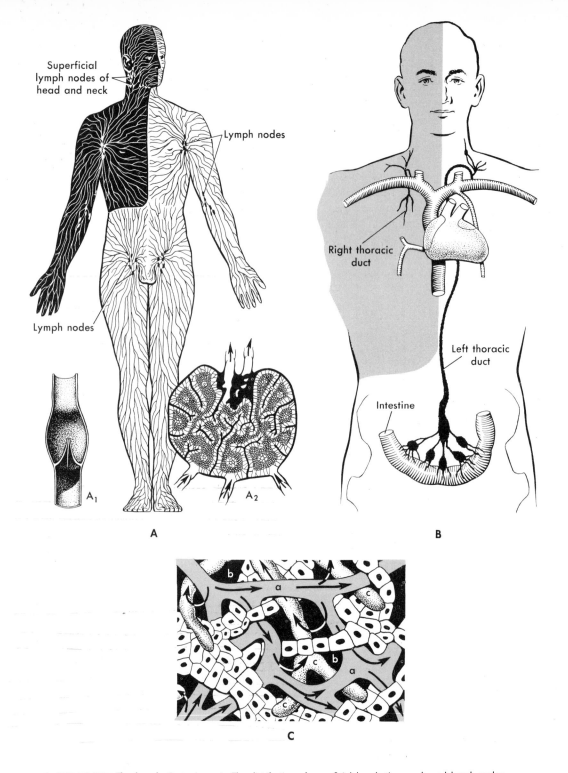

FIG. 10-17 The lymphatic system. A. The distribution of superficial lymphatic vessels and lymph nodes in man. A₁. A valve in a lymph vessel. A₂. A lymph node. B. The left and right thoracic ducts emptying into the veins (subclavian) that drain the arms. The left thoracic duct is the larger one, draining the whole of the unshaded area in A and B. It carries fats absorbed by the lacteals in intestinal villi (Fig. 10-18). C. Detail of blood and lymph capillaries. Plasma flows from the blood capillaries (a) into intercellular spaces (b) and then into the lymph capillaries (c), which end blindly.

oid tissues. Nodes are also filters which remove and destroy bacteria and solid particles. Lymph nodes near the lungs of city dwellers are often black with soot and dust particles. During infection, the nodes may become swollen and sore.

NUTRITION

Adequate nutrition supplies the organism with all the materials it needs for synthesizing the compounds that make up its structure and provide its energy. Autotrophic organisms, especially the green plants, can start their syntheses with simple inorganic compounds and elements. Heterotrophic forms must start their syntheses with complex organic compounds, such as sugars and amino acids. Man belongs to the latter group; he has low synthetic ability and requires a wide variety of elaborated foods. He thrives best on a diet containing, besides water and a considerable number of mineral salts, all three major classes of foods—carbohydrates, lipids, and proteins—with some diversity in each class. Any digestible food of any of these classes can furnish him with energy. In this respect the classes are largely interchangeable.

They are not interchangeable as building materials or as sources for the synthesis of enzymes and other compounds. For these needs, proteins (or a number of amino acids) are indispensable. A man who ate enough carbohydrates to satisfy his hunger and fulfill all his energy demands would, if he ate nothing else, be fatally undernourished. As a general rule, foods rich in carbohydrates are cheap, and those rich in lipids and proteins are expensive. What social implications does this have? Is deficiency in energy the major nutritional problem of underprivileged peoples?

There is another nutritional requirement, mentioned only in passing heretofore—vitamins. A man who has an apparently sufficient diet of carbohydrates, lipids, and proteins, with adequate material and energy intake, may nevertheless develop serious deficiency diseases. A deficiency disease is caused by a lack of substances essential for normal metabolism. One of the earliest such diseases to be studied was scurvy, a disorder producing bleeding gums,

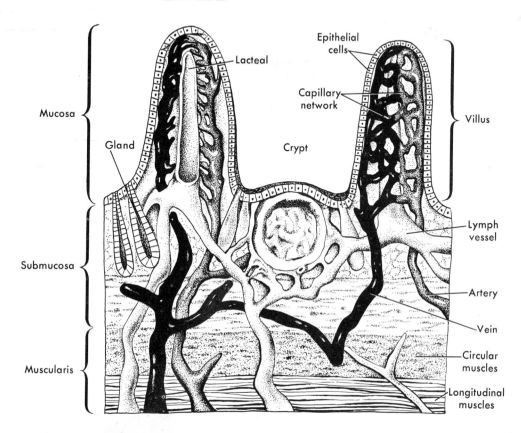

FIG. 10-18 Lacteals and capillaries in the intestinal villi. The lining of the intestine in vertebrates, including man, is molded into many villi, which serve to increase the effective absorptive area in the gut (cf. the earthworm, Fig. 10-6). Each villus contains blind-ending lymphatic vessels, the lacteals, into which fats enter. Each villus also is richly supplied with capillaries, which absorb other foodstuffs.

Mucosa

Submucosa

Muscularis

Lacteal

Gland

Epithelial cells

Capillary network

Crypt

Villus

Lymph vessel

Artery

Vein

Circular muscles

Longitudinal muscles

painfully swollen joints, and eventually death. It frequently appeared among sailors on long voyages in the days when fresh foods were not available on shipboard. Long before there was any knowledge of the cause of scurvy, it was discovered by chance that lime juice prevents it.

Later experiments with animals and clinical investigations with humans revealed that scurvy and a long list of other deficiency diseases result from a lack of vitamins. Vitamins are organic compounds required in small amounts for normal metabolism but not synthesized by the organism and therefore necessarily present in the diet. Vitamins do not belong to any one chemical family. The same substance may be synthesized by one organism, for which it is thus not a vitamin, and be required as a vitamin in the food of another. Some of the vitamins essential to man are listed in Table 10-3.

Although commercial advertisements of vitamin preparations give the opposite impression, it is a fact that the varied diet customarily eaten by all but the poorest Americans usually provides sufficient amounts of all the needed vitamins—particularly if the diet includes a considerable proportion of vegetables and fruit in addition to meat.

Most vitamins can be synthesized by one plant or another. Although the compounds are therefore not vitamins for plants, the fact that plants synthesize them suggests that they are necessary in plant metabolism, and their chemical roles are generally similar in plants and animals.

In animals these roles are well understood for all but a few vitamins. As we have seen (Chapter 2), almost all vitamins are converted in the body to coenzymes, in which form they participate in cell metabolism. Thus, for example, nicotinic acid is converted to the familiar coenzymes NAD and NADP. In nicotinic acid deficiency, these coenzymes are lacking, and the metabolic pathways upon which they depend function subnormally. This is the ultimate cause of the complex group of disorders constituting pellagra.

TABLE 10-3   *Some Vitamins Important in Human Nutrition*

Vitamin	Some deficiency symptoms	Some sources
FAT SOLUBLE		
A	Dry, scaly skin; night blindness	Milk, butter, liver oils, yellow and green vegetables[a]
D	Rickets (defective growth of bones and other hard tissues)	Milk, egg yolk, liver oils[b]
E	Degeneration of muscles (also sterility in rats and possibly in other organisms)	Green leafy vegetables, oils from seeds, egg yolk, meat
K	Delayed clotting of blood	Green leafy vegetables[b]
WATER SOLUBLE		
Thiamine (B_1)	Beriberi, polyneuritis (inflammation and degeneration of nerves)	Yeast, whole-grain cereals, lean meat
Riboflavin (B_2, G)	Soreness around mouth, inflammation of eyes	Vegetables, yeast, milk, liver, eggs
B_{12}	Anemia due to the inability of blood-cell precursors to synthesize DNA; nerve damage	Liver and lean meats
Ascorbic acid (C)	Scurvy	Citrus fruit, tomatoes, green peppers
Nicotinic acid or niacin	Pellagra (a disease affecting skin, alimentary canal, and nerves)	Yeast, meat
Folic acid	Anemia similar to that of vitamin B_{12} deficiency	Leafy vegetables

[a] Vitamin A is not required as such, since the human body can synthesize it from yellow pigments, carotenes. These are required if vitamin A itself is deficient.
[b] The human body can synthesize vitamins D and K, but the amounts synthesized may be inadequate.

Summary

Effects of large size on multicellular organisms.

Modes of food intake: in solid form by animals; by diffusion in protists and plants.

Digestion, as the converse of synthesis: extracellular and intracellular digestion; the necessity of intracellular digestion for the movement across cell membranes; digestive enzymes.

Assimilation: the incorporation of digested food into the organic system.

Transportation within the organism: its simplicity in protists; one of the major functions demanding special adaptations in large organisms.

Transportation in xylem and phloem of vascular plants: the transpiration–tension–cohesion theory explaining water movement in the plant.

Circulatory systems in animals: hearts; open and closed circulations.

Composition and function of blood: plasma, serum, and the formed elements of the blood; the clotting reaction; hemoglobin and the transportation of oxygen.

The mechanism and control of circulation: diastole and systole of the heart; blood pressure; control of heartbeat.

The lymphatic system; the movement of plasma from blood capillaries through intercellular spaces of lymphatic capillaries; the mechanism of one-way lymph movement; drainage into the subclavian veins; lymph nodes; fat transportation.

Nutrition and vitamins.

CHAPTER ELEVEN

THE ORGANISM: MAINTENANCE AND INTEGRATION: II

Respiration

THE MEANING OF RESPIRATION

In the language of the physiologists, breathing in is *inspiration,* breathing out is *expiration,* and the whole process is *respiration.* Inspiration draws in oxygen, and expiration expels carbon dioxide. Oxygen is not used solely in the lungs, any more than food is used solely in the stomach and intestine. In both cases the organs named are involved in the intake of materials used throughout the whole body. Thus, respiration is a process that takes place not in the lungs alone but in cells and tissues through the organism.

It is unfortunate when the same word comes to be used in more than one way, and this has happened to the word "respiration": it means breathing in and out of the lungs, and it also means the consumption of oxygen and production of carbon dioxide by metabolic processes in an organism. Popular writers to the contrary notwithstanding, plants and a great many animals never breathe. Practically all organisms and individual cells within organisms do respire, in the broader sense of the word. In this book we apply the term "cellular respiration" to the processes in cells and tissues comparable to chemical oxidation.

CELLULAR RESPIRATION

As we have noted, energy from solar radiation is bound into chemical compounds by photosynthesis. Among the first and simplest energy-rich compounds formed are simple sugars; the other, more complex, organic compounds also contain bound energy. Respiration, or oxidation-reduction, in cells includes the various processes by which this bound energy is released. We covered the fundamental chemical aspects of this respiratory-energy release in Chapter 4.

Part of the energy released in cells by respiration appears as heat and is eventually lost. Even this energy cannot be considered wasted. It helps to maintain body temperature in warm-blooded animals (birds and mammals), and even in other animals and in plants it influences the rates of other physiological processes. Much of the released energy is used in syntheses. The building up of complex from simpler compounds, for instance of proteins from amino acids, requires the expenditure of energy, and the energy comes from respiration. This is the reason that every cell must respire. It needs energy for building its own materials, even if it does not seem to be doing anything energetic. The released energy may also bring about physical changes in the protoplasm and in cell membranes. It may produce radiation and electrical phenomena. More familiarly, it may be expended as motion.

RESPIRATORY RATES

Even though anaerobic respiration (without oxygen) also occurs, most plants and animals have respiratory cycles that are aerobic (with oxygen) at one stage or another. This means that their oxygen consumption is at least roughly in proportion to their total energy consumption. This, in turn, is proportional to the total amount of activity, or work, of all kinds going on throughout the organism as a whole. Thus oxygen consumption is a valuable and interesting measure of organic activity. The amount of oxygen consumed per hour or day and in proportion to the weight of the organism is the respiratory rate.

Many measurements of respiratory rates in plants and animals have been made, and some of the results are surprising. The rate in a man at rest is comparable to that in a carrot. It is much lower than in bacteria, some of which have the highest rates known. Protists also tend to have high rates, but rates are generally low in the lower multicellular animals. Cold-blooded animals often have rates about as high as in man and other warm-blooded animals. Warm-bloodedness is not a matter of greater heat production but of more even production and better maintenance of heat level.

RESPIRATORY SYSTEMS

As was seen to be true of digestion, respiration usually involves no special organs in protists or in aquatic plants and many small and relatively simple aquatic animals. The required oxygen simply diffuses from solution in the surrounding water into the organism through cell membranes. Carbon dioxide similarly diffuses out from the cell into the water of the environment. In land plants a similar process of diffusion occurs between cells and the surrounding air. Many of these forms also develop air-filled spaces among internal cells, and these spaces often have special openings—stomata—which open and close through the mechanism of guard cells.

In higher animals, on the other hand, elaborate anatomical organs and systems have evolved (Figure 11-1).

Most relatively large and complex animals require more oxygen than can be readily taken in by diffusion through the unmodified body surface. Moreover, in many of these forms, both aquatic and terrestrial, there is a protective skin through which diffusion is slight or absent, a necessity for regulation of their water content. It is among such animals that the most specialized respiratory organs have evolved. In aquatic forms these are usually *gills*, which have arisen independently in various groups and are highly diverse. Most of them have in common a filamentous or platelike structure, which crowds a large surface area into a small bulk, and some means of circulating water past or through the gills (Figure 11-2).

Gill-like structures have become adapted to

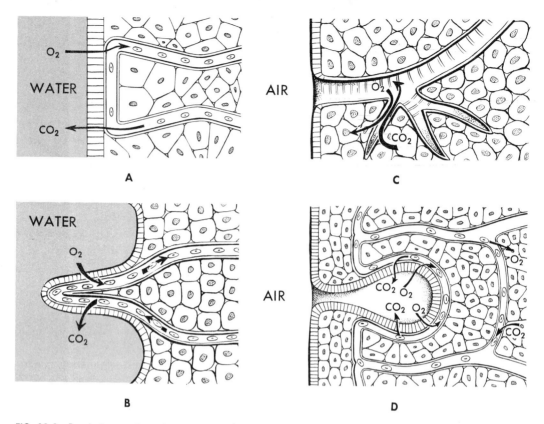

FIG. 11-1 Respiratory systems. In aquatic animals respiration is usually through the external body surface, either (A) generally or (B) in localized areas where the surface for O_2–CO_2 exchange is greatly increased by the development of gills. In land animals the respiration surfaces are internal because they must be kept moist. The two most common systems are tracheae (C) and lungs (D). Tracheae (in insects and some other arthropods) are tubular ducts through which air passes directly to and from tissue cells. The fine ultimate branches (tracheoles) are filled with water and supply individual cells. Lungs are internal cavities whose moist surfaces are richly supplied with blood vessels that transport O_2 and CO_2 to and from tissue cells. Animals like the earthworm, which respire all over their body surfaces, are not fully terrestrial; they are restricted to moist soil. Why?

O_2–CO_2 exchange with the air in some land-living forms, such as the spiders and scorpions. Other air-breathing forms have developed lunglike pouches, as in certain snails. True *lungs,* like man's (Figure 11-3), occur in some fishes, most amphibians, and all reptiles, birds, and mammals. A different and unique system for air breathing has evolved in the insects. In them there is a system of tubes, the *tracheae* (Figure 11-4), with paired openings, *spiracles,* through the body wall. The tracheae branch repeatedly, and their smallest terminal extensions deliver air to the cells throughout the body. In many insects rhythmic movements of the abdomen and synchronized opening and closing of the spiracles produce a definite circulation of air through the tracheal system.

In animals with gills or lungs these organs facilitate O_2–CO_2 exchange between the blood and the external water or air. It is the blood that exchanges O_2 and CO_2 directly with the cells in which respiration occurs. In the insects, however, the body fluids are not involved in respiration (with unimportant exceptions), and O_2–CO_2 exchange is directly between air in the tracheae and the cells of the body.

Control of Breathing

The basic chemical processes of respiration occur in cells; in man and most other organisms the cells sooner or later use O_2 and produce CO_2. These substances are carried from and to the lungs in the blood. For the body as a whole, rate of respiration

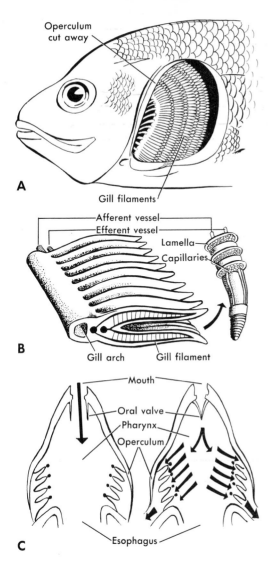

A

Operculum
cut away

Gill filaments

B

Afferent vessel
Efferent vessel
Lamella
Capillaries

Gill arch   Gill filament

C

Mouth
Oral valve
Pharynx
Operculum

Esophagus

FIG. 11-2 Gill respiration in fishes. The principal structural feature of gills is the way they are organized to offer as great a surface as possible to the water flowing over them; the greater their surface, the greater their capacity to pick up oxygen and give up carbon dioxide to the external water. A. The gill cover, or operculum, of the fish has been cut away, and four gills can be seen. Each gill carries a double row of gill filaments. B. Each gill filament is arranged as a series of lamellae. An afferent blood vessel carries blood to the gills, where it breaks up into a fine capillary bed at the surface of each lamella. Here gaseous exchange occurs. An efferent vessel carries the oxygenated blood away from the gills to the rest of the body. C. The water that carries oxygen into the gills enters through the mouth into the pharynx. As it is compressed by contraction of the pharynx, it is prevented from escaping through the mouth by the closure of the oral valves. The water is thus forced through slits between the gills, finally leaving under the operculum.

FIG. 11-3 Lung respiration in man. Air, drawn in through the mouth or nose, reaches the lungs through the trachea and its branches, the bronchi and bronchioles. The cartilaginous rings around the trachea give it sufficient rigidity to prevent its collapse and thus guarantee a continuously open air passage to the lungs. The bronchioles lead into small cavities, alveoli, which are richly supplied with blood capillaries (p. 215). Gaseous exchange occurs in the alveoli. The increased internal surface of the lung achieved by its organization into alveoli may be compared with the increased external surface of the gill achieved by its aggrangement into filaments and lamellae (Fig. 11-2). What is the significance in both cases? All the alveoli in the lung are bound tightly together by a surrounding epithelium, the pleura.

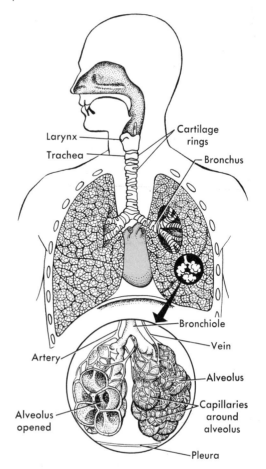

Larynx
Trachea
Cartilage rings
Bronchus
Bronchiole
Vein
Artery
Alveolus
Capillaries around alveolus
Alveolus opened
Pleura

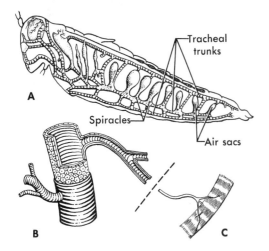

FIG. 11-4   Tracheal respiration in a grasshopper. A. The distribution of spiracles, main tracheal trunks, and air sacs on one side of the insect. The air sacs are reservoirs. B. A portion of a main tracheal trunk and its branches, showing the cells and the internal support of chitin (a protein substance) that they secrete (cf. the cartilage rings around the human trachea, Fig. 11-3). C. Ultimate tracheal branches supplying muscles.

depends on how fast O_2 is taken up and CO_2 given off in the lungs. These exchanges in the lungs depend, in turn, on the rate and depth of breathing.

The lungs themselves have no muscles. They are forced to expand and are permitted to contract again by movements of the ribs, which form a box around the lungs, and of the *diaphragm,* a muscular partition that closes the lower side of the box. Since this motion continues rhythmically even when a person is paying no attention to it or is asleep, the muscles might seem to have an inherent rhythm like the heart muscles. It is, however, easy to see that this is not so. A person can stop breathing immediately if he wishes to, but he cannot commit suicide by holding his breath; even if he had will power enough to hold it as long as he were conscious, breathing would start immediately when he lost consciousness. This suggests that the rib and diaphragm muscles used in breathing are fully controlled by nerves (Figure 11-5).

The rhythm of breathing is maintained not in the lungs themselves nor in muscles of ribs and dia-phragm, but in a nerve center. This breathing center is located in the *medulla oblongata,* which is the lower part of the brain at the top of the spinal cord (Figure 11-6).

In usual circumstances the rate of breathing and even the fact that breathing occurs at all is controlled by the amount of CO_2 in the blood. CO_2 acts on the respiratory center and causes it to send out its impulses to the muscles of breathing. The more CO_2, the faster the rhythm of the impulses. If there is extremely little CO_2 in the blood (a condition not normal but one that can be produced experimentally), the impulses stop and so, of course, breathing stops. The effect of CO_2 on the respiratory center is a powerful one. When a person tries to hold his breath for a long time, CO_2 accumulates until its influence is so strong that he starts breathing again in spite of himself. Production of CO_2 by the cells and its diffusion into the blood are approximately propor-tional to the consumption of O_2. Thus there is an automatic regulation that is unusually direct and simple compared with other organic processes. Con-sumption of O_2 in cells leads to an increase of CO_2 in blood, which leads to an increase in depth and rate of breathing, which leads to an increase of O_2 in the blood available for use by the cells. Another interesting point is involved here. CO_2 is a waste product, harmful in any considerable concentration, and rapidly discarded by the organism. Yet it is also an essential part of the bodily mechanism, and on its way out it acts as a messenger from the body as a whole to the respiratory center.

Control of Temperature

Life can exist only within a relatively narrow range of temperatures. Particular types of organisms are at their best in an even narrower range than that of life as a whole. The rates and even the kinds of reactions in cells are strongly modified by changes in temperature. The physical properties of protoplasm, such as fluidity and elasticity, are also affected by temperature.

It is not surprising that temperature regulation should have evolved as part of the mechanism stabi-lizing the internal environment. It *is* surprising that such regulation is poor or absent in the great majority of organisms. Man happens to be among the relatively few forms in which the temperature of the internal

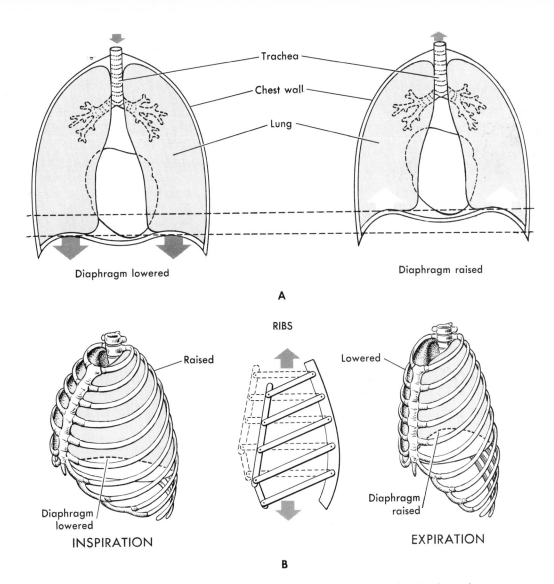

Trachea

Chest wall

Lung

Diaphragm lowered

Diaphragm raised

A

RIBS

Raised

Diaphragm
lowered

INSPIRATION

Lowered

Diaphragm
raised

EXPIRATION

B

FIG. 11-5 Mechanics of breathing. Ventilation of the lungs (movement of air in and out) is due to the bellows-like action of the thoracic cavity (bounded by the chest wall and the diaphragm), in which the lungs lie. Air is forced into the lungs when the cavity is enlarged by (1) the elevation of the ribs and (2) the depression of the diaphragm. Air is forced out of the lungs when the thoracic cavity is decreased in volume by (1) the depression of the ribs and (2) the elevation of the diaphragm. A shows the extent to which the diaphragm moves during inspiration (*left*) and expiration (*right*). B shows the extent to which the ribs move during inspiration and expiration. The central figure schematizes the way in which the ribs are loosely joined to the spinal column and the sternum (breastbone); it shows how elevation of the ribs enlarges the thoracic cavity.

environment is closely controlled. This is so exceptional that use of man as an example should be preceded by a brief review of the very different conditions in other organisms.

The ranges of environmental temperatures in the sea are much narrower than those in other environ-ments. The whole range of surface temperatures is about − 2 to 40°C (about 28 to 104°F), and these are very local extremes in different places. At any one place and depth, the range is usually only a few degrees. Marine organisms are markedly affected in their distribution by water temperature. Those living

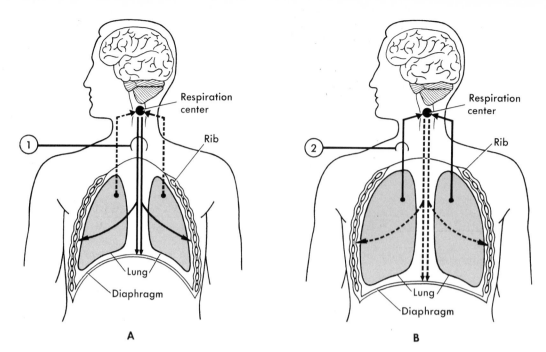

FIG. 11-6 Control of breathing. The thoracic cavity is expanded by the muscles of the diaphragm and the intercostal muscles, which elevate the ribs. A. These muscles are stimulated into action, thus enlarging the thoracic cavity, by nerve impulses that reach them (via channel 1) from a respiratory nerve center in the medulla. B. The expansion of the thoracic cavity enlarges the lungs and thus draws air in. In the lungs are nerves sensitive to the tension developed when the lungs are fully stretched. Stimulated by the stretch of the lung walls, these nerves initiate impulses that are transmitted (via channel 2) to the medulla's respiratory center, whose activity they inhibit. This inhibition of the respiratory center causes the diaphragm and the intercostal muscles to relax and, consequently, the thoracic cavity to collapse, resulting in expiration. When expiration is complete, impulses from the "stretch receptors" in the lung cease, and so, consequently, does inhibition of the respiratory center. Its renewed activity again stimulates (via channel 1) the appropriate muscles to expand the chest cavity.

in warm seas are quite different from those of colder water. In each place, however, the temperature changes are slight. Usual fluctuations pose no severe problems, and temperature regulation has never evolved in sea animals. (Penguins, seals, and whales have highly developed temperature regulation, but they inherited this from ancestors that lived on land.)

Fresh water has more variable temperatures than sea water, but still the variation is limited. Its temperature cannot drop much below freezing or rise above the temperature of the adjacent air. Organisms in waters with relatively great seasonal variation in temperature often pass the winter in an inactive state. It is the land that is the most difficult environment. Here temperature ranges are extreme, not only over a continent but also in single localities through the year. In the tropics, temperatures change little from

one season to another, but they have a daily rise and fall that may be much greater than any seasonal change. Tropical animals, from mosquitoes to monkeys, commonly have a daily rhythm. They are active at the times of day or night when the temperatures suit them; they stay in shelter when temperatures are much higher or lower.

The most extreme seasonal changes occur in the so-called Temperate Zone, where the climates are most intemperate. If you live anywhere in the central region of the United States, you probably have some summer days hotter than any in the tropics and some winter nights as cold as those in the far north. In this zone, land animals frequently either hibernate (as many mammals do) or migrate to warmer climes (as many birds do) in winter. There are many annual animals and plants. These die when cold weather comes, and their offspring survive the winter as inactive, well-protected eggs or seeds. Many insects and most leafy plants meet the problem of temperature range in this way. Perennial plants and trees become quiescent in winter, and most of them shed all their leaves in the fall. Some shed all their aerial parts and grow them again from the subterranean parts when warm weather returns. In one way or another all plants suspend activity in the coldest weather. It is noteworthy that those most successful in meeting low winter temperatures may be most susceptible to a late spring frost that comes when they have started active new growth.

Among the vertebrates, some are "cold-blooded" (fishes, amphibians, and reptiles) and some are "warm-blooded" (birds and mammals). A "cold-blooded" animal may very well have a higher temperature than a "warm-blooded" one. The difference is not in coldness or warmth but in the fact that "warm-blooded" animals have mechanisms for keeping the internal temperature constant and "cold-blooded" animals do not. Since the terms "warm-blooded" and "cold-blooded" are therefore flatly wrong, it is better to call those with internal temperature-regulating mechanisms *homeothermous,* and those without, *poikilothermous.*

Poikilothermous animals tend to take on the temperature of their environments. This is only a tendency: poikilotherms do have some heat-regulating ability. A swiftly moving animal, even a fish, raises the body temperature well above that of its surroundings, and this warming in turn helps to speed up the reactions that produce it. Reptiles often bask in the sun on cool days, and absorption of radiation can raise their temperatures above that of the air. On hot days they avoid the sun and may burrow into cooler earth.

Only homeotherms tend to maintain a constant temperature by entirely internal mechanisms. The efficiency of the mechanisms varies. Variations of as much as 15°C in internal temperature may not be fatal in some birds, but under usual conditions the temperature range is kept within a degree, more or less. In man the body temperature is normally close to 98.6°F (37.0°C); a rise of less than 2°F may mean trouble. (Although 98.6°F is marked as "normal" on clinical thermometers, this is not necessarily true for all individuals. Perfectly healthy individuals may have somewhat lower or higher temperatures normal for

them, and, in the same individual, a slight temperature change need not signify illness.) The temperature of a normal, healthy man remains nearly the same whether the air around him is at 115°F or at −40°F. Obviously we have some means of producing heat, some means of losing it, and some means of striking a balance between the two.

Heat is produced by oxidative processes in the cells. The most important source is the muscles, which produce much heat when exercised or even when tensed. We tend voluntarily to move about more when it is cold than when it is hot around us. Even if we do not, our muscles automatically become tense in the cold. If the tenseness is extreme, the muscles begin to quiver, and we say we are shivering. When we warm up, the tenseness disappears, and we feel relaxed.

Heat is lost by radiation and evaporation. The blood flows through a network of capillaries in the skin, where it is so near the surface that it loses heat by radiation. The more blood flows here, the more heat is lost. The amount of flow is regulated by constriction or enlargement (dilation) of the capillaries. In cold air the capillaries constrict; less blood flows near the skin, and less heat is radiated. In warm air the capillaries dilate; more blood flows, more heat is lost. Evaporation causes heat loss and hence is cooling, as everyone knows who has ever put a wet cloth on his brow. Cooling evaporation occurs all over our skin, mostly from sweat glands which secrete more liquid when the air is warm, less when it is cool. There is also much evaporation from our lungs.

In summary, these mechanisms work as follows:

When it is cool
- skin capillaries are constricted—and less heat is radiated.
- sweat glands are inactive—and less heat is lost by evaporation.
- muscles are tenser—and more heat is produced.

When it is warm
- skin capillaries are dilated—and more heat is radiated.
- sweat glands are active—and more heat is lost by evaporation.
- muscles relax—and less heat is produced.

These diverse mechanisms are put into action by nervous impulses in nerves outside the sphere of conscious control. We cannot stop sweating when we want to, even to the extent that we can control breathing. The nerve impulses involved originate and are coordinated in a temperature-regulating center at the base of the brain. The center reacts automatically to signals from sensory nerves in the skin where the sensations "hot" and "cold" originate. It is also possible that the center reacts directly to the temperature of the blood around it.

SECRETION

Secretion occurs widely, indeed universally, in multicellular organisms. Specialized secretions include those responsible for odors and tastes and the poisons formed in mushrooms and many flowering plants. Numerous other organisms, from protists to snakes, also secrete poisons that are useful for defense or for the capture of food. All kinds of synthesized molecules in both plants and animals are called secretions if they are used by the organisms elsewhere than in the cells where they are elaborated. Groups of cells active mainly in producing secre-

FIG. 11-7 **The human salivary glands.** The three pairs of glands pour saliva containing digestive enzymes into the mouth cavity. As the names imply, the sublingual gland lies under the tongue, the submaxillary under the jaw, and the parotid near the ear.

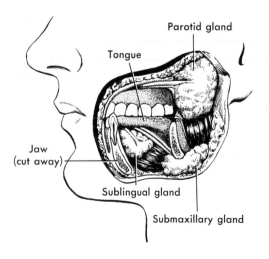

Parotid gland

Tongue

Jaw
(cut away)

Sublingual gland

Submaxillary gland

tions are called *glands*. They are more common and varied in animals than in plants. In some flowers the nectaries secrete a sweet fluid. In man the salivary glands (Figure 11-7) and others secrete digestive juices. The lachrymal glands secrete a fluid that moistens the eyes and has a peculiar tendency to overflow in the act of weeping. The secretions of the endocrine glands are the hormones, which we will consider a little later.

EXCRETION
IN HIGHER ANIMALS

What we have already learned of metabolism should suggest to us the major substances that have to be excreted by animals. The end product of respiration is CO_2. This usually leaves the body through the same organs that acquire O_2, that is, through the respiratory organs—gills or lungs in most animals. Respiration and numerous other metabolic processes also produce water, in addition to the water that is taken in as such. Water formed by metabolism is as useful as that drunk and is commonly retained for longer or shorter periods.

All animals do lose some water. In some situations this is an unavoidable loss of a needed substance rather than excretion of an unneeded end product; but water is often in excess and actively excreted. Water is a necessary part of urinary excretion, as we shall see in a moment. Water may also be lost in larger or smaller amounts from any surface of the organism. In man large quantities are lost from the lungs. This is not active excretion, but evaporation as an incidental result of the lung mechanism. We also lose much water through our sweat glands. Even when we are not actively sweating (when no visible drops of water appear on our skins), we lose a pint or so of water per day in this way. Several quarts may be lost on a hot day. This water is secreted by glands, but its significance is in heat regulation, not excretion. The loss of heat through the evaporation of sweat serves as a cooling mechanism.

Regulation of salt concentration and the production of salts by the metabolic breakdown of some compounds require that there be some mechanism for excretion of inorganic salts. In fishes that drink sea water and thus acquire excess salts, the gills are excretory organs for salt as well as for CO_2 (see Figure

11-8). Some salts are always excreted in fishes' urine, and this is usually the most important means of salt excretion, as it is in man. Because sweat is salty, it is widely believed that perspiration is an important route of salt excretion. Such is not the case. Loss of salt in sweat is quantitatively insignificant in comparison with loss of salt in urine and usually plays no essential part in body salt regulation. Exceptions may, however, occur in situations in which men sweat copiously for prolonged periods.

Contrary to another common impression, the intestine is primarily an organ of absorption, not of excretion. The feces consist almost entirely of undigested food (or indigestible matter taken in with the food) and masses of bacteria from the intestines—

materials that have not really been absorbed into the body and therefore cannot have been excreted. There is, however, some important excretion into the intestines. Dark brown bile pigments are excreted by the liver and flow into the intestines. These pigments are mainly end products of the destruction of hemoglobin in the liver and spleen.

All these modes and avenues of excretion in animals still fail to account for a large, important, and often toxic class of end products—those containing nitrogen. They are the end products of protein metabolism; you recall that proteins are the major category of body materials that contain nitrogen. Among the common end products are urea, $CO(NH_2)_2$, uric acid ($C_5H_4N_4O_3$), and ammonia (NH_3) (see Chapter 4). All three occur in human urine, largely as the result of the breakdown of different proteins. Urea is, however, about 20 times as abundant as the other two put together. Here is a curious fact. In almost all mammals uric acid is converted into a different compound before it is excreted. The exceptions are men, apes, and Dalmatian dogs. Except for that one breed, dogs follow the general rule and differ from man in the composition of their urine.

Animals differ greatly in their most abundant nitrogenous end products, and some interesting relationships are involved. Almost all aquatic animals, both invertebrates and vertebrates, excrete more ammonia than anything else. Ammonia is highly soluble, but it is also extremely poisonous. Its excretion involves solution in large amounts of water and copious, continuous or frequent flow of urine. Land animals excrete predominantly urea or uric acid. Almost all animals that lay eggs outside of water excrete more uric acid: land snails, insects, reptiles, and birds. Land animals that lay eggs in water or that do not lay eggs at all excrete more urea: adult amphibians and mammals. Uric acid is almost insoluble and leaves the body in solid crystals. It may also be safely stored for long periods because its insolubility prevents absorption. Urea is highly soluble and must be excreted in solution, but it is not seriously toxic except in unusually high concentrations. Can

FIG. 11-8 The maintenance of water balance in fishes.

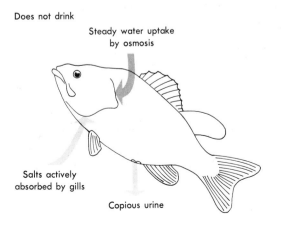

Continuously drinks sea water

Steady water loss by osmosis

Water in from gut

Salts actively excreted by gills

Little urine

A

Does not drink

Steady water uptake by osmosis

Salts actively absorbed by gills

Copious urine

B

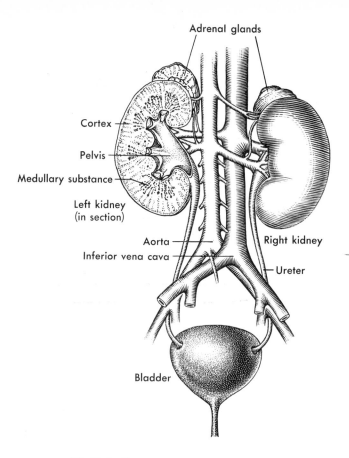

Adrenal glands

Cortex

Pelvis

Medullary substance

Left kidney
(in section)

Aorta

Inferior vena cava

Right kidney

Ureter

Bladder

FIG. 11-9 The urinary system in man, viewed from behind.

you think of any relationships between the ways of life of these various animals and their nitrogen excretion?

The Kidney

All the animals we have just mentioned have special organs that excrete nitrogenous wastes. These organs also largely affect the amount of water that leaves the body. In vertebrates the organ involved is the kidney, and we shall study the human kidney as an example (Figure 11-9).

The work of the kidney is done in minute tubules, over a million of them in each kidney. At one end of the tubule is a filter (called *Bowman's capsule*) closely applied to a ball of blood capillaries (the *glomerulus*) (Figure 11-10). Here a filtrate of plasma passes into the tubule. Its composition is essentially unchanged at this point, but the formed elements of the blood and colloidal proteins are filtered out

and do not enter the tubule. As the plasma filtrate passes down the tubule, which is also surrounded by capillaries, most of the water is reabsorbed and returned to the blood. Other substances such as glucose are also returned. Oddly enough, so is about half of the urea. Some additional substances also here move from the blood into the tubule. At the end of the tubule the fluid, which must be now called urine and is greatly altered in compositon from the plasma, flows into branched collecting tubes and finally through the ureter into the bladder. The bladder is only a storage reservoir and does not further alter the urine.

One of the more remarkable aspects of kidney function is the quantitative relationship between the amount of plasma filtrate that forms in the glomerulus and the amount of urine that eventually leaves the kidney. In an average-sized man, for example, the total volume of blood plasma is about 3200 milliliters. It has been shown that 130 milliliters of plasma filtrate are produced in the glomeruli each minute. This means that the whole plasma volume is reworked by glomerular filtration and tubular reabsorption 58 times a day or once every 25 minutes. It also means that about 187 liters (48 gallons) of glomerular filtrate are formed each day. Since only 1 to 2 liters of urine emerge from the kidneys each day, the kidney tubules must reabsorb 185 to 186 liters of water and selected solutes each day. Thus the kidney operates by first excreting everything and then taking back those items (in whole or in part) that the body needs to retain.

This process does more than excrete waste products. Selective absorption in the tubule and selective return of constituents of the plasma do much to regulate the composition of the blood. Substances in less than normal concentration in the blood are usually not retained in the tubule, and substances in more than normal concentration are usually retained in part. For instance, blood sugar is usually wholly returned to the blood, but if its concentration becomes abnormally high some is excreted in the urine. The tubules also retain and pass on to the bladder more water when the water content of the body is high and less when it is low. Thus control by the kidneys of the composition and volume of the blood, and hence of the internal environment of all body cells, is most effective.

Chemical Coordination

We have repeatedly emphasized that an organism is a unit, whose component parts interact with one another in a highly coordinated manner. Now let us think a little more about how the organism is unified, what ties it together. In the first place, it is bound together mechanically. It is enclosed in a skin of some kind. The various internal cells and tissues are in contact with each other and fastened together in various ways and at many points. There are skeletons, a bony framework, an external shell, connective tissue, the united cell walls of plants, or other arrangements that enclose part or all of the organism and to which tissues are fastened.

Another kind of unification is achieved through the nervous system. A nervous system is absent in protists, plants, and a few animals but is present in the great majority of animals. We know that it is of supreme importance in man, so much so that it will be considered at some length later in this chapter.

Still another mechanism of coordination exists, and this one is present in *all* organisms: it is the movement of chemical substances from one part of the organism to another. Chemicals diffuse and flow in the protoplasm among the parts of a protist within its single, cell-like mass. In nonvascular multicellular plants and animals, substances also diffuse from one cell to another and may be carried by water of the external environment in cavities or otherwise in the immediate vicinity of the organism. In vascular organisms, movements within and between cells occur too, and another feature has been added, especially apt for carrying chemical substances through the organism. There are internal fluids which, sooner or later, may move from any active cell of the body to any other.

As multicellular organization has been more intensively studied, it has become evident that all living cells must have some influence on adjacent cells. This influence is chemical in large part, although it may also have mechanical, electrical, and other elements. It has also become clear that any cell may produce substances that influence parts of the body quite distant from it. In other words, chemical

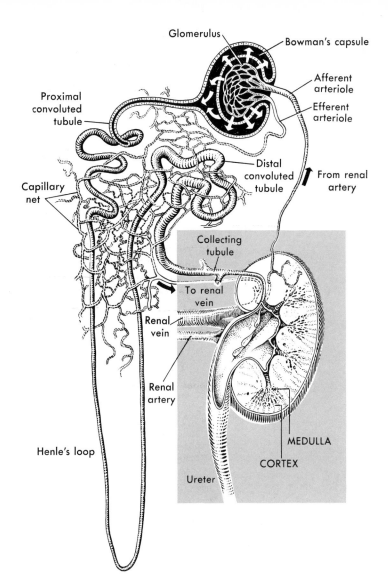

FIG. 11-10 Detail of a single kidney tubule in man.

coordination occurs everywhere in the organism, from and to all its cells, and not just between particular organs. A good but relatively simple example is provided by CO_2. Produced by all actively respiring cells, CO_2 passes into the blood stream and produces a specific effect at one point, the respiratory center, through which it initiates changes in the whole body.

Chemical coordination seems to be a general phenomenon of life, occurring in and between all the living parts of all organisms. However, certain organs produce specific chemical compounds that diffuse into the blood and have special, sometimes spectacular, results in the organism. These compounds, the hormones, have been intensively studied in man and other vertebrates.

The organs that produce hormones are the *endocrine glands*. It is interesting to realize that the two systems bearing the major responsibility for the control and integration of body functions—the endocrine system and the nervous system—have much in common. In both, the process being controlled is located some distance from a control center. And, to a great extent, both operate according to classical feedback principles (Chapter 4). There are also important differences between the two systems. The controlling messages of one system are nerve impulses, which travel along anatomically defined fibers and activate a limited number of cells within the influence of their peripheral endings. The messages of the endocrine system are the hormones, which enter the blood and, spreading widely, may influence cells and tissues in every part of the body. In general, nerve impulses control rapidly changing activities such as skeletal-muscle movements. Hormones, in contrast, act by altering the rates of cellular metabolic processes (Chapter 4). Thus it appears that hormone action is only a special instance of a much more general phenomenon. With this in mind, we may consider the hormones of man as our first examples of chemical coordination.

HORMONES OF THE HUMAN BODY

The human hormones are produced by endocrine glands or by endocrine tissues in organs that also have other activities. The word "endocrine" derives from the Greek and means "inside separation"—that is, *internal secretion*. The secretion is called internal because the secreted substances, the hormones, diffuse directly into the blood and do not leave the tissue—go outside of it—through tubes, as do the secretions of the so-called *exocrine glands*. In man, but not in all other organisms, each separate endocrine gland is definitely localized in the body, whether it constitutes a whole organ or not. The

various local endocrine glands are scattered through the head, neck, and trunk without any particular anatomical relationship to each other or to their activities (Figure 11-11). In fact, their activities characteristically affect many or all parts of the body.

Since the secretions of endocrine glands are rapidly carried everywhere by the circulatory system, no particular placement is necessary for their effectiveness. It seems logical, somehow, that the male hormone should be produced in the same organs

FIG. 11-11 The locations of the human endocrine glands. The left side of the illustration includes one of the pair of glands (testes) characteristic of the male, and the right side one of the pair of glands (ovaries) characteristic of the female. Since the parathyroids are not visible in the over-all view, they are shown from the back in the separate drawing.

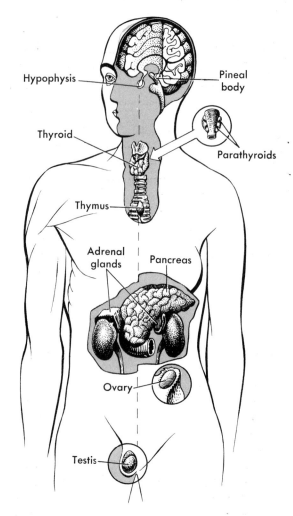

that produce the male sex cells, sperms. Undoubtedly there is a relationship, but it is historical rather than functional. The male sex hormone also affects processes of the body far distant from the testis, for instance, growth of hair on the face and changes in the vocal cords. The hormones resemble each other only in that they are all secreted into the blood and influence processes at various other points in the body, or throughout the body. They are all chemical messengers, mechanisms of coordination. They are not members of any one family of chemical compounds. At least one (insulin) is a protein, but others belong to quite diverse groups of simpler compounds.

Table 11-1 lists some of the better-known endocrine glands, their hormones, and their effects. The list is not exhaustive. For example, the duodenum produces secretin. The stomach and liver also produce hormones. Other organs, such as the pineal body in the brain and the thymus gland at the base of the neck, may be endocrine glands, but their activities are not yet clearly understood.

Note the kinds of functions that hormones control. Some influence chemical balances, especially in the blood. In other words, they help importantly to stabilize the internal environment. Others affect the rates of reactions concerned with growth and general bodily activity. Still others operate at particular times or periods of life to coordinate special developments and processes. Try making a classification of hormones along these lines. You will find that the distinctions are not clear-cut. The hormones, too, interact and are parts of an integrated system in the unified organism.

HORMONES OF PLANTS

Everyone has heard of "plant hormones." They are widely advertised both as stimulants for the growth of desirable plants and as killers for weeds. Plants differ from the more highly evolved animals in that their hormones are secreted by unspecialized tissues.

Since plants have no other active system of organic coordination but are nevertheless well-coordinated organisms, their hormones are particularly important. Each plant grows at a particular time of the year; each grows in its own characteristic way, each flowers at a definite time, and the fruits and leaves of some perennials also drop at definite times. There is nothing haphazard about these activities. They are coordinated processes of the organism, and the coordination must be largely if not altogether chemical in nature. It is, in fact, well established that hormones are involved in these and other processes. Yet only a few of the hormones have been definitely identified, so that this is a pioneering field of research at present. A special difficulty is the fact that the hormones are not secreted in endocrine tissues, where their isolation would be less difficult. The most fully known plant hormones are those called *auxins*. They are involved primarily in growth processes.

Auxins

"Auxin" is another invented word, coined from a Greek root meaning "to increase" or "grow." The term is still fairly precise in application to one definite class of plant hormones that promote elongation in growing cells, although they also have other activities. Their existence and some of their properties can be shown by simple experiments.

If oat seeds are germinated (Figure 11-12), they first send upward a bluntly pointed, leafless shoot. Actually the shoot has a leaf inside it. Botanists call the shoot a sheath, or *coleoptile,* because it surrounds the first leaf of the plant. If you cut off the tip, the shoot stops growing. Now place the tip, cut side down, on a little cube of gelatin or, better, agar jelly (a seaweed product much used in biological work) and leave it there for about 2 hours. Put the cube of agar on the cut end of a decapitated shoot. The shoot starts growing again. Something diffused from the tip into the agar, and the something—an auxin—promoted growth in the shoot (Figure 11-13).

Does the experiment as we have outlined it really prove this? As a matter of fact, it does not. Before you read on, try to think of alternative explanations and of ways to test them as hypotheses.

There are at least two other possible explanations: (1) perhaps growth of the shoot was only temporarily

TABLE 11-1 *Some Human Endocrine Glands and Hormones and Some of Their Effects*

Endocrine gland	Hormone	Processes affected or controlled	Symptoms of excess	Symptoms of deficiency
Thyroid	Thyroxin	Level of metabolism, oxidation rate, etc.	Irritability, nervous activity, exophthalmos	Cretinism when severe in infancy; lethargy, myxedema
Parathyroids	Parathyroid hormone	Calcium balance	Bone deformation	Spasms; death if severe
Adrenal medulla	Epinephrine	Stimulation similar to that of sympathetic nervous system	Increased blood pressure, pulse rate, blood glucose	None
Adrenal cortex	Aldosterone	Salt balance	Accumulation of body fluid	Addison's disease
	Corticosterone and cortisol	Carbohydrate metabolism, etc.	Abnormality of sugar and protein metabolism	
Pancreas	Insulin	Glucose metabolism	Shock, coma	Diabetes
Ovary	Estrogen	Female sex development and menstrual cycle		Interference with menstrual cycle and sexual activity
	Progesterone	Control of ovary and uterus during pregnancy		Sterility or miscarriage
Testis	Testosterone	Male sex development and activity		Lessened development of male characters and lessened sexual activity
Hypophysis (pituitary) Adenohypophysis	Adrenocorticotropic hormone (ACTH)	Control of adrenal cortex	Symptoms related to glands controlled.	
	Thyrotropic hormone	Control of thyroid		
	Gonadotropic hormones	Control of sex glands, etc.		
	Growth hormone	Growth	Gigantism	Dwarfism
Neurohypophysis	Antidiuretic hormone (vasopressin)	Kidney action	Excessive water in body	Excessive loss of water
	Oxytocin	Milk production and contraction of uterine muscle		Lessened or no milk production

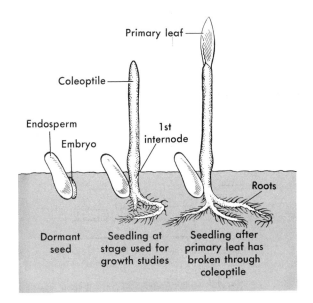

Primary leaf
Coleoptile
Endosperm
Embryo
1st internode
Roots

Dormant seed | Seedling at stage used for growth studies | Seedling after primary leaf has broken through coleoptile

FIG. 11-12 **The germination of an oat seed.** Left, before germination. Center, after germination. The young shoot system consists of a tubular sheath, the coleoptile, which contains within it the primary leaf. Right, after the primary leaf has emerged. The coleoptile itself is the subject of growth experiments undertaken to study plant hormones. (Adapted from *Principles of Plant Physiology*, by James Bonner and Arthur W. Galston. W. H. Freeman and Company. Copyright © 1952)

Three distinct but chemically related auxins have been isolated from plants and identified. The most widespread and only biologically active auxin is a simple derivative of the amino acid tryptophan, indole-3-acetic acid:

$$\text{CH}_2\text{—COOH}$$

Oddly enough, the same substances are common in animals, and one of them is present in human urine.

FIG. 11-13 **Plant hormones.** A, B, C, and D are a series of experiments demonstrating the existence of a diffusible growth hormone (auxin) in the tip of the oat coleoptile.

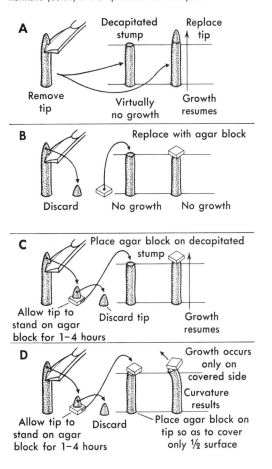

A Remove tip | Decapitated stump | Replace tip
Virtually no growth | Growth resumes

B Discard | Replace with agar block
No growth | No growth

C Allow tip to stand on agar block for 1–4 hours | Place agar block on decapitated stump
Discard tip | Growth resumes

D Allow tip to stand on agar block for 1–4 hours | Discard | Place agar block on tip so as to cover only ½ surface
Growth occurs only on covered side
Curvature results

stopped when it was decapitated and would have started again in a couple of hours anyway; or (2) perhaps the agar alone would have caused growth. To test these hypotheses the experiment requires *controls*. Decapitate three shoots at the same time. On one, put an agar cube that has had an opportunity to receive diffused material from a tip. On another put a cube exactly the same except that it has not been in contact with a tip. On the third do not put anything. Only the first shoot will grow, and the presence of a growth substance in the tip is substantially proved. It is still better to run multiple tests, giving each of the three treatments to three or four shoots.

Now try another experiment. Put a cube of agar that contains diffused auxin on a cut shoot in such a way as to cover only one side of the cut end. As the shoot grows, it will bend away from the side in contact with the jelly. That side receives more auxin and therefore grows faster, and the shoot is forced into a curve. This important reaction explains many of the motions and growth patterns of plants.

Here is further evidence of the unity of life, although the relationship is not wholly clear.

In extremely small concentrations, auxins cause the elongation of cells and hence growth in length, but with an increase in concentration, they inhibit growth. The effect is different on different plant tissues. A concentration producing the most rapid elongation of stems stops the growth of roots. Thus auxins are not merely growth promoters. They are growth *regulators,* either stimulating or retarding growth depending on the circumstances. In addition, they may directly initiate or promote mitosis. The mechanism of this effect is unknown.

A number of chemical compounds not normally present in plants have auxinlike effects due to resemblances to the natural auxins in molecular composition and structure. Such chemicals can be synthesized in commercial quantities and have many increasingly practical applications. Probably the most familiar at present is 2,4-D (2,4-dichlorophenoxyacetic acid). This compound produces abnormal, distorted growth and eventually death in wide-leaved plants but has little effect on the narrow leaves of grass. It can therefore be used as a spray to free a lawn of weeds. (It kills clover, though.) Auxins and auxinlike synthetics are also used to stimulate root formation on cuttings, to produce seedless fruits, to keep stored potatoes from sprouting, and to delay or force blooming in flowers.

Other Plant Hormones

The presence of several other hormone-like substances in plants is known or inferred. The *gibberellins* are a family of at least nine different but closely related compounds. They affect growth but in ways different from auxins. For example, they do not cause a shoot (or coleoptile) to bend, as auxins do; rather, they induce elongation of the whole stem. In addition, gibberellin is active in such diverse developmental phenomena in plants as increase in flower and fruit size, relieving genetic dwarfness in corn and peas, and replacement of a winter cold period in biennial plants which results in earlier flowering. Thus, gibberellin is active in a wide range of phenomena, and it appears highly likely that in the future we will learn of many more places where it is active. Other compounds that can promote cell division are derived from purines and nucleic acids and are known as *kinins.* Although they are effective in experiments, it is still uncertain whether they have an essential role in natural development.

Among the most important activities of plants are the induction of flowering and the consequent fruiting. These are influenced by the environment. The environmental control is usually the length of darkness, although it is commonly and confusingly referred to as the day length. "Short-day" (really "long-night") plants, such as ragweed and cocklebur, blossom as the ratio of light to dark decreases seasonally below a characteristic value. "Long-day" (or "short-night") plants, such as plantain and coneflower, bloom when the ratio increases to a fixed value. Elaborate experiments indicate that the ratio of light to darkness influences the formation of some substance in the leaves, perhaps only by the modification of the rate of formation. After its formation the substance moves only through living tissues, especially phloem, to the parts most concerned with flowering. The pigment, *phytochrome,* which absorbs the light has been isolated, but the controlling substance has not yet been surely identified. Part of the difficulty may be that it is not *a* hormone but a mixture or succession of different compounds. Also, it (or they) may not directly induce flowering but may overcome an inhibitor, which could be an auxin. This is a significant problem of plant physiology.

Nervous Coordination

In all but the lowest animals the most essential and characteristic part of the mechanism for specific responses to stimuli is the nervous system. All special receptor organs in animals transform stimuli into nerve impulses. A nerve impulse is an electrical signal transmitted along fiberlike extensions of nerve cells. The nerves are the conductors from receptors to effectors. Their pathways and connections determine what, in the end, the response will be. Increasing complications along these pathways are mechanisms for coordination of actions, for memory, for perception, for association, and finally for all the richness of our own mental lives. The nervous system, too, has come to share with chemical integration the wisdom of the body automatic maintenance of the internal environment. The nervous system of a clam or of a worm is truly remarkable. What can we say of the nervous system of man, so vastly more complex? It is this that makes us mankind, organisms beyond the potentialities of any others that have ever existed.

NERVE CELLS

One of the most remarkable facts about the nervous system is that, with all its complication and flexibility of reaction, it is made up of cells all of which perform essentially the same action. The action is produced by the extremely complex, interlocking processes so characteristic of life, but the action itself is rather simple; it is merely the transmission of impulses from one end of the cell to another. The impulses are the same sort in all nerves, although they may be involved in seeing red (either literally or figuratively), in composing a poem, in telling us that we are hot or cold, or in the coordinated contracting of muscles that eventuates in a song or a swift kick. It is not the separate nerve cells but their arrangements and connections that determine the qualitatively different outcomes. We see that in many ways the properties of an organism are different from and more complex than those of its separate parts.

The unit of the nervous system is the nerve cell, or neuron. For all their differences in size and shape, neurons are fundamentally alike in all animals that have them. The nucleus lies in a central cell body that is drawn out into two or more fibrous projections. The projections may be short, but usually are long fibers, much thinner than hairs. Nerve impulses can pass in either direction along these fibers. In some lower animals an impulse may come into the cell body along any fiber and then move away through all the others, out to their tips. Most neurons in higher animals, however, are so arranged anatomically that impulses always travel through them in

the same direction. A frequent, although not the only, arrangement in these cases is with numerous, shorter branching fibers, the *dendrites,* on one side, through which impulses come into the cell body, and one longer fiber, the *axon,* on the other side, carrying impulses away from the cell body. The fibers are often enclosed in one or more sheaths. The sheaths are not essential to conduction, for unsheathed fibers also occur and transmit impulses of the same sort. Not only do the sheaths look rather like insulation on electric wires, they also include partial insulators that increase the speed of impulse transmission. One of the sheaths, when present, is also known to play a crucial role in the regeneration of injured fibers.

A nerve such as you are likely to see when you dissect an animal in the laboratory is not a single fiber but a whole bundle of fibers belonging to different neurons. In vertebrate animals most of the cell bodies of nerves are in or near the brain and spinal cord. Some of the fibers may run through nerves for long distances. In man some extend down to the toes from cell bodies in the small of the back. It is exceedingly difficult to follow a single fiber through its whole length, and earlier students could not believe that a fiber in a toe was actually part of a cell with its nucleus several feet away. However, experimentation and more delicate dissection have proved that this is true.

NERVE IMPULSES

The nature of the nerve impulse has been the subject of long, ingenious investigation and of much dispute. The main features now seem to be well established, although certain details remain unknown. How would one go about finding what chemical and electrical changes are going on in a fiber much smaller than a hair? Just to make it more difficult, the changes take place in a small fraction of a second, and everything is back as it was before the impulse passed. Despite these difficulties, so much has been learned of the nerve impulse that we can only indicate its general nature here. The impulse is electrical, although associated with and set up by chemical changes. It is not simple conduction of an electrical current, as in the transmission of a message over a wire. The impulse accompanies a zone of electrical charges in the nerve fiber, a zone that moves alone with the flux of small, purely local currents and ions between the fiber and the fluids immediately around it.

The mechanism of the nerve impulse has a bearing on the properties that, in turn, help in understanding the whole process of reaction to stimuli in animals. One consequence of the mechanism is that the impulse moves much more slowly than a current in a wire. The speed varies greatly from one nerve to another and one animal to another but is always slow enough that conduction takes appreciable time. In the fastest fibers of mammals, including man, the rate is about 100 meters per second. This is a little less than 225 miles per hour, which does not seem very fast to us in this age of much faster planes. In some of the slow invertebrate fibers, the rate is as low as 5 centimeters per second, or about 0.1 mile per hour. A tortoise can walk faster than this. Even in some human fibers the rate is lower than 2 meters per second, which is no faster than we can walk.

Another point about the mechanism of nerve conduction is that the strength of the impulse is standardized. It is not like putting an impulse of variable strength into a wire. The reaction is local in each part of the fiber. If an impulse is started at all, it starts at full strength and the strength is not affected by the length of the fiber. A usual way to make this sort of process understandable is to compare the fiber with a sprinkled line of gunpowder. If the powder is lit at one end, the flash travels to the other end. The rate of travel and the strength of the flash do not depend at all on the heat of the match with which it was lit or the length of the line. A nerve fiber similarly transmits impulses by local power at each point and has an *all-or-none reaction.* Comparison with the gunpowder cannot be carried further, because the reactions involved are really quite different.

No matter how strong the stimulus is, the impulse in a given nerve has a fixed strength. How, then, does it happen that the impulses do have varied intensities in their effects? The answer is that a stimulus seldom starts a single impulse. Unless the stimulus is extremely brief, repeated impulses will pass along the fiber one after the other. A stronger stimulus will result in impulses that are closer together, and therefore more frequent. More of them arrive at the other end, and so they can have a stronger effect even though each has the same intensity.

All protoplasm reacts to stimulation and conducts impulses. Nerve cells do not have unique properties, but are only specialized in the sense of heightening the particular property of conductivity and directing it anatomically. Nerve cells also carry on respiration and other metabolic processes of protoplasm in general. In fact nerve cells have particularly high oxidation rates (nerve cell mitochondria, the loci of this oxidative activity, can be seen in Figure 8-15) and are especially sensitive to variations in concentration of sugar, the principal source of energy. Thinking really is work, not just because some of us are reluctant to indulge in it, but because it does use energy even though in amounts smaller than for muscular activity.

NERVE CONNECTIONS

In some lowly animals, receptor cells are in direct contact with an effector. The receptor or sensory cell receives a stimulus and transmits an impulse (as if it were a neuron) direct to a muscle cell (Figure 11-14A), which contracts when the receptor is stimulated. In the next stage of complication, the sensory cell starts an impulse in a separate nerve cell, through which the impulse travels to a muscle fiber or other effector (Figure 11-14B). In either of these systems, the reaction is necessarily simple and entirely inflexible. A sufficient stimulus, one above threshold, on the sensory cell invariably and necessarily results in an impulse to one particular effector, which responds in a way that usually varies only in duration.

In higher animals sensory cells are rarely in direct contact with effectors, and they never are in verte-

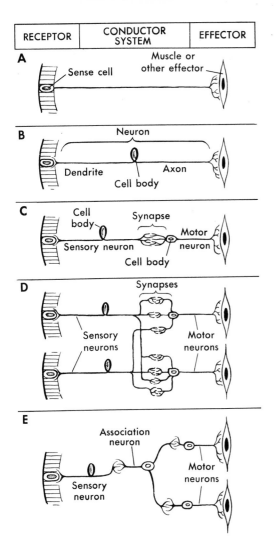

| RECEPTOR | CONDUCTOR SYSTEM | EFFECTOR |

A
Sense cell
Muscle or other effector

B
Neuron
Dendrite
Axon
Cell body

C
Cell body
Synapse
Sensory neuron
Motor neuron
Cell body

D
Synapses
Sensory neurons
Motor neurons

E
Association neuron
Sensory neuron
Motor neurons

FIG. 11-14 Receptor–conductor–effector systems.

brates. Almost always there is more than one nerve cell between receptor and effector, with branches in the possible lines traveled by nerve impulses. A *sensory neuron* carries impulses from the receptor and passes them on to a *motor neuron*. The motor neuron in turn conducts the impulse to an effector, characteristically a muscle fiber, which reacts. This is still a simple chain from receptor to effector. It is a *reflex arc* (Figure 11-14C). Even this relatively simple arrangement brings in the possibility of more effective and flexible response than direct connection between

a receptor and an effector. When there are separate sensory and motor neurons, one sensory neuron can stimulate more than one motor neuron (Figure 11-14D). Response to stimulation can be more extensive, and continued stimulation can spread so as to involve more and more effectors. Yet the reaction must still be a simple reflex, a connection from one particular receptor to one particular set of effectors.

The next complication, which has become practically universal among animals such as insects or vertebrates, is the occurrence of still other nerve cells, one or many, between the sensory and the motor neurons (Fig. 11-14E). These additional cells are *association neurons*. Through them, an impulse may be passed on selectively to any of a number of different effectors. Impulses from different receptors may also be brought together and routed to the same or different effectors. Simple reflexes can still occur, but the possibilities for more complex and flexible reactions are tremendously increased.

The fibers through which an impulse is passed from one neuron to another are not continuous or fused to each other. They may be pressed close together, but there is always a tiny gap between them, a separation by cell membranes, at least. The point of transfer, with its tiny gap, is called a *synapse*. The actual mechanism of transfer is still incompletely known. When an impulse reaches a synapse, a minute quantity of a chemical compound appears there. The compounds that have been detected (there are at least two of them) have a stimulating effect on nerves. One of them is very like epinephrine, and the other is acetylcholine. These chemicals bring about the transmission of the nerve signal, an electrochemical impulse, from one nerve fiber to another.

The fact that impulses are not conducted through fibers from one neuron to another has some important consequences. One or a few impulses or widely spaced impulses may arrive at a synapse and not cross it. If numerous impulses arrive at close intervals, they add up (*summation* occurs, technically speaking), and finally they are transmitted across the synapse. A brief, weak stimulus produces few and widely spaced impulses. These may cross no synapses, so that no response occurs, or few synapses, so that response is weak and local. A long, strong stimulus produces many and closely spaced impulses. These readily cross synapses, so that response definitely occurs, and can cross many synapses, so that response may become strong and widespread, especially as association neurons become involved.

Another important property of synapses is that once an impulse has been transmitted across them, subsequent impulses pass more readily. It may take a long volley of closely spaced impulses to cross a synapse, but once this has occurred, a short sequence of impulses or even a single impulse may cross. The fact that impulses have already been transmitted facilitates transmission of later impulses; this phenomenon is called *facilitation*. If no further impulses do come along, the effect fades out, often in a matter of seconds or minutes. If impulses keep coming along before facilitation has entirely faded out, the facilitation is maintained and increased. Continual crossing of a particular synapse at appropriate intervals can maintain facilitation there for a lifetime. Thus there are established pathways in the nervous system, routes across facilitated synapses, along which impulses move more readily and rapidly.

Once a response or an association has occurred, it occurs more readily soon thereafter. If it occurs often, its readiness increases and it may be maintained

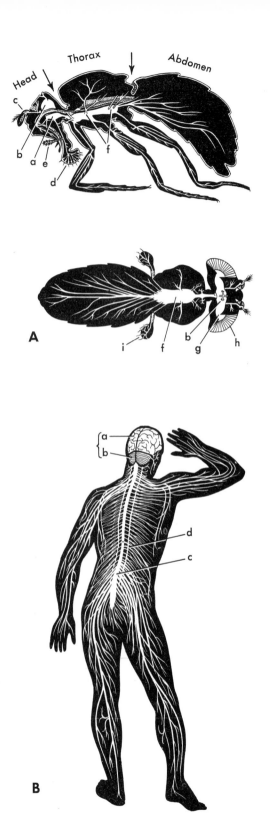

FIG. 11-15 **Nervous systems.** A. An arthropod nervous system, that of the fruit fly *Drosophila*. Note in the side view how the central nervous system (white) lies ventrally to the gut (stippled), which is shown only as it passes through the head and thorax, except in the head, where the brain encircles the esophagus: a, ventral portion of the brain; b, dorsal portion of the brain; c, antenna carrying diverse kinds of sense organs; d, sucking structure leading to the mouth; e, maxillary palp (d and e are also endowed with sense organs); f, large concentration of nerve cells in the thorax. The dorsal view shows also g, optic nerve from the compound eye (h), and i, balancer, a remarkable sense organ that assists the fly to maintain its orientation in flight. B. A vertebrate nervous system, that of man, showing the organization into brain (a, cerebrum; b, cerebellum) and dorsal spinal cord (c), from which individual nerves supply all parts of the body. The two sympathetic nerve trunks (d) lie on either side of the spinal cord.

indefinitely. Clearly this is a mechanism that goes far toward explaining habit, learning, and memory.

The termination of a nerve fiber on an effector, such as a muscle, is anatomically unlike a synapse, but it has similar properties of summation and facilitation.

STRUCTURE OF THE VERTEBRATE BRAIN

The precise number and pattern of nerves of course differ greatly from one species to another and even among individuals of the same species. Those anatomical details do not concern us here. In the vertebrates the tendency for concentration of central control reaches a peak, and the evolution of the brain is the most important single factor in the success of this group.

The central nervous system of all vertebrates consists of a *single, hollow* nerve cord that runs along the *back* (dorsal part) of the body. These basic anatomical characteristics of the nervous system do not occur in any living invertebrates—reason enough to infer that none of them preserve just the same structure that was present in those ancient invertebrates from which vertebrates evolved. The brain of the great majority of modern higher invertebrates is a ring of nerve tissue surrounding the esophageal part of the alimentary canal. The ring consists of two *ganglia* (masses of nerve-cell bodies) lying above the esophagus and connected to two others lying

below. Two solid nerve cords leave the *sub*esophageal ganglia and extend backward along the length of the body under (or *ventral* to) the gut. The fact that the brain is an anterior inflation of the nerve cord is the principal similarity in the gross anatomy of the central nervous system of the more advanced living invertebrates and vertebrates (Figure 11-15).

The most primitive vertebrate brain consisted mainly of three irregular swellings of the hollow nerve cord, each with various thickenings of the walls. The three enlargements are the *forebrain, midbrain,* and *hindbrain,* which can still be distinguished in the human brain, with its vastly greater complications. Very early, even in primitive fishes, further complications occurred. The forebrain became divided into three parts: (1) the *thalamus* and associated structures; (2) a pair of swellings farther forward and higher, the *cerebral hemispheres* (or, taken together, the *cerebrum*); and (3) the *olfactory bulbs,* which project as swellings from the lower front of each cerebral hemisphere (Figure 11-16). The midbrain developed various swellings, especially an upper pair, the *optic lobes.* A large swelling developed on the forward, upper part of the hindbrain and became the *cerebellum.* The much thickened lower wall of the hindbrain is the *medulla oblongata.*

There are dozens of other distinguishable parts even in fairly primitive vertebrate brains, but the *main* parts from front to back are as shown in Figures 11-16 and 11-17.

FIG. 11-16 Parts of the vertebrate brain, in generalized and schematized representation. The lower figure is a longitudinal section showing local differences in thickness of the brain wall.

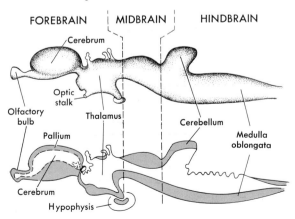

FOREBRAIN | MIDBRAIN | HINDBRAIN

Cerebrum

Optic stalk

Olfactory bulb

Pallium

Thalamus

Cerebrum

Hypophysis

Cerebellum

Medulla oblongata

Forebrain	{ Olfactory bulbs Cerebral hemispheres (the cerebrum) Thalamus (with an upper epithalamus, lower hypothalamus, etc.)
Midbrain	Optic lobes, in mammals four (two pairs) swellings called the *corpora quadrigemina,* "quadruplet bodies"
Hindbrain	{ Cerebellum (forward and above) Medulla oblongata (below)

All parts of the brain connect directly or through chains of neurons with the spinal cord through the medulla oblongata, which grades into the spinal cord without sudden change. The brain also has a series

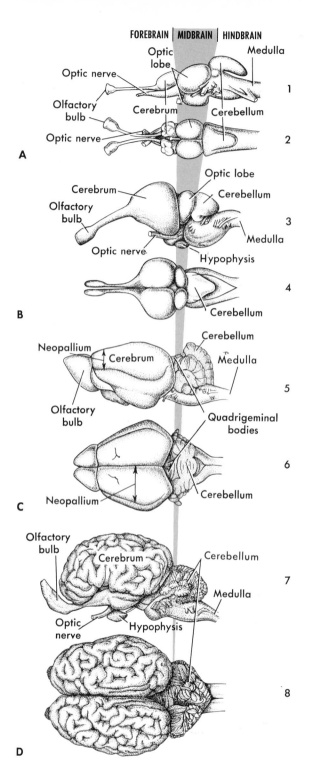

FOREBRAIN | MIDBRAIN | HINDBRAIN

A
Optic nerve
Optic lobe
Medulla
Olfactory bulb
Cerebrum
Cerebellum
Optic nerve
1
2

B
Cerebrum
Olfactory bulb
Optic lobe
Cerebellum
Optic nerve
Medulla
Hypophysis
Cerebellum
3
4

C
Neopallium
Cerebrum
Cerebellum
Medulla
Olfactory bulb
Quadrigeminal bodies
Neopallium
Cerebellum
5
6

D
Olfactory bulb
Cerebrum
Cerebellum
Medulla
Optic nerve
Hypophysis
7
8

FIG. 11-17 The expansion of the forebrain in vertebrate evolution. Four vertebrate brains are shown in side view (odd numbers) and from above (even numbers). The proportionate sizes of fore-, mid-, and hindbrains may be judged from the width of the stippled pathway, which approximates the midbrain in each case. The huge proportionate increase in size of the forebrain is obvious. Although the forebrain was originally principally concerned with olfaction, its expansion is due to the growth of the cerebrum, which is concerned with general association and control.

of paired nerves of its own that connect it directly with some sense organs and muscles. The forebrain is connected with the smell receptors in the nose. The midbrain is connected with the light receptors in the eyes and, by two separate pairs of nerves, with the eye muscles. The hindbrain has a whole series of nerves—usually six pairs in lower forms and eight in higher forms, including man—that connect with the more scattered receptors and with the muscles of the head.

NERVE PATTERNS AND RESPONSES

In animals with well-developed nervous systems, specific reactions to stimuli depend mainly on how nerves act and how they are arranged. The kinds of reactions that may occur depend on the nerve pattern: how many nerves there are, what receptors stimulate them, how they run to synapses and to effectors, what associative paths are present, and so on. This arrangement is determined mostly by heredity, although it may also be somewhat affected by the conditions of early development. The reactions that actually *do* occur depend first of all on the stimuli that an individual happens to receive, next on the mainly inherited nerve pattern, and finally on the past experiences and current condition of the individual. Facilitation, in particular, depends largely on what responses the individual organism has already made.

Thus in higher animals what an animal does, its whole pattern of behavior, and indeed what sort of creature it is, are more closely related to its nervous system than to any other one factor. As neurons become more abundant and patterns more complex, culminating in man, responses and associations become more varied, too, and so do the experiences imprinted on the nervous system. Herein is the basis not only of the high and numerous capacities of mankind, but also of individuality and of personality.

Receptors

The nervous system is largely involved in handling information about the environment. It also handles information about the organism itself. It is involved in responses to changes in the environment and also, with increasing complexity, with sorting out and associating information, storing impressions for future responses, varying responses according to current situations, and other activities all of which go back to the receipt of information about the environment. (Can you imagine what your mental life would be like if you could have no knowledge about things outside your own body?)

We have inherited from antiquity the popular notion that we have just five senses: sight, hearing, taste, smell, and touch. A little thought or simple experimentation suffices to show that this is false. We have five large, complex, and definitely localized sets of sense organs: eyes, the hearing mechanism of the ears, an organ of equilibration connected with the inner ear but producing very different sensations, the taste organs in the mouth, and the smelling organs in the nose. It is significant that all these localized organs are in the head. Elsewhere throughout most parts of the body we have an extremely large number of small, anatomically simple, scattered receptors. These vary and intergrade so much in structure and in the sensations produced that it is really impossible to say how many senses they represent.

In the skin, especially well provided with scattered receptors, there are at least four distinct senses, that is, there are at least four kinds of receptors each of which on stimulation produces a different sort of sensation. The sensations are: warmth, cold, pain, and touch or pressure. A little exploration with a pin and small warm and cold rods will convince you that these sensations have receptors definitely localized at certain spots and distinct from each other. Many other receptors of diverse sorts occur within the body. We feel the tenseness of muscles, the motion of joints, hunger, thirst, internal pain, nausea, sexual orgasm, and other distinct sensations that originate inside ourselves.

An ameba or almost any single, undifferentiated cell reacts to stimuli of many different kinds. Now we are interested in the development of special receptors that react to particular sorts of stimuli. Such specialization clearly depends on protoplasm and has evolved from its general reactivity. In all but the simplest animals it has resulted in the development of organs in which stimulated receptor cells start impulses in nerve fibers. Light receptors will serve as an example.

LIGHT RECEPTORS

All protoplasm is sensitive to some kinds of radiation, including the radiation that is visible to us and that we therefore call *light*. (But sensitivity in most protoplasm is usually greater to ultraviolet, which is invisible to us.) As a stimulus giving information about the environment, light is in a class by itself in the amount of information it can give and in giving information about things at a distance from the organism. Comparisons of simple and more complex light receptors, or photoreceptors, are especially interesting because they show how more and more information can be gained from the same stimulus.

The very simplest sorts of light receptors—one could hardly call them "eyes" at this stage—occur even in some protists as well as in simple multicellular animals (Figure 11-18). They are sensitive spots of light-absorbing pigment. They really give no information from a distance but only indicate whether light is present or absent where the animal is. Some or all of these simple animals also react to increase or decrease in intensity of light.

More complex eyes, such as occur in most invertebrates, have evolved with great diversity of details in form and structure. They almost always involve one or both of two features: the presence of a lens and of several to many separate light-sensitive cells, each capable of starting impulses in a nerve fiber. A lens concentrates light on the sensitive cells. It

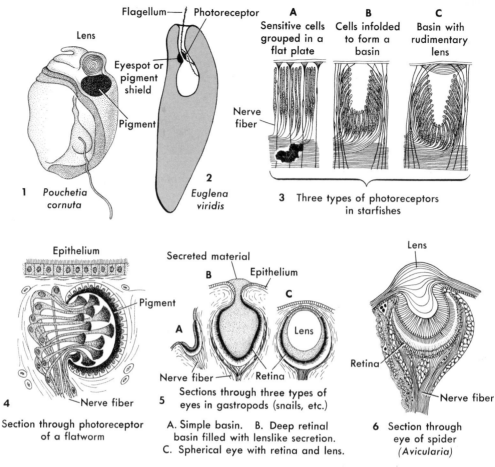

Flagellum — Photoreceptor

Lens

Eyespot or pigment shield

Pigment

1 *Pouchetia cornuta*

2 *Euglena viridis*

A Sensitive cells grouped in a flat plate

B Cells infolded to form a basin

C Basin with rudimentary lens

Nerve fiber

3 Three types of photoreceptors in starfishes

Epithelium

Pigment

Nerve fiber

4

Section through photoreceptor of a flatworm

Secreted material

Epithelium

B

C

A

Lens

Nerve fiber — Retina

5 Sections through three types of eyes in gastropods (snails, etc.)

A. Simple basin. B. Deep retinal basin filled with lenslike secretion.
C. Spherical eye with retina and lens.

Lens

Retina

Nerve fiber

6 Section through eye of spider *(Avicularia)*

FIG. 11-18 **A variety of photoreceptors.** The eyes illustrated belong to a diverse array of organisms. In groups as different as snails, starfishes, and spiders, there has been an evolutionary tendency to develop special light-absorbing cells and a lens that concentrates or focuses the light on these cells. The frequency with which this system has evolved in unrelated organisms attests to the importance of photoreceptors. Light energy is actually absorbed by pigment molecules in the receptor cells of the eye. The absorbed light energy initiates in these cells chemical reactions that ultimately stimulate associated nerve cells. 1 and 2 are examples of very simple photoreceptors in unicellular organisms. In some protists, like *Pouchetia* (1), a simple lens concentrates the light on the absorbing pigment molecules in the cell behind the lens. 3. A simple kind (A) of photoreceptor in starfishes consists of a flat plate of nerve cells that contain the light-absorbing pigment. Other starfish photoreceptors (B, C) illustrate the evolution of a more efficient system with infolded nerve cells and eventually a simple lens formed by a thickening of the epithelium. 4. In the flatworm's eye light-absorbing pigment is concentrated in a separate layer of cells lying in front of the nerve cells they ultimately stimulate. 5. Snails (gastropods) have eyes of varying degrees of complexity. The simplest (A) is a basin of pigment-carrying cells supplied with nerves. The most complex (C), which has surely evolved from a simple beginning like (A), has a spherical lens. 6. The eye of the spider *Avicularia* is similar to that of the snail but arose entirely independently.

therefore permits reaction to weaker intensities of light and also finer discrimination between different intensities. An eye with a lens also gives a new sort of information: the direction from which light is coming. This clearly facilitates and directs the re-

sponse, widespread in animals, of moving toward or away from light. Increase in number of sensitive cells also makes response to light and to changes in intensity more delicate. Moreover, if there are many sensory cells back of the lens, different cells will be stimulated in succession when light or dark objects move in front of the lens. In the simple kinds of such eyes no true image is formed. The organism cannot tell *what* is moving in front of its eye, but it can distinguish and respond to the fact that motion has occurred. This is a great advance in amount of information received, and it can include information (even though of a vague sort) about happenings at some distance from the animal.

There is no doubt that lenses first evolved not as image-formers but merely as mechanisms for concentrating light from particular directions. It is, however, a fact (you can call it a peculiarly fortunate coincidence) that lenses can form images by focusing light on a surface. If a lens is of appropriate shape, if the number of sensitive cells increases greatly, and if all the cells are arranged as a *retina* on the curved surface where the lens focuses an image, then it is possible for the eye to receive an image and to translate it into a pattern of nerve impulses (Figure 11-19).

These evolutionary developments have occurred more than once. There need not have been, and quite surely was not, a definite point or sudden change when eyes began to receive images. Increased discrimination of light intensity, direction, and movement would gradually begin to produce a vague image. Variation such as occurs in all groups of animals would mean that the image was a little less vague for some than for others. It is definitely an advantage for a sufficiently complex animal to be able to discriminate what is approaching it; this becomes possible as even vague images are formed. On an average, animals with clearer images would have better chances to survive and to pass their characteristics down to posterity. Thus extremely slow but steady improvement in the image would occur. What do you think of the claim, sometimes made, that eyes like ours must have appeared all at once because they would be of no use at all until they were perfect?

Eyes with single lenses forming useful images have evolved, entirely independently, at least three times: in some of the more active and complex mollusks (such as the octopus), in some spiders, and in the early vertebrates, from which we and all other vertebrates have inherited them.

There is another sort of information that can be conveyed by light and that may be useful in identifying objects and discriminating among them; this is *color*, which depends on the wavelengths of light transmitted or reflected. Animals may, and many do, see very well by light of various wavelengths without discriminating *differences* between the wavelengths. Such animals do not have color vision. (It really is not correct to call these species colorblind, because most of them simply never had color vision.) Color vision, the ability to distinguish different wavelengths of light, has evolved several times. Some crustaceans have it, and so do many insects. Some insects, including honeybees, not only see ultraviolet but also see it as a color, as different from, say, green. Of course we have not the slightest idea what ultraviolet color looks like to a bee, any more than a bee could imagine (if it had an imagination) what red looks like to us. Red is black (absence of light) to a bee, as ultraviolet is to us.

Strangely enough, color vision may have been lost and regained in our ancestry. Many fishes and reptiles and most birds have color vision, but most mammals do not. Primitive mammals probably lacked color vision. At least this is slight or absent among most present-day mammals except man and his nearest relatives, the apes and some monkeys. Dogs, cats, horses, and most other mammals may in some cases have very feeble discrimination of colors, but more probably they have no color vision.

The evolution of image-forming eyes has involved other refinements and extensions of the capacity to obtain information from light. Many of these refinements can be seen in our own eyes, which are about as highly developed as any. The whole apparatus is enclosed in a ball, which can be turned by its own muscles. Both eyes habitually focus on the same point, and the stereoscopic effect is a clue to distance. This is uncommon in animals other than man; man also uses other clues to distinguish distance, and many other animals rely wholly on clues other than the stereoscopic effect. The lens is elastic and can be focused. A variable diaphragm, the *iris*, automatically adjusts to light intensity. The sensory, retinal, cells are of two sorts, one set (the *rods*) especially sensitive

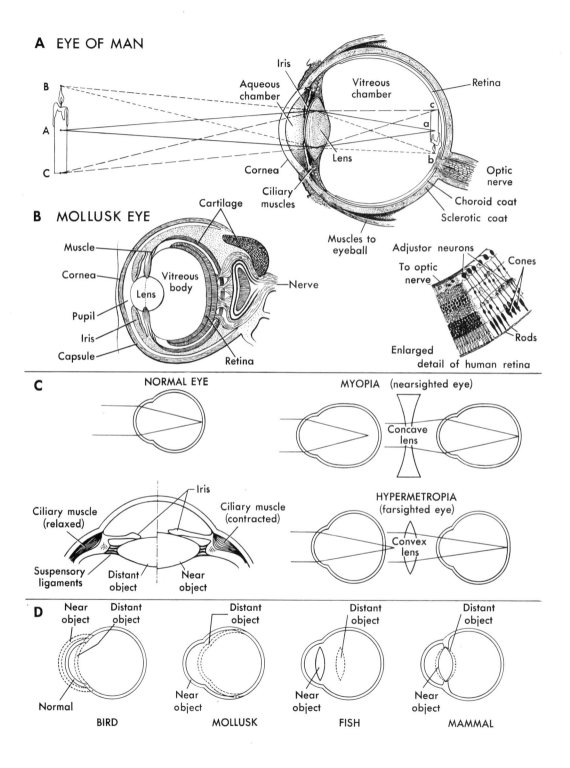

A EYE OF MAN

Iris

Aqueous chamber

Vitreous chamber

Retina

B

A

C

c
a
b

Optic nerve

Cornea

Lens

Choroid coat

Ciliary muscles

Sclerotic coat

Muscles to eyeball

Adjustor neurons

To optic nerve

Cones

B MOLLUSK EYE

Cartilage

Muscle

Cornea

Vitreous body

Lens

Nerve

Pupil

Iris

Capsule

Retina

Rods

Enlarged detail of human retina

C

NORMAL EYE

MYOPIA (nearsighted eye)

Concave lens

Iris

Ciliary muscle (relaxed)

Ciliary muscle (contracted)

HYPERMETROPIA (farsighted eye)

Convex lens

Suspensory ligaments

Distant object

Near object

D

Near object

Distant object

Distant object

Distant object

Distant object

Normal

Near object

Near object

Near object

BIRD

MOLLUSK

FISH

MAMMAL

and active in dim light, the other set (the *cones*) active in bright light. Only the cones are involved in color vision. Altogether, the eye in the higher vertebrates—perhaps even more in birds than in man or other mammals—is the most complex receptor that has ever evolved.

Before leaving the subject of light reception, we must mention another point of great importance here. There is much more to the sense of vision, or any other sense, than the receptor. Complex as it is, the eye does no more than send a series of signals, all of the same sort and intensity but varying in frequency, along a large number of nerve paths. If these signals were diverted to a muscle, the muscle would contract, and that is all. The fact that an optical image was involved in their formation would have no meaning. The image becomes meaningful—it is really information to the organism—only if all the separate signals are somehow associated into a whole pattern simultaneously grasped. This process does not occur mainly if at all in the eye. It takes place through an incredibly complex arrangement of extremely numerous associative and conductive neurons in the

brain. Thus the image formed in the eye is transformed into a *perception* in the brain.

It follows that an eye that is optically image-forming is not really image-forming for the organism unless it is accompanied by a complex associative system precisely related to it. The advanced sort of receptor could not evolve without this evolution in the brain. Organisms without brains or with simple brains can have only simple light receptors or none. At each level of complexity there is only so much information that can become meaningful for the organism and that can, therefore, really be information for it.

The effector system is also involved in the interrelationship that starts with the receptor. The more complex receptors make finer discriminations. A simple eye receives information adequate to conclude, "Something is moving." But a complex eye provides enough information for the discriminating observa-

FIG. 11-19 Image-forming eyes of the camera type. Image-forming eyes comparable to cameras have evolved in at least two different groups of animals. The lens system has been transformed in the course of evolution from a mere light-concentrator to a precise optical device that focuses an image on a light-sensitive retina. A. The eye of man, a vertebrate. B. The eye of the squid, a mollusk. Essentially both eyes consist of a light-sensitive retina; a light-focusing system, cornea and lens; an iris that controls the amount of light entering the eye by adjusting the diameter of the pupil; and a protective coating. In the squid the protective coating is a complex and heavy cartilaginous casing; in man it is the sclerotic coat, a strong elastic connective tissue. (The cornea is the transparent and strongly curved anterior portion of this sclerotic coat.) The detail of the inset shows how the rods and cones are arranged in the human retina. Note how the nerve fibers from the retina run over its surface on their way to the optic nerve. C. Accommodation (or focusing) of the human eye. Incoming light rays are focused on the retina mainly by the strongly curved surface of the cornea. Final adjustment is made by the lens, which is suspended by ligaments immediately behind the iris. The curvature of the lens surface is regulated by the tension of the ciliary muscles. When the ciliary muscles contract, ligamentous tension on the lens decreases, and the elasticity of the lens causes it to bulge, increasing its surface curvature and bringing near objects into focus on the retina. Myopia (top right in C) is an abnormal condition in which the eye cannot focus on distant objects. Its usual cause is an eyeball too long for its lens system, so that, even when the ciliary muscles are fully relaxed, the focal plane lies in front of the retina. The condition can be compensated for by the use of concave lenses in eyeglasses. Hypermetropia (bottom right in C) is the reverse condition, in which the eyeball is too short. Convex lenses are used to compensate for this condition. D. Diverse methods of accommodation in camera eyes. Mammals generally, like man, accommodate by varying the curvature of the lens surface (far right in D). Other ways of adjusting focus have, however, been evolved in various animal groups. Accommodation is of unusually great importance in a bird of prey, which must focus on its victim not only when at a great distance above ground but also, following its swoop to earth, when its victim is immediately in front of it. Predatory birds accommodate by a radical change in the curvature of the cornea rather than of the lens. Some mollusks accommodate, not by changing the curvature of the refractive surfaces, but by shortening the eye itself. With the lens thus closer to the retina, the eye accommodates to distant objects. Fishes lack ciliary muscles and hence cannot change the curvature of the lens; instead muscles within the eye change the position of the lens, pulling it back closer to the retina to accommodate to distant objects.

tion, "A yellow house cat a foot long is coming toward me slowly from 10 feet away a little to my left." Such varied and detailed discrimination is of no use to the organism unless the possible responses are also varied and detailed. An ameba's responses are just about exhausted when it rolls into a ball, moves one way or another, or puts out a projection and engulfs a food particle. Discriminating precisely what was touching it would have no significance in the life of an ameba because the limited repertory of possible reactions would be precisely the same in any case. Discrimination in receptors simply does not evolve unless it is accompanied both by a correspondingly complex association system and by appropriately varied effector responses. Does this have a bearing on the near lack of receptors in plants?

Summary

The meaning of the term "respiration": (1) gas exchange, as in breathing; (2) intracellular processes of oxidation that liberate energy.

Respiratory rates.

Respiratory systems: their diversity of form related to the peculiarities of the environment; control of breathing, especially the role of CO_2 as chemical messenger.

Control of body temperature.

Glands and secretion.

Excretion: in higher animals; ammonia, urea, and uric acid; the organization and functions of the kidney in man.

Coordination through chemical communication—the endocrine glands; the hormones of man; plant hormones.

Nerves: the structure of a neuron; the nature and speed of the nerve impulse; nerve patterns and behavior.

Structure of the vertebrate brain: its complexity; comparison of vertebrate and invertebrate; central nervous system; the three parts of the vertebrate brain (forebrain, midbrain, and hindbrain).

Receptors: light receptors—their diversity, lenses as light concentrators and their subsequent utilization in image-forming eyes, color vision, complex eyes related to complex brains.

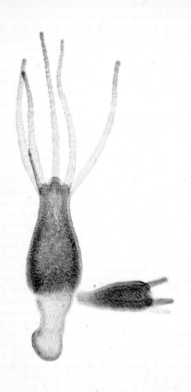

Adult Hydra showing budding. Medusa of *Aurelia flavidula*. (Courtesy Carolina Biological Supply Company)

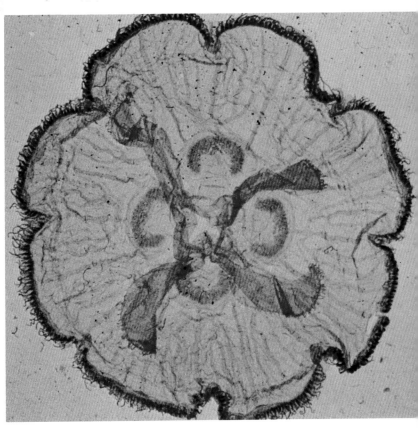

 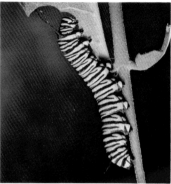  

Life cycle of Monarch butterfly. Left to right. Monarch eggs hatching. Larva feeding. Skin of larva begins to be worked upward. Pupa resting inside chrysalis. New body inside chrysalis. Body of monarch drops out of chrysalis. Monarch resting on chrysalis. Adult butterfly with wings spread. (W. Clifford Healey from National Audubon Society)

Stages in blossoming of dogwood. Left to right. Dogwood bud opens. Protective scales called bracts unfold. When the bracts are fully extended, the flowers show. The tiny flowers in the center open for only a brief period. The dogwood in full bloom. (James P. Jackson)

Yellow warbler with young. (Left, Alvin Staffan from National Audubon Society; right, C. O. Harris from National Audubon Society)

Hatching of crocodile. Adult crocodile on the Nile. (Top, N. Smythe from National Audubon Society; bottom, Dick Hufnagle from Monkmeyer)

PART FIVE

THE MECHANISM
OF EVOLUTION

The photograph introducing Part 5 shows a population of Peruvian Boobies on their coastal nesting ground where they congregate each year to propagate. Over thousands of years, such congregations have built up thick deposits of guano that have been important to man as a source of nitrogen for agricultural fertilizers. The scene points up two major features of our present topic, the mechanism of organic evolution: (1) The evolutionary process can be understood only in terms of populations; what evolves, as we shall see, is the pooled hereditary constitution of a population of individuals. (2) The mechanism of natural selection—key feature in the mesh of evolutionary causes—focuses on reproductive and genetic process we have previously outlined.

Boobies are descendants of early reptile-birds such as *Archaeopteryx*. Their evolution has been a history of change of habitat and way of life with a corresponding change in bodily structure, function and social behavior. But in another, more fundamental, view, their evolution has been a history of change in hereditary constitution. In the last analysis the evolution of organisms is change in their genetic make-up—a gradual rewriting, so to speak, of their inherited message.

The first task in explaining evolution has already been performed, in preliminary fashion, by Part 3: to discover the factors that introduce variations, or innovations, into the hereditary make-up of organisms. The mechanisms of heredity do not guarantee a perfect similarity of offspring to parent; mutation and genetic recombination ensure that innovations will continually appear in successive versions of the chromosomal blueprint. Each seal in our photograph, for example, surely differs to some minor extent from the others in its private version of the basic seal genotype that they all possess. There is, however, more to organic evolution than the variations that mutation and recombination constantly produce. For these processes, being completely mechanical and blind to the organism's needs, result in all manner of little changes, few of which improve the adaptive organization of the living thing. And one of the most conspicuous features of evolution is the way it has maintained and increased the adaptation of organisms to their environment.

The second task in explaining evolution is therefore the search for the processes that, given the random hereditary changes of mutation and recombination, mold from them the organized, nonrandom change that fits the organism to new environments or, just as importantly, enhances its fitness for the accustomed habitat. Those processes—complex and subtle in their detail—giving this direction and order to evolutionary change are what we refer to collectively as natural selection.

Chapter 12 is concerned with the fundamentals of population genetics; it discusses the nature of natural selection as basically a process of differential or nonrandom reproduction.

Chapter 13 deals with the fundamental concept of adaptation; it gives a fuller meaning to natural selection as an adaptive historical process.

Chapter 14 treats those factors in the evolution of populations that cause an increase in life's diversity through the formation of new species.

ELEMENTARY PROCESSES

OF EVOLUTION

Individuals, Populations, and Species

THE FOREST AND THE TREES

Not to see the forest for the trees has become a common metaphor for taking a short-sighted view of things, for being tangled up in details and failing to grasp the whole situation. If you look, literally, at a forest and try to understand it, you are likely, and quite rightly, to look first at trees. First questions are, "What is the structure of this particular tree? What is it doing? And how does it do it?" But even as you look at a single tree, you become conscious that it is not living alone. It is affected by surrounding trees and other plants with which it must share the necessities of life: space, water, other materials, and sunlight. Still more important, it reproduces. It is a temporary link in the continuity of its kind. If (as is usual) its reproduction is biparental, the process of continuity brings together substance and characteristics of different trees in the forest. In a matter of years, or of centuries at most, the one tree you are looking at will be gone, but the forest may endure without significant change.

To understand life it is necessary to see *both* the trees and the forest. So far we have been looking mostly at trees. Preceding chapters have reviewed the biology of individual organisms. Here and there relationships in groups of organisms have been touched on, for there are no really hard and fast divisions of knowledge. Yet even when we discussed continuity and genetics (Part 3), this was mainly in terms of basic processes as seen in individuals and their offspring.

253

Now the time has come to look at the forest. We have started to consider diversity, the different kinds or species of organisms. The species are groups. They cannot be understood in terms of individuals only. From here on, most of this book will be devoted to the biology of populations and of communities, which are composed of populations.

UNITS OF LIFE

Organisms and Populations as Biological Units

An obvious unit of life in nature is the individual. We have seen that the cell is a basic unit at a different level and that it is the pertinent unit when some, especially biochemical, processes of life are under consideration. In many protists, cell and individual are identical. In multicellular organisms they are not identical. The difference in organizational level is a crucial element in our study. Whether of one cell or of trillions, the individual is the pertinent unit as regards physiological organization, total metabolism, responsiveness, development, and some other essential phenomena of living things. The individual is the separate and objectively concrete biological unit. Intracellular processes take on full biological significance only when they are considered in relationship to the whole individual within which they occur.

Now, however, that we are turning more explicitly to the subject of evolution, the individual organism is no longer the most pertinent unit. Just as processes within cells must be related to individuals composed of cells, so must processes in individuals be related to populations composed of individuals. Evolution is something that takes place through long sequences of generations in which the individuals are evanescent and only the populations are continuous. In this continuity the discreteness of the individual tends to be lost. The continuity occurs by the passing on of hereditary codes of information, and as a rule the lineages of the transmittal are not discrete. They anastomose, separating when numerous descendants arise from one ancestral individual or pair and uniting when, as is usual, an individual derives parts of its genetic code from multiple ancestors.

The Deme: A Local Population of Similar Individuals

Consider the individuals of a protist, say *Paramecium,* in a pond. All are much alike, they may reproduce for long periods without much interbreeding, and they have no social organization. They are about as independent from each other as individual organisms ever are. Nevertheless, the whole population of paramecia in the pond does constitute a naturally defined unit. That population as a whole fills a certain unitary role in the life of the pond. Descendants of any individual in it may spread anywhere in the pond, and, as far as the role of the population is concerned, it does not matter what particular individuals or progeny are carrying forward the activity at any time or place within the pond. Moreover, this population in this pond is a unit separable from other, similar populations of paramecia in other ponds in the vicinity.

Coming out on dry land, we may observe a grove of pine trees or a population of squirrels living in those trees. Here, too, there are clearly units of population, definable like the populations of paramecia because the group as a whole has a role that continues, regardless of what particular individuals happen to be there at any given time. Here, however, there is still another factor that helps to define the group: the individuals composing it are all related and they are interbreeding. The future populations of the unit may be derived from any or all individuals now present in this local group. They are less likely to be derived from any individuals of other pine groves or their squirrel occupants.

As another example, we may find among the pine trees a large anthill. Here is a still more sharply defined unit of population. All the ants swarming in the hill are closely related. Usually they include one resident queen and her daughters. Future populations, as long as the colony persists here, will be of the same descent. The population is also more closely knit than those previously exemplified because it has a complex social organization. The whole population works together as a cooperative unit, with division of labor among the several castes.

A general term for any definable local unit of

population, like those of paramecia, pine trees, or ants, is *deme*. The examples have shown that demes can be several sorts or, at least, that they can be defined by different characteristics. When a deme is defined in part by interbreeding among its individuals, as in demes of pine trees or of squirrels, it can also be called a *genetic population*. (Some authorities use the synonymous term *Mendelian population*.) Social demes are usually also breeding units so that they tend to correspond with genetic populations. This need not, however, be strictly true, as the example of the anthill shows. Few individuals in a social deme of ants ever breed. When they do, they usually crossbreed with individuals from other social demes (anthills) and set up new ones. In the long run, the genetic population thus includes members of a large number of social units. All the anthills over a considerable area may represent the real genetic population, or a genetic deme of a larger and more permanent sort than the social demes.

Do you think the biological concept of demes is applicable to human populations? If so, how would you define various sorts of demes among mankind?

The Species: A Group of Similar Demes

Adjacent demes often intergrade, and the distinction of any one deme may be quite temporary. It is, in fact, characteristic of demes that they are commonly vague in definition and fluctuating in numbers. A grove of pine trees is distinguished as a deme and a genetical population because its continuity depends for the most part on interbreeding of individuals within the unit. It is, however, more likely than not that some pollen from other demes will reach this one and affect its reproduction, and also that some pollen from this deme will spread to others. There is some genetical unity in the deme, but it is not absolute. If pines grow up between this grove and the next, the two former demes may

become quite indistinguishable. In a large pine forest, trees in one area are more likely to interbreed among themselves than with distant trees in the same forest. There are vaguely separate genetic populations in the forest, but they intergrade so continuously that it would be entirely arbitrary to divide the forest into definitely bounded demes (Figure 12-1).

Similarly, the squirrels in any one deme are likely on occasion to interbreed with those of surrounding demes. Heredity does pass from one deme to another. Adjacent demes may interbreed so freely as to become essentially one deme: the demes fuse. If all the squirrels in one grove or one part of a forest die out, a deme ceases to exist, but squirrels of surrounding demes may soon occupy the territory, or migrants may give rise to a new deme of the same sort. No essential or permanent change in the squirrel population has occurred. Demes fluctuate and intergrade, but there are larger units of population in nature which tend to be both more permanent and more clear-cut. These are species.

A *species* is a group of organisms so similar in structure and heredity that their demes intergrade, may fuse, and may take the place of each other without essential change in the nature and role of the group as a whole. All biologists agree that species are important units in nature and that they correspond more or less with that definition. It is, however, difficult or impossible to frame a really precise, fully meaningful definition which applies without question to all organisms in nature. This is the *species problem*, which will be discussed in Chapter 14. In order to understand the problem and the processes by which species arise, it is necessary first to know more about heredity in populations.

Genetics of Populations

A deme or any sort of population as it occurs in nature tends to persist for years, centuries, or millennia. It has *continuity*, as we have already emphasized. We have also emphasized that an essential element in that continuity is the passing on of

chromosomes, with their genes, from one generation to the next. The persistence of a population without significant change in its characteristics implies that there has been little or no change in its genetic or environmental factors. Change in a population over

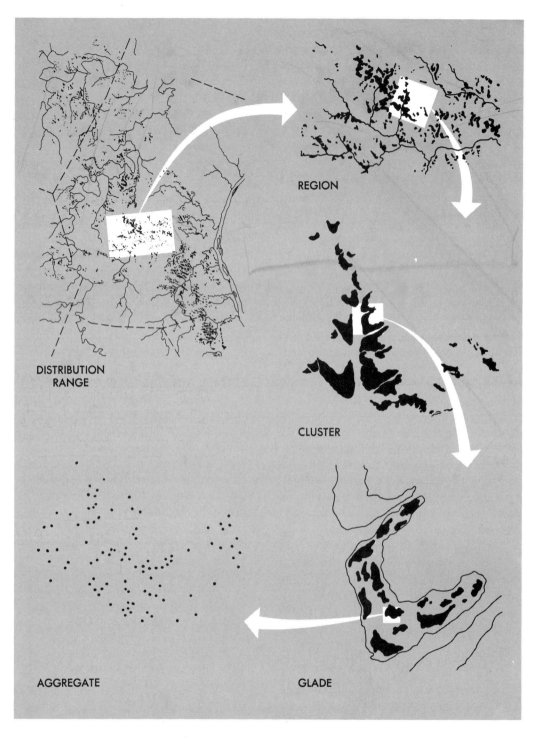

FIG. 12-1 Population structure in the plant Clematis fremontii. The arrows indicate the details of distribution in hierarchical fashion down to a deme in a particular glade.

the generations—in other words, its evolution—must indicate change in genetic or environmental factors, or both. Since changes *directly* due to environmental factors are not heritable, we may for the moment ignore these. Changes in heredity are in the strictest sense the basis of evolution. To understand life and its history it is therefore necessary to know something about the heredity not only of individuals but also of continuously reproducing groups. This is the subject of *population genetics*.

VARIATION WITHIN SEXUALLY REPRODUCING POPULATIONS

There is always variation among the individual organisms within a population, and the variation of prime importance for evolution is genetic. Every sexually reproducing population that has ever been studied has been found to exhibit genetic differences among its individuals. *Drosophila* populations in local orchards and woodlands have been intensively investigated as examples. All have proved to contain genetic variation, including many of the mutant alleles studied in the laboratory. This is really not surprising in view of what we know about mutation. A big enough population of any organism is bound to include different alleles at many gene loci in the whole set of chromosomes. The evidence indicates, moreover, that each gene locus may mutate to many more than just two allelic forms. With just two alleles present (A_1 and A_2) three diploid genotypes are possible among the individuals in a population: A_1A_1, A_1A_2, and A_2A_2. With three alleles (A_1, A_2, A_3) there are six genotypes possible. (What are they?) The number of possible genotypes as regards a single locus increases rapidly as the number of alleles increases. Then, too, because of crossing over and chromosome reshuffling at meiosis and recombination in zygote formation, each of the genotypes possible at one locus can be combined with any of the several possible at all other loci. The known processes of mutation and recombination in sexually reproducing populations guarantee enormous variation within the population as a whole.

It will also appear in the course of our further discussion that variation in a population is commonly adaptive in itself and then is maintained by natural selection. The conclusion is that, with the trivial

exception of identical (monozygotic) twins, genetic identity between any two individuals in even the largest populations is extremely rare or probably nonexistent. Most, if not all, of the individuals in natural populations are genetically unique.

EVOLUTION AS A CHANGE IN GENETIC POOLS

The Idea of a Population's Genetic Pool

One way, and for the purposes of this chapter the best way, to define evolution is as a change in the genetic constitution of a population. As individuals are almost always genetically unique, there is of course constant change from one generation to the next in the genetic constitutions of individuals within the population, but we do not consider that evolutionary change has occurred unless it involves the hereditary characteristics of the population as a whole, the pertinent evolutionary unit.

If we were to count all the alleles of the genes in a population, a tabulation of their ratios or percentages would be a measure of the genetic constitution of the population. It is this pooling of all the individual counts that characterizes what has been picturesquely called a *gene pool*. To encompass total heredity, we speak of a *genetic pool*, and not simply a gene pool. Evolution is any sustained change in the genetic pool of a species. It is, however, convenient at first to explain some of the more important processes of evolution in terms of alleles alone.

Processes Within Genetic Pools

The processes that go on within genetic pools and that are therefore potential causes of evolutionary change are in part already familiar to you from Chapters 6 and 7. Others that emerge clearly only in the new context are as follows:

1. Mutation in a broad sense, including both gene and chromosome mutations.

2. Recombination in a broad sense, including crossing over and chromosome assortment in meiosis

as well as sexual recombination of chromosomes of gametes.

3. Gene migration or hybridization, that is, the introduction into a population of chromosomes (with their included genes) from some other population.

4. Natural selection.

Each of these processes can and in fact does on occasion produce changes in a genetic pool. They are, indeed, the elementary processes of evolution. Of course, the actual outcome in any given case depends on a multitude of other factors, including the conditions under which the processes take place and the way in which they interact. In some circumstances mutation and recombination lead not to change but to equilibrium. Gene migration may be classed as a special type of recombination. Each of the first three processes is normally random with respect to natural selection, which is the nonrandom, oriented, and adaptive process in evolution. But all three also interact with natural selection, so that their direct effects are modified and they, in turn, partly determine the effects of selection.

GENETIC EQUILIBRIUM

Mutational Equilibrium

By definition, mutation in its various guises is the process that produces entirely new hereditary variations and that consequently is the ultimate source of evolutionary change. Mutations are, however, repetitive; the same ones (in different individuals) occur over and over again. Furthermore, they are to some extent reversible; a mutant allele can mutate back again to the original allele.

As a simplified example, let us consider a gene with two alleles, A_1 and A_2. Suppose that we start with an experimental population having only the allele A_1 in all individuals. In the course of many generations, this gene will mutate to A_2 in a few gametes. Rates of mutation vary greatly, but they are usually low, often on the order of one mutation per million gametes. In spite of the low rate, if we have a large enough population and maintain it through enough generations, A_2 will accumulate through repeated mutation and subsequent reproduction, and evolutionary change will result. Some of the A_2 alleles may, however, mutate back to A_1, so that the situation at this one locus for the two alleles can be represented thus:

$$A_1 \xrightleftharpoons[\text{back mutation}]{\text{forward mutation}} A_2$$

The absolute number of mutations from A_1 to A_2 will at first be much larger than from A_2 to A_1, because we started with all A_1 and this allele will long remain abundant. As the process continues, however, the number of A_1 alleles, and hence of mutations to A_2, will decrease, while the number of A_2 alleles and of mutations back to A_1 will increase. A time will come, therefore, when the absolute numbers of mutations in the two directions will be equal. Change in the proportionate numbers of the two alleles will then cease, genetic equilibrium will have been reached, and evolution by mutation alone will stop. The exact point of this occurrence, in terms of the proportions of the two alleles, will depend on the relative rates of forward and back mutations.

Although these considerations are logically impeccable, and although such an equilibrium may occasionally be reached in nature, it is probably extremely rare and of quite minor importance in evolution. In the first place, back mutations are not so common as was once believed. Another different mutation, say from A_2 to A_3, is likely to intervene, greatly reducing the chances that descendants of the particular gene will ever mutate back to A_1. In the second place, the attainment of mutational equilibrium is normally so slow that some other process intervenes before it is reached. The most likely intervention is by natural selection favoring the spread of one allele or another in the population regardless of the mutational equilibrium point.

Combinational Equilibrium and the Hardy-Weinberg Law

A tendency toward genetic equilibrium more important than that arising from mutation is involved in recombination in biparental populations breeding at random.

Let us set up an imaginary experimental population of *Drosophila* and follow the history of its genetic variation from one generation to the next. Let A_1 symbolize one of two alleles of a particular gene and A_2 the other. We begin our experiment by introducing 200 *Drosophila* (100 males and 100 females) into a breeding cage, where one generation follows another without break so long as we continue to supply food. We cannot wait for mutation to produce variation in our experimental population, and so we deliberately include both alleles (A_1 and A_2) among the initial flies. Of the 100 flies in each sex, 49 have the genotype A_1A_1, 42 A_1A_2, and 9 A_2A_2. Thus we have an initial population as follows:

100 females				100 males		
A_1A_1	A_1A_2	A_2A_2	$\times$	A_1A_1	A_1A_2	A_2A_2
49	42	9		49	42	9

We allow the males and females to mate at random. Can we predict the relative frequencies of the genotypes that will appear in successive generations? It is common for people first confronted with this problem to have two impressions: (1) that the less common allele, A_2, will gradually be lost from the population; and (2) that the task of predicting exactly what genotypes will result from indiscriminate matings among so many flies is quite hopeless. Neither impression is correct.

The prediction problem would certainly be formidable if we had to figure out, one at a time, all the matings that could possibly occur and summate their outcomes. Fortunately the problem is much

TABLE 12-1 *Gene Frequencies in an Experimental Population*

Flies	Gametes		
	A_1	A_2	Totals
49 males are A_1A_1 and produce	490	0	(490)
42 males are A_1A_2 and produce	210	210	(420)
9 males are A_2A_2 and produce	0	90	(90)
The 100 males as a group produce	700	300	(1000)
Ratio of different gametes in the pooled population of sperms as a decimal fraction	0.7	0.3	(1.0)

simpler than that. We can treat all the females as though they were one female and ask: What kinds and frequencies of eggs will be produced through meiosis and gametogenesis by the population's "composite female"? Treating males similarly, we can determine what sperms the "composite male" will produce.

Let us begin with the males. Every male produces enormous numbers of sperms, but we can simplify our arithmetic by assuming the number to be 10. This reduction in total numbers does not affect *ratios*, which are our real concern. The 100 males will produce gametes as shown in Table 12-1. The table shows that 3 out of every 10 sperms produced by the total population of males are A_2 and that 7 out of every 10 are A_1. The ratio between alleles is often conveniently called the *gene frequency*. The frequency of the gene (allele) A_1 in the present population is 0.7. Since the initial females in our experiment had the same genetic constitutions as the males, it follows that in their pooled gametes (eggs) the frequency of A_1 will again be 0.7 and that of A_2 0.3. The sum of the gametic gene frequencies should total 1.0 (for example 0.3 plus 0.7 equals 1.0).

The next step in calculating what genotypes will appear in the next generation is to set up the genetic checkerboard shown in Figure 12-2A. You are familiar with the checkerboard method from Chapter 6. There we used it to predict what genotypes would result from meioses and fertilizations made from gamete pools taken from *one* female and *one* male. The method is just as applicable here where we have simply pooled all the gametes from 100 females and 100 males rather than from one each.

When we crossed two single heterozygote flies, the gene frequencies in the gamete pool of each parent were of course $0.5A_1 : 0.5A_2$ (cf. Figure 6-1). In our experimental population, however, gametes are produced in the ratio $0.7A_1 : 0.3A_2$. The checkerboard in Figure 12-2A shows that the zygotes produced by random matings in our population will have genotypes as follows: $0.49A_1A_1 : 0.42A_1A_2 : 0.09A_2A_2$. Comparing this ratio with that of the

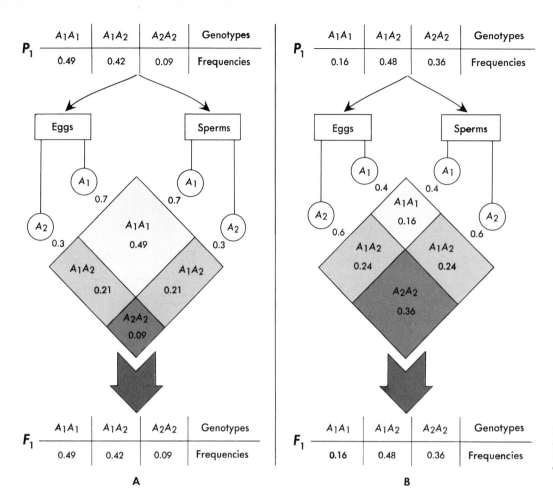

	A_1A_1	A_1A_2	A_2A_2	Genotypes
P_1	0.49	0.42	0.09	Frequencies

	A_1A_1	A_1A_2	A_2A_2	Genotypes
P_1	0.16	0.48	0.36	Frequencies

	A_1A_1	A_1A_2	A_2A_2	Genotypes
F_1	0.49	0.42	0.09	Frequencies

	A_1A_1	A_1A_2	A_2A_2	Genotypes
F_1	0.16	0.48	0.36	Frequencies

A B

FIG. 12-2 Genetic checkerboards illustrating the Hardy-Weinberg law. For an explanation, see the text.

initial parental population, we notice that the two are identical.

Parental population
with genotypes

A_1A_1	A_1A_2	A_2A_2	{ Gene frequency
0.49	0.42	0.09	{ is $0.7A_1 : 0.3A_2$.

↓

F_1 population
with genotypes

A_1A_1	A_1A_2	A_2A_2	{ Gene frequency
0.49	0.42	0.09	{ is $0.7A_1 : 0.3A_2$.

We must of course conclude that the F_2, F_3, and all subsequent generations would continue to have the same gene frequencies and genotype ratios among individuals.

This result may well surprise you. It was certainly not self-evident to the early geneticists. The rule, discovered independently by two men and called after them the Hardy-Weinberg law, is one of the most fundamental laws of genetics. It states that under certain conditions gene frequencies and genotype ratios remain constant from one generation to the next in sexually reproducing populations. This is true no matter how many alleles there are at each gene locus or what their relative frequencies may be in the initial population. Of course, if the proportion of alleles differs in different populations, the genotype ratios will also differ. Figure 12-2B gives, as further illustration, a checkerboard for a population in which the gene frequencies are $0.4A_1 : 0.6A_2$.

Mathematically inclined readers will have recognized before now that our genetic checkerboards are only graphic ways of expanding the binomial expression $(p + q)^2$, where $(p + q) = 1.0$. If we let p = the frequency of the allele A_1 in a population and q = the frequency of the allele A_2, then the algebraic expansion of $(p + q)^2$ describes the frequency of the three genotypes (A_1A_1, A_1A_2, and A_2A_2) in the population. Taking our experimental fly population (Table 12-1 and Figure 12-2A) as an example, we have $p = 0.7$ = frequency of A_1; $q = 0.3$ = frequency of A_2. Then it follows that

(1) $(p + q)^2 = p^2 + 2pq + q^2$
(2) $\qquad\quad = A_1A_1 + A_1A_2 + A_2A_2$
(3) $(0.7 + 0.3)^2 = 0.49 + 0.42 + 0.09$

Line 1 gives the expansion of the binomial; line 2 shows the equivalence of zygote genotypes to the three terms in the expanded binomial; and line 3 shows how the frequencies of zygote genotypes are computed from the binomial. The familiar Mendelian F_2 ratio for a single pair of alleles is only a special case of this same general rule, in which $p = 0.5$.

The Hardy-Weinberg law explains one of the most striking and fundamental facts of nature: that while biparental populations always contain a variety of genotypes, the population as a whole, including its variations, may continue for generation after generation without significant change. Variation, which makes evolutionary change possible, is maintained even when evolutionary change is not occurring.

Conditions for Hardy-Weinberg Equilibrium

The Hardy-Weinberg law can be restated in this form: the relative frequencies of alleles ($A_1 : A_2$ in our simplified example) and genotypes ($A_1A_1 : A_1A_2 : A_2A_2$ in the example) in a population tend to be constant through successive sexually reproduced generations. This tendency in nature partly explains the usual stability of populations and species over limited numbers of generations. Nevertheless, evolutionary change does eventually occur. It is therefore obvious that the Hardy-Weinberg law is not followed absolutely or indefinitely. It would be strictly applicable only under the following conditions:

1. Mutation either must not occur or must have reached its own equilibrium.
2. Chance or random changes in gene frequencies must be insignificant.
3. Gene migration either must not occur or must be a precisely balanced interchange between populations.
4. Mating patterns in reproduction must be random.

These conditions are rarely, indeed probably never, exactly met. Practically, then, Hardy-Weinberg equilibrium is only a tendency and not the actual course of the genetics of real populations.

EVOLUTION AS A DEVIATION FROM GENETIC EQUILIBRIUM

Basic Causes of Genetic Change in a Population

The four conditions just listed are necessary for genetic equilibrium, or lack of evolutionary change. It follows that their opposites are the basic causes of evolutionary change. Thus for such change to occur, one or more of the following conditions must apply:

1. Mutation must occur and must not have reached mutational equilibrium.
2. Random changes in sexual recombination and reproduction must be significant.
3. Gene migration must not be in precise balance.
4. Mating patterns in reproduction must be nonrandom.

These conditions for evolution are clearly related to the four processes of population genetics given on p. 257. The first three will be briefly discussed in sequence, and the remainder of the chapter will be devoted to the last, most important, and most complex condition.

Mutations and Evolutionary Change

Mutations are the ultimate raw materials for evolution. Obviously a mutant allele, or chromosome, or set of chromosomes, cannot be incorporated into the genetics of a population if it has never appeared in that population. It is, then, equally obvious that the possibilities for evolutionary change are dependent on the mutations that occur. This is, however, far from being all or even the greater part of the story. Mutations are of innumerable different kinds. Not all of them but, indeed, only a relatively small proportion do in fact eventually become characteristic of whole populations. Further, a mutant gene or chromosome does not act independently or in isolation. Its actual effect depends in considerable measure on the already established genetic system in which it appears and on the new combinations into which it is introduced in meiosis and sexual recombination.

Although mutation is necessary for continued evolutionary change, the fate of a mutation within a population depends largely on external factors. The spread of the mutation in the population, if it occurs, is a gradual process over the course of generations. The actual outcome rests on factors that impede or promote the spread, the most important of which is natural selection. Contrary to some early geneticists, and contrary to one of the favorite themes of science fiction today, mutation alone cannot determine a sustained direction of evolution and rarely determines the nature of any evolutionary change. It is a well-established observation that the most frequent mutations are not likely to be in the direction of past or apparently present evolution in the population in question.

A final pertinent point is that all natural populations have tremendous stores of genetic variation at any given time. Furthermore, the potentially possible combinations of alleles generally vastly outnumber the individuals in the population. This variation, both realized in individuals and potential through recombination, is the material on which natural selection can act. The variation is derived from earlier, ancestral mutations, and it can finally be exhausted. It does, however, permit extensive evolutionary change without the occurrence of any new mutations.

Chance Changes in Gene Frequencies

When Mendel crossed two pea plants heterozygous for the flower-color gene (Cc), he obtained 23.1 per cent (224 out of 929) cc (white) homozygotes in his F_2 instead of the theoretical or ideal proportion, 25 per cent. We noted in Chapter 6 that such departures from the ideal genetic ratios are always experienced in practice. The gametes employed in

producing any family are only an *approximate representation*—or *sample*—of the total population of gametes from which they are drawn. This is true whether we are considering the progeny from mating two individual organisms or the total progeny raised by a whole population of organisms. One hundred sperms taken at random from a population of males in which the gene frequency is 50 per cent A and 50 per cent a will contain *approximately* 50 a gametes, but the actual number is quite likely to be 53 or 48 or some other number in the general vicinity of 50. These chance departures from the ideal ratios are called *sampling errors,* and they become increasingly serious the smaller the sample becomes. Conversely, they are less serious in larger samples; you tend to get closer to a 50 per cent incidence of heads the more often you toss a coin.

In the reproduction of large populations of organisms, sampling errors are usually negligible; the initial ratios of alleles are fairly accurately represented in the large sample of gametes that initiates each new generation. But in small populations a considerable number of errors may accumulate because the sample of gametes that initiates each new generation is small. Thus the equilibrium of the population's genetic pool can be changed (can evolve) by purely chance processes. Such evolution is said to be *indeterminate* because, since the changes are due to chance, the genetic equilibrium is as likely to drift one way (for example, toward loss of the allele A) as the other (toward loss of the allele a).

There is debate among biologists as to the extent and importance of such indeterminate evolution, or genetic drift, but there is little doubt it plays a role, perhaps a minor one.

Another cause of chance change in genetic frequencies is embodied in what has been called the *founder principle.* When a species colonizes a new area, the individuals moving into that area are usually few—possibly only one, generally more, but probably never comparable in number to the main body of the species. These founding individuals, from whom new populations develop, rarely if ever include the whole genetic repertory of the species. The new populations thus represent only a sampling of the genetic pool. Especially if the sample is small, they may right from the start differ markedly and in a more or less random way from the parental population. The effect is most apparent on islands, which tend to isolate new populations, and it helps to account for the differentiation of island populations from their mainland relatives. Even in the continuous expansion of a species, the marginal populations invading new areas are likely to differ genetically from the populations near the center of the species' whole region of distribution. The founder principle probably has had more total influence on evolution than indeterminate evolution, or genetic drift, within a single small population.

Gene Migration

Gene migration from one population to another, generally called *hybridization* if the populations are markedly different, has analogies with both mutation and recombination. It may, indeed, be imperfectly distinguishable from them as an evolutionary factor. Hybridization may introduce a genetic variation quite new to a population, as mutation does. The chances of its survival and spread may, however, be greater than for a mutation, because it has, as a rule, already been integrated into a genetic system similar to that of the population to which it has migrated. (Why is the genetic system of the donor population necessarily similar to that of the recipient population?) If the two populations involved are closely related—if, for in-

stance, the populations are adjacent demes of the same species—then the phenomenon is hardly distinguishable from sexual recombination within a single deme.

An intermediate situation may be particularly important for adaptive evolution under the influence of selection. In ways that will be made clearer later on, a local population tends to become selectively adapted to its locality (environment). Achievement and maintenance of such adaptation require some degree of genetic isolation from populations adapted to other localities. However, complete isolation and perfect local adaptation may restrict variation and reduce the possibility of further adaptive change, or of survival, if the local environment changes. A local population that is partly isolated but still has some genetic exchange with other populations (migration) can be adequately adapted to current conditions and yet have genetic access to further variation when those conditions change. An abundant, widespread species split up into many incompletely isolated local populations is in the best position to achieve and maintain adaptation throughout its range.

Natural Selection

NONRANDOM REPRODUCTION

Seen in broad perspective, the historical course of evolution has two major features: it produces *diversity* among living things; and it gives rise to their *adaptation,* their ability to survive and to reproduce in the environments they inhabit. The evolutionary factors that we have just reviewed are, in the main, random with respect to adaptation. That is, they have no direct and causal connection with adaptation, so that, in themselves and if other things are equal, they are as likely to be inadaptive as adaptive; indeed, under the usual natural conditions they are more likely to be inadaptive. There must also be an evolutionary process that is nonrandom with respect to adaptation, that tends specifically and

directionally toward the adaptedness of populations. That process is *nonrandom reproduction,* which in modern usage is synonymous with *natural selection.*

An Example of Nonrandom Reproduction

The effect of natural selection on the frequency of mutant alleles in a population can be illustrated by hemophilia. You recall that hemophilia is an inherited disease in man affecting the ability of the blood to clot. Hemophiliacs are liable to die from loss of blood because a defective clot may fail to halt bleeding from even a small cut. This disability of the blood is caused by a mutant allele that we shall designate H_2. Blood in subjects with the allele H_1 clots normally.

The mutation $H_1 \rightarrow H_2$ occurs at what is, as mutations go, a fairly high rate, about once in every

50,000 gametes. The rate of the back mutation $(H_2 \rightarrow H_1)$ is not known exactly, but it is much lower than the forward rate. (Indeed, it is not certain that this back mutation occurs.) Consequently, if the mutational processes at the H gene locus were to reach an equilibrium, hemophilia (H_2) ought to be a common inherited disease in man. In fact, however, the disease is comparatively rare; the ratio of H_2 to H_1 alleles in human populations is about 1 : 10,000. Clearly H_2 is much rarer than it would be if mutation and a possible mutational equilibrium were the only factors involved.

The cause of this discrepancy is not hard to find. Hemophiliacs commonly die while still too young to have reproduced. Even when they survive to sexual maturity, they are less likely to be accepted for marriage or (if married) are likely to raise fewer children than people with normal blood-clotting mechanisms. What does this difference in reproductive competence between normals and hemophiliacs imply in terms of the human population's gene pool?

We can clarify this problem by supposing that we have for study a population in which H_1 and H_2 *have* reached a mutational equilibrium. Since we do not know what the back-mutation $(H_2 \rightarrow H_1)$ rate is, we do not know what its equilibrium is, but for purposes of illustration we may assume it to be $0.3H_1 : 0.7H_2$. The mutant allele is more common than the normal one because the forward-mutation rate exceeds the back-mutation rate; thus hemophiliacs are common in the hypothetical population.

We would normally set up a genetic checkerboard (Figure 12-3) in order to compute what zygote genotypes would appear in this equilibrium population. A checkerboard that assumed that all zygotes were equally competent reproducers would take the values $0.3H_1$ and $0.7H_2$ as the frequencies of alleles in the population's pool of gametes (Figure 12-3A). On this assumption we would expect zygotes to appear generation after generation with the frequencies $H_1H_1(0.09) : H_1H_2(0.42) : H_2H_2(0.49)$. This assumption of *random* (or equally successful) reproduction on the part of the two alleles in our hypo-

thetical population however, would be quite unjustified. We have seen that hemophiliacs (carriers of the allele H_2) differ from nonhemophiliacs (carriers of H_1) in being (1) more likely to die before sexual maturity, (2) less likely to marry, and (3) if married, likely to have less than average-sized families. Thus in the sample of gametes that actually initiates the next generation (those that actually reach the genetic checkerboard, so to speak) the proportion of H_2 alleles is substantially reduced from the initial value of 70 per cent to something more nearly like 20 per cent (Figure 12-3B). Zygote frequencies in the next generation will accordingly be different from those in the first generation: hemophilia will be rarer.

This can be summed up in a different way by saying that if the gametes that go to make up a new generation were drawn at random—were a fair sample of the parental population—the ratio of H_1 to H_2 would not change. But because a gamete containing H_2 is less likely to be passed on to the next generation the sample is not a fair (or random) one; it is *biased,* as the statisticians say. Therefore, the proportion of H_2 in the population tends to decrease. H_2 would, indeed, eventually be eliminated entirely if it were not continually replenished by mutation. The actual ratio $H_1 : H_2$ is determined neither by mutational equilibrium nor by the Hardy-Weinberg equilibrium but by the relationship between mutation rate and nonrandom reproduction or natural selection.

Elements in Nonrandom Reproduction

As it affects populations over successive generations, sexual reproduction involves (1) the bringing together of male and female gametes by mating or otherwise, (2) the production of offspring in the form of viable zygotes, and (3) the development and survival of the offspring until they are capable of producing offspring in their turn. In the present context, reproduction means a continuous sequence of life cycles and not just the production of offspring at one stage in the life of one generation. If the whole process is random, each of the three phases specified must be random. A male must be as likely to mate with any one female in the population (or the gametes of the two must be as likely to get together somehow) as with any other, *regardless of the genotypes involved.* Any two gametes must be as likely to produce a viable zygote as any others, also regardless of genotypes. And every individual zygote, again regardless of its genotype, must have the same chance of developing into a sexually mature and reproducing organism as any other. In other words, the whole reproductive process must be quite independent of—uncorrelated with—the genotypes.

From the opposite and more relevant viewpoint, reproduction may be and usually is *non*random in

each of the three specified phases of reproduction and in several or many different ways. Nonrandom, in the sense pertinent here, means in some degree dependent on—correlated with—the genotypes. Thus reproduction that is nonrandom tends to produce directional, nonrandom changes in genetic pools and

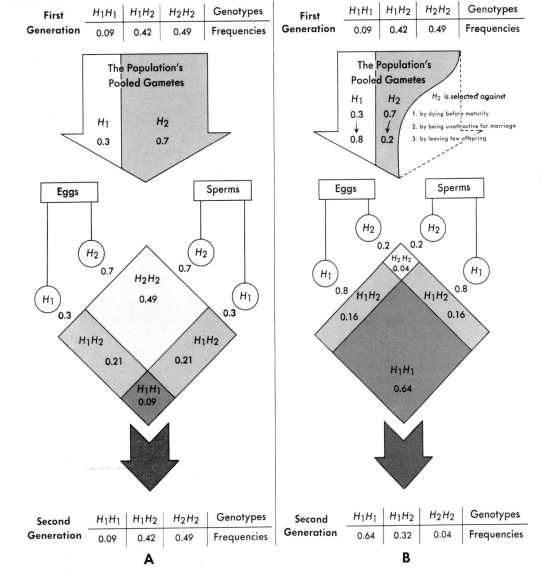

FIG. 12-3 Genetic checkerboards showing the effect of natural selection on the frequencies of hypothetical alleles in a human population.

hence directional, nonrandom evolution. The three specified phases of reproduction will now be separately considered from this point of view.

Nonrandom Mating

There is a mutant allele (w) that causes white eyes instead of the usual red eyes (W) in *Drosophila*. If we set up an experimental fly population containing these alleles, we run into evolutionary change immediately. White-eyed males are unsuccessful in the courtship of both white- and red-eyed females;

FIG. 12-4 **An experimental demonstration of natural selection due to nonrandom mating.** *Drosophila* females discriminate against white-eyed males in favor of red-eyed males. By measuring experimentally a coefficient of their preference, it is possible to predict the rate at which the gene w (white eyes) will be naturally selected out of a population. Experiments to test the prediction are performed in population bottles—a population of *Drosophila*, in which the initial proportion of W and w genes is known, is allowed to breed in bottles, and the entire population is transferred to fresh bottles with new food at fixed intervals. The proportion of red-eyed to white-eyed flies is followed generation after generation. The graph shows the observed rate, as well as the calculated rate, at which the gene w is eliminated. The agreement is close.

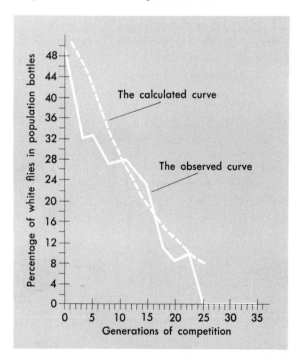

at least they are much less successful (literally have less sex appeal) than red-eyed males. As a result the white-eyed allele is quite rapidly lost by the population as a whole. The relative attractiveness of red- and white-eyed males to females can be measured, and the rate of elimination of the gene from the population can therefore be predicted. Figure 12-4 shows that the experimentally observed evolution of the population closely follows the predicted course. In one sense the evolution of this population is only a change in frequency of the gene w from 70 per cent to nearly 0. But in another and more important sense it is an evolutionary improvement in the mating (hence reproductive) efficiency of the population as a whole. Nonrandom mating has inevitably caused the evolution of adaptive improvement in the population.

A moment's thought reveals that mating customs, the accepted pattern of courtship, within a species constitute one of the most powerful and direct sources of nonrandom reproduction. Gene mutations that cause deviations from the common, accepted pattern of courtship will be immediately selected against; they will have little chance of entering the next (and therefore *any* subsequent) generation. On the other hand, accepted courtship patterns can act not only as a conservative agent, eliminating deviants (like white eyes in *Drosophila*), but also as agents of new evolution. In fishes, birds, and some other animals, bright-colored or showy parts may act as a stimulus to the opposite sex, the inherited "password" required before copulation is begun. When, as in some fishes and birds, the courtship password is a color spot or a showy pattern, almost inevitably larger spots and showier patterns evolve. Why? Any new mutations that make the courtship password more readily perceived or more effective are more likely to succeed in courtship than their longer-established alleles. The new mutant alleles have a favored entree into subsequent generations. In the examples given there is sexual acceptance or refusal of one animal by another. This is what Darwin called *sexual selection,* one type of natural selection.

Differential Reproduction

The sheer production of more offspring must plainly affect natural selection. If individuals with, say, an allele X_1 regularly produce 10 offspring while those with X_2 produce only 1, the proportion of X_1 in the population will surely tend to increase. This is, indeed, the most obvious form of natural selection—*differential reproduction*. Offhand, it might appear that selection would always favor more offspring per couple and that the rise of organisms, such as man, that have comparatively few young would be an anomaly. There is, however, a balance between the factor of fecundity and the factor of survival, next to be considered. If individual chances of survival are low, then selection will favor fecundity. This situation applies, for example, to parasites with the hazards of complex life cycles and to many fishes with tremendous mortality among the young. Such organisms have become extremely fecund, with one female often producing literally millions of eggs. If, however, chances of individual survival are high, there may be no selection for fecundity. In fact, there may be selection against fecundity, because the production of many offspring may reduce the chances of their survival—for instance, by reducing the effectiveness of maternal care, as in many birds and mammals. If one female produces three offspring, all of which survive to breed in their turn, while another female produces 20 young, only one of which survives to breed, then selection clearly is favoring the genetic characters of the first female. Not only is there an interplay of different factors, but also, as in so many aspects of evolution, there are alternative solutions to the same problem: high fecundity, low survival; low fecundity, high survival.

Survival to Reproduce

We have seen how mating (or, more generally, union of gametes) and relative fecundity are sources of nonrandom reproduction and of natural selection, therefore leaving their mark on the evolutionary process. They are not the whole story; most organisms have to go through a longer or shorter period of development, growth, and sexual maturation before they ever enter the final reproductive contests, so to speak. And it is nonrandom success in surviving to and through reproductive age that has given rise to many of the more obvious features of organic adaptation. The ultimate significance of the lion's speed, strength, and cunning is not that these adaptive features promote his survival in the sense of merely staying alive; it is that they promote his

survival up to and throughout the period of his sexual maturity when he can make a contribution to the next generation's gene pool.

The crucial issue in natural selection is the leaving of offspring. In terms of our genetic checkerboards, the crucial issue is whether or not an organism succeeds in getting his gametes into those listed on the checkerboard as the source of the next generation. From the point of view of natural selection, what counts about a hen or a lioness is its capacity to produce offspring. Natural selection will never lead to improved survival capacity at the expense of reproductive efficiency. It could well be that a lion might gain in strength, cunning, and longevity from genetic changes that lower his fertility or his attractiveness to lionesses, but improved survival at such a cost will never endure in the evolutionary process revealed by population genetics. Such improved survival capacity does not get the genes causing it onto the genetic checkerboard.

Survival beyond the reproductive age is rare in nature. What happens to an organism after it has exhausted its possibility of contributing genes to the new generation rarely matters to natural selection. It is true that in some social groups, among insects or men, nonreproducers may help the population as a whole to raise the next generation and so promote significant survival, but that is an exceptional situation. Even in man the ailments that strike increasingly after the age of 45 or 50 testify to the fact that natural selection in our ancestors did not tend to promote survival after reproduction was completed. Medical science is more and more devoted to combating this unpleasant but quite natural consequence of the way we originated.

PHYSICAL ENVIRONMENT. It is obvious that survival of the individual to sexual maturity demands competence to withstand the rigors of the physical environments.

Insects have never been able to become big because of their external skeleton and their mode of respiration. Their small size has been a source of danger to them as land animals because it means that their surface is large in relation to their volume. Land animals tend to dry out by evaporation of their water into the unsaturated air which they inhabit, and the danger of death by water loss (a function of surface area) is proportionately greater the smaller the animal.

In insect populations those individuals whose genotypes render the outer coating less permeable to water are more likely to survive and therefore contribute to the next generation than are their brothers and sisters whose genotypes have opposite effects. Insects possess a host of diverse adaptations that are directed at conserving water, and the origin of those adaptations by natural selection is clear enough. Similarly, all physical environments make demands that must be met for survival and that consequently are determinants of natural selection.

BIOTIC ENVIRONMENT. The environment in which an organism must make a living, survive, and raise a family contains important biological as well as physical elements. The organism has to live amid other organisms and the dangers and opportunities they afford. The major feature pervading any community of organisms is its traffic in energy and materials—the scramble to eat and avoid being eaten. This pattern of community life universally imposes natural selection on the community's members.

At the bottom of the heap are the plants, confronted with two sources of natural selection due to other organisms. First there is competition for soil room and sunlight arising from the abundance of other plants constantly showering the ground with seeds or thrusting in roots and runners from adjacent locations. Secondly, there is the constant threat of being consumed by herbivorous animals of all kinds before the season's crop of spores or seeds can be produced. These two *selection pressures* will elicit, in the long run, their appropriate adaptive adjustments.

In the desert, plant life is in a most difficult environment, and it comes under special threat of extinction largely because, being scarce to begin with, it is the more likely to be totally destroyed by hungry animal life; here as nowhere else adaptations are developed that discourage the hungry consumer. Thorns abound, as on cactus and euphorbia, and acrid juices, as in sagebrush.

Animals are under a whole complex of pressures in the web of relationships involved in the community's food economy. Most are under pressure to avoid being eaten as well as to find food themselves. Most birds *are* early birds because they have descended from ancestors who caught the worm. Keen vision in the hawk is always at a premium, and for this reason so are all genetic factors that improve vision. Good eyesight is no less important in the mouse or rabbit; alleles in mouse populations that help to promote quick recognition of the hawk's sinister silhouette floating above make a greater contribution to the next generation's genetic pool than alleles that impair this recognition—by no matter how little.

NATURE OF NATURAL SELECTION

Selection and Adaptation

Evolutionary changes resulting from nonrandom reproduction can have only one general direction. They are always of such a kind as to maintain or improve the average ability of populations to reproduce in the environments they inhabit. Effective reproduction is the only purpose that natural selection has or can possibly have. There are many different ways—literally millions of them—by which effectiveness of reproduction can be promoted, so that the specific effects of natural selection are various and innumerable. All, however, tend toward the same biological end.

We have mentioned that natural selection is the directive and adaptive factor in evolution. Adaptation is the subject of the next chapter, where it is defined and extensively exemplified. Here we must make just one point about it. If adaptation were defined as success in reproduction, then it would be a mere tautology to say that natural selection is adaptive. If, however, we define adaptation (as, with some further qualifications, we shall) as any feature of an organism that promotes its welfare, then it does not follow that natural selection is invariably or directly adaptive. Natural selection directly and always promotes the effective reproduction of populations. It promotes individual welfare only indirectly and only to the extent that individual welfare itself promotes population reproduction, as it does much more often than not.

Natural selection, then, does not always promote

the welfare of individuals. It commonly (not necessarily or invariably) leads to the death of individuals before maturity; their individual welfare is obviously not promoted. Since it requires variation in populations, it also entails the probability that some individuals will be less well adapted than others and will, in a sense, suffer so that others may survive.

Changing Concepts of Natural Selection

Old ideas about natural selection have become so deeply ingrained that they reappear even in some present-day discussions of the subject. To many of Darwin's contemporaries natural selection seemed to be a brutal struggle for survival in the universal carnage of "nature red in tooth and claw." Such catchwords as "the struggle for existence" and "the survival of the fittest" appear repeatedly even in Darwin's own works, although his views were less extreme than those of many of his followers.

From such concepts there developed a doctrine called "social Darwinism," although it was not supported by Darwin himself. Natural selection was believed to warrant as "right" all kinds of cutthroat competition, including wars between classes and nations, on the grounds that thus the "fittest" would survive and progress would ensue. The doctrine was completely unjustified, for two reasons. First, it is not a true picture of the way natural selection actually operates. Second, natural selection is not an ethical or moral principle that indicates what is right in human behavior. It is like the law of gravitation, a fact about nature which we must recognize as existing and affecting our lives but which is neither good nor bad in itself.

The question whether natural selection is "right" or "wrong" is not a scientific one, and there is no reason to discuss it here. Questions about what natural selection is and how it operates are scientific. The modern concept of natural selection, set forth in earlier pages of this chapter and now familiar to you, has developed from Darwin's, and yet it differs in some essential respects from nineteenth-century ideas on the subject. Natural selection is not struggle, competition, or survival; it is simply nonrandom reproduction.

Of course, animals do sometimes fight, and plants do compete for space, water, and sunlight. The competition has no bearing on populations and their genetic, evolutionary changes *unless* it leads to nonrandom reproduction. That is the real point of natural selection, and not the winning or losing of a struggle by one individual or another. Competition, struggle, and red-tooth killing often result in nonrandom reproduction, but not always. The concept of competition as a combat or literal struggle is also usually inapplicable to competition as it really occurs in nature. Moreover, the competitive aspects of nature are not the only ones that result in nonrandom breeding. An animal that gets along best with its neighbors may be precisely the one that has the most offspring. Then selection by nonrandom breeding favors absence of competition. Well-integrated plant and animal communities and, finally, animal (including human) social organizations have arisen under the directive influence of natural selection.

Creative Selection

Some nineteenth-century critics of natural selection objected that its effects would be only negative and noncreative. It could, they admitted, account for the elimination of the unfit but not for the origin of the fit, a more important problem. Their objection had considerable force with the older concept of natural selection, which centered on the idea of survival or failure to survive. The objection is, however, completely answered by the modern concept, based on population genetics and centered on (indeed, identical with) nonrandom reproduction.

In the light of modern theory, it is easy to see that natural selection does have a positive and creative role in evolution. In the first place, the elimination of one allele from a population by selection does not occur unless there is an alternative allele that is, under the existing conditions, superior in terms of effective reproduction. The negative effect of elimination of the "unfit" allele and the positive increase in frequency of the "fit" allele are two sides of the same coin. You cannot have one without the other. In an example to be discussed in Chapter 13, selection for darker color literally *created* a moth population better fitted to survive and reproduce in the pine woods.

There is a second, more complex, and still more important way in which natural selection is creative. The various characteristics of an organism are not determined separately and independently by individual genes. As a rule, each gene affects numerous different characteristics, and each characteristic is affected by numerous different genes. Genes also commonly interact, so that a given allele may produce different effects when associated with different alleles of other genes. As will be further emphasized in a moment, natural selection acts not only on each allele but also on the genetic system as a whole. It tends to produce gene associations and integrated genetic systems that would have little or no chance to arise and to spread through populations by any random process. This is a truly creative action.

Natural Selection, Variation, and the Genetic System

For the sake of simplicity and clarity, we have so far discussed natural selection for the most part in terms of simple alternatives of alleles at a given gene locus. In fact, it is the whole genetic system, taken all together as a unit, that determines what the organism will be, and effective selection acts not only on each allele but also on the whole system in all its aspects. An important outcome of these facts is that selection does not tend simply to increase the frequency of the "best" or "fittest" allele of each gene and so eventually to produce a population completely homozygous for all those alleles.

One basic consideration here, which we have already mentioned in passing, is that variation is in itself adaptive for a population. A completely homozygous population would have nothing on which natural selection could act and no possibility of evolutionary change. If—or we can say "when," for it is inevitable in the long run—the environment changed, the population would no longer be well adapted and could not become so. The most rigorous of all the sanctions of natural selection would be applied: the population would become extinct. Populations that have survived have necessarily always maintained enough variation to permit adaptive change. Observations on natural populations of flies have shown that their genetic pools change cyclically in adaptive response even to the brief alternations of the seasons. Such adaptation requires continuous preservation of the appropriate variations.

Another consideration pertinent here is that in many known instances a heterozygote is distinctly fitter for survival and reproduction than either of the corresponding homozygotes. But the highly fit heterozygotes cannot be maintained in the population unless comparatively unfit homozygous individuals are also regularly produced. (Why is this so?) Depending on the relative fitnesses, or selective values, of the heterozygotes and the two homozygotes, there is a definite ratio of alleles (or of different forms of homologous chromosomes) in the genetic pool that results in the optimum proportions of heterozygotes and homozygotes—optimum in the sense of being most effective for continued reproduction of the population. This kind of preservation of variation by selection is called *balanced polymorphism*. There is increasing evidence that the fittest populations, those that are reproductively most effective, maintain a high degree of heterozygosity.

Still another way in which natural selection acts on the genetic system and the genetic pool as a whole is by tending to bring and to keep together genes that act in unison, as a group, to produce an adaptive characteristic. Such genes, sometimes called *polygenes*, have additive or complementary effects and are less effective singly. They are more likely to be inherited together if they occur on the same chromosome than if they occur on different ones, and the closer together they are on the chromosome, the less likely they are to be separated by crossing over, as you will recall from Chapter 6. There are also genetic mechanisms that prevent crossing over so that blocks of cooperating genes can be kept together indefinitely. Once such an association has arisen by mutation, natural selection preserves it and spreads it through the population. The probabilities of its occurrence are increased by the selection of alleles that are near each other and that interact favorably.

Stabilizing Selection

We have so far been concerned with natural selection as producing evolutionary change. We have also seen that change could occur without selection but that such change would ordinarily be inadaptive. Another important role of natural selection is to limit or prevent inadaptive change. The simplest example is selection against harmful mutations, preventing their spread in populations and maintaining a steadily high ratio of more adaptive alleles at the same loci. This stabilizing effect undoubtedly occurs in all populations (including human). In a more general way, stabilizing selection often favors the reproduction of individuals near the mean, which are generally best adapted, at the expense of less well-adapted extreme deviants. One of the earliest students of natural selection in wild populations found after a storm that killed many birds that mortality had been relatively highest among the largest and smallest birds and lowest among those of average size. In a more subtle way, stabilizing selection seems to favor genetic and hence developmental systems that tend to produce normal organisms in spite of varying environmental influences during development. This flexibility in the production of what one might call standard items in the face of environmental modification apparently requires a considerable degree of heterozygosity in a population.

Limitations of Selection

Natural selection obviously is not all-powerful. It can operate only on genetic variations actually present in a population, and so the changes that can occur ultimately depend on the mutations that have previously occurred. As mutations are most often inadaptive, the material for adaptive selection may be comparatively little, although selection usually assures that mutations are efficiently used. Within any one population over a limited span of time, selection can generally produce only relatively slight modifications of what was already there. Mutations with really large effects are almost always so poorly integrated with the rest of the developmental system that they yield monstrosities and are immediately eliminated by stabilizing selection. A dog cannot mutate into a viable cat. Changes of comparable and far greater scope indeed result from natural selection, but only by the slow accumulation of lesser changes over great numbers of generations. The time scale of evolution is in millions of years. Moreover, mutations and recombinations of them that might be highly adaptive may simply not occur, although once a potentially

adaptive mutation has occurred selection tends to bring it into adaptive combinations and to integrate it with the whole genetic system.

We have seen that selection can act at any point in the whole reproductive cycle from generation to generation. It can act directly on the genotype, for instance in requiring that the mitosis of the zygote be normal. Usually, however, it acts on the phenotype and hence at a point one or many steps removed from the actual genetic system, changes in which control the course of evolution. A fully recessive allele in a heterozygotic individual has no phenotypic expression and hence is shielded from natural selection. (It will, nevertheless, be exposed to comparatively slow natural selection in the whole population. How?) The many environmental modifications or acquired characters that contribute to variation in populations do not correspond with variations in genotypes and therefore selection on them has no direct evolutionary effect. Further, an adaptive phenotypic character may be produced by an allele that also has other and inadaptive effects. Selection for that character may therefore be inadaptive in other respects. The outcome will be a compromise, so to speak, balancing help against harm.

The limitations of natural selection have had a remarkable result in the history of life, one that probably will surprise you: the great majority of populations have failed to maintain continuous adaptation. Failure of adaptation is the general cause of extinction, and the fact is that most of the millions or probably billions of species that have ever lived became extinct without issue. Conditions changed. For all these extinct species, either variations suitable for the adaptive action of natural selection were lacking, or selection could not act rapidly enough. Natural selection is a limited and blind process that cannot produce perfect or even adequate adaptation in any and all circumstances. The whole world of living things nevertheless attests that its over-all action is adaptive and that in the long run it is tremendously powerful and exceedingly delicate in that action. The next chapter will provide some striking evidence of its significance.

Summary

Individuals, populations, and species: populations as the appropriate units for the study of evolution; the deme, a local population of similar individuals and a genetic population of interbreeding individuals; the species, a group of similar demes.

Genetics of populations: the universality of genetic variation in populations; the concept of a genetic pool—processes of possible change in genetic pools; mutation, recombination, gene migration, natural selection.

Genetic equilibrium: mutational equilibrium between forward and back mutations, rarely if ever attained; the Hardy-Weinberg law in biparental populations; necessary conditions for genetic equilibrium, involving mutation, chance changes in gene frequencies, gene migration, and random reproduction.

Evolution as a deviation from genetic equilibrium: changes due to mutation, chance changes in gene frequencies, and gene migration random with respect to adaptation.

Natural selection: equivalence to nonrandom reproduction; cause of basic evolutionary phenomena of diversity and adaptation; example of selective departure from Hardy-Weinberg equilibrium in hemophilia; elements in nonrandom reproduction; nonrandom mating; differential fecundity; nonrandom survival—the effects of physical and biotic environments on survival and selection.

Nature of natural selection: an indirect cause of adaptation; a promoter of individual adaptation to the extent that adaptation promotes effective reproduction; changing concepts of natural selection; natural selection as a creative process; the relation of selection to variations and to the whole genetic system; stabilizing selection; the limitation of selection by materials available and modes of action.

CHAPTER THIRTEEN

THE EVOLUTION

OF ADAPTATION

Evolution and the Problem of Purpose

In ancient times and in primitive societies man's concept of his place in the universe was centered around himself and the place where he lived. The rise of modern science was accompanied by a physical reorientation. It was learned that the earth is not the center of our solar system, then that our sun is a relatively mediocre one among myriads in our galaxy, and finally that our galaxy is only one of the millions in the observable cosmos. Those discoveries dealt heavy blows to human self-importance and the age-old ingrained idea that man is the center, in some sense the purpose, of creation. Still, even among well-educated men, until 1859 the vast majority could cling to the belief that although our habitat may be only a speck in an inconceivable vastness, the world of living things was created to be under the dominion of man. In 1859 Darwin shattered this last basic prejudice. No other truth revealed by science compares with that of organic evolution in impact on human thought.

Many people growing up today go through a similar sequence of reorientations and suffer the same shocks. The child's world centers on himself, and as he develops further it expands, still around that center, to include family, community, nation, earth, and physical universe. He may be well along in his education before evolutionary biology invades his comfortably self-centered cosmos and carries him into unfamiliar and emotionally uncertain realms. He learns that the earth existed for billions of years before man entered the scene. He learns that man is only one among millions of species all akin to each other. He learns that all living things are products of the same natural processes by which life arose on the sterile planet Earth in forms simpler than the simplest cells of today and expanded into its present awesome complexity. It is impossible to contemplate the grand sweep of evolution and our own true place in nature without

FIG. 13-1 Morphological adaptation in insect mouth parts. The basic insect mouth parts are as follows: a labrum, or upper lip; a pair of mandibles; a hypopharynx; a pair of maxillae (technically the first maxillae); and a labium, or lower lip (technically a fusion of the second pair of maxillae). A. The mouth parts of a primitive biting and chewing insect like a cockroach. The labium and maxillae manipulate the food, keeping it in the mouth cavity while it is being chewed by the mandibles. The food is salivated through the hypopharynx. B. The mouth parts of a moth and a butterfly, adapted to sucking nectar from flowers. Superficially these mouth parts bear no resemblance to those of a biting and chewing insect, since they have been evolved to suit a very different activity. The mandibles are reduced and functionless, as are the labrum and labium, and the only functionally important element is the proboscis, a long tube formed by the close apposition of the two maxillae. Nectar is sucked from flowers through this proboscis. 1. The mouth part of a butterfly. 2. A cross section through the proboscis, showing how it is formed by the two maxillae. 3. A sphinx moth sucking nectar from a flower.

Many insects have evolved complex modifications of their mouth parts enabling them to pierce the surfaces of other animals or plants and then to suck nutritive body juices from their prey. Mosquitoes pierce the skins of animals and suck their blood, whereas the true bugs (Hemiptera) pierce plants and suck juices from their tissues. (Some, however, like the bedbug, have turned to animals as a source of food.) C. The mosquito's mouth parts. The labium serves as a scabbard in which other mouth parts are housed. The labrum, mandibles, maxillae, and hypopharynx are all elongate, needle-like structures, modified to form collectively an elaborate "hypodermic needle" in which there are two distinct channels. One of these is the hypopharynx, down which saliva flows, facilitating the insertion of the mouth parts by providing lubrication. The saliva contains a chemical agent that prevents the victim's blood from coagulating and thus clogging the other delicate channel—in the labrum—through which the blood is sucked up into the pharynx. The sucking is done by a simple structural adaptation of the pharynx itself (3): muscles anchored to the exoskeleton of the head are also inserted on the wall of the pharynx; their rhythmic contraction and relaxation causes the pharynx to act as a bellows. This mechanical adaptation is found in many other sucking insects and is shown for the bug (D1) and a dipterous fly (E2). D. A plant bug's mouth parts, simpler than those of the mosquito. The labium again functions as a sort of protective scabbard for the long needle-like stylets, formed this time only by the maxillae and mandibles. A comparison of the mosquito and the bug brings out an interesting generalization about adaptations and their evolution: different (even though related) organisms are likely to solve a common adaptive problem in different ways. This may be called the principle of multiple solutions. The bug, like the mosquito, pumps a lubricating saliva down through one channel and sucks food up through another channel; but the morphological bases of food and saliva channels differ for the two types of insects. In the bug the maxillae are complexly sculptured so that when closely apposed they form both channels, whereas in the mosquito the food canal is in the labrum and the saliva canal in the hypopharynx. E. The mouth parts of a housefly or other dipterous fly, adapted for sucking juices from free surfaces like those of fermenting fruits and decaying foods. The mouth parts collectively comprise the proboscis and are normally withdrawn under the head (3). Functionally they may be likened to a vacuum cleaner. At the end of the proboscis is the labellum, the tip of the labium. Flattened out and covered with capillary grooves, it is well fitted to sponge up fluids from wide surfaces. The necessary suction for the vacuum is supplied by the pharyngeal pump mechanism.

experiencing emotions of wonder and humility. It was with these emotions that Darwin closed *The Origin of Species,* beginning the final sentence, "There is a grandeur in this view of life . . . ."

The grandeur of which Darwin spoke so eloquently elicits many questions from us: "What is the meaning of this vastly greater world of which man is only a recent and minute fragment?" "What has caused evolution?" "What is its purpose?" These questions span both science and philosophy, for science rests on a philosophical foundation and cannot be absolutely separated from it. That our perceptions can be reliably related to objective phenomena, that the universe is orderly, that we can approach a true picture of its orderliness by observation—these and other propositions necessary for science are philosophical postulates than cannot be proved by scientific methods.

Yet, as we have already seen in Chapter 1, there is a touchstone by which many questions can be designated clearly as either scientific or philosophical. A question is scientific if it elicits answers testable by observation. "What has caused evolution?" is a scientific question because it has elicited answers that are testable and that have been reliably tested. "What is the meaning of the universe?" is a philosophical question because in an ultimate sense no observations seem to permit a choice among the many answers that have been given. Like any other man, a scientist seeks answers to the philosophical questions as well, and with his store of tested observations he is in a better position than most to find them. The point to stress here is that he should as far as possible distinguish between the two types of questions and that when he is speaking purely as a scientist he should stick to scientific questions and answers.

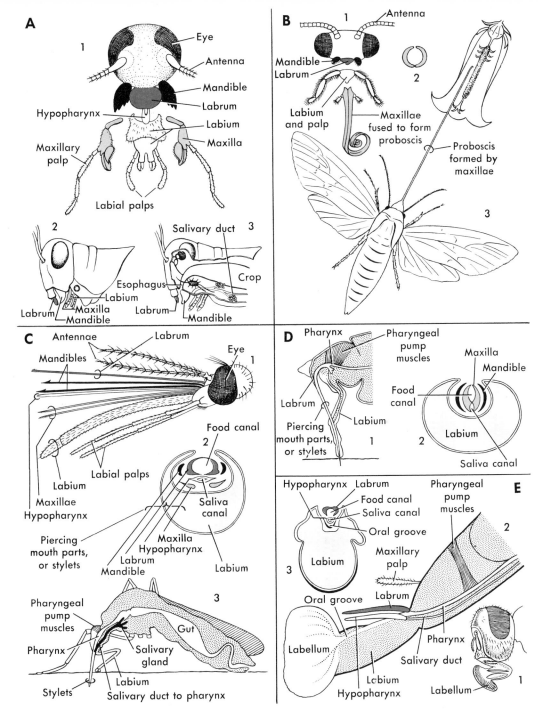

The greatest problems arise from questions that elicit both scientific and philosophical answers. Here our role as scientists, as biologists in the present instance, demands that we first consider and test the strictly scientific answers. Only if all those answers fail or when we push inquiry beyond the scope of testability should we enter the realm of philosophy, and we shall not enter that realm but only attempt to delimit it in this book devoted not to philosophy but to science. "What is the purpose of evolution?"

is one of the questions that almost imperatively elicits both scientific and philosophical answers. A possible answer is that man is the goal toward which all evolution has been purposefully directed. Thus stated, this answer is untestable. It is strictly philosophical, and the scientist, as scientist, cannot argue with it. It has, however, been asserted that the facts demand this answer, that it can be tested, and that it is in accordance with observation. This assertion brings the answer into the field of science, and our conclusion as scientists is that in this field, on this level of inquiry, it is wrong.

Observation indicates unmistakably that there is no single direction of evolution. As far as evolution has yet gone, man is one end point or, if you like, pinnacle, but so is a tapeworm or a mosquito or any of the millions of existing species. There is a purpose-ful aspect in the world of life. That world is, in fact, permeated with what could in some sense be called "purpose." The highest purpose that is *scientifically* discernible is the universal one of survival to reproduce. More immediate purposes, already quite familiar to you, are diverse: food-getting, escape from enemies, and so on. The specific means of achieving these purposes are incomparably more diverse still, numbering in the millions. They are adaptations.

"How are adaptations achieved?" is the most important of all scientific questions about evolution—if not, indeed, about biology in general. Any theory of evolution must be judged by its success in answering that question. You already know the answer that most biologists now consider most reasonable: adaptation is the result of natural selection acting in and with the whole complex of biological factors—genetic, populational, ecological, etc. The rest of this chapter is devoted to the scientific examination of adaptation and its relationship to natural selection.

Nature of Adaptations

We have encountered the phenomenon of adaptation in previous chapters and restrict ourselves here to a brief systematic review and definition of it.

A DEFINITION

Like so much else in biology, adaptation is not easy to define in a thoroughly exact manner. As in the case of life itself, adaptation is better defined by the whole discussion of it here and elsewhere in the book than by any statement condensed within the limits of a sentence. Nevertheless, its essentials are covered in the statement that *an adaptation is any aspect of an organism that promotes its welfare, or the general welfare of the species to which it belongs, in the environment it usually inhabits.* Individual welfare here means simply the organism's success in obtaining food, avoiding predators, and generally surviving and satisfying its whole range of biological needs. The welfare of the species is not only that of its individual members but also that of the group—in the maintenance or increase of the population. Adaptations are thus the apparently goal-directed features of living things that constantly impress us with the notion that organisms do have purposes, even though we cannot assume for any organisms other than ourselves that these purposes are conscious or that they are predetermined beyond the universal goals of survival and reproduction.

DIVERSITY OF ADAPTATIONS

Adaptations take any form—morphological, physiological, or behavioral—by which the welfare of the organism or the species is enhanced.

Morphological adaptations are among the most obvious and well documented. Examples are provided by the great structural diversity in insect mouth parts (Figure 13-1) and the feet and beaks of birds (Figure 13-2), all of which relate to the efficient functioning of these species in their special environments (compare grasshopper, mosquito, and butterfly mouth parts, and the feet of duck and eagle). Other clear morphological adaptations are the shapes and colors (discussed later in this chapter) by which animals are protectively

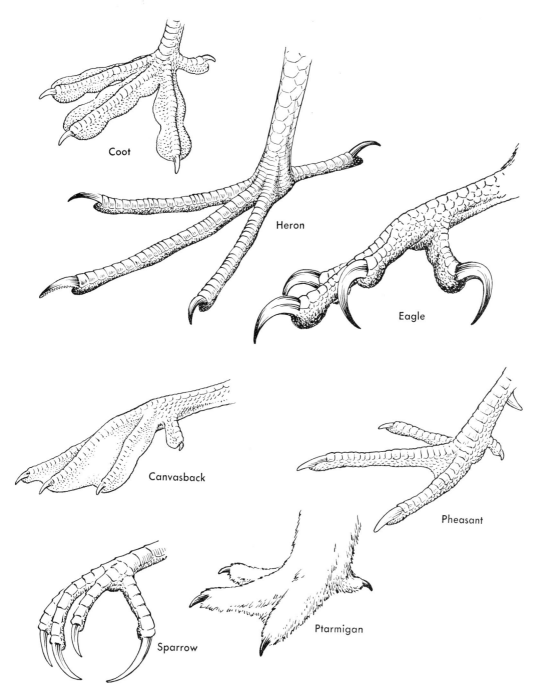

FIG. 13-2 Adaptive specialization of feet among birds. The coot swims or paddles with its feet, which have lobed toes. The elongate toes in front and in back of the feet of the heron, a tall and large bird, give it a firm base for walking. The eagle is typical of birds of prey in having long talons on each toe with which to grasp its prey. The canvasback duck is a swimmer with fully webbed feet. The pheasant has feet suited to walking and scratching the ground for food. The sparrow is a typical perching bird, with feet equipped for grasping a branch. The ptarmigan, inhabitant of very cold regions, has feet stockinged by feathers.

FIG. 13-3 **The Indian leaf butterfly, *Kallima*.** (Photo, Charles Halgren)

present in organisms. The shipworm *Teredo*, which causes so much trouble in the wooden pilings of wharfs and in the hulls of wooden ships, is able to exploit its remarkable habitat because it possesses special enzymes that digest wood. Shrimps that inhabit salt lakes like the Great Salt Lake in Utah have highly specialized powers of regulating their internal osmotic pressures.

Behavior in animals is almost as conspicuously adaptive as structure. Figures 13-4 and 13-5 provide examples, and the termite provides one still more remarkable. A termite, which like *Teredo* is able to live on wood, does so not because it can manufacture the enzymes necessary to digest wood but because its gut is always inhabited by flagellated protists that can digest the wood for it. A termite, like any other insect, must shed its skin periodically in order to grow. In the process it sheds the lining of its hindgut and with it loses the wood-digesting flagellates. The problem this raises—loss of a digestive system—is overcome by a behavioral adaptation: as soon as it has shed its skin, the termite eats it and thus reinfects itself with the flagellates it needs. A young termite freshly hatched from the egg case acquires the protists it needs by the appropriate if indelicate action of licking the anus of an adult termite.

concealed. A famous example is the leaf butterfly (*Kallima*) of Asia, which at rest is hard indeed to recognize in foliage (Figure 13-3). Desert plants, possessing water-storage tissues, reduced or otherwise specialized leaves, and still other features, are spectacularly adapted to the problem of conserving water in arid conditions.

Physiological adaptation, if less obvious, is always

BROAD AND NARROW ADAPTATIONS

Adaptations so far mentioned are extreme and obvious. Too often in biology there has been a tendency to think of all adaptation in this way. The

FIG. 13-4 **Adaptive behavior.** The male of the (marine) 15-spined stickleback (*Spinachia vulgaris*) ensures good aeration of the eggs developing in his nest by fanning a current of water over them with his pectoral fins. (Photo, © Douglas P. Wilson)

FIG. 13-5 Morphological and behavioral adaptation in the moth Venusia. The moth always rests by day on the leaf of a tree lily, with the striations of its wings carefully aligned with the vein striations of the leaf. The moth is thus inconspicuous and safe from predators.

phenomenon has been regarded as a collection of bizarre curiosities whereby creatures succeed in unusual habitats or in usual habitats in unusual ways. Such a view is in fundamental error. Properly viewed, any entire organism is a bundle of adaptations; it is all adaptation insofar as it is appropriately organized to survive and reproduce in its habitual environment.

We may get a more useful perspective on kinds of adaptation if we classify them as broad and narrow rather than as morphological, physiological, and behavioral. Let us consider the adaptations of a woodpecker on this basis. It shows several obvious *narrow* adaptations to its special way of life; these include its posture, its ability to hop up the vertical face of a tree trunk, its powerful neck muscles, which operate the head like a hammer, its large and chisellike beak, and its long tongue, used to probe insects from the crevices it cuts (Figure 13-6). In all these respects it is adapted to the narrowly defined occupation of extracting insects from tree trunks. But it is also more *broadly* adapted to the bird's way of life generally. Both its wings and its bones, which combine lightness with strength, are adaptations to flying shared by thousands of bird species. Its respiratory system, while similarly specialized to the bird's way of life, nevertheless is to be seen primarily as one of its broadest adaptations. It is shared by all birds, reptiles, and mammals as a fundamental and essential part of the vertebrate organization adapted to life on land. Of still wider adaptive significance is the woodpecker's possession of muscles and nerves intricately organized in relation to each other and to bones, effecting the precisely coordinated movements on which its whole life depends. Again, the fact that

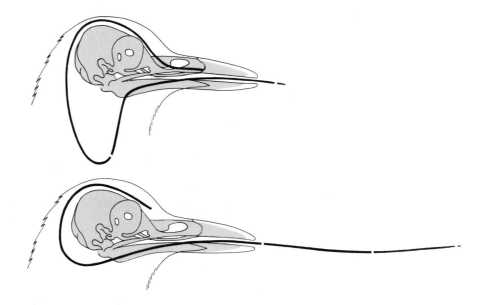

FIG. 13-6 Adaptive specialization in a woodpecker's hyoid cartilage. In all higher vertebrates the tongue skeleton is the hyoid cartilage. In woodpeckers it is enormously long, adapted for probing insects from deep crevices in trees. The tip of a woodpecker's tongue is equipped with barbs.

muscles and nerves are possessed by every animal group of higher organization than sponges must not blind us to their adaptive nature. Broadest of all adaptations is the woodpecker's capacity to reproduce itself or, more strictly, to copy and pass on the hereditary message that it inherited from its parents. The mechanisms that copy chromosomes are as surely adaptive as the chiseling beak and the long probing tongue. But this ability to pass on genetic information is shared by all organisms. It is an adaptation of life in general.

INDIVIDUAL ADAPTABILITY

A nearly universal kind of adaptation, developed to a greater or lesser degree in different organisms, is exemplified by the response of *Paramecium* to increasing salt concentrations of the water in which it lives. The adaptation concerned is a capacity to adjust or habituate to changed conditions. The *Paramecium* is a fresh-water creature whose environment usually contains little salt; in fact, the animal can readily be killed by a sudden and large increase of salt in its water. If, however, the salt is added gradually, the *Paramecium* adapts or habituates to the salt; the concentration necessary to kill it becomes greater. Similar phenomena are known in other organisms, including man, whose ability to habituate to arsenic has been the central theme in many a mystery story. The prospective murderer slowly habituates himself to arsenic and then invites his victim to a dinner of which they both partake; the dinner has been spiced with arsenic adequate to dispose of the guest but not the habituated host.

Habituation to specific toxic compounds is a special example of a much more general phenomenon of somatic adjustment or *individual adaptability*. Mice or men raised in the lowlands have severe respiratory difficulties at high altitudes where oxygen is scarce. In the course of time their performance improves, however, because the body adjusts to the new stress placed on it by increasing the number of red cells and, thus, the oxygen-carrying capacity of the circu-

lating blood. Many other instances of somatic adaptability are familiar in man: well-exercised muscles respond to the special and prolonged work load by appropriately increasing their size; exposure to a new infective agent elicits manufacture of an appropriate antibody; and so on.

Seen in broad perspective, even the capacity of animals to *learn* is itself just another example of the same phenomenon: behavior is appropriately adjusted in the light of past experience in such a way as to heighten the efficiency of living. Thus, whether earlier experience takes the form of unfavorable osmotic conditions, drug intake, low oxygen content, extra muscle work, or a behavioral problem, the organism possesses the ability to improve its organization for survival efficiency. In all these instances, the adaptation occurs within an individual's life span.

We must therefore distinguish carefully two uses of the verb "to adapt." Looking back over the history of man, we might comment that some of his ancestors *adapted* to life in trees by evolving modifications of forelimb structure. That is a radically different process from the one referred to in a sentence like "Mr. Smith eventually *adapted* to high altitudes and decided to stay in Peru." The adaptation in man's ancestors involved an overhaul of their genetic make-up; it was an adaptive modification of the inherited chromosomal information that specified relatively rigidly the structure of limbs. But the process of adaptation in Mr. Smith took place with no change in the chromosomal specifications he received from his parents and transmitted later to his children. The physiological flexibility of Smith's body is guaranteed by his heredity; it is within his inherited reaction range. It is as though his chromosomes had given these instructions for his development: "Build a blood system that includes the following special physiological equipment that will permit automatic adjustment of the red cell content to a level appropriate to local conditions."

Individual adaptability is in itself an adaptation of the highest order. Were a population to inhabit a rigorously stable environment, inherited information could be simplified by specifying a quite inflexible bodily organization appropriate to the enduring conditions. But no environments are completely stable; the biological environment is constantly changing, and other ecological changes are inevitable. The time eventually arrives for all populations when, in order to survive, they must move into new environments or must meet changing conditions where they are. In such circumstances those populations with the capacity to adjust somatically (that is, bodily or phenotypically) are at an advantage. Mutational modifications of inherited information causing development of an *adjustable* body in species meeting changing conditions are favored by natural selection as surely as the mutations that increase simpler fixed adaptive features like protective coloration.

Inheritance of Acquired Characters

LAMARCKISM OR NEO-LAMARCKISM

Two main scientific (as opposed to philosophical) hypotheses have been proposed to account for adaptation. One already familiar to you, natural selection, has successfully undergone such thorough testing that it has advanced to the status of an established theory. The other, the inheritance of acquired characters, failed to meet the tests of observation and has been almost universally discarded by biologists. Michurinism, one of several nineteenth-century forms of this hypothesis, has had political support in the Soviet Union, but (to say the least) political sanctions are not criteria for scientific acceptability. That there are still also a few non-Soviet supporters of the hypothesis is hardly more significant than that there are still a few people who maintain that the earth is flat. We might, therefore, ignore the inheritance of acquired characteristics here were it not for the fact that it played an important part in the history of evolutionary thought. Moreover, it sometimes has so strong an appeal to beginning students of evolution that reasons for its rejection still need to be spelled out.

The hypothesis of the inheritance of acquired characteristics states that the results of individual, somatic adaptability are passed on by heredity to the offspring of the individual. If it were true, some adaptations, at least, could be explained by the accumulation of such modifications in the genetic system through the generations. A classic but grotesque example is the view that the giraffe's long neck is an evolutionary consequence of long-continued exercise in stretching as generation after generation of giraffes strove to reach leaves at the tops of trees. Frequently included in the hypothesis was the further idea that modifications from strictly environmental sources, including inadaptive changes due to injuries or malnutrition, also became heritable.

It is customary to call the hypothesis of the inheritance of acquired characters *Lamarckian* and the acceptance of it *Lamarckism,* after Lamarck, the most thorough of the pre-Darwinian evolutionists. It is important that you know these terms because of their frequent use in discussions of the history of evolutionary thought. They are, however, both inaccurate and unfair and would be abandoned if scientists were as meticulous in historical study as in science itself, for the following reasons: the hypothesis of the inheritance of acquired characters was only a minor and subsidiary feature of Lamarck's theory of evolution; Lamarck was not, by many centuries, and never claimed to be the originator of the hypothesis; Lamarck himself did not accept the hypothesis in just the same form or to the same extent as that now labeled "Lamarckian".

When Lamarck wrote his *Zoological Philosophy* (1809) and still when Darwin wrote *The Origin of Species* (1859), the inheritance of acquired characters was a legitimate and indeed a good scientific hypothesis. It could be tested, and it was necessary for the advance of biology that it should be thoroughly tested. It was an age-old belief, and it also had at least two seemingly common-sense features that suggested its application to the newer concept of evolution. One of these is its apparent analogy with social or cultural evolution, in which the new acquisitions of one generation are indeed inherited by the next. The other is that, as we have seen, individual organisms do to a limited extent become somatically adapted. Why should not such adaptation lead to or even be identical with organic evolution? The same verb, "to adapt," is applied to both processes. In fact, here as in the comparison with social evolution, this version of "common sense" turns out to be misplaced trust in a false analogy.

FAILURE OF THE HYPOTHESIS

Intensive testing in the latter part of the nineteenth and early part of the twentieth centuries revealed many and insuperable weaknesses in the Neo-Lamarckian hypothesis. Most of these relate to five main points.

1. The hypothesis demands that hereditary information be passed backward, so to speak, from body cells to germ cells within individuals. Our present vastly expanded knowledge of heredity not only discloses no mechanism by which such a transfer could occur but also demonstrates that it is virtually impossible.

2. Enormous effort has repeatedly been put into experiments designed to demonstrate the inheritance of acquired characters. All these experiments have failed.

3. It seems quite impossible that many adaptations could be achieved either by efforts of the organisms themselves or by the direct effects of their environment. For example, the green coloration of insects that escape predation because they look like leaves is an evident adaptation. But how can an insect practice becoming green? And how can green leaves directly cause insects to become green with completely different pigments?

4. There are other adaptations that, for a different reason, cannot possibly result from the inheritance of acquired characters. The most noteworthy examples are among the neuter worker or soldier classes of insects, which do not breed and therefore cannot pass on any characters that they may acquire. Each individual must in fact inherit the capacity to develop its caste characters from parents that did not have those characters.

5. If, as the usual Neo-Lamarckian form of the hypothesis demands, effects of the environment were directly heritable as such, inadaptive effects such as are caused by injury or malnutrition would inevitably accumulate along with any adaptive effects. For example, by now we must all have had many ancestors who lost a finger or toe before producing offspring, but possession of the normal five on each limb continues to be just as much a part of our inheritance as it was 300 million years ago.

At each point where the hypothesis fails or is inadequate, natural selection agrees with the observations and provides a sufficient explanation for them. The occurrence of natural selection in nature is abundantly attested, and its explanation of adaptation is consistent with everything we know about genetics and the history of life.

We do not mean by all this that acquired characters have nothing to do with adaptation. We have already stressed that individual *ability* to acquire adaptive characters is itself an adaptation *developed by natural selection.*

Natural Selection and Adaptive Coloration

Colors and color patterns, some brilliant and some subtle, are present in organisms of many different kinds. They are adaptive in highly diverse ways, and they provide some of the most striking illustrations of adaptation. Some of them have also provided crucial evidence in controversies about the role of natural selection in producing adaptations. From this point of view we shall briefly consider two kinds of adaptive coloration—cryptic coloration and warning coloration.

CRYPTIC COLORATION

The Theory of Cryptic Coloration

It is a common observation that many animals are colored or shaped in such a way as to be hard to recognize in their natural surroundings (Figure 13-7). *Cryptic,* or *concealing, coloration* is widespread among mammals, birds, and some other groups, but insects are perhaps the most obvious examples. Grasshopper species in the lush grass of meadows and stream banks are green; other species in dry prairie grasslands match the drab straw color of their backgrounds. Their relatives the stick insects can change their color to suit different backgrounds, and they add to the deception by being elongate and twiglike in shape. The common moths of birch and pine trees differ in wing coloration, each appropriately matching the surface upon which it habitually rests. Pale moths from birch trees are nearly invisible in their usual habitat, but if they land on the dark bark of a pine, they stand out clearly—fair game for any bird hunting insect food.

A more subtle kind of cryptic coloration is exhibited by most protectively colored mammals and

FIG. 13-7 **Protective coloration and warning coloration.** Above, warning coloration in the larvae of the cinnabar moth. Note the conspicuous crossbanding and the clustering together. Below right, cryptic form as a protective device in the pipefish, *Entelurus aequoreus,* which rests amidst eelgrass, *Zostera Marina.* Below left, cryptic coloration in the flatfish topknot, *Zeugopterus punctatus,* which rests on a shell-gravel bottom. (Photos, below left and right, ©️ Douglas P. Wilson, above, from N. Tinbergen, *Social Behaviour in Animals,* Methuen & Co. Ltd.)

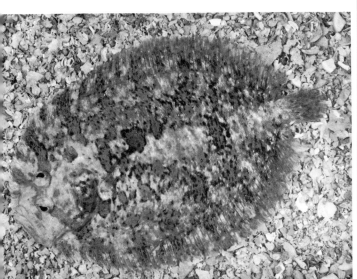

birds, which are darker on their backs than underneath. Under ordinary conditions, with light coming mostly from above, this color arrangement tends to conceal the body by eliminating the comparative brightness of the upper, more illuminated parts and darkness of the lower, more shadowed parts. Some bold color patterns of stripes, irregular blotches, and the like, highly conspicuous when seen in isolation, are in fact protective in the natural habitat because they break up the outline of the body and make it unrecognizable as prey; the same device is used in military camouflage.

The theory of the origin of cryptic coloration by natural selection is as follows. In a population of animals subject to predation, as almost all are, there is hereditary variation in color and pattern. Some variations are more likely to deceive predators than others. On an average, the predators will find and kill more of the less well-protected variants than of the better-protected variants. This lethal form of natural selection will therefore produce, through the course of generations, a population as a whole more adequately protected.

Let us consider two similar but separate light-winged moth populations on trees with dark bark. Both are conspicuous and are heavily preyed on by birds. Suppose now that in population 1 but not in population 2 mutations occur that slightly darken the wings. It is a common error to assume that because the darker wings are only *slightly* less easily seen they are not an adaptive improvement. Even if the mutants are overlooked only 1 per cent more often than the individuals with normal alleles, natural selection will result. The proportion of individuals with darker wings will increase in succeeding generations, and eventually the mutant allele will entirely replace the original allele. It will do so because it is more effective and more adaptive, and the process of replacement is natural selection. This phenomenon of progressive darkening of the wings of moths more nearly to match a dark background has been observed in nature, and careful study has proved conclusively that the phenomenon is indeed caused by the selective pressure of predation.

TABLE 13-1 *The Adaptive Value of Warning Coloration*[a]

	Accepted as food by monkey	Rejected as food by monkey	Totals
Warningly colored insect species	23	120	143
Cryptically colored insect species	83	18	101

[a]The monkey accepted as food 83 per cent (83/101) of all cryptically colored species but only 16 per cent of all warningly colored species; 87 per cent (120/138) of all species rejected were warningly colored.

WARNING COLORATION

The existence of alternative adaptations is pointed up by the fact that flashy color patterns, just the opposite of cryptic coloration, may also (but in quite a different fashion) protect their bearers against predation. There are many insects among beetles, bugs, bees, butterflies, and others that have unpleasant tastes, bristles, or stings making them disagreeable food for most predators. These features profit the insect nothing if they are noted only after it has been killed. If, however, it advertises its unacceptability by *warning coloration,* predators learn to leave it alone (see Figure 13-7). The advertising message is "This is the color pattern that gave you trouble before."

The theory of warning coloration predicts that predators learn to recognize and not to molest distasteful, warningly colored insects. Repeated experiments have borne out the prediction. In the example summarized in Table 13-1, G. D. H. Carpenter offered to a monkey over 200 species of insects, some warningly colored and some cryptically colored. We do not expect, and the theory does not demand, 100 per cent efficiency, but it is clear that the warning coloration was, on an average, highly protective.

OTHER KINDS OF ADAPTIVE COLORATION

Obviously there are more ways of avoiding being eaten than by evolving cryptic coloration. Another, also involving coloration and pattern, is by *mimicry.* In one of the several kinds of mimicry, the mimics are animals (especially insects) that are quite acceptable as food but that look and act like others, usually with warning coloration, that are obnoxious to some predators. If a mimic is mistaken for an unpalatable species, its chances of survival are increased, and natural selection will tend to favor and to reproduce the mimicry, which is, of course, quite unconscious. (Can you think of still other ways of escaping predation?)

Coloration may also be adaptive without having anything to do with predation. Conspicuous colors may be recognition marks, helping birds of a feather to flock together. They may also be releasers or, so to speak, passwords that elicit sexual acceptance and appropriate mating behavior. Colors may be adaptive to the physical environment. For example, dark

integuments may facilitate heat radiation from within and screen off shorter frequencies (light, ultraviolet) from without, whereas light integuments may have the reverse effects. The colors and patterns of flowers commonly serve to attract and guide pollinators such as insects and birds. The omnipresent green of chlorophyll in fields and forests is adaptive in yet another way: it is incidental to the absorption of energy from light.

We have by no means exhausted the ways in which color is adaptive in organisms, but have mentioned only a few of them.

Natural Selection as a Historical Process

We have stressed that natural selection is not necessarily a process of competitive combat and strife. Nevertheless, competition, which is usually unconsciously entered, does play an important role in the direction of evolution. Competence to find food and make a living up to and throughout reproductive maturity is an essential part of that more general competence to leave offspring which is *the* feature of organisms that selection constantly maintains or improves.

The natural selection that results from competition for food and a place to live leads to a variety of evolutionary consequences. Broadly speaking, these may be (1) a narrowing and further specialization in competence, (2) an increased diversification and broadening in competence, or (3) a change to a different mode of life and kind of competence. Which of these evolutionary effects is realized depends on a variety of circumstances, some of which will now be considered.

OCCUPATION
OF NEW ENVIRONMENTS

Pressure to Diversify

All species of organisms are adapted to a particular environment that is limited, to a greater or lesser extent, in size and resources (food, a place to live,

etc.). Sooner or later the reproductive capacity of the species raises the population to a limit determined in large part by the availability of resources. This situation creates a selective process in which those individuals able to make use of otherwise unexploited environments and resources are at an advantage; their probability of successfully leaving progeny is heightened by the low competition in the new environment. Thus the theory of natural selection leads to an explanation of the diversity that is one of life's most striking features. When we survey the nearly incredible range of habitats, or environments, exploited by organisms—from hot springs to arctic waters, from ocean floor to mountain streams, deserts, rain forests, and the air above, from the intestines of other animals to the pages of library books—we are viewing the diverse habitats that have constituted opportunities for organisms to escape from competition in other, well-occupied environments.

It is surely unnecessary at this point to labor the fact that, when we speak of "escape from competition," we are not envisaging a deliberate attempt on the part of a squirrel, bird, or bacterium to find a new way of life where the going is easier. The universally present structural devices and behavior patterns that ensure random dispersal of a species cause it constantly (and for the most part quite unwillingly) to sample new environments.

Conditions for Entry into New Environments

To enter a new mode of life a species must be given the *opportunity* to do so in three distinct senses.

First it must have the *physical opportunity* to enter. This is the most obvious of the three conditions and needs little amplification. Conceivably, a butterfly species now limited in distribution to South American forests might be competent to exploit some new and so far unused environment in African savannahs, but its evolutionary potential in this respect will remain unfulfilled so long as it lacks physical access to South Africa. The intestines of other animals have been exploited as new environments only by those groups (protists and worms with aquatic larvae) that have had prolonged physical access to animal intestinal tracts through their presence in drinking water and food.

Prolonged physical access to a new environment does not, however, guarantee its successful evolutionary invasion by a species. A *constitutional opportunity* must develop. We can put this another way by saying that a species has constitutional access to a new environment only when it already possess some minimal adaptation adequate to sustain survival and reproduction while it gains a footing. Once entry is established, selection will steadily raise the level of adaptation to the new conditions. Examples given later in the chapter show that we are not begging the question of how new modes of life evolve when we say that a minimal degree of adaptation must exist before new habitats are entered. It is a commonplace of life's history that the adaptations which permit exploitation of *new* modes of life are only temporary makeshifts initially acquired as adaptation to *old* modes of life, and subsequently improved or sometimes completely replaced.

Physical and constitutional access are both necessary, but even together they are not in themselves sufficient to ensure invasion of new habitats. The species concerned must also have *ecological opportunity;* the ecological conditions prevailing must be appropriate. Ecological access always means that the competition encountered in the new habitat must be slight enough to permit survival of the new invader during

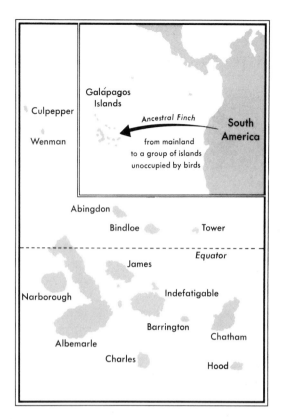

FIG. 13-8 The Galápagos Islands, home of Darwin's finches.

its initial phase, when its adaptation may still be poor.

Much of life's history becomes understandable in terms of exploitation of constitutional and ecological opportunities to enter new environments and thus escape the heavy competition in those that are fully occupied.

Darwin's Finches: An Adaptive Radiaion

The role that ecological opportunity plays in determining evolution is well illustrated by the history of a group of small land birds, the Geospizinae, or Darwin's finches, on the Galápagos Islands (Figure 13-8). These islands are a compact group lying about 600 miles off the coast of Ecuador. Darwin's visit to them when he was serving as a naturalist aboard the exploration ship H.M.S. *Beagle* in 1832 strongly influenced his later thought about evolution.

The biologists' interest in the Galápagos stems from the fact that they are oceanic islands thrust up from the ocean floor. They have had no connection with the mainland at any time in their history. Coming into existence late in the history of life, they initially constituted a completely unoccupied environment, and a remarkable ecological opportunity for such land organisms as could reach them. The nature of the present flora and fauna completely gives away the story of how the islands were initially colonized by life. The groups now present on the Galápagos are an extremely spotty sampling of those present on the South American mainland. In the absence of a land connection with the islands, only a few kinds of organisms have ever reached them. Their successful immigration was a rare event brought about by the chance movement of winds and of debris floating along where currents drove them. As soon as vegetation became established on the islands, immigrant animals were free to enter any of the several new environments they encountered and to which they had constitutional access.

All the small land birds of the Galápagos today are descendants of a small finch from the South

American mainland. Since its arrival, this finch has evolved into at least 14 distinct species, each of which specializes to some extent in exploiting the resources of the islands. (Figure 13-9). The evidence indicates that the ancestral finches were ground birds feeding mainly on seeds and other vegetation. Of the 14 species that evolved from this stock, three, of different sizes are still ground finches feeding on seeds, two are mainly cactus finches, and one combines ground and cactus feeding. All the others have become tree finches, the majority of which are insectivorous. Within these broad categories (ground, cactus, and tree finches, some vegetarian and others insectivorous) still further specialization has developed. The species differ markedly in beak size and structure; this relates to the size of the food they capture and eat. One of the tree finches has become essentially a woodpecker. It lacks the long tongue that is an adaptation

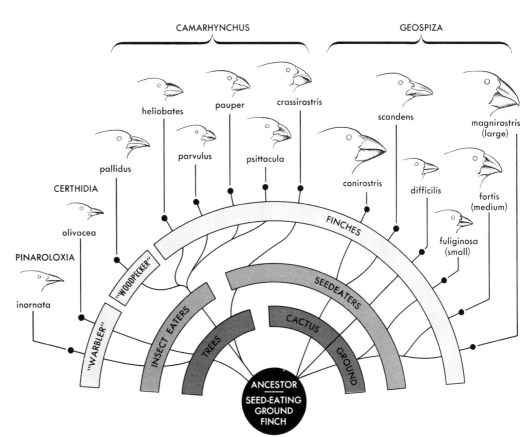

FIG. 13-9 The adaptive radiation of Darwin's finches.

The difference in evolutionary future between the initial finch immigrants to the Galápagos and their brothers and sisters who remained on the mainland is striking. All the Galápagos finches of today have departed so far from their original ancestor that we can no longer identify them among the mainland finches. But we are sure of this—not one of the mainland finches (including the ancestor of the Galápagos birds) has been able to undergo the extensive adaptive diversification that occurred on the Galápagos, in spite of having identical physical and constitutional opportunities to do so; the mainland birds lacked the ecological opportunity that had been created by the vacant habitats of the Galápagos (Figure 13-11).

The evolution of new species on the Galápagos Islands was further enhanced by the island nature of the new territory. Island-to-island movement of small birds like the finches is extremely limited, though adequate to ensure the population of all the islands in time. The geographic isolation of each new island population promoted the initial breaking up of the finch population into new species. The various species specialized to some extent according to local conditions but ultimately spread all over the archipelago. The result has been that most of the islands now support a number of species. Roughly the same ecological opportunities existed on most of the islands. On all of them openings existed, for example, for large, medium, and small vegetarian ground finches. These openings were filled on all the islands, although not always by the same species. Even among the Galápagos finches themselves, we can discern how

FIG. 13-10 *Camarhynchus pallidus.* The adaptive radiation of Darwin's finches has produced one species that is essentially a woodpecker. It has mastered this way of life by evolving, not the morphological specializations of the familiar woodpecker, but a behavioral substitute. It uses cactus spines instead of a long tongue to probe insects from trees.

of the tree woodpeckers but substitutes a remarkable piece of behavior. After chiseling with its beak, it snaps a cactus spine and uses it to probe its insect prey from the crevice it has chiseled (Figure 13-10). Another of the tree finches has become to all intents and purposes a warbler.

FIG. 13-11 **Evolutionary opportunity, or access: prerequisite to adaptive radiation.** A. Habitat (or niche) 1 is filled by species A (consider it to be a bird like the ancestral ground finch that colonized the Galápagos Islands). Competition within the species constitutes a perpetual pressure on the population to diversify, to exploit new and unoccupied niches. The species can diversify only when it has physical, constitutional, and ecological access to (opportunity to enter) a new habitat. (a) Such is the case for species A with respect to habitats 2, 3, and 5. (b) Although species A has physical and constitutional access to habitats 4 and 6, it lacks ecological access, for these niches are already occupied by the well-adapted species B and C. (c) Species A (a bird) has ecological and physical access to habitat 7 (say, that of a cat), but it lacks constitutional access. (d) Species A could, constitutionally and ecologically, enter habitat 8, but it lacks physical access, for habitat 8 is on another island. B. The consequences of the conditions in A are as follows: (e) Three new species (A_1, A_2, and A_3) evolve as the original species A exploits the combined evolutionary opportunities afforded to it. (f) Habitats 4 and 6 are never entered because, in its transitional stage of incomplete adaptation, A cannot compete with the well-adapted occupants B and C. (g, h) Habitats 7 and 8 remain unoccupied. C, D. The Galápagos Islands versus the mainland. The figures compare schematically the evolutionary opportunities afforded the same species of finch on the South American mainland and in the Galápagos. For the most part, the adaptive radiation of the finches in the Galápagos has been limited only by the constitutional opportunities of the initial ground finches; having gained physical access to the islands, they had virtually unlimited ecological opportunities.

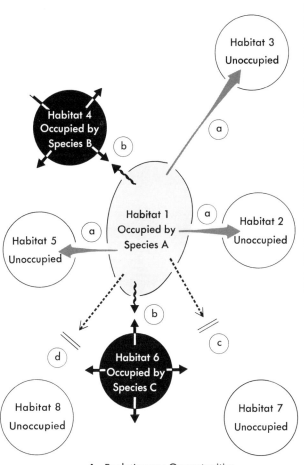

A Evolutionary Opportunities

NO ADAPTIVE RADIATION

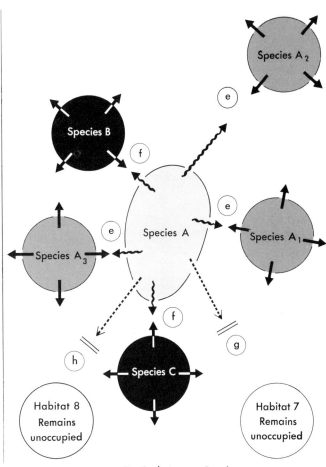

B Evolutionary Results

LARGE-SCALE ADAPTIVE RADIATION

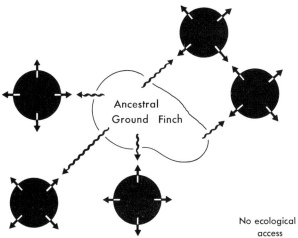

C Mainland— Niches filled

No ecological access

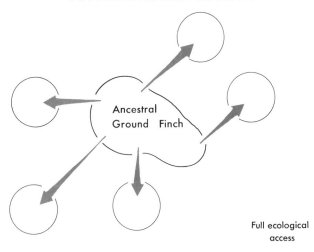

D Galapagos— Niches open

Full ecological access

local differences in ecological opportunity from island to island have affected the history of individual species (Figure 13-12).

The evolutionary phenomenon exemplified by the Galápagos finches is a general one called *adaptive radiation*. The descendants of an ancestral species that was itself adapted to a typically restricted way of life have radiated out into a diversity of new habitats. Adaptive radiations have characterized the evolution of life throughout its long history. Whenever for one reason or another a group of organisms has been confronted with a diversity of new ecological opportunities to which it has physical and constitutional access, radiations have occurred. Some radiations, like those of the Galápagos finches, are trivial in extent

even if beautifully clear in understood detail. Other radiations have taken place on a more massive scale with far-reaching importance for the history of life in general.

MAJOR ADAPTIVE RADIATIONS

The total evolutionary opportunity afforded the Geospizinae on the Galápagos Islands was limited in two ways. First, the diversity of open habitats (ecological opportunities) was limited; the variety of vegetation types was restricted. Second, vegetarian ground finches have limited constitutional opportunities; many ways of life, for instance those of cats or of large rodents, remained open on the Galápagos, but the finches had no access to these ways of life because they lacked teeth and unspecialized forelimbs. Cats and rodents themselves did not exploit the opportunities on the Galápagos because they lacked

FIG. 13-12   The exploitation of local evolutionary opportunities by *Geospiza* species in the Galápagos Islands. Several of the small outlying islands (Fig. 13-8) have never been colonized by some species from the central islands. *G. magnirostris,* for example, has failed to reach Hood and Culpepper. Its absence from these islands left open the large-ground-finch niche to which *G. conirostris* had physical and constitutional access. On Hood *conirostris* has a larger beak than in the central islands and occupies both the large-ground- and cactus-ground-finch niches; on Culpepper it has a still larger beak and occupies the large-ground-finch niches. In the central islands *G. difficilis* is a small ground finch of humid woodlands, a habitat not found in the arid outlying islands. In these outer islands *difficilis* has succeeded only where *fuliginosa* (the common arid-zone small ground finch) is absent and where it has had, therefore, the ecological opportunity to enter the new niche.

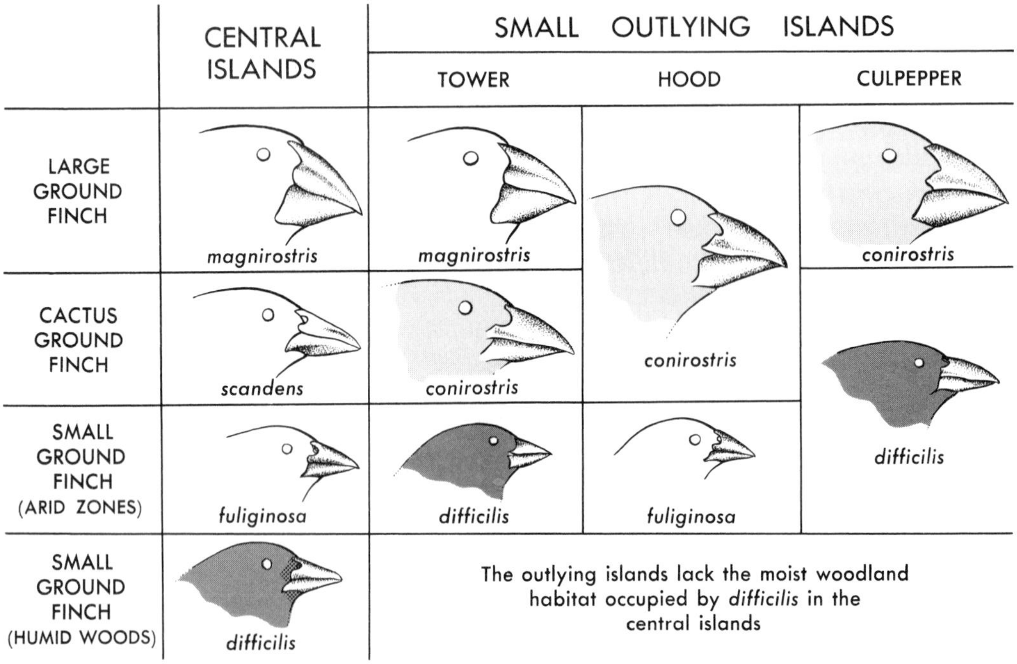

	CENTRAL ISLANDS	SMALL OUTLYING ISLANDS		
		TOWER	HOOD	CULPEPPER
LARGE GROUND FINCH	*magnirostris*	*magnirostris*	*conirostris*	*conirostris*
CACTUS GROUND FINCH	*scandens*	*conirostris*	*conirostris*	*difficilis*
SMALL GROUND FINCH (ARID ZONES)	*fuliginosa*	*difficilis*	*fuliginosa*	
SMALL GROUND FINCH (HUMID WOODS)	*difficilis*	The outlying islands lack the moist woodland habitat occupied by *difficilis* in the central islands		

physical access; they did not cross the sea barrier between South America and the islands. Evolutionary opportunity of far greater scope and significance has been created when organisms with fewer constitutional limitations have been confronted with a wider range of ecological opportunity.

A major adaptive radiation of great importance in our own history followed the first conquest of land by vertebrates. The earliest vertebrates that could emerge even temporarily on the land were fishes that (1) could breathe air to a limited extent with lungs that were extremely crude by modern standards and (2) could walk or wriggle in still cruder fashion with the aid of slightly modified fins. The evolution of these minimal constitutional prerequisites took place as part of a strictly fish radiation. What is important here is the fact that, once able to colonize the land to any extent, the vertebrates had clear sailing from then on; being the first large terrestrial animals, they met with no competition. Amphibians, reptiles, and mammals successively evolved through subsequent geological periods. The reptiles were the first fully competent land vertebrates. Equipped with improved reproductive apparatus, they could move inland away from water and exploit the rich array of wholly unoccupied land habitats. The reptile radiation was a grand one; it produced herbivores in rich assortment, a diversity of carnivores, a host of flying forms, and even forms that successfully returned to water, making a good living in spite of fish competition.

Two special points should be noted in connection with the reptilian radiation. First, it removed the ecological opportunity earlier open to the fishes that were becoming amphibious. The fact that fishes once evolved into land vertebrates but can no longer do so has proved puzzling to many people. How could fishes have accomplished the feat 300 million years ago if they cannot do so now? The answer is simple enough: the evolutionary step from water to land involves a transitional stage, neither fully aquatic nor fully terrestrial, that was extremely unlikely to be successful once efficient competitors were established on the land. No fishes today would, to put it plainly, stand a chance.

The second special point concerns the history of mammals. It is clear from the fossil record that one branch of the early reptilian radiation produced animals that later gave rise to mammals. Indeed, mammals of a sort were in evidence throughout the prolonged heyday of the reptilian dinosaurs, but they were of restricted variety and abundance. For reasons still obscure, many reptiles became extinct about 70 million years ago. With their passing, all the ways of life they had formerly filled became available. Into these now open environments the mammals, which had survived the great dying amoung the reptiles, were free to radiate.

As in the earlier great radiations, the ensuing adaptive radiation of mammals was rapid. Forms appeared that converged toward most of the earlier reptilian adaptive types: herbivores, carnivores, flying forms, swimmers, and so forth. The history of mammals has involved a whole series of still later, more restricted radiations, some of which will be discussed in later chapters.

THE EVOLUTIONARY LOTTERY

Multiplicity of Evolutionary Directions

In any given situation, a combination of physical, constitutional, and ecological opportunities controls the directions of evolution. It does not limit evolution to a single direction but repeatedly produces adaptive radiations like that of the reptiles, the first vertebrates to emerge fully onto the land. This is decidedly not a random process. It is strictly determined by the opportunities presented and by the resultant force of natural selection. These factors, however, depend on the past history and present status of any given population. They do not and cannot take account of the future, as is evident from the fact that the eventual fate of most populations is extinction. With reference to the ultimate outcome, then, the process may be likened to a lottery in which most of the ticket-holders are losers (extinction), some just happen to make limited gains, and a small minority become big winners.

Small Winners

Two examples will sufficiently illustrate how features highly adaptive in their own way may nevertheless limit future opportunities for further or still broader evolution.

The ancestral arthropods arose in the first great

radiation of animals. They themselves have radiated and reradiated repeatedly, giving rise among other things to the exceedingly diverse insects. One reason that they prospered was that they acquired external skeletons. Nevertheless, that very characteristic forever debarred them from the further and in some sense higher opportunities open to the vertebrates with their internal skeletons.

Parasitic flatworms make up another highly successful but even more limited group. Their adaptation to parasitism entailed the loss of sense organs and other structures adaptive to nonparasitic life. Parasitism forever closes all other opportunities of evolution. No parasitic group known has escaped into a nonparasitic existence.

Big Winners

Man shares a common ancestry with other mammals, with birds, with reptiles and fishes, with arthropods, and even with parasitic flatworms. Like all of them, he is descended from animals that underwent the first great adaptive radiation resulting in the animal phyla. His history traces through the later radiation of fishes (first vertebrates), through the still later radiation of reptiles, and so on.

The evolutionary advance that man represents when compared with all his relatives, close and distant, is the product of the same lottery process in which so many organisms lost future opportunities. Man simply happens to be the descendant of a long line of organisms that drew winning tickets in every successive adaptive radiation. The basic adaptations of his ancestors have proved, in hindsight, not to have closed out the evolutionary future.

An essential part of our present adaptive organization is our respiratory system. We owe our lungs to the happy accident that some Devonian fishes developed them, under pressure of selection, as an adaptation to strictly fish problems. They turned out to be more than valuable adaptations in the radiation of fishes; they helped to confer upon some early fishes constitutional access to environments then unoccupied. The sequence of causes here is clear: fishes did not evolve lungs *in order to* become land vertebrates; their descendants became land vertebrates because the ticket the earlier fishes drew in the lottery of fish radiation was a winning one.

So it is with all our adaptations. All arose in response to the generally quite different conditions under which our ancestors, near and remote, lived. All just happened to be winning tickets that opened opportunities for further evolution eventually culminating in man. The many millions of populations that drew other tickets—evolved different adaptations—therefore either became extinct or evolved into species other than *Homo sapiens*.

Natural Selection and Inherited Information

We have repeatedly emphasized the fundamental problems posed for the biologist by the fact of life's complex organization. We have seen that organization requires work for its maintenance and that the universal quest for food is in part to provide the energy needed for this work. But the simple expenditure of energy is not sufficient to develop and maintain order. A bull in a china shop performs work, but he neither creates nor maintains organization. The work needed is *particular* work; it must follow specifications; it requires information on how to proceed.

Our treatment of the subject of genetics was presented in this light. We envisaged embryological development as leading to complex adult organization, and the study of heredity proper as the search for the inherited information that specified how the work of development must proceed. This search led us to the nucleus and its chromosomes, which proved to be the carriers of the inherited specifications ultimately responsible for the organization of the living system.

In showing that the organization of living matter is controlled by information in the chromosomes, genetics provides only the beginnings of a full explanation. We need to know not only where the information is and how it is decoded by the organism, but *how it got there*. The answer to this final question is given by the historical processes of evolution that we have reviewed.

The processes of mutation introduce new modifications into the inherited instructions; genetic recombination always reshuffles the variations of the inherited information that exist among the individuals of a population. Many of the variants thus produced in the chromosomal instructions are disadvantageous; they distort an otherwise clear and appropriate set of inherited specifications. In that case, however, they never persist long in the succession of generations, for their very inappropriateness guarantees their reproductive inefficiency. Natural selection keeps the population's inherited patterns in good

repair. But it does more than that. *Some* of the novelties in the message *happen* to specify a more appropriate organization—a better-adapted organism—than did the original instructions. And as a result of natural selection this more appropriate information ultimately becomes the prevalent pattern throughout the population. Thus natural selection is the agent that *created* the coded information pattern in the first place as the appropriate set of specifications which guarantee the adaptive organization of living things.

Summary

Evolution and the problem of purpose: the impact of the knowledge of evolution on human orientation; the interdependence of science and philosophy; testability as the touchstone for scientific questions and answers; the purposive aspect of adaptation open to scientific examination.

Nature of adaptations: a definition; the diversity of adaptations—morphological, physiological, behavioral; broad and narrow adaptations; individual adaptability.

Inheritance of acquired characters: an alternative to natural selection as a hypothesis to explain adaptation; the misleading label "Lamarckism"; failure of the hypothesis—incompatible with principles of heredity, not supported by experiments, incapable of explaining many kinds of adaptations (insect coloration, neuter insects); the success of natural selection where inheritance of acquired characters fails.

Natural selection and adaptive coloration: the cryptic coloration evolved by selective predation; the example of cryptic coloration in moths; warning coloration, the opposite of cryptic coloration but also caused by selective predation; mimicry and other kinds of adaptive coloration.

Natural selection as a historical process: the pressure to diversify generated by intraspecific competition; physical, constitutional, and ecological opportunities as conditions for entry into new environments; adaptive radiation exemplified by Darwin's finches on the Galápagos Islands—the ecological opportunities not previously exploited on the islands and radiation into 14 species in different niches; major radiations—reptiles, mammals.

The evolutionary lottery: evolution in many directions, determinate but not oriented toward the future, with ultimate extinction as the usual outcome; small winners—arthropods, parasites; big winners—the human ancestry; adaptations to ancestral conditions opening new opportunities for descendants.

Natural selection as the process that creates the information content of the chromosomes.

CHAPTER FOURTEEN

VARIATION, SPECIES, AND SPECIATION

The first reaction of a newcomer to a coral reef or a tropical rain forest is one of confusion. In such places life is most obviously abundant and diverse. The lavishness of nature is overwhelming, and no meaningful pattern is evident at first sight. If perception is not too dulled by familiarity, the same emotion may arise nearer home. A meadow parti-colored with wild flowers or a swarm of insects around a light has in its own degree the same massing of life and bewildering variety. The diversity of life is a product of the evolutionary process, a product arising from the principles of adaptation. It is basically a diversity of adaptations to different ways of life—a topic we have repeatedly touched upon in preceding chapters. One of the fundamental problems in the study of evolution is how diversity arises. That is the topic of this chapter.

Species: Unit of Population Diversity

Were we to look closely at all the individual organisms on a reef, in a forest, or in a meadow we would find every individual different in at least some minor respect. Armed with the genetic facts we have already discussed, this would not surprise us. On the other hand, we would be more impressed with the fact that the individual organisms seemed to fall into natural groups of *nearly* similar forms. We might notice the differences among buttercups in the meadow, but we would more certainly recognize their similarity. We would perceive that buttercups form a distinct kind of organism, a natural group of similar individuals—a *species*. The differences that would impress us would be those between species, as between buttercups and daisies. The diversity of life is a diversity of populations, and the species is a significant unit of population.

Intraspecific Variation

Diversity begins at the lowest level, with the fact already repeatedly mentioned that no two individuals are ever exactly alike. No matter how small a unit of population we study, there is always variation among its members. That very fundamental generalization lies at the heart of the diversity of life.

SOURCES OF VARIATION

The sources of variation have all been mentioned in previous chapters. Let us briefly review them as background for the present subject.

The characteristics of organisms arise in the course of their development by the interaction of heredity and environment. Heredity determines a reaction range. The circumstances of development (through the entire life span) determine just where in that reaction range an individual's characteristics will actually be. In the long run, the differences that count the most are differences in reaction ranges and therefore in heredity.

Variation due to differences between reaction ranges is of major biological importance and is the source material for evolutionary change and for the diversity of life. Within a population, the variation arises mainly from the shuffling of genes and chromosomes, especially in sexual reproduction. The different kinds of genes and chromosomes involved in this shuffling originated by mutation.

BELL-SHAPED DISTRIBUTION
OF VARIATION IN DEMES

In order to convince yourself of the reality of variation, and to learn something of its nature, you should now examine 50 or 100 specimens from one deme of some one sort of organism. (If the specimens were collected in a limited area and over a brief period of time they are probably from a single deme.) These may be available in museum or college collections, but they will be more interesting and instructive if you gather them yourself. Among the innumerable possibilities are flowers, leaves (full-grown, each from a different plant of one species); seeds; shells; ants, grasshoppers, beetles, butterflies, or other insects; or field mice (skins, skulls, or both). Whatever you collect, some measurements of size will be possible. Probably also there are characters that can be counted (petals on a flower, scales of a pine cone, ribs on a shell, etc.). Other characters, perhaps colors and color patterns, may best be noted in words. These are the principal sorts of observations used in studying variation and classifying diversity.

In your sample some features will be the same in all the individuals. After all, it is characteristic of a deme that the organisms in it are similar. For instance, if you collect simple flowers, all will probably have the same number of petals and other flower parts, although they may not. Other characters are sure to vary in your sample. This is especially true of measurements of size and weight or of counts of such multiple parts as ribs on a shell or scales on a snake or lizard. Observations of such characters may be grouped and tabulated in the form of a *frequency distribution*. Examples of frequency distributions of a common sort are given in Table 14-1.

These observations can also be presented pictorially in graphs, as in Figure 14-1. You see that these graphs have definite patterns, which are similar but not identical in the two examples. In both there is a particular range of values, a *class*, that is most frequent. You might say that this class is the fashion among these animals, and it is called by a name for a fashion; it is the *mode*. On each side of the mode, the frequencies fall off, with fewer and fewer (and finally no) individuals in each class.

Most variable characters that can take any one of a considerable number of values in the individuals of a deme tend to have frequency distributions similar to those of Figure 14-1. This is the most important single generalization regarding variation in demes. The pattern approximates a bell-shaped mathematical curve, one which is a member of a particular family of curves that is known collectively as the normal curve of probability. Some differences from the precise mathematical curve always occur, because nature is not as tidy and regular as mathematicians, but the correspondence of a nearly symmetrical distribution (like Figure 14-1A) may be quite close. This is the basis for some of the essential statistical methods in

FIG. 14-1 Frequency distributions.

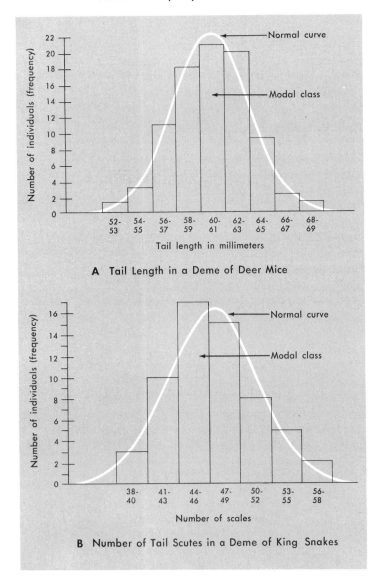

A Tail Length in a Deme of Deer Mice

B Number of Tail Scutes in a Deme of King Snakes

TABLE 14-1 *Frequency Distributions*

a. A measurement of size. Tail lengths of individuals from a deme of deer mice.

Measurements in millimeters	Numbers of individuals (frequencies)
52–53	1
54–55	3
56–57	11
58–59	18
60–61	21
62–63	20
64–65	9
66–67	2
68–69	1

b. A count of multiple parts. Numbers of scales (scutes) along the tails of individuals from a deme of king snakes.

Number of scales	Numbers of individuals (frequencies)
38–40	3
41–43	10
44–46	17
47–49	15
50–52	8
53–55	5
56–58	2

the technical study of variation. Some frequency distributions are distinctly lopsided (like Figure 14-1B) or may otherwise differ from a normal curve. In statistical analysis the differences are also studied and may reveal important facts about variation in a deme.

It is easy enough to demonstrate that variation in demes often has a bell-shaped frequency distribution. In your own sample you can almost certainly find some variation that has this sort of pattern. The fact is interesting, but it does not have much real scientific meaning unless we can link it with biological principles. What does the bell-shaped pattern mean? We know that variation may result either from hereditary differences in reaction ranges under similar conditions or from different environmental conditions interacting with similar reaction ranges. Either or both of these principles may be involved in the bell-shaped distributions.

If organisms with similar or identical genotypes

(Figure 14-2B), and hence similar or identical reaction ranges, develop in similar (but not identical) conditions, the phenotypes will tend to be similar. Most of them will fall into a modal class representing the usual interaction of genotype and conditions of development. Conditions of development producing phenotypes far from the modal class will be comparatively rare. Thus the effects of environment often tend to produce a bell-shaped distribution even apart from hereditary variations. This can be checked by comparing mature leaves from a single plant, actually parts of one individual and identical in genotype. Their variation in size usually has a bell-shaped distribution.

FIG. 14-2   **The bell-shaped curve of population variation.** A bell-shaped distribution of phenotypic characteristics (size, weight, color, etc.) in a population may be due theoretically to either (A) variation among the genotypes of the population's members or (B) variation in the environmental conditions encountered by the population's members. The bell-shaped distributions of variation encountered in natural populations are nearly always the result of variation in both environmental conditions and individual genotypes.

Absolutely Constant Environment; Variation
Caused Entirely by Heredity

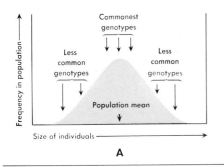

A

Absolutely Constant Genotype; Variation
Caused Entirely by Environmental Conditions

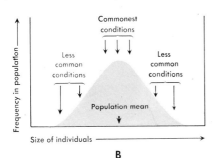

B

On the other hand, we have seen that characters influenced more or less equally by several or many genes also tend to produce a distribution that you now recognize as like a bell-shaped distribution in a deme. In the experiment previously studied (Chapter 6), crossing of large and small parents produced a broad, bell-shaped distribution in F_2. In natural populations with the same genes, the same sort of distribution results from interbreeding in a deme and tends to persist through the generations. When a distribution of this pattern (Figure 14-2A) has a genetic basis, the most probable inference is that the genetic system is one with several or many genes affecting the character being studied.

Thus either environmental or hereditary factors may produce a bell-shaped distribution. In most instances both are involved simultaneously. It is difficult to disentangle the two, but this can be done approximately at least. One way is to conduct an experiment like that just mentioned, crossbreeding extreme variant individuals from a deme. If the results are similar to those of that experiment, hereditary variation is present, and further analysis can determine its nature and extent. Another way is to perform selection experiments of the type shown in Figure 14-3. Of course, it is impractical to conduct breeding experiments on many of the millions of demes present in nature, and such experiments are wholly impossible for the even more numerous demes now extinct. Still, it is possible for us to obtain an approximate idea of the amount of variation that is truly hereditary by the statistical analysis of variation within demes and among demes living under similar and different conditions.

POLYMORPHISM

We have just considered variation that seems to intergrade continuously or that has a sequence of numerous classes, usually with a bell-shaped distribution. There is also variation with a few classes, often strikingly different forms which may occur in varying proportions in different demes. Among some birds a mixture of dark and white forms is usual in demes.

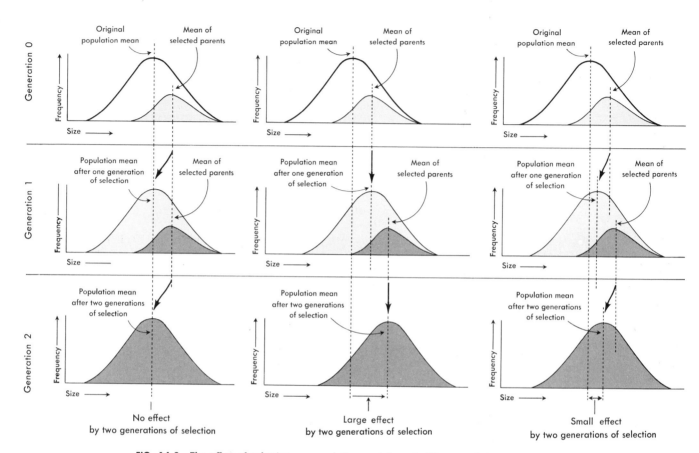

A. Phenotypic Variation Caused Entirely by Environmental Conditions

B. Phenotypic Variation Caused Entirely by Variation in Heredity

C. Phenotypic Variation Caused by Variation in Both Heredity and Environment

Generation 0

Original population mean / Mean of selected parents — Frequency / Size

Generation 1

Population mean after one generation of selection / Mean of selected parents — Frequency / Size

Generation 2

Population mean after two generations of selection — Frequency / Size

No effect by two generations of selection

Large effect by two generations of selection

Small effect by two generations of selection

FIG. 14-3 The effect of selection on population variation. A. When population variation is caused entirely by variation in environmental conditions, selective breeding from one generation to another will fail to change the distribution of population variation. Generation 1, the progeny bred from a select group of large individuals of generation 0, will show (if raised in the same range of environmental conditions) the same distribution of phenotypes that characterized generation 0 as a whole. B. The result is different when environmental conditions are constant and the population variation reflects an array of different genotypes in the population. In this case the mean size of generation 1, bred from selected parents, is considerably larger than the mean size of generation 0 as a whole. In fact, it is the same as the mean size of the selected parents. C. When both hereditary and environmental variations contribute to the variation of a population's phenotypes, selection leads to a generation 1 whose members are larger than those of generation 0, but the effect is relatively slight. The mean size of generation 1 is smaller than that of the selected parents. The reason is clear: although he carefully breeds from large individuals, the selector cannot avoid picking some individuals that are large because of favorable environmental factors and in spite of relatively poor genotypes. (Adapted from *General Genetics*, by A. M. Srb and R. D. Owen. W. H. Freeman and Company. Copyright © 1952)

There are herons among which demes normally include both gray and white birds, which interbreed. Sometimes there are about three white to one gray, a suggestive approach to the Mendelian ratio for combinations of equally numerous dominant and recessive alleles. In some bitterns (relatives of the herons), brown, white, and black (or unusually dark brown) forms commonly occur within single demes.

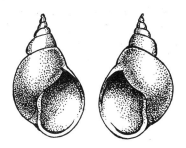

FIG. 14-4 **Polymorphism.** Two members of the same snail population differ in the direction of shell coiling; one shell has a right-handed coil (the common condition), and the other has a left-handed coil.

On the other hand, some species of herons are always white and some always colored in the same way.

The natural occurrence of two or more sharply distinct forms in a single deme is *polymorphism* ("many forms"). Polymorphism is a widespread sort of variation and may be seen, in some respect and to some extent, in most demes. It involves not only color but many other characteristics. For instance, a deme of snails may be polymorphic in its direction of coiling, some individuals having shells coiled left-handedly and some shells coiled right-handedly (Figure 14-4). Most human populations are polymorphic in blood types, which do not show but which are sharply distinct biochemically. The number of forms in a deme is usually small: two (colors of some herons, direction of coiling in some snails), three (colors of some bitterns), or four (the human A, B, AB, and O blood types). Less commonly, many forms may occur; more than 120 distinct patterns have been found in a single species of platyfish (small tropical fish often kept in home aquariums).

What underlies polymorphism? In Chapter 6 you learned that alleles of single genes may accompany striking and sharply distinct differences in particular characters. Such were the characters studied by Mendel, and these are the genes of classical Mendelian experimentation. Polymorphic characters in demes are like the flower colors and seed characteristics of Mendel's peas. They are determined by one or a few genes, each with two or a small number of alleles in various members of the population. They contrast with characters determined by the interaction of larger numbers of genes, which usually have a bell-shaped distribution in demes. This is not an absolute distinc-

tion. There is a continuous scale of intensity of gene action and of single to multiple gene effects on phenotypic characteristics. Similarly, polymorphic and bell-shaped distributions intergrade in populations. They are, however, distinct in their more extreme or characteristic forms as well as in convenient methods for studying them and in some of their implications for evolution. In several well-documented cases, two or more forms in a polymorphic population undergo cyclic changes in ratios due to differences in seasonal adaptations.

FIG. 14-5 **Differences among populations in blood group frequencies.** Each of three distinct populations of Montana Indians is characterized by the relative frequency (as percentage) within it of the three blood group alleles O, A, and B.

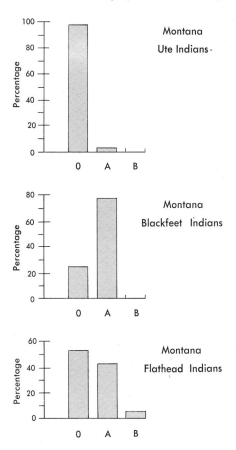

DIFFERENCES BETWEEN DEMES

Within a species divided into more or less distinct demes, as most species are, there are two kinds of variation. One is variation within any one deme, some features of which have been mentioned. The other is variation of the species in the form of differences between demes, for two demes are not likely to be precisely similar.

In species with sexual reproduction, there is occasionally and often regularly interbreeding between adjacent demes. Offspring from one deme may move into the other. For these reasons, adjacent demes almost always intergrade and are seldom completely distinct from each other in any characteristic. Adjacent demes often differ but still usually intergrade in polymorphic characters. It is rare for the individuals of one deme to be all of one form and those of another, adjacent deme all of a different form. If a character takes two forms, adjacent demes will usually have both forms. If the demes differ in this character, the difference is, as a rule, in the percentages of individuals of each form. Variation of this sort between demes is exemplified in Figure 14-5. The basis for these relationships is that the same genes and alleles are present in the adjacent demes but that some alleles are more frequent in one deme than in another.

Two demes of the same species do not usually

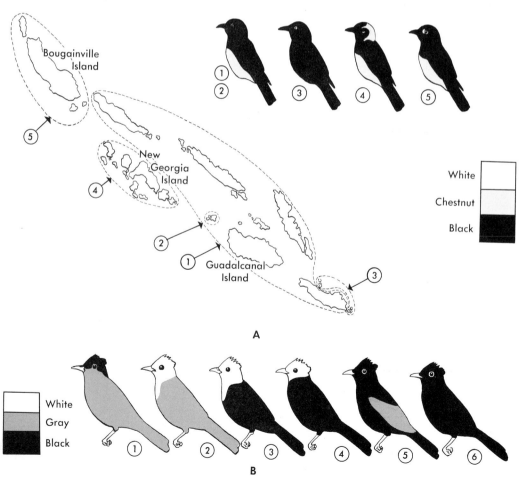

White
Chestnut
Black

A

White
Gray
Black

B

FIG. 14-6 Two examples of bird species subdivided into distinct subspecies. A. Geographic subspecies, and their distribution, of the flycatcher *Monarcha castaneoventris* in the Solomon Islands. Four color patterns (involving white, chestnut, and black) are found among the five subspecies. B. Six subspecies of the Asiatic bulbul (*Microscelis leucocephalus*), distributed from India through China.

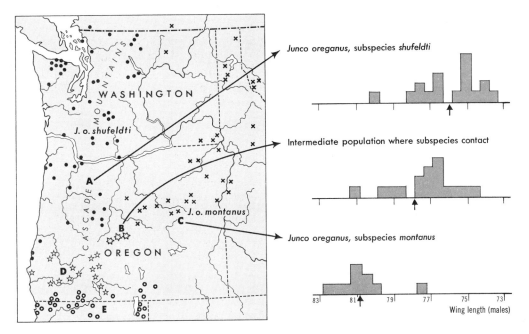

FIG. 14-7 Intergradation where subspecies come in contact. The map shows the distribution in Oregon and Washington of three subspecies of the small snowbird *Junco oreganus* and of intergrading populations between subspecies. Each symbol identifies a locality from which samples have been studied. The three subspecies are as follows: A (• symbol), *J. o. shufeldti*; C (✕ symbol) *J. o. montanus*; E, (O symbol), *J. o. thurberi*. B (✿ symbol) represents intermediate populations between the two neighboring subspecies *shufeldti* and *montanus*. D (☆ symbol) represents intermediate populations *shufeldti* and *thurberi*. Frequency distributions for male wing lengths are given for *shufeldti*, *montanus*, and the intergrading population (B), where these two subspecies meet. Population means are indicated by the arrows on the segmented line.

occur and never continue long in just the same place at the same time. If they did, the demes would fuse and become one. Variation between demes therefore has geographic patterns. The patterns are of great interest because they throw light on many problems such as the genetics of populations, the relationships of populations with their environments, and the origin of species and other units of classification.

It is unusual for each deme to be sharply distinctive or for the differences among demes to be highly irregular. Usually all the demes over a considerable area are closely similar. Such similarity is maintained by interbreeding between demes. Interbreeding over the whole area may, indeed, be so common that in effect the whole regional population is a large unit, a single deme or a complex without distinct division into demes. The large deme or complex of similar demes may constitute the whole of a species. More

commonly there are two, several, or many such complexes, their demes also similar among themselves but different from those of other complexes. In classification, the large demes or deme complexes in such a situation are usually designated *subspecies* (Figure 14-6). Where two subspecies of one species are in contact, there is usually a zone of intergradation, due to interbreeding, but away from this zone the subspecies may be quite distinct in their characteristics. Figure 14-7 illustrates this frequent sort of distribution of variation within a species.

Zones of intergradation between demes (or groups of similar demes) are not always narrow and well-defined as in the last example. In fact, a whole regional population may intergrade from one end of its distribution area to another. For instance, southern and northern individuals of a species may be quite different, and yet when the population is followed

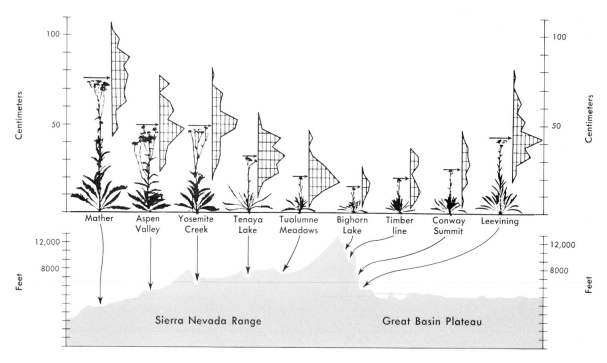

FIG. 14-8 An altitudinal cline in Achillea. The plant species *Achillea lanulosa* occurs at all altitudes in the Sierra Nevada Mountains of California, exhibiting considerable adaptive intraspecific variation in relation to the different environments at various altitudes. Populations at lower altitudes are taller and those at higher altitudes are shorter. Beside the plant representative of each altitudinal population is a graph showing the distribution of height variation within the population.

from south to north there may be no definite line or zone where the change is localized. Or differences may appear gradually as populations are followed from lower to higher elevations (Figure 14-8) or from wetter to drier situations. Continuity and complete intergradation imply that the interbreeding of adjacent demes is common, and that the gradual change is usually correlated with gradients of environmental conditions. The technical term for a sequence of poorly separable demes with gradual, regular change from one area to another is *cline*.

Environmental gradients are common in nature. Every mountain range has a gradient from bottom to top, from warmer to colder, and usually simultaneously from drier to wetter, with gradients also in other climatic conditions and in soils. Plains or lowlands have similar gradients from south to north. Gradients of temperature, of salinity, and of light occur in lakes and seas. These gradients in physical environments are often accompanied by gradients in

characteristics of the organisms inhabiting them. The gradients may be similar in a number of different species. There are, for example, three famous rules (generalizations with some exceptions) that apply to many mammals and birds:

1. Within any one species, the average size of the individuals tends to be smaller in warmer climates and larger in colder climates (Bergmann's Rule).
2. Within any one species, protruding parts such as tails, ears, or bills tend to be shorter in colder climates than in warmer climates (Allen's Rule).
3. Within any one species, colors tend to be darker in warm, moist climates and lighter in cold, dry climates (Gloger's Rule).

There are numerous other rules of this kind that apply to various groups of animals and plants. There is nothing especially mysterious about such rules. They are only special examples of a broader and profoundly important generalization that states: *Differences among demes tend to be correlated with differences in their environments.*

Another way to state the generalization about differences between demes is this: variation among subspecies or local populations of a species is largely adaptive. Most students of the subject agree that some nonadaptive variation also occurs in species and may even be common *within* demes, where variation

involves *particular* characteristics of *individuals*. It is, however, probable that most of the variation represented by differences *between* demes is adaptive, for there variation involves *average* characteristics of natural *populations* of individuals.

Species and Speciation

THE SPECIES PROBLEM

It has already been noted that the basic unit of population in nature is the deme. There are still smaller units, such as a family consisting of parents and their offspring. Such units are obviously very temporary. They are distinguishable only for a generation or so. Their distinction and naming are not practical or significant for the broader study of the evolution of populations and the diversity of life. The same situation often applies to demes, which are not likely to persist indefinitely as distinct units. The smallest unit that is persistent in nature is the species.

All biologists think that they have a pretty good idea of what a species is, at least among the particular organisms on which they work. Yet for centuries biologists have been battling and baffling each other about "the species problem." The problem is simply to produce a clear, fully satisfactory answer to the question, "What is a species?"

It is one of the facts of life that an exact definition of a species applicable without question to all sorts of organisms is inherently impossible. It is no waste of time to discuss what species are; on the contrary, that is one of the most important subjects in the whole science of biology. It is, however, a waste of time to try to agree on one, infallible definition of species. In the first place, there are many ways, all valuable, to approach the subject. A geneticist naturally thinks in terms of breeding and an anatomist in terms of structure. In the second place, population units tend to be of different sorts among the tremendously varied products of evolution. Why should

we expect to find precisely the same sorts of units among, say, yeasts, tapeworms, bees, and primroses? Third, natural populations are not static things that stay put neatly within the confines of rigid definitions. They are constantly changing, splitting up, reuniting, becoming more or less similar to each other, expanding, contracting, acquiring new habits, discarding old structures, and, in a word, *evolving*.

We have already characterized a species as a group of organisms so similar in structure and heredity that their demes intergrade, may fuse, and may take the place of one another without essential change in the nature and role of the group as a whole. A species may not be clearly subdivided into smaller units that can be called demes. Usually it is so subdivided, and then the point is that the demes do not necessarily have evolutionary continuity as distinct units. A species does tend to have long evolutionary continuity and distinctiveness. That, really, is what makes it such a significant unit. The species may then be defined as *a sequence of ancestral and descendent populations evolving independently of others and with its own separate and unitary evolutionary role and tendencies.* It is an essential part of the concept that a species is a sort of population, a group, the individuals within which are rather closely related to each other and therefore more or less similar in essential characteristics, although there is always variation among them. The kind and degree of variation are important features of a species. A species is not a group of individuals all of which have the same pattern; that is a nonevolutionary and old-fashioned idea, as will be evident when we discuss classification in Chapter 15.

The thing that maintains a species as a unit among biparental organisms is interbreeding. As long as the individuals of a group can interbreed, producing fertile offspring, and as long as they do so with some frequency, the whole group shares in a genetic pool and tends to have the unity and continuity that we have noted as characteristic of species. Thus we have the basis for another definition: *a species is a group of actually or potentially interbreeding natural populations that are reproductively isolated from other such groups.* This definition, stressing the genetic structure of a species, does not conflict with the previous definition, which stresses its evolutionary role. Provided that it reproduces sexually (as most species do), the evolutionary species as seen *at any one time* almost always corresponds with the genetic species.

Neither definition demands that two distinct species never interbreed. In some groups of organisms hybrids between two closely related species are rather common. The genetic distinction of the species and their integral evolutionary roles are nevertheless maintained if breeding between them is decidedly less common than breeding within each one separately, or if the hybrids are distinctly less fertile than the offspring of parents both of the same species.

Of course there is no absolute distinction between separate demes of one species that interbreed more freely and produce more fertile offspring, and separate species that interbreed less freely and produce less fertile offspring. The two sorts of groups intergrade in nature. The intergradation is part of the process of evolution. That is a reason that a species is not really an absolutely delimited unit and that it is futile to try to define it as such. But if the process goes a little further, until all the hybrid offspring are completely infertile or interbreeding can never occur, then the delimitation has become absolute and no one would seriously question that the two groups are different species.

SPECIATION

Chapter 12 dealt with the genetics of populations and how populations change. Such changes are part of the basis for the diversity of life. Obviously

two species, necessarily derived from a common ancestry some time in the past, will not be different unless one or both have changed. It is also obvious that there will not be two species rather than one unless there has been another sort of change, a splitting of one group into two. Changes in a continuous population make for differences between earlier and later forms, but they do not increase the number of different populations or species. Another basis for the diversity of life is thus necessarily the splitting of a population into two or more. An eventual outcome of this process is adaptive radiation, discussed in the preceding chapter. We did not there consider just how the process goes on at the basic level where one species divides into two or more, and that is the topic to which we now turn.

Geneticists and other biologists now adhere to the view set forth by Darwin: that speciation is usually a gradual process. Demes or groups of similar demes (such as the subspecies of classifiers) often develop somewhat distinctive genetic characters. This may be just a matter of having different allele ratios in their genetic pools. There is somewhat freer interbreeding within these groups than between them. Usually that is all that happens. The groups continue to be subdivisions of a species and do not become so distinctive as to be considered separate species. Sometimes, however, interbreeding between groups becomes less and less frequent, and its resulting hybrids less and less fertile, or both. If this process continues, the groups eventually become different species, although there is no sharply definable point at which speciation can be said to have occurred.

The key processes in evolution down at the level of the populations are thus two: genetic change within populations; and the splitting up of populations by sudden or, more commonly, gradual decrease of interbreeding between demes or other units of populations.

ISOLATING MECHANISMS

Anything that decreases interbreeding between groups or organisms is called an *isolating mechanism.* Isolating mechanisms are of many different kinds, and some of them are very curious.

The most generally effective isolating mechanism

is simply space or geographic separation. Some students believe that speciation rarely or never occurs (always excepting new polyploid species of plants) unless the groups becoming isolated are in different areas. There may be rare exceptions, but certainly spatial separation is usually involved. Sooner or later other isolating mechanisms also arise, even if the effective isolation is purely geographic at first. Two nonmigratory animals a hundred or a thousand miles apart obviously cannot interbreed, and two plants at such distances are most unlikely to do so. If plants or animals of the same species occur fairly continuously in the intervening region, there is still little isolation as far as the whole population is concerned. Individuals at opposite ends of the occupied region cannot interbreed directly, but they can pass on genes to any part of the population in the course of reproduction over a few generations. Often, however, there are spatial breaks in the distribution. Then there is less interbreeding across the gap, and in time the populations on the two sides of it may become different species.

There are rather similar populations of tuft-eared squirrels on the north and south rims of the Grand Canyon (Figure 14-9). They must originally have come from one population, but in their present positions they seldom or never interbreed because they do not cross the canyon. They have become visibly different: the northern squirrels have darker underparts and whiter tails. The difference is not yet very great, but the two populations are usually considered distinct species, Abert squirrels on the south rim and Kaibab squirrels on the north rim. The distributional break involved in geographic speciation need not be so spectacular as the Grand Canyon. A stretch of grassland between two forests may represent a break between plant and animal populations of the forest. Narrow or wide discontinuities in distribution are abundant, and if they long persist, they frequently lead to specific separation between the populations on each side of them.

Geographic isolation alone is seldom permanently effective in decreasing interbreeding. Even the Grand Canyon might not entirely prevent the squirrels from interbreeding; some might cross, and populations can spread around the ends of the main barrier. (Also in broad geological view, even so tremendous a barrier

Kaibab squirrel

Abert squirrel

FIG. 14-9   The Kaibab and Abert squirrels.

as the Grand Canyon is only temporary.) In almost all instances of speciation, biological as well as geographic factors eventually decrease interbreeding. It is the biological isolating mechanisms that are strangest and most varied.

Interbreeding between otherwise similar populations in the same region is often reduced simply because they have slightly different habitats in that region. In Florida there are two groups of turtles that do interbreed to some extent and are considered as belonging to the same species, but interbreeding is reduced by the fact that one group prefers to live in lakes and ditches and the other in running rivers. Anyone who has ever climbed a mountain knows that both plants and animals tend to live at characteristic elevations. Interbreeding between similar populations may be reduced by their preferences for different altitudes.

Interbreeding may also be reduced or even eliminated if animals have different breeding seasons or plants produce pollen at different times. In eastern and central United States there are two groups of common toads, considered distinct species. They can hybridize and occasionally do, producing fertile offspring. The populations as a whole are, however, kept quite distinct by the fact that one breeds early in the season and the other late.

In higher animals, especially insects and vertebrates, sexual isolation is frequently effective. Males and females of different populations simply do not like each other, or perhaps it would be more strictly scientific to say that they do not effectively stimulate each other sexually. Choice of partners may be exercised by males, females, or both. Some experiments with flies (*Drosophila* again) suggest that the males do not care but that the females rebuff "foreigners." In some tropical fishes, however, the males do the selecting. The females have distinctive color patterns, and the males pick out the patterns of their own species and even show preferences for certain particular variants of pattern within their species.

Many animals have elaborate courtship procedures. In these species a female does not breed unless she is properly stimulated by courtship characteristic of the male of her own species. A relatively simple instance familiar to most of us is the strutting display of male turkeys. Some birds go through much more elaborate performances (and so do some men). Even among fishes there may be complex courtship. There are, for example, specific differences in their breeding patterns (Chapter 14). Male sticklebacks build nests and then induce females to lay eggs in them. Differences in the procedure in different species are effective isolating mechanisms, for a female is persuaded only by the performance of her own sort of male. Some of the many differences between two species are

The male of one species	The male of the other species
Builds a nest with separate entrance and exit, hanging on water plants.	Builds a nest with entrance only, on the bottom.
Leads the female to the nest in a series of zigzags and gets her to enter with a little prodding.	Puts on a special mating play in front of nest and then forces the female in.

Interbreeding in plants is often restricted by the tendency of pollinating insects to visit only one species of plant on a single foraging trip. This sort of isolation is carried to a high degree in orchids, for instance, which commonly have flowers that attract one species of bee or fly to one species of orchid.

The mechanisms so far discussed reduce interbreeding even if the organisms concerned are completely fertile with each other. They are thus of particular importance in early stages of speciation, when the populations are still quite similar and may still be interfertile. Sooner or later another factor enters the picture: *genetic isolation,* reduction of the genetic capacity for reproduction between two populations. Genetic isolation may set in early in the process or may not become significant until long after the species are fully separated, but it does always occur in the long run. The main reason most of the diverse sorts of organisms do not interbreed is simply that they cannot produce fertile offspring.

Distantly related species usually cannot produce hybrid offspring at all. They are so different genetically that the chromosomes cannot get together and produce a zygote that will develop. More closely related species may produce hybrid offspring, but continued reproduction between them may be reduced or impossible. The hybrids may be inferior in survival capacity, or may have reduced fertility or be entirely sterile. Cats and dogs are both carnivores, but they belong to families that have been distinct for scores of millions of years. Their gametes do not produce hybrid zygotes. Goats and sheep belong to the same family but to long-distinct lines in the family. Their gametes form a hybrid zygote that begins to develop but dies before birth. Horses and donkeys are distinct but rather closely related species. Hybrid zygotes develop normally and produce vigorous, long-lived animals, mules, but the hybrids cannot reproduce, probably due to faulty gametogenesis. Some crosses of closely related kinds of cotton result in fertile hybrids, but reproduction among the hybrids produces a majority of abnormal, short-lived offspring.

Genetic isolating mechanisms include the following: (1) gene and chromosome differences which prevent normal fertilization or development, and (2) abnormal meiotic processes in hybrids that prevent normal gamete formation or severely reduce fertility.

Once genetic isolation is fully established, the evolutionary destinies of the two populations are

forever separate. They are unquestionably and irreversibly established as distinct species, and the diversity of living things has been increased. The process has been repeated countless millions of times during the history of life, and it has been responsible for the production of the millions of separate species that fill the world of life.

Interspecific Selection

We previously (Chapter 12) discussed natural selection primarily in terms of single populations. Now we should mention a kind of selection that depends on principles familiar to you but the genetic aspect of which has hitherto been mostly implicit: *interspecific selection,* which is selection not within but between populations or especially species. If species are in contact with each other and if they must share some necessity of life in limited supply, competition will ensue. This generalization, earlier made in other contexts, also has a strong bearing on natural selection. Two different outcomes are possible. In the first case, the competitively more effective species may be more successful in reproduction, and its population may increase while that of the less effective species decreases, usually to local or total extinction. This is natural selection not by the increase of some and

the decrease of other particular genetic characters within a population but by the increase of one whole isolated genetic pool at the expense of another genetic pool.

In the other case, the intensity and direction of natural selection change within each of the two separate genetic pools. Competition intensifies selection, and in each population selection favors variants ecologically least similar to members of the other population and hence least competitive with them. As a result, the two species diverge, evolving until they occupy ecological niches sufficiently distinct so that competition is no longer significant. This is plainly one of the basic factors in adaptive radiation, although it applies only after speciation has occurred and the species in question are genetically isolated. (Why?)

Summary

Species and diversity: the diversity of life as a diversity of populations adapted to different environments; the species (contrasted to the deme) as the significant unit of population diversity.

Intraspecific variation—its sources: variation within a deme—its bell-shaped distribution exemplified, the modal and the less frequent classes, the approximation of empirical bell-shaped distributions of variation to the normal curve of probability, heredity and environment as causes of bell-shaped distributions, polymorphism; variation between demes—continuously varying characters like size and weight, geographic subspecies, interbreeding and the intergradation of subspecies, interdeme variation correlated with different environments (Bergmann's, Allen's, and Gloger's rules).

The species problem: the problem of defining a species—the variety of approaches to a definition, the difficulty in giving a truly general definition because all species are always evolving; the species as the smallest *persistent unit* of population in nature; the general similarity of species members as a result of free interbreeding within the species, whose members therefore share a common genetic pool (a common heredity).

Speciation—the evolutionary process whereby one species population splits into two populations that no longer interbreed: speciation not a single step (saltation) except in the special case of new polyploid, usually plant, species; Darwin's correct view that speciation is gradual; the genetic divergence of isolated segments of a species population (genetic pools gradually changing) until interbreeding is permanently prevented.

Isolating mechanisms preventing interbreeding between populations: the importance of geographic isolation, especially in initiating speciation (the Abert and Kaibab squirrels of the Grand Canyon); the evolution of biological isolating mechanisms— ecological isolation (as in Florida turtles), sexual isolation because of periodism or courtship patterns in animals (*Drosophila* and sticklebacks) and habits of the pollinating insects in plants; hybrid sterility as the ultimate barrier separating species.

Interspecific competition: the outcome either expansion of one species at the expense of the other or divergent evolution until the two occupy different niches.

This bright blue bullfrog was found near Fort Knox, Kentucky. It has been theorized that his unusual color is the result of yellow pigment in his skin. (Karl Maslowski)

A patternless and a normal copperhead. The patternless snake may reflect an evolutionary change since it is better camouflaged in its habitat, the prairie. (Henry S. Fitch)

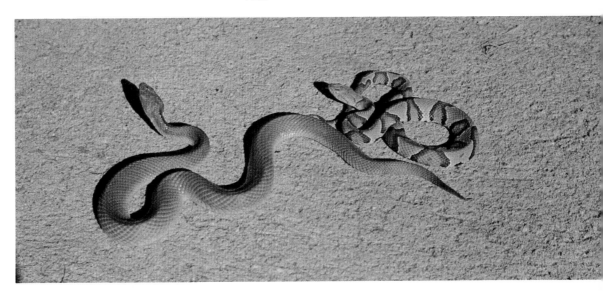

The hornet clear wing moth *(Sesia api-formis)* is a strikingly effective mimic of the large yellow and black hornet. (Magnified several times.) (S. Beaufoy)

When the ilia underwing *(Catocala ilia)* moth is at rest during the day, its brilliantly colored wings are normally concealed by its barklike front wings. The cryptically colored and patterned wings of the geometrid moth *(Lytrosia unitaria)* make it difficult to see. (Alexander B. Klots)

The caterpillar of the oleander hawk moth can mimic parts of the oleander bush. When disturbed, the moth jerks its hidden eyespots into view to scare off the predator. (Miriam Rothschild)

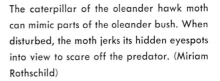

Pair of giraffes different in color and pattern showing intrademe variation. (George G. Simpson)

Lithops karasmontana in full flower. The resemblance of these plants to stones may be adaptive camouflage. (E. Javorsky)

Red anemone traps an unsuspecting sculpin. The tentacles of the anemone contain a poison which stuns the fish. (Anthony Mercieca from National Audubon Society)

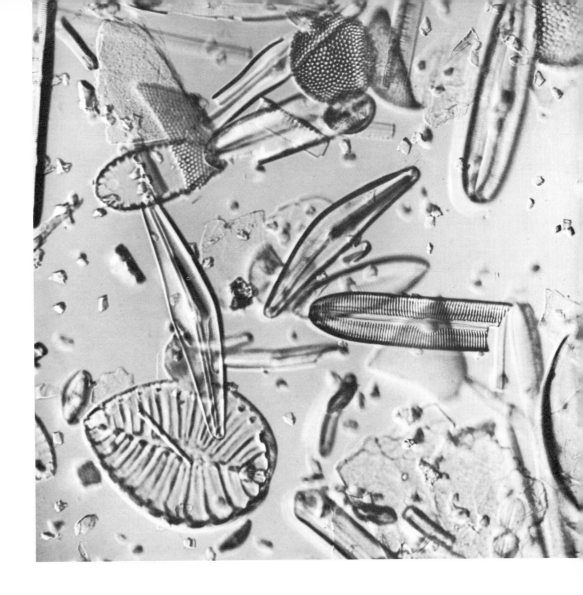

PART SIX

THE DIVERSITY OF LIFE

The photograph introducing Part 6 displays a rich assortment of diatoms—photosynthetic protists—in a drop of water. Diverse as it is, the life in this drop can only suggest the over-all variety that confronts the biologist when he turns—as he must—to study the total array of different organisms that evolution has brought into existence. The truly immense diversity of life, attested to by the existence of well over a million species today, is bewildering. But bewilderment gives way to understanding as we perceive two general themes running through the vast variety of life.

The first theme is that the diversity of species is essentially one of mode of life: species differ in the adaptations they have evolved to diversified environmental opportunities.

The second theme is that all the different organisms are related to each other, some to greater, others to lesser, degree. Organic reproduction, under the control of heredity, is basically a conservative process. The adaptive innovations and diversity that have come about in life's evolution have rarely obscured, or transformed beyond our recognition, a fundamental and ancient pattern of organization. The trained observer can detect this organizational pattern underlying the more special adaptations wrought by natural selection. And to this extent he can trace the line of evolutionary descent by which an organism has come to its present condition. The elucidation of evolutionary relationships is the basis of the natural classification of organisms by which life's diversity is most effectively rendered understandable.

Chapter 15 deals with the evolutionary principles that underlie the process of classification. Chapters 16 and 17 survey the major groups of organisms: the protists, plants, and animals.

PRINCIPLES

OF CLASSIFICATION

Variation within demes and species and the nature and origin of species, as discussed in Chapter 14, are fundamental aspects of the diversity of life. Still, they leave us far from real comprehension of that diversity. Even if all species were clearly delineated, we would end up with over a million units among living organisms alone. We need to arrange the units in a more comprehensive, orderly way. In short, we must *classify* them. The most meaningful classification must rest on principles that are biologically significant. The next step, then, is to consider what principles best apply to the problems of classification.

Doubtless you already know that organisms are ordinarily classified on evidence derived, in large part, from their anatomy and physiology. Classification by anatomy and physiology is not a simple and clear-cut matter. It is not really meaningful to classify by some such procedure as this: a gray squirrel has 10,001 anatomical and physiological resemblances to a red squirrel, 8346 to a cat, 3921 to a frog, 2754 to a fish, and 172 to a daisy. The figures used certainly are not correct. We have no idea what the correct figures are or how they could be established; that is one of several reasons the most meaningful classifications are not based solely on anatomical and physiological resemblances.

Classification by anatomy and physiology requires that characters be selected and interpreted. The fact that the ovary is superior (i.e., higher in position within the flower) in spiny euphorbias and inferior (i.e., lower) in cacti is considered more important than the fact that both have spines. What characters are selected, what meaning is assigned to them, and finally what classification is devised depend on the way in which the characteristics of organisms are interpreted. They depend on a decision as to one of the most profound questions of biology and of philosophy: What is the nature of a systematic unit among organisms, and how do the characteristics of such units originate? The principles on which biological classification is based arise from answers to that question.

Nature of Systematic Units

The form of classification of organisms still in use today is conventionally dated from the middle of the eighteenth century. It is dated especially from the book *Systema Naturae* by the Swedish botanist Carolus Linnaeus (Karl von Linné, 1707–1778), which appeared in 1735 and went through many editions. This dating applies, however, only to the *form,* the terms and names used. There have been two revolutionary changes in the principles of classification since Linnaeus. The result is that although a classification of plants or animals today *looks* almost the same as one of two centuries ago, it *means* something altogether different.

In Linnaeus' day classification was based on the philosophical doctrine that species are fixed, unchanging units, and that all the units were created as such by God at the beginning of the world. Some slight change within a species was admitted as possible, on the example of the various races of domesticated animals. There were also a few biologists who considered the evolution of new species possible. These ideas, however, had not yet had any real influence on systematics. The systematists' task then was supposed to be simply to recognize the units of divine creation. The units were presumed to be sharply distinct, like cats, dogs, sheep, pines, or maples, and to pose no "species problem." Linnaeus had little doubt that the 4235 species of animals listed by him were actually the "kinds" of the Creator and subject to no further revision by human systematists.

For most systematists of Linnaeus' day a species had its characteristics because it was created just so. This implies a pattern, one for each species. Deviations from that pattern, so evident in nature as variation within species, were considered accidental and irrelevant. The essential thing, the ultimate or transcendental reality of a species, was believed not to be material and tangible but a pattern, a divine idea, a *type* or, as then often designated, an *archetype* ("primeval pattern"). The way for a systematist to look at organisms, then, was supposed to be to ignore individuals, to brush aside variation and all characteristics of populations as such, but to abstract an idea of what the individuals have in common. That abstraction was the type or archetype of the species. The same concepts were applied to groups of wider scope than species.

These were the classical principles of systematics, the ones with which the science was established. The first revolution occurred when it was learned that species are not separate and unchanging creations but that they have evolved, one from another, in the long course of the history of life. This concept of species, and of all systematic groups made up of species, is profoundly different from the special-creationist and type concepts. Species are now known not to be fixed units but rather changing things, in continual flux over immense periods of time. Hence the "species problem," because you cannot give a fixed definition to units that change and grade one into another.

Even more important than the new concept of evolving species was the discovery that relationships among species are not abstractions, reflections of metaphysical archetypes. Species are related to each other in the fully material sense that one descends from another and several or many have descended by the processes of organic reproduction from the same ancestral species. The principle became, and still is today, that all species in any systematic grouping are of common ancestry.

Revolutionary change in the principles underlying classification made no difference in the form and, at first, little difference in the practice of classification. Preevolutionary classification grouped organisms according to the anatomical and physiological characters common to all within the group, interpreting these characters as physical manifestations of a metaphysical archetype. Evolutionary classification established groups in just the same way and, indeed, took over most of the groups already established by Linnaeus and other nonevolutionary biologists. The only real difference was that the characters in common were now considered as physically inherited from the common ancestry of the whole group.

Classification as it was practiced by the evolutionary systematists of the later nineteenth century did not fully do away with the preevolutionary archetype. As far as it really affected classification, the archetype was simply relabeled and differently interpreted. Each species had a type, now an individual specimen, supposed to be a sort of standard, a model, in a sense really an embodied archetype. Other individuals were compared one by one with type specimens and placed in the species the type of which they most nearly resembled.

Higher groups, including several or many species, also continued in practice to have archetypes in more or less veiled form. The groups were defined by characters in common, abstracted patterns quite like archetypes even though considered as somehow representing the characteristics of an ancestor. Thus, although classification soon became evolutionary in principle after publication of Darwin's *The Origin of Species* (1859), it remained largely preevolutionary in practice.

The second major revolution in principles of systematics since Linnaeus was the change from a typological to a *population* concept of the nature of systematic units. The turning point cannot be associated with one man and date, as that of evolutionary systematics can with Darwin and 1859. Some earlier students, including Darwin, did grasp the rudiments of a systematics of populations rather than of types. Full comprehension, however, required the discovery of Mendelian genetics and then the development of population genetics on that basis. Systematics clearly based on populations and explicitly nontypological is mainly an achievement of the second quarter of the twentieth century. In fact, this revolution in systematics is still going on.

The following, then, is the modern, fully evolutionary concept of systematic units:

A systematic unit of organisms in nature is a population or a group of related populations. Its anatomical and physiological characteristics are simply the total of those characteristics in the individuals making up the population. The pattern of characteristics is neither a real individual nor an idealized abstraction of the characters of an individual. It is a frequency distribution of the different variants of each character actually present at any given time. Species are populations of individuals of common

descent, living together in similar environments in a particular region, with similar ecological relationships and tending to have a unified and continuing evolutionary role distinct from that of other species. In sexually reproducing species, the distinctiveness and continuation of the group are maintained by extensive interbreeding within it, and less or no interbreeding with members of other species.

The best and the only *direct* evidence that an individual belongs to a particular species is not the anatomy or physiology of the individual as such, but the observation in nature that the individual is living with the specific population and functioning as a member of that population. Such direct evidence is not available in practice for organisms that have been removed from the context of their natural environment—that are specimens in collections rather than parts of living populations. Fully direct evidence is also lacking for fossils. It is also usually impossible to obtain entirely direct evidence that a group of species is of common descent and hence is properly classified as a higher systematic unit. In all these cases pertinence to a systematic unit must be judged by indirect evidence. There are many kinds of indirect evidence, anatomy and physiology among them.

The one other point to make here is that use of anatomy, for instance, as *evidence* that an organism belongs to a particular species does not mean that a species as a systematic unit is *definable* in anatomical terms. A species or other systematic unit is defined in terms of populations and their biological, evolutionary relationships. These relationships have anatomical consequences, among others, from which they may be inferred. If two people look exactly alike, that is evidence that they are, or may be, identical twins. But they are not twins because they look alike; they look alike because they are twins. Similarly, typological systematics maintained that organisms belong to the same systematic unit because they have the same anatomical pattern. Modern systematics has learned that they have the same anatomical pattern (to the extent that they really do) because they belong to the same biological, evolutionary population or group of populations. An up-to-date systematist is not now engaged in classifying anatomy or any other sort of evidence. He is engaged in using the evidence to classify populations of organisms according to their evolutionary relationships.

It is true that some groups just are not well enough known as yet to achieve evolutionary classification, even though what is known is interpreted by evolutionary principles. There is some doubt whether truly evolutionary classification is really possible in a few groups, mostly among the protists and notably including the bacteria, and the old typological method continues in use there mainly because no one has come up with a more practicable method. The old method has been improved and updated, however, by use of computers to obtain a complex statistical estimate of over-all typological resemblance.

Interpretation of Form and Descent

If classification is to have an evolutionary basis, the decisive factor is whether resemblances between organisms have or have not been inherited from a common ancestry. Interpretation and application in classification depend on some historical, evolutionary principles and processes, which must now be reviewed.

HOMOLOGY

Homology is correspondence between structures of different organisms due to their inheritance of these structures from the same ancestry. Such structures are called *homologues* and are said to be *homologous.*

If the bones of a man's arm and a dog's foreleg are compared (Figure 15-1), the number and arrangement are remarkably similar. The resemblance also extends to the way the limbs arise embryologically and, in greater or less degree, to the arrangement in them of muscles, blood vessels, and nerves. A reasonable explanation is that the limbs are homologous.

If, now, comparison is made with the wing of a bird, the similarity is less striking. Nevertheless, it can be established beyond any doubt that man's arm, dog's foreleg, and bird's wing are all homologous, and even that some homologous bones are present in all three. The evidence involves anatomical and embryological comparisons and, still more convincingly, fossils of early mammals (from which men and dogs later evolved), of ancient birds, and of still older reptiles from which both mammals and birds arose. Separation of the reptilian ancestries of mammals and birds occurred not less than 200 million years ago, but a fundamental genetic resemblance has not been obliterated.

Let us now add the front (pectoral) fin of a fish to the comparison. The resemblance is even slighter, and this is not surprising because we are now comparing animals whose nearest common ancestry is more than 300 million years in the past. The fish's fin as a whole is still certainly homologous with the forelimb of bird, dog, or man, but it is no longer possible to designate homologous individual bones

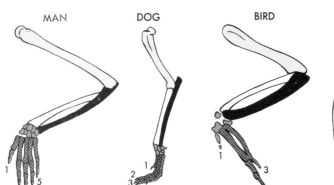

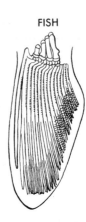

MAN   DOG   BIRD   WHALE   FISH

FIG. 15-1 Vertebrate forelimbs. Homologous bones in the limbs of man, dog, bird, and whale are indicated as follows: light gray, humerus; white, radius; black, ulna; dark gray, carpals; crosshatching, metacarpals and phalanges (finger bones). Numbers refer to digits (or fingers).

in the limb with any assurance. Extremely ancient fish fins are known from which both modern fish fins and the limbs of air-breathers have evolved, but the separate lines of evolution have undergone changes so profound that the homologies of the individual bones have been practically obliterated.

The degree of homology in the examples given is the basis for phylogenetic inferences which, in turn, are involved in the classification of these organisms. Man and dog are more nearly related to each other than either is to a bird. Man, dog, and bird are more nearly related than any is to a (modern) fish. Homology is the anatomical evidence for degrees of relationship among organisms. A main problem, then, is to distinguish between resemblances that are homologous and those that are not.

HOMOPLASY AND ANALOGY

Anatomical features that resemble each other but that are not inherited from the same feature in a common ancestry are called *homoplastic,* and the phenomenon is *homoplasy.* Thus correspondences in anatomy between two plants or between two animals are either homologous or homoplastic. If they are homologous, they are evidence of relationship or genetic affinity. If they are homoplastic, they are not such evidence. The terms are, of course, interpretive. They express an opinion or a deduction from the available evidence. The use of comparative anatomy in classification depends on this decision of whether anatomical resemblances are homologous or homoplastic.

The front leg of an insect has some sort of anatomical correspondence with the front limb of a dog or the arm of a man. It is, however, certain that the limbs of insects and mammals evolved wholly independently and were not inherited from an ancestry common to the two. Insects and mammals did have a common ancestry, but this was extremely remote, more than 600 million years ago, and the limbs of the two groups evolved after their ancestries had separated. The limbs are not homologous, but they are to some extent homoplastic.

The homoplastic forelegs of insects and arms of men do not function in the same way. If an insect and a dog are compared, however, there is a resemblance in function, for in both the limbs are used mostly for walking. When structures that are not homologous have a functional resemblance, they are *analogous* and are called *analogues*. The wing of an insect is to some extent homoplastic and is completely analogous with the wing of a bird (Figure 15-2A). It is certainly not homologous.

Homoplastic structures are usually also analogous. It is a rule of evolution that resemblance in structure not due to inheritance from a common ancestry is generally correlated with similarity of function. Homoplasy usually results from similar adaptations of organisms of different ancestry. Like almost all biological rules, this one has exceptions but is true in the majority of instances. Structures may, indeed, be analogous without having any noticeable degree of anatomical resemblance. The gills of a fish and the lungs of a mammal are anatomically so different that they would hardly be called homoplastic, but both are organs of respiration and are in that respect analogous. The homologue of the lungs in fishes is the swim bladder (Figure 15-2C).

TRANSFORMATION

Homologous structures may differ markedly both in anatomy and in function. In most living fishes the swim bladder is a simple closed sac filled with gases that decrease the specific gravity of the fish and help it to maintain a favorable depth in the water—a sort of internal water wings. It has nothing to do with breathing. In one group of fishes it has become even less lunglike and acts as a sounding board or resonating chamber, the vibrations of which are communicated to the brain through a series of bones. It is, in fact, analogous to an eardrum (fishes do not have real eardrums), although still homologous with the lungs.

It is odd enough that fishes should hear by means of a structure homologous with part of our breathing apparatus. It is at least as peculiar that *we* hear by means (in part) of structures homologous with parts of the jaw apparatus of reptiles, including our own reptilian ancestors. Two of the three little bones that transmit vibrations from our eardrums to our inner ears are homologous with the bones that form the joint between upper and lower jaws in reptiles.

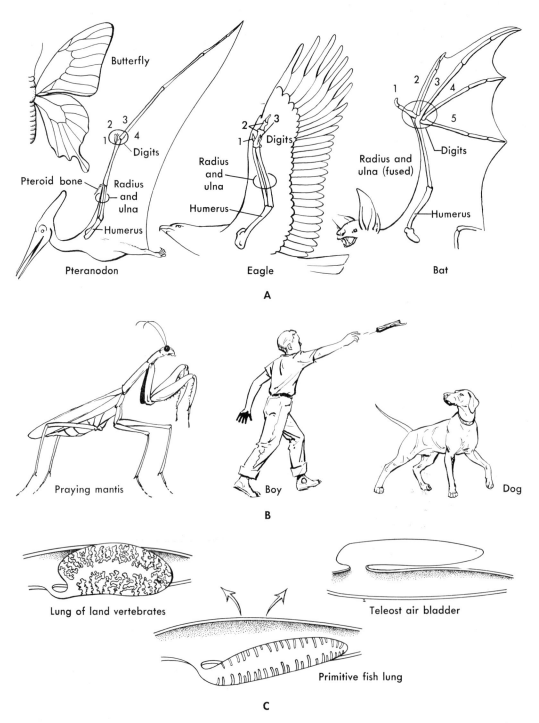

FIG. 15-2 Homology, homoplasy, and analogy. A, B. The wings and legs of insects bear a homoplastic relation to those of vertebrates. The wings in *Pteranodon* (an extinct flying reptile), eagle, and bat evolved separately from walking forelimbs and so are homoplastic as wings, but they contain homologous bones. The wings of insects and of these vertebrates are analogous: they perform similar functions. The forelimbs of man and praying mantis are not only homoplastic but also analogous, for both are used to manipulate. The forelimbs of man and dog, which are homologous, are not fully analogous; the dog's forelimb is nearly exclusively for locomotion. C. Lungs of land vertebrates and air (or swim) bladders of fishes are homologous but not analogous.

One of the most fascinating things about comparative anatomy, phylogeny, and classification is that homologous structures can be so very different both in form and in function. From the point of view of their evolution, this means that structures can and often do change radically both in appearance and in the way they work. Such radical changes are known, logically enough, as *transformations,* and they have been rather common in the history of life. They are especially likely to be involved in the origin of major new groups of organisms, such as the rise of mammals from reptiles or of flowering from nonflowering plants.

The widespread occurrence of transformations emphasizes that new sorts of organisms, new organs, or new adaptations evolve from what is already there. A good engineer should be able to design a better reproductive apparatus than a magnolia flower, a better means of walking than a salamander's leg, or a better sound receptor than an opossum's ear. The point is that these structures were not designed. They evolved on the basis of mutations affecting earlier structures that functioned differently. And even though they are not perfect, they do work. They have been molded by and have stood the test of millions of years of natural selection.

IRREVOCABILITY OF EVOLUTION

The fact that evolutionary change occurs on the basis of what is already there—that is, of the results of all previous evolution—has extreme and widespread consequences. It makes evolution *irrevocable.* What has already happened before any given time necessarily affects and limits what can and does happen next. The future cannot change the past; what is past is irrevocable. Evolutionary change never wholly eradicates the effects of previous evolution. The most radical transformation does not wipe out influences of the previous condition of the structure transformed. If the little mammalian ear bones had not been part of the reptilian jaws they would certainly not have the relationships that they do, in fact, have. If any of our ancestors, back to 2 billion B.C. or earlier, had been different from what they were, we too would be different in some respect and to some degree.

There is also another side to the principle of irrevocability. If the past cannot be wholly lost,

neither can it be fully regained. Nothing quite like an earlier form of life ever evolves again, for the simple reason that time does not double back on itself.

The principle of irrevocability is of great importance in systematics. An example should make its relevance clear. Land vertebrates, such as reptiles and mammals, arose remotely from aquatic forms, fishes. Some reptiles and mammals, such as the whales, became aquatic and fishlike in habits. Their evolution reversed the way of life, but of course this did not make them fishes again. The effect of irrevocability can be seen throughout their anatomy, as clearly in their flippers as elsewhere (see Figure 15-1). The flipper functions like a fish's fin, but it is quite different because, unlike the fin, it has passed through a stage when it was a leg. This is one aspect of irrevocability. However, even though the flipper has become finlike, it has not lost the effects of its land-living ancestry, and the bones in a whale flipper are still plainly homologous with those in the leg of a land mammal. This is the other aspect of irrevocability. The application to classification is that even though a whale is more fishlike in habitat, habits, and general appearance, it is more closely related to land animals than to fishes. It is classified as a mammal.

CONVERGENCE AND PARALLELISM

The example of whales and fishes shows that organisms may be alike in living conditions and appearance even though they are of quite different ancestry and relationships. Such resemblances may arise between organisms even more distantly related. Spending an evening in a southwestern garden, a visitor was astonished to see what were apparently large numbers of hummingbirds gathering nectar in the dusk. A closer look showed that they were not hummingbirds but hummingmoths, insects almost identical with the birds in actions, size, and superficial appearance (Figure 15-3). The evolutionary development of resemblance between organisms whose ancestors were less alike is called *convergence.* In Australia, an island continent, the isolated evolution of marsu-

FIG. 15-3 Hummingbird and hummingmoth, examples of convergent evolution. The bird and the moth have converged in form, flying habit, and feeding procedure in their exploitation of flower nectar as a food source. None of these resemblances existed in their extremely remote common ancestry.

pials has produced kinds convergent toward many different nonmarsupial (placental) mammals of the rest of the world. There are not only native "wolves" but also native "mice," "cats," "anteaters," "moles," and "sloths," as well as the squirrel- and flying squirrel-like phalangers and the groundhog-like wombats. These marsupials are only distantly related to the placental true wolves, mice, cats, anteaters, moles, sloths, squirrels, and groundhogs. The resemblances result from convergent evolution (Figure 15-4).

In such examples, the separate ancestries of convergent forms were so different that the convergent nature of the resemblance is obvious with a little study. Things become more difficult if the ancestries were not very different, and still more so if the ancestries were related and evolution in the descendent lines has simply followed more or less the same course. This sort of evolution intergrades with convergence and is not always clearly distinguishable, but it is given a different name: *parallelism*. Parallelism is even more common than convergence. Moreover, close parallelism may be practically impossible to distinguish from close community of ancestry unless the actual ancestors have been found as fossils. It was,

for example, long assumed that the American and Old World porcupines are closely related and that their spininess is homologous and part of the evidence for that relationship. Later work raises a strong possibility that this is a case of parallelism, that the common ancestor was really very remote and was spineless. If this is so, the spines (and a number of other resemblances) have evolved independently in the two groups and are homoplastic, not homologous. The fossil evidence is still insufficient and the question remains open, but most systematists now think that parallelism is involved in the history of porcupines. In recent years it has become apparent that parallelism has occurred far more widely among all sorts of organisms than was formerly recognized. This is one of the major problems of systematics today.

DIVERGENCE

If you try to predict the future of two evolving groups of organisms there are plainly three possibilities: the groups can become more similar (convergence); they can evolve in much the same way, so as to remain about equally similar (parallelism); or they can become less similar (*divergence*). It is obvious that divergence is extremely common. Indeed, it is the universal rule for directions of evolution and is necessarily the basis for the whole of the diversity of nature. Within a species there is fluctuating, reversible divergence as demes or other subdivisions of the species develop differences from each other. As soon as speciation occurs, two (or more) species arise from one, and divergence between the two becomes essentially irreversible and tends to increase as time goes on.

Special examples of divergence are unnecessary because it is illustrated by the manifest differences between any two species or organisms. The pattern of divergence recurs in all groups of organisms. It is the basic element reflected in classification. When we list the species of a genus, we are listing populations that have diverged from a single ancestral population. The genera of a family, the families of an order, and so on, are also the representatives and results of divergence of increasingly long standing and on an increasingly large scale.

The frequent occurrence of convergence and parallelism do not at all contradict the fact that

PLACENTALS

MARSUPIALS

Wolf
(Canis)

Tasmanian
wolf
(Thylacinus)

Native cat
(Dasyurus)

Ocelot
(Felis)

Flying
squirrel
(Glaucomys)

Flying
phalanger
(Petaurus)

Ground
hog
(Marmota)

Wombat
(Phascolomys)

Anteater
(Myrmecophaga)

Anteater
(Myrmecobius)

Mole
(Talpa)

Mole
(Notoryctes)

Mouse
(Mus)

Mouse
(Dasycercus)

FIG. 15-4 The convergent evolution of some placental and Australian marsupial mammals.

divergence is universal in evolution. There can be neither convergence nor parallelism unless there has been previous divergence. Furthermore, in comparing any two groups of organisms of near or remote common ancestry it never has been found that they are completely, in every respect, convergent, parallel, or divergent. In some respects the two have always retained some ancestral features unchanged; in some features they are always divergent; in others they may or may not be convergent or parallel.

The Practice of Classification

Classification consists mainly of three operations: (1) recognizing and describing related smaller and larger groups of organisms according to the principles of populations and of phylogeny; (2) fitting these groups into a formal hierarchy; and (3) providing names for the various groups. Only the first of these operations involves the direct observation and interpretation of nature. The second and third put the results of the first into meaningful form and supply the names by which we can think and talk about those results. The second and third operations are, however, necessarily subjective and more or less arbitrary. The third nomenclature, involves completely artificial legalistic symbolic devices.

THE SYSTEMATIC HIERARCHY

By general consent, a particular form of hierarchy, modified from that of Linnaeus, is now in general use, and a special term is applied to each recognized level or category.

1 Kingdom
2 Phylum (plural, phyla)
3 Class
4 Order
5 Family
6 Genus (plural, genera)
7 Species (identical in singular and plural; "specie" means "coin" and has no application in biology)

There is no reason in nature that the hierarchy should have seven steps. Groups of almost any inclusiveness could be recognized, for in nature there is no fixed size inherent in the facts.

A full classification of a human subspecies, with the names applied to the groups at the various levels, shows how the system works.

Kingdom Animalia
Phylum Chordata
Subphylum Vertebrata
Superclass Tetrapoda
Class Mammalia
Subclass Theria
Infraclass Eutheria
[Cohort Unguiculata—optional]
Order Primates
Suborder Anthropoidea
Superfamily Hominoidea
Family Hominidae
Subfamily Homininae
Genus *Homo*
Subgenus *Homo* (*Homo*)
Species *Homo sapiens*
Subspecies *Homo sapiens sapiens*

For reasons that will be apparent from the following discussion, no two authorities agree exactly as to how all organisms should be classified. There is, however, a reasonably good consensus on the most important features. A brief, modern, but conservative classification is provided in this book. It is mainly for reference purposes, and it has been placed at the end (Appendix) where it can be easily turned to. It should be consulted throughout the study of the rest of the book, whenever it is desirable to see how any one group fits in among its relatives or among organisms as a whole.

Sample and Population

A species is a special sort of category in nature and in evolution, and therefore also in classification. It is a population that may be subdivided in various ways but that has an essential internal unity and continuity in evolutionary role, in geographic and ecological distribution, in genetic relationships, and in physical, phenotypic characteristics. It has some degree of external discontinuity, sometimes relative but tending to become absolute, from any other species. Groups higher in the hierarchy than species are less unified and continuous because they generally include more than one species. Groups lower than species are less clearly bounded because there is less or no discontinuity between them within the species. The species, then, is the fundamental population unit of classification.

Classifying a species involves determination of the characteristics of a population. The procedure can be compared with what you would do if, for example, you were a wholesaler who planned to buy the output of a large apple orchard. You would need to know what the whole crop is like, and you would be sure that the apples would vary considerably in size, color, ripeness, and other characteristics important to you. Surely you would not pick one apple and base your price and plans on the idea that the apple (a type) is sufficiently representative of the whole lot. Obviously, too, it would not be practical for you to examine every one of tens of thousands of apples in the orchard. (In systematics, examination of all individuals of a species is usually not merely impractical but downright impossible.) What you would do would be to take a sample of perhaps a hundred apples, being careful that the selection was at random so that it covered the range of variation fairly well and was not loaded with the better or poorer apples. If you really knew your business, you would know methods (derived from the science of statistics) for deciding how many apples you need as an efficient sample for your purposes. By related methods you would estimate from the sample the average quality of the crop and its variation, and you would calculate how close your estimates are likely to be to the actual characteristics of the whole crop (the population).

That, in principle, is the modern procedure for determining (or more strictly speaking, for estimating) the characteristics of a species or smaller natural population unit in systematics.

Higher Categories

Placing species into genera, genera into families, and so on upward in the hierarchy is not based on inferences from samples about populations. The basic population units, the species, are successively com-

bined in increasingly larger groups according to interpretation of their evolutionary relationships. In principle and with certain exceptions, all the species of one genus have evolved from one ancestral species, all the genera of one family from one ancestral genus, and so on. Of course, we do not yet know the natural relationships of all organisms with high probability and in sufficient detail to produce a definitive, final classification on which everyone can agree. Classification is constantly changing in some respects as we learn more about the course of evolution, and experts often disagree about details of classification.

Even when evolutionary affinities are adequately known and there is no disagreement about them, classification in higher categories does not automatically follow. It is impractical to express *all* the intricacies of relationships in a classification simple enough to be understandable and usable. All that can be done is to assure that the classification is *consistent* with a reasonable theory of evolutionary affinities. Different arrangements may be equally consistent with the same theory. Choice is a matter of usage and personal taste. Since stability is desirable, conservative systematists hold that a classification in general use should not be changed unless new study shows that it is probably inconsistent with the affinities of the organisms concerned.

NOMENCLATURE

Systematists come in for a good deal of derision because they call a rose by another name or stutter *Rattus rattus rattus* when they mean plain "rat." It is true that there are people who like to make things sound mysterious and difficult, but systematists have been forced into a complex and stuffy nomenclature whether they like it or not. There are millions of species that must be named, not to mention all the other groups up and down the hierarchy. No everyday language has enough names to go around. Innumerable sorts of plants and animals simply do not have common names. This situation applies, naturally, to all extinct organisms, but also to many still living. Worse yet, the common names that are available are usually vague in application, often misleading, and almost always are applied indiscriminately to different groups that the systematist must distinguish. In New Mexico, alone, there are 13 species of wild roses. In the Old World there are more than 560 species and subspecies of the genus *Rattus* and hundreds more called "rats" that do not even belong to this genus.

The systematists had to invent an artificial system for naming organisms, and fortunately they agreed to use the same names everywhere, regardless of native language. This is one useful holdover from the days when all scholars wrote in Latin. Linnaeus wrote in Latin, and naturally he also named plants and animals in Latin. Innumerable scientific names are also derived from Greek, and in modern usage they may be derived from any language or from none, just made up. However, they are always latinized and treated as if they were Latin words.

The name of any group from a kingdom down to a genus is a single capitalized word. Names of genera are usually printed in italics, but those of higher groups are not. The name of a species is two italicized words: the name of the genus followed by a name (not capitalized) peculiar to the species. For example, the name of the human species is the two words *Homo sapiens*. This is why the nomenclature is called *binomial* ("two-named"). For subspecies, a third italicized word (not capitalized) is added to the name of the species.

It frequently happened that different workers applied different names to the same group or the same name to different groups. Frequently, also, some systematist has decided that two or more groups that had different names should be combined into one, or that a group with one name should be split into two. Even after systematists had agreed in principle on a system of nomenclature, such duplications and changes tended toward chaos. Finally, international congresses and biological unions drew up codes of nomenclature designed to solve these problems and to settle on one name for each group and a different name for each. The codes depend heavily on the *rule of priority*. The valid name of a group is the first published name applied to it (if it was published after a fixed date and if it complied with certain requirements). If the same name has been given to two groups, the name belongs to the group to which it was first applied, and the other group must have a different name.

Summary

The accepted system of classification based on anatomical and physiological characters; the problem of selecting significant characters in classification; its relation to the nature of systematic units.

Modern classification, still Linnaean (eighteenth century) in form but justified by principles radically different: the twofold revolution in post-Linnaean systematics—(1) the advent of evolutionary thought and rejection of the concept of archetypes or divine patterns; the recognition that species are related in the material sense of common ancestry; but early evolutionary systematics still typological—concept of morphotype; (2) the replacement of a typologoical by a population concept of systematic units; the systematic unit as a varying population or group of populations related genetically; the nature of evidence in systematics.

Interpretation of form and descent: homology—structural correspondence between organisms due to inheritance from a common ancestor (exemplified by vertebrate forelimbs), homoplasy and analogy—homoplasy a structural correspondence not caused by common ancestry, and analogy a functional correspondence (exemplified by wings and legs in insects and vertebrates); transformation—a radical evolutionary change in structure and function (exemplified by the histories of fish lungs and swim bladders and of the mammalian ear mechanism); irrevocability of evolution—past structural evolution never wholly eradicable, old structure never wholly regainable, past evolution as a commitment setting conditions for future evolution (exemplified by aquatic mammals); convergence and parallelism—convergence as the evolution of resemblance between organisms with dissimilar ancestors (exemplified by hummingbirds and hummingmoths and by the history of Australian mammals) and parallelism as a comparable and more common phenomenon involving ancestors less remotely related than in convergence; divergence, the opposite of convergence and parallelism, and its universality.

The practice of classification: (1) treatment of species—sample and population, the special status of the species in systematics (more clearly bounded than either higher or lower categories in the hierarchy), the use of population samples for characterization of species; (2) treatment of higher categories—inference of evolutionary relationships, existence of alternative acceptable bases, consistency with evolutionary affinity as the main criterion of acceptability; (3) nomenclature—the practical need for technical nomenclature, the binomial system, rules of nomenclature, the priority rule, nomenclatural types (not to be confused with archetypes).

CHAPTER SIXTEEN

PROTISTS AND PLANTS

In an appendix to this book there is a summary outline of one way in which living things can be classified. It is relegated to an appendix, not because it is unimportant, but because it is reference material. It cannot be read with pleasure, and memorizing it, although possibly useful, would not make you particularly wise. We have now covered some of the principles underlying the fact that living things are and have long been of such an amazingly large number of different kinds. Next to be considered is what those different kinds are, how they resemble each other and how they differ, and what roles they play in the drama of life.

We shall be dealing mainly with the major subdivisions of each kingdom of living things, the large groups called *phyla* (singular, phylum). Some individual examples will of course be mentioned, but it is not necessary (or possible) in a study of the basic principles of biology as a whole to enter into much detail as to the anatomy, physiology, and other peculiarities of many of the extremely numerous kinds of organisms. In some of the more important and more familiar phyla some of the lesser included groups, especially the *classes,* will be separately discussed. Further detail in this more descriptive and taxonomic part of the broad science of biology is the special province of the systematic biological subsciences: protistology, botany, and zoology.

Few people have ever seen even one representative of the most abundant organisms in the world. The great majority of them are too small to be seen clearly, if at all, with the naked eye. They include a few giants as much as 2 centimeters in diameter, or even a bit more, but almost all of those present in our usual environments are between about 0.1 and 200 microns in diameter. (A micron, symbolized as μ, is one millionth of a meter.) They are therefore nearly or completely invisible as individuals, as you can readily understand if you convert those sizes into more familiar

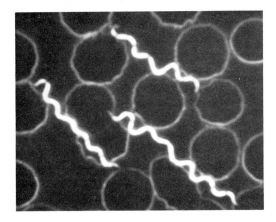

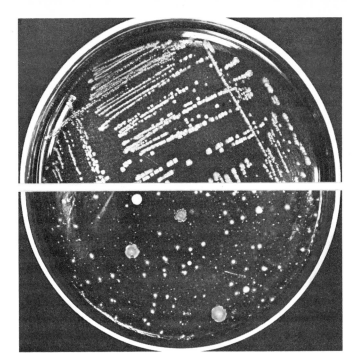

FIG. 16-1 Bacteria. Left, Spirochetes, the pathogenic (disease causing) agents of relapsing fever in blood (×1100). Right, bacterial colonies growing on plates of agar jelly. The figure is compounded from photographs of two agar plates. In the top half-plate the bacterial cells used to make the inoculation—that is, to start growth of the large colonies now visible—were streaked across the jelly with a needle. Individual cells left on the surface started the hundreds of round colonies that now lie along the paths of the needle. In the bottom half-plate the cells used in the inoculation were first suspended in water, which was then spread uniformly over the plate. Each of the colonies now visible again grew from a single cell. (Photos, left, Carl Strüwe; right, C. E. Clifton)

terms (see Figure 3-4). Sometimes they pile up in such numbers that it is obvious that *something* is there, but only a microscope can reveal the fact that the something consists of uncounted millions or billions of tiny organisms. In nature such a situation occurs, for instance, in the red tides that sometimes sweep an ocean shore. In the laboratory, bacteria entirely invisible as individuals become easily visible as groups when they are cultured in large colonies (Figure 16-1).

The fact that there is a whole world of life smaller than the eye can see has had a profound influence on human thought and history. Most of the organisms that cause human diseases belong in this microscopic realm. In the long millennia before their existence was suspected it was impossible to have a rational idea of the causes of disease, and irrational ideas became deeply embedded in human thought. This gap in the possibility of observation was also partly responsible for the fallacious notion of spontaneous generation. More widely still, the invisible protists have indispensable parts in the operation of nature, in the intricately intermeshed cycle of life. Life itself could not be understood, even in a superficial way, until these tiniest of its manifestations were discovered. The fortunate man who made the discovery of protists was Anton van Leeuwenhoek, a minor Dutch official and amateur biologist, who lived from 1632 to 1723. His must have been one of the most exciting experiences anyone ever had! He saw a whole new world more truly than did Columbus or any other explorer. Think of him the next time you look at a drop of pond water under a microscope.

General Characteristics

We have had several occasions before to mention that protists are, in general, one-celled or, in another sense, noncellular organisms. Most of them are organized like single cells; they are not highly developed systems of many cells specialized for different functions within the over-all organism. This description seems at first sight to be a clear definition, but nature (or evolution) rarely deals in absolute distinctions. The boundaries of the kingdom Protista are in fact vague and correspondingly disputed.

On the one hand, there are objects having some of the attributes of life, and therefore sometimes considered protists, that do not have all the vital attributes and that lack cellular organization. Prominent among these are viruses (see Figure 3-3). When they are complete, viruses are comparatively simple combinations of nucleic acids and proteins. They are not self-reproducing; replication occurs only through the action of their nucleic acids within a living cell of a true organism. But in spite of their great biological importance, viruses are not themselves true organisms.

The protists apparently represent a variety of organisms not now very closely related to each other or to anything else. They include the bacteria, the blue-green algae, the flagellates and their allies, the slime molds, and three more animal-like phyla sometimes grouped together as Protozoa.

Bacteria

GENERAL CHARACTERISTICS

The most striking physical characteristic of bacteria (Figure 16-2) is their extremely small size. They are the smallest indisputably living things; only some viruses (which do not meet usual definitions of living organisms) are smaller. The smallest bacteria are about 0.1 micron in diameter. A giant among bacteria may be as much as 60 microns long by about 6 microns in transverse diameter. With bacteria of usual size, between these extremes, it takes about a trillion (1,000,000,000,000, more simply written as 10^{12}) to weigh 1 gram.

With ordinary (light) microscopes, organisms of such almost inconceivably small size are barely visible. It can be seen that some are spherical, some elongated or rodlike, and some variously spiral. They commonly occur singly or heaped up more or less at random in highly populous colonies, but in a few species individuals are attached to form chains. Further study with the electron microscope has shown that bacteria have rather rigid cell walls outside the cell membranes, which is a plantlike characteristic. Many of them have at least one and usually many hair- or whiplike flagella so delicate that they are commonly not seen in classroom preparations of bacteria. The flagella provide some limited power of movement.

Bacteria are now known to possess chromosomes, and their heredity is mediated by DNA as in higher organisms. Some bacteria even demonstrate a phenomenon resembling sexuality. In a large population of *Escherichia coli*, for example, a few organisms are capable of transmitting a chromosomelike body to other organisms through *conjugation*. Such occasional sexual exchanges of genetic material within a large population that normally reproduces by fission provide an invigorating redistribution of genetic substance that is beneficial because it tends to prevent an accumulation in the population of altered and thus debilitating genes. Thus, the advantages of a process analogous to sexual reproduction are available even to the lowly bacteria.

The most extraordinary thing about bacteria is that these minute and seemingly simple objects are extremely complex in molecular composition and structure. They carry out all the really basic processes of life. They do not differ fundamentally from other organisms, up to man or to a higher plant, in the complexity and general nature of their transformations of matter and energy. They testify to the unity of life and to the common basis upon which, in the course of evolution, the extraordinary diversity of living organisms has developed.

USEFUL AND HARMFUL BACTERIA

The great majority of bacteria are useful in the sense that their activities are essential for the continuous maintenance of living communities. Indeed, the whole scheme of life as it has evolved depends upon bacteria. This is true especially because bacteria are the principal (but not the only) organisms of *decay* and almost the only organisms capable of

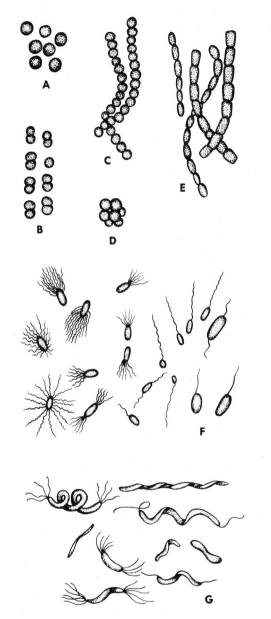

FIG. 16-2 A diversity of bacterial cell types. A–D. Cocci (singular, coccus, are round cells that may grow singly, in pairs, or as long chains. E. Bacilli (singular, bacillus) are rod-shaped. They, too, may grow singly as well as in chains. F. Many bacteria are flagellated. G. Spirilla (singular, spirillum) are helical cells.

nitrogen fixation, although some blue-green algae can also fix nitrogen.

When a plant or animal dies, much of the material in its body is in the form of organic compounds that cannot be directly utilized by green plants. Many of these compounds are quite stable and do not tend to break down into simpler, usable materials by inorganic processes under usual conditions. Nitrogen, for instance, is mainly in the form of proteins, amino acids, and other compounds more elaborate than the nitrates required by most green plants. Carbon occurs in the same compounds and also in lipids and carbohydrates, not as the CO_2 required by green plants. If the compounds in dead plants and animals were not somehow broken down, by now some crucial materials for green plants would all be locked up in the remains of the dead, and life would have become extinct except, perhaps, for a few autotrophic bacteria.

This is where the bacteria of decay demonstrate their usefulness. Decay is simply the breaking down of organic compounds by bacteria and by some nongreen plants. An essential part of the process is the successive breaking down of proteins into amino acids and then of amino acids into ammonia. Other bacteria then oxidize the ammonia to nitrites, and still others oxidize the nitrites to nitrates, available as the principal nitrogen source for green plants.

Some bacteria, to be sure, go too far with the breaking-down process and produce free nitrogen, which cannot be used by green plants. This loss is, however, compensated for by those bacteria that can fix nitrogen. They are able to use free nitrogen, which constitutes nearly 80 per cent of the atmosphere, in the synthesis of their own proteins. By further metabolism and decay those nitrogen compounds eventually become available to other organisms. The nodules on the roots of many plants of the pea family (legumes) contain colonies of bacteria that obtain energy from the carbohydrates of the host plant and utilize part of the energy to fix nitrogen. Soils that have become depleted of nitrates, and therefore have become infertile for green plants, can be restored by planting with nodule-bearing plants such as clover or alfalfa. The cycles of energy and materials involving bacteria are further considered in Chapter 19.

Although most bacteria are useful in that they help to keep the cycles of life going, many kinds are parasites. They are responsible for most of the infectious diseases in man and other animals and for certain of the diseases of plants. Bacteria may invade any part of the body of any larger organism. If the bacteria produce *toxins,* poisonous to the host, disease usually ensues. Many of the bacterial toxins are proteins. Some are excreted by the living bacteria, and others are part of the bacterial cell, liberated after death of the bacterium.

Disease-producing bacteria must have arisen far back in the history of life. The survival of other organisms has depended on their evolving one or more of a triple set of defenses: resistance to invasion by bacteria, resistance to their survival or multiplication in the host, and resistance to the effects of their toxins.

Blue-green Algae

In spite of the name, only about half the *blue-green algae* (Figure 16-3) are blue-green. The others are highly varied in color: blue, green, yellow, red, and intermediate hues. Some blue-green algae are unicellular and solitary, but most consist of clumps or colonies of attached cells, with little or no differentiation. Probably the most characteristic form is a filament made up of cells attached end to end. In all blue-green algae the cell or the whole colony has a mucilaginous outer wall. The cells contain nucleoproteins and their heredity involves DNA, but as in bacteria, there are no nuclei. Reproduction is vegetative or by cell division, and no evidence of a sexual or parasexual process has yet been found.

Blue-green algae are extremely abundant in the seas. The Red Sea may have been so named because of the presence of red "blue-green" algae. They also abound in lakes, streams, and the soil. Some species grow in especially rigorous environments such as hot springs, heavily mineralized waters, antarctic pools, and other places where they (and often some bacteria) may be the only forms of life. How would you account for such structurally simple organims as bacteria and blue-green algae existing in places where complex, higher plants and animals are unable to live?

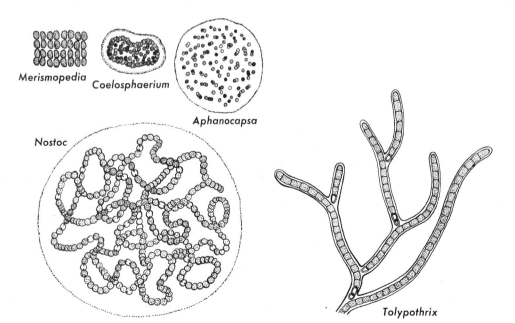

Merismopedia

Coelosphaerium

Aphanocapsa

Nostoc

Tolypothrix

FIG. 16-3   A variety of blue-green algae.

Flagellates (Euglena)

The flagellates (Phylum Mastigophora) (Figure 16-4) and their allies deserve special emphasis because they are transitional between strictly plantlike and strictly animal-like organisms and because they also illustrate a possible transition from protistan to multicellular structure. It is evident that no flagellate living today can preserve in detail the characteristics of the ancient protists ancestral to multicellular organisms. Sponges and numerous true plants, especially among the algae, have cells or life stages that are almost indistinguishable from flagellates. Moreover, some flagellates form colonies in which there may be some functional differentiation and also a degree of coordination among the individuals. It then becomes a mere matter of definition whether we consider such an aggregation as an advanced colonial union of individual protists or as a rudimentary grouping of cells in an individual of a higher order.

Flagellates are so called because almost every one of them has one or a few long whiplike appendages, the flagella (singular, flagellum). They drive or pull the protist along by lashing. The body usually is more definite and fixed in form than in such protists as the amebas and commonly has some differentiation

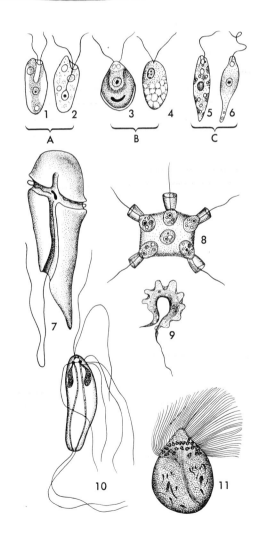

FIG. 16-4   Flagellates. 1. *Cryptomonas ovata*, photosynthetic; 2. *Chilomonas paramaecium*, nonphotosynthetic closely related to *Cryptomonas*. 3. *Chlamydomonas monadina* ($\times$610), photosynthetic; 4. *Polytoma uvella* ($\times$870), nonphotosynthetic, closely related to *Chlamydomonas*. 5. *Euglena pisciformis* ($\times$195), photosynthetic; 6. *Astasia klebsii* ($\times$300), nonphotosynthetic, closely related to *Euglena*. 7. *Ceratodinium asymmetricum* ($\times$600), a dinoflagellate from brackish waters. It possesses two flagella, one of which beats within the confines of a groove running around the cell wall. 8. *Protospongia haeckeli* ($\times$320), a simple colony of eight collar-flagellate cells embedded in a common matrix. [See Chapter 17 for comment on the resemblance between *Protospongia* and the ancestors of sponges (Porifera)]. A collar flagellate feeds by trapping debris and microorganisms on its collar; like perpetually moving flypaper, the collar maintains a surface streaming that brings the trapped food down to the cell surface proper, where it is engulfed in a food vacuole. This is also how sponge cells trap and ingest food. 9. *Trypanosoma giganteum* ($\times$400), a parasitic flagellate from the blood of fishes. Other trypanosome species attack livestock and man, causing sleeping sickness. The flagellum runs alongside the cell, and an "undulating membrane" of protoplasm is stretched between the cell and the flagellum, much as a soap film can be stretched between wires. 10. *Hexamitus intestinalis* ($\times$2000), a parasitic flagellate from the gut of frogs and other vertebrates. *Hexamitus* is one of the few flagellates having more than one nucleus per cell. The nuclei are pearshaped bodies near the top of the cell. (The two long rodlike structures running down the cell connect the granules at the base of each flagellum; their function is unknown.) 11. *Calonympha grassii* ($\times$630), a symbiotic flagellate from the gut of termites. (See Chapter 13 for comment on the significance of these and related flagellates to the termite hosts.)

of organelles, although much less than in the ciliates. One of the most interesting facts about flagellates is that their various kinds have just about every sort of nutrition and associated physiology that is conceivable for organisms of their size. Some (*Euglena* and *Volvox* are common examples) contain chlorophyll, perform photosynthesis, and are generally much like plants, among which they are frequently classified. Others ingest chunks of plant or animal food and are thoroughly animal-like in nutrition.

Animal-like Protists

Several major groups, phyla, of protists are particularly like animals and are often, indeed, classified as animals. They are the phyla Sarcodina, Sporozoa, and Ciliophora of the classification in the Appendix. Those who prefer to classify them as animals rather than as protists generally unite them in a single phylum, Protozoa. That name means "first animals" and refers to the belief that they preserve something of the characteristics of the earliest organisms that could, by any possible definition, be considered animals. This may be true in an extremely broad sense, but again we must note that all "protozoa" now living have surely undergone profound evolutionary changes.

The most animal-like features of these groups of protists are, first, that they eat plant or animal food, ingesting it in chunks into the protist body, and, second, that most of them are quite active. Within their small worlds they move about, scouring their surroundings for nourishment. Often there is even a sort of purposiveness in their movements, or, it would be better to say, an orientation: they tend to move toward food or better environmental conditions and away from obstacles of poor living conditions. Thus they do exhibit the rudiments of animal-like behavior. Moreover, as we shall see, the more complex among them have simple organs or organelles that are also more animal- than plantlike.

All of them are small, some as little as 2 microns in diameter, as small as many bacteria. A few, the

Many are organisms of decay, absorbing molecule by molecule through the cell membrane the breakdown products from the remains of other, dead organisms. Many are parasites and cause serious diseases, although some are relatively innocuous. The trypanosomes, which cause African sleeping sickness and some other diseases, are flagellates.

Flagellates are very abundant in the sea and there share with the diatoms (p. 336) basic roles in the turnover of organic materials. The producers of the red tides previously mentioned are flagellates. So are the commonest of the organisms causing "phosphorescence" in sea water. One of these has the appropriate name of *Noctiluca,* the "night-shiners."

largest of all protists, reach 3 or 4 centimeters in largest dimension. Most of them range from 100 to 300 microns, too small to be seen clearly if at all with the naked eye but a comfortable size for being studied with a light microscope.

In these protists the usual apparatus of heredity is fully established. They have visible nuclei and chromosomes and reproduce by cell division. The young protist generally starts out in life not only with a full set of parental chromosomes but also with its bodily structure and material directly derived from the parent.

AMEBAS AND THEIR KIN

An ameba appears as simple as a fully developed organism can be, and it is famous on that account (Figure 16-5). It has become a living symbol of the primitive, as in the common expression of evolution "from ameba to man," although it is improbable that anything quite like an ameba ever did really figure in our ancestry.

There are a great many protists more or less similar to amebas in structure and function; tens of thousands of species of this phylum (Sarcodina), living and fossil, have been described. The most varied and perhaps the most interesting are the Foraminifera (or forams, for short), most of which secrete limy shells. The shells, when suitably magnified, are often of great beauty and amazing complexity (Figure 16-6). It is

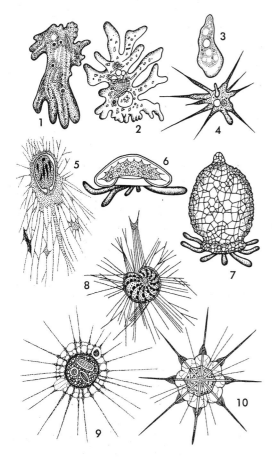

of the ages of rocks and can readily be recovered when a well is bored in rocks originally laid down in the sea. For these reasons their study is useful in the petroleum industry, and they are the principal object of the science of micropaleontology. Forams have made an even greater contribution: much of the petroleum itself has probably been derived from their soft organic parts through the ages, although other organisms have also contributed.

The evolution of the sarcodines (amebas, forams, radiolarians) from flagellates nicely illustrates two common evolutionary principles—overlapping functions and opportunism. Pseudopodia evidently arose first as useful supplementary feeding devices in animal flagellates. Some still-living flagellates exemplify

FIG. 16-6   The empty cases of various Foraminifera (greatly magnified). (Photo, Carl Strüwe)

FIG. 16-5   Ameba and its kin: the Sarcodina. 1–4. Members of the order Amoebina, showing different forms of pseudopodia. 1. *Amoeba proteus* ($\times 40$); 2. *Amoeba dubia* ($\times 40$); 3. *Vahlkampfia limax* ($\times 280$); 4. *Amoeba radiosa* ($\times 170$). 5–7. Members of the order Testacea, each of which possesses a shell, or test, of chitinous material, which in some species (6) is heavily thickened and in others (7) is supplemented by the addition of foreign particles. The animal can withdraw completely inside its shell or extend its pseudopodia all over it (5). 5. *Gromia ovoidea* ($\times 25$); 6. *Arcella discoides* ($\times 34$); 7. *Difflugia urceolata* ($\times 100$). 8. *Polystomella crispa* (order Foraminifera ($\times 15$). Note the long filamentous pseudopodia. 9. *Actinosphaerium eichhorni* (order Heliozoa) ($\times 27$). Note again the filamentous pseudopodia. 10. *Acanthometron elasticum* (order Radiolaria). Note the siliceous spikes.

especially remarkable that such intricate structures, characteristic for each species and fixed by heredity, can be built by what look like completely structureless blobs of living material. Forams, most of which are marine, are so abundant in the seas that much of the bottom ooze is made up of their shells. Forams are also common as fossils. They are good indexes

transitional stages that must have occurred in the evolution of pseudopodia (Figure 16-7).

SPOROZOA

The phylum Sporozoa especially well illustrates two characteristics that are widespread among the animal-like protists: parasitism and complicated reproductive cycles.

Many of the parasitic sporozoans cause severe disease. They vie with the bacteria in the amount of misery they have caused man and other animals. The combination of parasitism and a complex reproductive cycle is well seen in the sporozoans that cause malaria. While living as parasites in mosquitoes, the malarial sporozoans have a sexual process, followed by multiple fission. Introduced into the human blood stream by a mosquito bite, they reproduce asexually and periodically. The cycle is completed when the biting mosquito acquires individual sporozoans from the human blood.

CILIATES

The ciliates (Figures 16-7 and 16-8) are so called because they have numerous tiny hairlike projections, or cilia (singular, cilium), which beat rhythmically and drive these protists through the

water in which they live. They are by far the largest and most complexly organized of the protists. *Paramecium*, one of the most abundant ciliates, occurs almost everywhere in fresh water, although, curiously enough, the way in which it colonizes isolated streams or pools is unknown. It has become a famous labora-

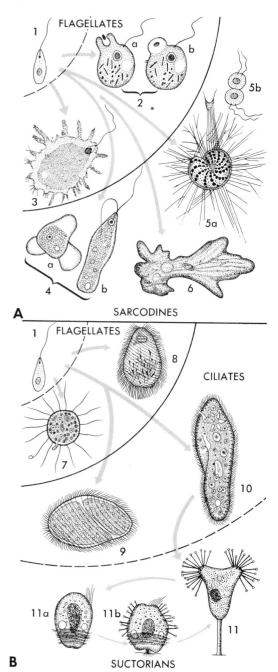

FIG. 16-7 Protozoan descendants of flagellates. A. Flagellate–sarcodine relations. 1–3. Flagellates: *Oikomonas* (2) and *Mastigamoeba* (3), which utilize pseudopodia for feeding. 4–6. Sarcodines, revealing their flagellate ancestry: *Naegleria* (4) alternately pseudopodial and flagellate; *Polystomella* (5), a foram with flagellated gametes (5b); *Amoeba* (6), with pseudopodia (a flagellate feeding device) as organs of locomotion. B. Flagellate–ciliate relations. 1. A flagellate. 7, 8. Flagellates approaching the ciliate condition: *Multicilia* (7), with pseudopodia as a feeding device, many flagella, and more than one nucleus —the last two characters being ciliate-like; *Holomastigotoides* (8), from termite gut, with huge numbers of flagella organized in rows, like cilia. 9, 10. Ciliates: *Opalina* (9), which lacks the differentiated macronucleus and micronucleus characteristic of true ciliates; *Paramecium* (10). 11. *Acineta*, a suctorian and thus a ciliate descendant, as is evidenced by its macronuclear and micronuclear organization and the temporarily ciliated larva (11a), which eventually settles down (11b) and develops the stalk and suctorial tentacles of the adult.

tory organism. It is easy to propagate and to study under a microscope; the range of length is about 100 to 300 microns. Its behavior is complex for a protist, and its genetics is especially enlightening, in part because it goes through the rather odd sexual process called conjugation.

The ciliates dramatically illustrate how much structural and physiological differentiation can occur in a small space and how far from simple even a protist may be. Although there is no division into cells, they have well-developed structures, organelles, analogous to the organ systems of multicellular animals. In various ciliates there are locomotor systems (the cilia), the operation of which is finely coordinated; "muscular" systems of contractile fibers; reactive coordinating and conductive tracts analogous to an incipient nervous system; an alimentary canal with "mouth," "gullet," and "anus"; excretory organelles; stiffening plates analogous to a skeleton; and other organelles.

Like the sarcodines, the ciliates were probably derived from early and primitive flagellates, and there are flagellates still living that are more or less intermediate between the two phyla (see Figure 16-7B).

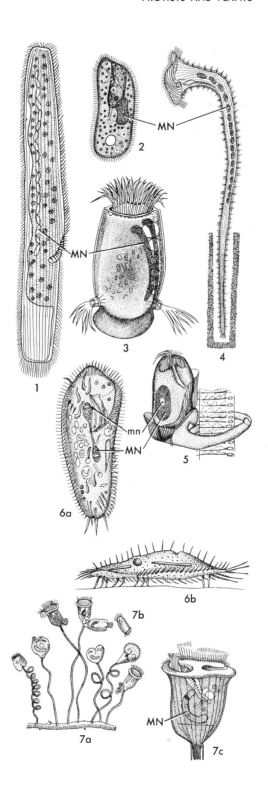

FIG. 16-8 **Ciliates.** Note the distinction between macronucleus (MN) and micronucleus (mn), which is visible in some of the drawings. The macronucleus is often a long chainlike structure, as in 1 and 4. 1. *Spirostomum ambiguum* (×40), a large fresh-water ciliate. Note the oral groove curving inward on the right side; the large area shaped like an inverted hatchet and unstippled is the contractile vacuole. 2. *Paramecium bursaria* (×100). The dots in the cell are symbiotic green protists. 3. *Cycloposthium bipalmatum* (×210), a parasitic ciliate from the gut of horses. The cilia are compacted together into robust paddle-like processes, the cirri. The elongate structure to the right of the macronucleus is a skeletal rod. Note several contractile vacuoles lying near the macronucleus. 4. *Stentor mulleri* (×48), which lives in a case it secretes. The large cilia around the "top" of the animal set up feeding currents in the adjacent water that bring microorganisms into the oral groove and mouth. 5. *Ellobiophyra donacis* (×600), attached by two armlike processes to the gill bar of the mussel *Donax*. Recall how pelecypods feed (Fig. 10-2); the gill of a mussel is a rich hunting ground for a ciliate that feeds on microorganisms. As in *Stentor*, the ring of cilia sets up local currents that lead to the mouth. 6. *Stylonichia mytilus* (×140), a ciliate that uses its cirri (cf. 3) as highly coordinated leglike structures; it literally walks (6b) on the bottoms of ponds or on leaf surfaces under water. 7. *Vorticella* sp. (×80), a ciliate with a contractile stalk that quickly pulls the main cell body away from a source of stimulation. 7b. A free-swimming individual budded off from the colony. 7c. Detail of the cell. The ring of cilia around the oral groove (leading deep into the cell) creates a feeding current.

Suctorians, derived from ciliates and referred to the same phylum, also exemplify the extent of complication possible at the protistan level (see Figure 16-7B). Unlike other protists, some of them go through definite developmental stages. A young suctorian has larval characteristics and is not simply a small adult.

SLIME MOLDS

At one stage in their life history, slime molds (Figure 16-9) are unicellular organisms with flagella and might well be classified as animal-like flagellate protists. Later, those that survive lose the flagella and become thoroughly amebalike. They reproduce by cell division, with mitosis of the nucleus, which is haploid in these stages. Eventually many of the ameboid individuals clump together. Then the separate cell membranes usually break down, and the result is a single mass of protoplasm with hundreds or even thousands of nuclei. This mass moves about and ingests food like a gigantic ameba; it may reach a diameter of 25 centimeters or more.

So far the slime mold's life cycle is like that of a protist, at first solitary and later colonial in a peculiar way. The colonial mass (*plasmodium*) may undergo an extraordinary differentiation that is plantlike, at least superficially. From the basal mass stalks grow upward, and bulblike expansions develop at the ends of the stalks. The remaining basal cells or nuclei, those in the stalk and those coating the bulbs, do not further reproduce. They die, just as the somatic cells of higher plants and animals die while the germ cells continue the race. In the slime molds, the inner nuclei of the bulb fuse two by two in a sexual process, resulting in diploid nuclei. Meiosis then occurs, and haploid spores are formed. The spores are scattered, and, with luck, each may produce an individual of the flagellate stage as the cycle continues.

FIG. 16-9 Life cycle of myxomycetes, right. Left, Plasmodium of *Physarum polycephalum* on agar in Petri dish (courtesy C. J. Alexopoulos).

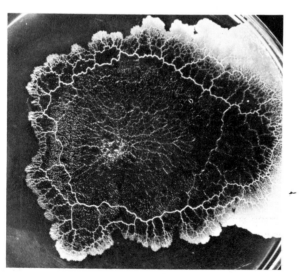

A

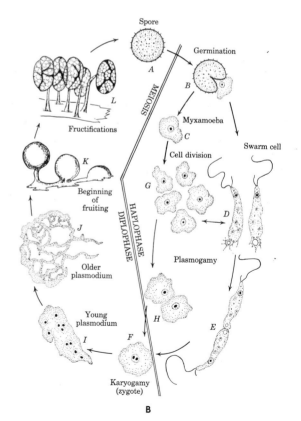

B

Are such organisms animals or plants? Are they protistan or multicellular? The alternatives are not clear-cut, and the question hardly makes sense. Perhaps the most likely phylogenetic answer is that the slime molds evolved from protists that somehow struck off on a peculiar line of specialization of their own, not like that followed by any other organisms. This can be viewed as another independent approach toward large size and more or less multicellular organization. It was successful enough to ensure survival of some forms, but it was a blind alley that led no further.

Algae, the Grass of the Waters

We have emphasized that photosynthesis is the basic dynamic process of life. Although it may not always have been, now practically all the energy of living things is first made available to them by photosynthesis, which is also one of the key processes in building up organic compounds. Most of the photosynthesis so important in the economy of life occurs in water, especially in the sea.

Algae are symbolically the grass of the waters, not only in the sense that they are the principal energy-fixers of the meadows of the sea but also in the sense that they are the original food source for most of the untold billions of aquatic animals. This greatest of all food sources has hardly been touched by man as yet. The only significant human use—and it accounts for only a small fraction of the food consumed by humans—is indirect: the eating of fish and to still less extent of other seafood. Now that the human population has outrun land-food production over large areas, experiments are under way for the cultivation and more direct utilization of algae. The results are not very meaningful as yet, but these efforts may assume importance if the world population continues to increase rapidly.

Some algae are as small as bacteria. Others are more than 200 feet in length. Most of them are multicellular, but some are unicellular. The unicellular algae are not classified as protists because they seem to be related to or even derived from multicellular algae. They are, it seems, cells that get along alone but that are of essentially the same kind as those in their multicellular relatives. The vegetative parts of algae have little differentiation of tissues or organs. In many, all the vegetative cells are practically alike. Others do have some distinctions of size, shape, and function among their cells but without differentiation of such organs as roots or leaves or of such tissues as the vascular, tubelike, sap-conducting bundles of cells that occur in land plants. For this reason the algae are included among the *nonvascular* plants, as opposed to the *vascular* plants, which include most of the familiar land plants. The reproductive structures of algae, in contrast with their vegetative parts, may be highly differentiated and complex.

Most algae are fully aquatic. Others grow in soil, where they are abundant, or in such odd places as inside or among the tissues of other plants, but always in damp or wet situations. Almost all have pigments of the chlorophyll family and are photosynthetic, but a few have lost the pigment and have become organisms of decay.

In popular language, the main groups of algae are usually characterized by their predominant color: green, yellow-green, golden-brown, brown, and red. As we have already noted for the so-called blue-green algae, however, colors are not infallible means of recognizing the groups. More fundamental are details of anatomy, especially in reproductive structures, and of the life cycle. The essentials of reproduction in algae and their widely diverse life cycles have already been discussed in Chapter 9.

Although there is a tendency to lump all the algae together, botanists believe that they represent at least four main groups, each of which may have arisen independently from protists. An evolutionary classification should, then, recognize each of these groups as a primary subdivision of the plant kingdom. (See the classification in the appendix.) The algae of popular speech are the phyla Chlorophyta, Chrysophyta, Phaeophyta, and Rhodophyta of our classifica-

FIG. 16-10 **Diatoms.** Left, a variety of diatom cell walls from New Zealand waters, showing the diversity of form ($\times 67$). Right, the diatom *Aetinoptychus* ($\times 130$). (Photo, Carl Strüwe)

tion. The Cyanophyta, here considered protists, are also sometimes considered as algae—the blue-greens.

Algae include the familiar seaweeds and the green scum of still ponds. Among other groups peculiar in various ways are the diatoms. *Diatoms* (Figure 16-10) are tiny plants, usually unicellular but occasionally found in small, colonylike aggregations. They secrete unique skeletal structures made of silica (SiO_2, the same compound as that of rock crystal), sometimes complex and with a delicate beauty. Diatoms are especially important because, despite their small size, they are often so amazingly abundant as to be the main photosynthetic organisms over wide areas, especially in the sea but also in lakes and streams. The productivity of the oceans, from the tiniest animals up to the whales, depends largely on diatoms.

Fungi

The great majority of algae and of other true, multicellular plants have chlorophyll and perform photosynthesis. This is true to such an extent that "green" and "plant" are words almost automatically associated. However, the members of one large and important group of plants do not perform photosynthesis. They are the *fungi* (Figure 16-11). Everyone has seen some parts of fungi, and many fungi grow to considerable size, but they are for the most part hidden organisms. The basic unit of their structure is a threadlike element, or *hypha*. The hypha consists of an elongate cylindrical wall containing a mass of cytoplasm and hundreds of nuclei that are not separated by cross walls. The mass of hyphae that constitutes a fungal growth is collectively referred to as a *mycelium*.

The mycelium of *molds* visibly spreads on old food in damp, dark places, and sometimes on the surfaces of other plants or even of animals. *Yeasts* are familiar to the housewife, although what she sees is a mass of organisms rather than the small individuals. Structurally, yeasts are atypical fungi, for they consist not of hyphae but of single cells.

Mushrooms are delicacies; toadstools are a recognized danger. (This is not a scientific distinction; "toadstools" are mushrooms that are poisonous or believed to be so.) *Bracket fungi,* sometimes also called "conks," form spongy-looking but hard shelves on stumps and tree trunks. Farmers can readily see the *smut* or *rust* that may infect their grain and ruin a crop. All these easily visible organisms are fungi—masses of tightly packed hyphae—but hundreds of other fungi are not visible. Even among the readily visible ones what are seen are often only reproductive structures. The vegetative mycelium often lies hidden in the soil or inside the tissues of a host plant or animal. It is the vegetative part of the fungus within plant and animal tissues that is harmful. When the spore masses appear, as in smuts and rusts, the damage is already done to the host.

All fungi are heterotrophs. Many of them require as organic food only a simple sugar and can carry on all the other necessary syntheses from there. Some have highly specific requirements for more complex organic foods. In any case, all must absorb through cell membranes a carbohydrate, at least, that has been synthesized by some other organism. They are all either parasites or organisms of decay, absorbing food from the living bodies or dead remains of other organisms.

Fungi reproduce asexually by spores, which may be as small as 1 micron in diameter, although they are usually several times that size. Such tiny objects float freely in air, and the air around us is rarely without a multitude of them. If they land on a suitable medium, the spores develop into vegetative bodies, which in turn develop anew the spore-bearing organs, often elaborate in shape and structure. Thus almost any piece of bread left exposed to air develops mold; damp shoes and luggage made of parts of dead animals become mildewed; a compost heap sprouts mushrooms—all developed from the ubiquitous air-borne spores. Most fungi also have sexual processes, and their life cycles may be quite complex (Figure 16-12).

Although some fungi do untold damage from our human point of view, many others are highly useful. Brewing and all the industrial operations involving fermentation depend on yeasts, which have the attractive property of metabolizing sugars into

FIG. 16-11 A variety of fungi. Top, *Amanita muscaria*, a poisonous mushroom. Bottom left to right, the mycelium of the mold *Penicillium chrysogenum*, showing individual hyphae. This fungus produces penicillin. Cells of brewer's yeast (*Saccharomyces cereviseae*) in the process of budding. A bracket fungus (*Fomes*) growing out from a tree trunk. (Photos, top, Hugh Spencer; bottom, left to right, Merck and Co., Anheuser-Busch, Inc., Hugh Spencer)

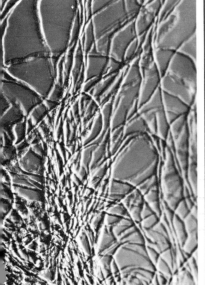
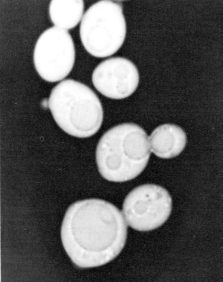

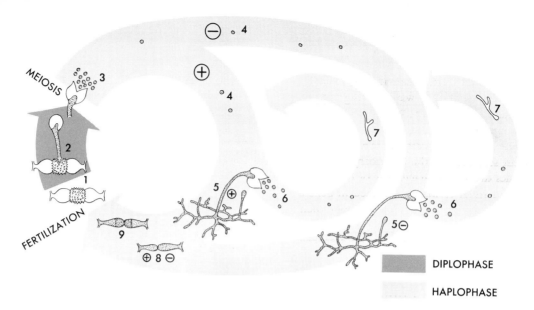

FIG. 16-12 The reproductive cycle of the bread mold *Rhizopus*. The diplophase is of minor significance, consisting only of the zygote and the sporangiophore, with its terminal sporangium that produces haploid spores (meiotic products). 1. Zygote. 2. Sporangiophore, grown out of the zygote, with the sporangium. 3, 4. Haploid spores of two mating types, $\oplus$ and $\ominus$. (The term "mating type" is used where there is neither morphological nor physiological distinction between the "sexes" other than that $\oplus$ will mate only with $\ominus$ and that $\ominus$ will mate only with $\oplus$.) 5. New mycelia (two mating types) germinated from the spores. 6. Spores. 7. New generation of vegetatively propagated mycelia. 8. Two hyphae (technically progametes at this stage), one from a $\oplus$ mycelium and the other from a $\ominus$ mycelium, which come in contact and (9) produce gametes at their tips; fertilization consists of a fusion of the two gametes.

alcohol and carbon dioxide. Bread raised with yeast utilizes the same reaction, but here the carbon dioxide bubbles in the dough are desired, not the alcohol. (What becomes of the alcohol?) A number of fungi, especially molds, synthesize compounds poisonous to competing organisms and particularly to bacteria. The term *antibiosis* is applied to the phenomenon in which organisms take the lives of others to preserve their own. The naturally synthesized antibacterial compounds are called *antibiotics*. They are metabolic products, formed regardless of any "need" the fungi may have for protection against invasion by or competition from bacteria. Some of them destroy bacteria that cause human diseases but are only mildly if at all toxic to the human hosts of the bacteria. The first of these life-saving products of fungi to be isolated, penicillin, was named for the mold that produces it, *Penicillium*. It has now been followed by streptomycin, aureomycin, and many others. Explorers all over the world are collecting soil samples from which fungi can be grown in laboratories. Each fungus is then tested for the antibiotic properties of its products. Some prove to be no more effective than others already known. Some turn out to be as injurious to humans as to the invading disease-producers. But one in many becomes a new weapon in the fight against disease—and our debt is increased to the fungi and to their intricate chemistry.

Lichens

Lichens (Figure 16-13) are familiar as the scale-like, varicolored patches on rocks or tree trunks. Those who have been in the far north know another lichen as "reindeer moss," which is not really moss.

A lichen is a composite of two quite distinct kinds of plants intergrown in close, obligatory association. A fungus forms a dense web of threads within which grows an alga. The fungus obtains organic food from the alga, and the alga obtains water and dissolved salts from the fungus. They are pioneers that often play an important role in the first steps of breaking down rocks into soils. Their relationship is an excellent example of symbiosis, a way of living happily together discussed in Chapter 19. The alga and the fungus that together constitute a lichen never grow separately in nature. In some cases it has been possible to grow them separately in the laboratory, but then neither assumes the form characteristic of the lichen. The combined natural forms are classified in genera and species as if they were single plants, but their placement in higher categories is anomalous because the single organic system is *both* an alga *and*

a fungus. A further complication exists if the "alga" involved is blue-green, and hence a protist and not a true alga.

The lichens are true land plants, just as much as the higher (vascular) plants, and indeed some of them can grow in drier, more exposed environments than any other plants, and even with no soil at all. They provide stunning examples of versatility in adaptation and of alternatives for meeting adaptive requirements.

More Complex Plants

If you were asked for examples of plants, it is unlikely that you would come up with any of those discussed earlier in this chapter. Fungi are, indeed, abundant all around you, but mostly as spores too small to see or else as developed plants largely hidden in the soil or in other organisms, living or dead. Some algae, to be sure, almost certainly are present somewhere near you, but most are so inconspicuous that you are hardly aware of them. The combinations of algae and fungi that we call lichens are true land plants, but they are rarely very prominent. It is the higher land plants, those that push up freely from the soil into the air, that are most conspicuous in our own environment. For the classification of these and other plants referred to in this chapter, see the appendix.

FIG. 16-13 **Lichens.** Left, a foliaceous (or leafy) lichen on a rock. Right, *Cladonia* growing tightly on the surface of a fallen tree. (Photos, American Museum of Natural History)

Conditions of Land Life

Every living cell must obtain water and other materials by absorption through the cell membrane, and such materials must be constantly available throughout the whole of an active organism. Difficulties arise when some cells are internal—out of direct contact with the environment—and especially if some parts extend into the air, distant from a source of water and dissolved materials. Then in a relatively simple plant like an alga or a fungus, water must be passed along from cell to cell by osmosis and diffusion. The processes are slow and ineffective over any considerable distance inside the plant.

This is a first barrier to any great extension of a plant into the air. It has been overcome most completely by the plants that have developed vascular tissues. These tissues, in some ways analogous to the circulatory systems of animals, make possible the prompt supply of needed solutions to cells far from an external source of water.

A differentiation of organs accompanies, or indeed even preceded, development of a vascular system. A land plant needs water and minerals (in solution) from below, from the soil, and it needs sunlight and CO_2 from above. Below there develops a specialized absorptive system, the roots, and above there develops a specialized photosynthetic system, the leaves. Between roots and leaves is the stem, a structural element containing the central conduits of the conductive system.

Another requirement for land life is especially associated with the stem. In water an organism may simply float, and in soil it lies among the mineral grains. There is no special requirement for support. A stem or other structure extending into the air must support itself and anything attached to it, such as fruits or a crown of leaves. Thus higher land plants have specialized supporting tissues. In plants growing to any considerable height, the support must be particularly strong and rigid; their stems are woody.

Still another limitation imposed by land life has to do with sexual reproduction. Gametes are, in effect, protistlike organisms that cannot long survive exposure to air. In an aquatic environment one or both of the gametes that are to unite can simply be shed into the surrounding medium. This is impossible in air. Conquest of this difficulty has involved a long series of specializations in land plants, culminating in pollen and seeds.

Bryophytes

Among living plants the *bryophytes* (Figure 16-14)—the *liverworts* and *mosses*—represent a group that might be called amphibious. They do not have well-developed vascular systems and are thereby restricted in size and in possible range of land environments, but they are considerably advanced over the algae in adaptation to the land. The better-developed among them do have structures superficially similar to roots, stems, and leaves.

Some bryophytes are aquatic, although none is marine. A few manage to live in arctic wastes and arid deserts. Those hardy species can survive cold and dryness by suspending vital activities until warmth and moisture come along, at which time they revive. Bryophytes grow most luxuriantly, however, in moist, shady places and in bogs. The low, tangled vegetation of mosses often holds water like a sponge, so that even on dry land they make for themselves what is practically an aquatic habitat. They reach a height of a few tens of centimeters at most (usually much less) and are rarely solitary. Usually they form an extensive, dense mat, a little world in itself, inhabited also by bacteria, algae, fungi, worms, insects, and snails. We have already learned something of the reproduction and life cycle of the bryophytes (Chapter 9).

FIG. 16-14 Bryophytes. Center, a liverwort, *Conocephalum conicum*. Right, sporophyte capsules of the moss *Pottia truncata*. Left, a mat of *Sphagnum* moss. (Photos, left and center, American Museum of Natural History; right, Hugh Spencer)

In comparison with the vascular plants, the bryophytes seem primitive and at a distinct disadvantage. Without true vascular tissue, they cannot rise high in the competition for light. They must be wet at some time if the usual life cycle is to be completed. The gametes are highly vulnerable. Yet the bryophytes have survived and are still abundant. One reason is that there are some situations for which they are really better adapted than other plants. A peat bog, characterized especially by the moss *Sphagnum,* is such a place. Another reason is that they are tough. If they cannot compete for the good things of life they manage, like the poor, to make do with what they have. If they cannot rise into the sunshine, they get along with more modest photosynthetic demands in shade too deep for most green plants. They are often pioneers, spreading into places not yet reached by other vegetation. When, in part through the activities of these bryophytes, conditions have been improved, other plants move in and the pioneers may be crowded out. Such is the usual fate of pioneers, plant or human.

Early Vascular Plants

All the groups of plants that are still to be dealt with have vascular tissue. All had the evolutionary potential to rise into the air and become upstanding growths. All have followed, to varying degrees, an evolutionary path nearly opposite to that of the bryophytes. In the bryophytes, as you know, the gametophyte became the principal or sole vegetative stage in the life cycle. In the vascular plants the gametophyte became reduced until in the latest and most progressive groups it is microscopic and transient. The female gametophyte became a well-protected parasite on the sporophyte, and the sporophyte is in all vascular plants the principal, and usually the only, vegetative, photosynthetic phase in the life cycle.

Plants that had reached only the early phases of these important changes were at first spectacularly successful in covering the land with vegetation. Later most of them were supplanted by plants with more specialized reproduction, by means of seeds. A few relicts of earlier groups live on, however, and one such group, that of the ferns, has survived in considerable abundance.

PSILOPSIDS

The earliest known vascular plants belong to the *psilopsid* group, for which there is no common name in English. It is nearly extinct, with only two relict genera surviving (*Psilotum,* Figure 16-15, and

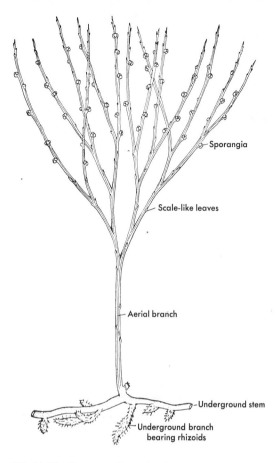

FIG. 16-15   The sporophyte of *Psilotum*.

some lycopods were great forest trees, 1 to 2 meters in diameter and 30 to 40 meters high.

Lycopods have true, although sometimes poorly developed, roots as well as differentiated stems and leaves. Their anatomy in general is more complex than that of the psilopsids. They show another advance over both the psilopsids and the nonvascular plants. Some produce two distinct kinds of spores (microspores and macrospores), one of which develops into a male gametophyte and the other into a female gametophyte. The gametophytes are tiny but independent organisms, sometimes photosynthetic, sometimes colorless and living on organic debris in the soil.

Selaginella displays another remarkable advance in mode of reproduction. The eggs develop in a well-protected case on the female gametophyte and are retained there even after they have been fertilized and begun to develop into embryonic sporophytes. The results resemble seeds.

It is unlikely that the seed plants evolved from

FIG. 16-16   **Sporophyte of the lycopod *Lycopodium clavatum*.** Note the upright branches with minute leaves (sporophylls) on which the sporangia are borne; the conelike structure formed by the sporophylls collectively is a strobilus. (Photo: Field Museum of Natural History)

Tmesipteris). There are no true roots, a subterranean part of the stem serving the same needs. Some psilopsids have small, simple leaves, whereas others are leafless; in the leafless plants the aerial part of the stem carries on the necessary photosynthesis. Gametophytes in the surviving forms are small, colorless, and subterranean.

LYCOPODS (CLUB MOSSES)

The *lycopods* are another group now represented only by relicts, four genera in this instance, but with fairly numerous and widespread species (Figure 16-16). Most of the living lycopods are low herbs, although some of the vinelike species may reach as great a length as 20 meters. In their time of glory, in the coal forests of the Carboniferous,

these particular lycopods, but they show clearly how such a momentous change could take place. They also illustrate the widespread occurrence of independent parallel selective processes leading to evolutionary advances.

SPHENOPSIDS (HORSETAILS)

Living *sphenopsids* all belong to one genus, *Equisetum,* with about 25 species. They are nevertheless locally abundant and are usually easy to find around bogs or in sandy soil near streams. They are commonly known as "scouring rushes" because the stems contain gritty silica and were useful for cleaning pots and pans in the days before soap operas and the products they advertise. Our native species are rarely over a meter tall, although some tropical equisetums reach much greater heights. The equisetums, too, are relics of a group that flourished in the ancient coal forests and then included large trees.

Nothing like a seed is known in any sphenopsids, and the spores are rarely, if ever, differentiated into microspores and macrospores. Otherwise, in degree of differentiation and in life history, the sphenopsids are quite like lycopods (or ferns). They are, however, quite different in appearance and in details of anatomy. The stems are vertically ribbed and jointed, with a whorl of leaves at each joint. In the living genus the leaves are small, and photosynthesis occurs mainly in the stems, which are of course green.

FERNS

From primitive psilopsids three major groups of plants evolved with divergent complication in their anatomical and functional differentiation but with little change in major features of reproduction or life cycles. All three reached their climax about the time of the Carboniferous coal forests. We have seen that two of those groups, the lycopods and the sphenopsids, greatly declined thereafter but still have a few living survivors. The still more ancient and originally ancestral psilopsids also straggled along even when overshadowed by their more exuberant descendants. The third of the progressive divergent groups, the *ferns,* also declined in importance but is still so abundant and varied that its members cannot be called unsuccessful or relics (Figure 16-17).

The reproductive and life cycle of ferns is similar to that of the vascular plants just described; it has been discussed in Chapter 9. In some respects the ferns are even less progressive than some of the ancient lycopods. Lycopods and ferns do not represent successive evolutionary steps, but are divergent groups that arose at about the same time and have remained at about the same level. The gametophyte in ferns is

FIG. 16-17   Ferns. Most ferns are relatively small, herblike plants like the Christmas fern (*left*). A few, however, have evolved the arborescent (tree) habit like the tree ferns in New Zealand (*right*). (Photos, left, Hugh Spencer; right, New Zealand Consulate)

small but is usually an independent, photosynthetic plant. The eggs are fertilized where they are formed, on the damp undersides of the gametophyte, but the sporophyte develops directly from the zygote, without the appearance of a seedlike, protected embryo. Sperms are still flagellated cells that must swim through an external watery medium if they are to encounter and fertilize the eggs. In this respect ferns are no better adapted to land life than are mosses. Ferns are also comparatively unprogressive in that only a few of them have differentiated microspores and macrospores. Vegetative reproduction is common in ferns. The leaves may be only a few centimeters in length, but in some tropical climbing ferns they may reach the astonishing length of 30 meters or more. Some ferns

have simple leaves, but most have leaves divided into leaflets, which may in turn be subdivided.

The spores are borne in sporangia on the undersides of the fronds. These are quite evident as little brown dots in many of our native ferns. In some species some of the fronds have no spores, and in some species the spores develop on specialized parts unlike the vegetative fronds.

The stems of ferns have a well-developed vascular system, and true roots are usually present. In the familiar species of our Temperate Zone the stems are usually horizontal, on or in the soil, with simple roots (occasionally absent) extending into the soil from the prostrate stem. In more uniformly warm climates many ferns have large, vertical stems or trunks which may grow to great heights and develop bark: such are the *tree ferns,* which are common in the tropics but do not extend far into the regions of cold winters.

Early Seed Plants

Abundant as they are, the ferns still do not represent completely successful adaptation of plants to land life. The gametophytes, particularly, are highly vulnerable to adverse environmental conditions. The sperms still require environmental water, even if only a film of it, if they are to fertilize the eggs. The most sensitive and vulnerable stages in the life cycle were eliminated in the plants that evolved *seeds*. In them, as you will recall (Chapter 9), the partially developed

male gametophyte becomes a *pollen grain,* which is often highly resistant to drying and can float for long periods in the air without dying. The female gametophyte is entirely parasitic and lives its whole life protected in the tissues of the parent sporophyte. The male gametophyte completes its development, and the zygote also forms within these parental tissues. The zygote then develops further into an embryonic sporophyte, which is enclosed in protective tissue and

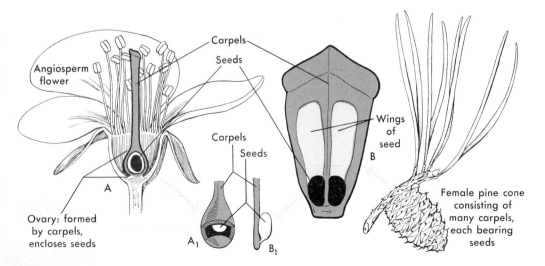

Angiosperm flower

Carpels

Seeds

Carpels

Seeds

Wings of seed

Ovary: formed by carpels, encloses seeds

A

A₁

B₁

B

Female pine cone consisting of many carpels, each bearing seeds

FIG. 16-18 The seed and the carpel in gymnosperms and angiosperms. In an angiosperm (A) the carpel or carpels form an ovary, which encloses the seed. In a gymnosperm (B) the carpel is a flat, primitively leaflike structure bearing the seeds nakedly on its surface. A₁ and B₁ are schematic representations of the relation of seed to carpel in angiosperm and gymnosperm, respectively; the ovary wall is cut away in A₁ to show the seed inside.

provided with food before it is freed from the parental plant. Then it is by some agency moved off to start a new, independent sporophytic generation.

Associated with the evolution of seeds is also the most extensive and effective development of root and stem systems and tissues and of leaves. These factors have made the seed plants incomparably the most abundant and widespread of land plants. Some seed plants have become aquatic, but the group is far from dominant in fresh water and is almost absent in the seas. Why has there been no significant tendency for seed plants to replace the far simpler algae in aquatic environments?

In the first seed plants to evolve, protection of the seeds was not yet perfected and flowers had not yet appeared. Spores, gametes, and seeds developed in organs sometimes of considerable complexity but without the still higher degree of organization seen in a true flower. The seeds arose on leaflike structures (technically known as *carpels* or *sporophylls*) that did not enclose them; thus the seeds were comparatively naked (although they had other protective coatings). Plants with such seeds are called *gymnosperms* (from Greek for "naked seeds"). Plants with flowers and with seeds encased in an ovary (whose tissues are in fact the carpels, or sporophylls, which bear the seeds) are *angiosperms* ("enclosed seeds") (Figure 16-18).

The gymnosperms, first seed plants on the scene, early (mainly in the latter part of the Paleozoic) underwent an extensive adaptive radiation. Numerous groups became divergently adapted to various environments and ways of life without, as a rule, much fundamental progressive change in basic characteristics. Some of the main branches of this basic radiation—the seed ferns, cycadeoids, and cordaites—have become extinct, probably through competition with more progressive or efficient plants. Others survive but are so diminished in numbers, diversity, and geographic distribution that they are today mere relicts: the ginkgos (Figure 16-19), cycads, and joint firs. Only one main branch of the early gymnosperm radiation has continued to the present in great abundance and diversity, although even it is past its heyday: the conifers.

FIG. 16-19 *Ginkgo biloba*, the maidenhair tree. The two sexes occur as separate trees. Below, A. A branch of a male tree with mature male strobili. B. A branch of a female tree with young ovules (female sporangia). C. A branch of a female tree with mature seeds. Right, a row of ginkgos. The ginkgo is a tough plant, vying with the plane tree in its ability to survive in the poisonous, sooty air of large cities. This plant has become virtually, if not completely, extinct in nature yet thrives in cultivation. (Photos, U.S. Forest Service)

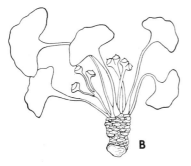
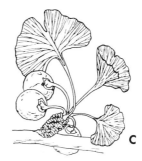

A   B   C

FIG. 16-20 **Conifers.** Left, mountain hemlocks, *Tsuga mertensiana*, in Washington State. Center, a monkey puzzle tree, *Araucaria araucaria.* Right, *Sequoia gigantea* and other conifers in Yosemite Park, California. (Photos, left, U.S. Forest Service; right, Helen Faye)

CONIFERS

The only really common living gymnosperms are the *conifers,* many of which are certainly familiar to you. They include the pines, firs, spruces, cedars, hemlocks, cypresses, redwoods, junipers, and many others; there are about 450 living species. All of them are woody perennials (living for several or many years), and most of them are trees, although some are shrubs. They are among the largest and oldest (as individuals) of all living things. Sequoias and redwoods (two closely related species) reach 10 meters in diameter, 100 meters in height, and 4000 years or more in age (Figure 16-20). Conifers are the dominant trees over much of the Temperate Zone and often form great forests made up of only one or a few species. In spite of this wide and dense distribution, it is evident that conifer forests are most common in relatively unfavorable situations: dry, cold, and windy, or with poor, sandy soil. In the most favorable situations angiosperm forests are more usual.

Most conifers have narrow, needle-like or scale-like leaves (Figure 16-21). A few have broad leaves, and a few have reduced leaves and perform photosynthesis mostly in the stems. Most of them are *evergreen,* and the whole group is sometimes called the evergreens. Evergreens do shed their leaves, as do all trees, but they do not shed them all at once and so always have some green leaves in place. However, some *deciduous* conifers shed their leaves all at once at the onset of the cold or dry season. Among conifers familiar in this country, larches and tamaracks are deciduous. There are also some evergreen angiosperms, and the contrast evergreen–deciduous does not completely coincide with gymnosperm–angiosperm.

Conifers have separate male and female cones. A pollen tube develops and the sperms are nonmotile and without flagella. As in the angiosperms, they are reduced to a minimum. Each sperm (two arise from each pollen grain or male gametophyte) consists merely of a haploid nucleus in the pollen tube.

Conifer pollen usually has small winglike projections; dispersal of the pollen so that it reaches female cones and fertilizes their egg cells depends entirely on the wind. The seeds, also sometimes with a wing, may be dispersed by wind or simply by falling, rolling, and bouncing. They are frequently dispersed by rodents, which carry them away and store them but fail to eat all they take.

Conifers as a group are abundant enough, but they are past their prime, and many kinds of conifers are extinct or are relicts. Araucarias (see Figure 16-20), for instance, were once worldwide but now occur only in a limited part of South America and in Australia and the southwestern Pacific islands. To us they seem highly exotic, but the famous petrified forest of Arizona consists largely of ancient members of the Araucaria group. Even more remarkable is *Metasequoia,* known as a fossil from many parts of the world. Its remains are common in the United States. It was long believed that *Metasequoia* had been extinct everywhere for tens of millions of years, but in 1944 a living *Metasequoia* forest was found in China. This resurrected fossil is now being cultivated by a number of people in the United States.

Flowering Seed Plants

The plants with flowers, the angiosperms, are far and away the most successful of land plants today. This is true by any reasonable criterion: individual abundance, number of species (probably about 175,000), area covered, or total metabolic activity. They are also by far the most important to man. Much the greater part of our food is of angiosperm origin, directly or indirectly. Almost all of our own food plants are angiosperms: cereals, vegetables, fruits, and the rest. Likewise, almost all our food animals live mostly or entirely on angiosperms, so that when we eat them we are still eating angiosperms, once or twice removed. Most of our ornamental plants are angiosperms, although here the conifers do play a considerable role. Of course all our flowers are angiosperms. Conifers are at present a more important source of wood and other forest products, but angiosperm forests are also productive. Man's existence, like that of all animals, depends on the plant kingdom, and man is one of the species that depends most heavily on the angiosperms. It is only fair to add that our most obnoxious weeds are also angiosperms.

The angiosperms arose later than other groups of plants of comparable scope. They had probably

FIG. 16-21 **The cones of white pine.** Left, a branch bearing a female cone. Right, a branch bearing several male cones. (Photos, U.S. Forest Service)

evolved by the early Mesozoic, but they were not dominant until toward the end of that era. The expansion of the angiosperms coincided with the decline or extinction of most groups of gymnosperms, and undoubtedly this situation involves cause and effect. Angiosperms represent the highest level of plant evolution up to now. It would be rash to predict that no higher will occur, but it seems impossible to imagine what that higher might be. They are highest not in extending their dominance over all, for far older groups continue to be dominant in some environments, but in living in environments farthest removed from the ancestral sea and in being most successful in those particular environments. There is a parallel here to animal evolution. Among animals old groups (mollusks, fishes) continue to dominate in the water, but the highest animals in an evolutionary sense are younger groups in more recently occupied environments.

Some angiosperms have wind dispersal of pollen and seeds. It is, however, among the angiosperms that the most elaborate or specialized means of dispersal by animals, especially insects but also birds and mammals, occur. The spread of the angiosperms, their modernization and increasing dominance over the older gymnosperms, broadly coincides with the evolution of special groups of insects, birds, and mammals. That is surely not pure coincidence. What are some of the evolutionary concomitants of this interdependence of broadly different groups of organisms?

Angiosperms are divided into *monocotyledons* and *dicotyledons*. The bulk of an angiosperm seed is made up of one or two leaflike structures (*cotyledons*) packed with food, especially starch, with which the young plant begins its development. Monocots have one such organ, and dicots have two. The distinction is obvious on comparison of a grain of corn (a monocot seed) with a peanut (a dicot seed). A monocot leaf generally has numerous longitudinal veins of about equal prominence, separating at the base and converging again at the apex, with small and short cross veins more or less at right angles to the longitudinal veins; a dicot leaf usually has a main central vein from which others arise by successive branching. In monocots, bundles of vascular tissue are scattered throughout the pith; in dicots the bundles form a cylinder around the pith. Some authorities think that monocots are

TABLE 16-1   *A Summary of Characteristics of the Major Groups of Plants*

(+ indicates that the stated character is the usual or the ancestral condition for the group; 0 indicates usual or ancestral absence of the stated character)

Group	General way of life	Dominance of Gameto-phyte	Dominance of Sporo-phyte	Roots, stems, leaves	Vascular tissue	Seeds	Flowers
Algae	Aquatic (secondarily in other moist situations); photosynthetic	Variable		0	0	0	0
Fungi	Aquatic and moist situations; non-photosynthetic; parasites and organisms of decay	+[a]	0	0	0	0	0
Bryophytes	Semiterrestrial, mostly in moist situations; photosynthetic	+	0	0[b]	0	0	0
Ferns (also psilopsids, lycopods, sphenopsids)	Terrestrial; photosynthetic	0	+	+	+	0	0
Gymnosperms	Terrestrial; photosynthetic	0	+	+	+	+	0
Angiosperms	Terrestrial; photosynthetic	0	+	+	+	+	+

[a] The terms "gametophyte" and "sporophyte" are not strictly applicable to many fungi.
[b] Leaves and stems of bryophytes (some authorities prefer to speak of them as scales and stalks) only superficially resemble those of vascular plants. The root-like structures bear little resemblance to true roots. Nevertheless, there is definite organ differentiation.

a more specialized group, derived from early dicots. Others think the two groups are of equal antiquity and represent a basic split that developed among the earliest angiosperms.

Familar monocots include grasses, sedges, cattails, lilies, onions, tulips, palms, and orchids. Dicots are considerably more numerous. They include magnolias, carrots, peas, mints, morning-glories, nightshades, potatoes, mustards, squashes, dandelions, sun flowers, spinach, poison ivy, and gardenias, as well as almost all the other broad-leafed shrubs and trees.

Most of our important angiosperm food plants have been cultivated since prehistoric times, although many varieties of them have been developed recently. Even early man exercised rigorous selection, so that the older cultivated plants have been changed, sometimes beyond recognition, from their wild ancestors. For instance, one of the most disputed problems in genetics and botany has to do with the wild plants from which pre-Columbian Indians evolved corn (or maize). The word "evolved" is used advisedly. The ability of man to develop new strains, even wholly

new species, of cultivated plants is convincing evidence that nature has done likewise, though more slowly and less systematically from the human point of view. Much has been learned about evolutionary principles from experiments with such plants. Knowledge of evolution has, in turn, assisted efforts to develop desirable new cultivated plants.

The bulk foods of most agricultural communities have always been those rich in starch and, in different parts of the world, have usually been monocot seeds (such as corn, wheat, or rice) or dicot tubers (such as potatoes, yams, or cassava). A really fascinating exercise, unfortunately one we cannot follow up here, is to chart agricultural food supplies among primitive peoples throughout the world and to trace the history of the plants down into our modern economy.

Table 16-1 summarizes some of the characteristics of the major groups of plants.

Summary

Protists: their size, diversity, and importance for man and for life as a whole; their unicellular nature; their systematic status.

Bacteria: their extremely small size; the absence of nuclei; useful bacteria—their role in decay and in nitrogen fixation; harmful bacteria—their role in disease; toxins.

Blue-green algae: not true algae; absence of nuclei and of known sexual processes.

Flagellates: their importance as little-modified descendants of forms transitional between plant and animal and transitional between unicellular and multicellular life; the flagellum as a locomotory organelle; the physiological diversity of flagellate types; their ubiquity, abundance, and importance in food chains.

Animal-like protists, the Protozoa: the ameba and its kin; Foraminifera; the sporozoans, parasitic protists with complex life cycles; the ciliates—their form, cilia, and complexity of structure for a unicellular organism; the slime molds—their life cycle, their fruiting bodies and spores.

Algae: photosynthetic organisms—simple plants; a primary food source for the majority of animals; the possibility of human exploitation as food; their wide range in size; unicellular and multicellular forms; their nonvascular nature; the complexity of their reproductive structures and cycles; their aquatic environments; types—seaweeds, the green scum of ponds, diatoms.

Fungi: nongreen (nonphotosynthetic) plants; the hypha as the unit of their structure; types—molds, yeasts, mushrooms and toadstools, bracket fungi, with the mycelium often hidden in soil or parasitized tissues; fungi as heterotrophs; their reproduction; the ubiquity of fungal spores; their possession of sex; fungi as agents of destruction and disease; useful fungi—yeast, penicillin and other antibiotics.

Lichens: tough symbionts of alga and a fungus.

Problems raised by land life, the condition for the more complex plants: the acquisition of water and nutrients; their transportation inside the plant (the significance of vascular systems); the differentiation of root and shoot systems; the mechanical problem of support in air as against water (the significance of supporting tissues); the problem of getting the sexes together (the significance of flowers).

Bryophytes—liverworts and mosses; their poorly developed vascular systems; their restricted exploitation of land, predominantly moist habitats; dominance of the gametophyte; dependence on water for fertilization; modest photosynthetic demands.

Early vascular plants—the evolution of sporophyte dominance with a vascular system: psilopsids—the most primitive vascular plants—formerly abundant, two surviving genera, no roots, simple leaves, small subterranean gametophytes; lycopods—club mosses—abundant in Carboniferous, true roots, microspores and macrospores, tiny gametophytes, ancient evolution of seedlike structures; sphenopsids—horsetails—abundant in Carboniferous (included tree forms), one surviving genus, leaves in whorls around the stem, no differentiation of macro- and microspores; ferns—the third main line of evolution from primitive psilopsid vascular plants—small independent gametophytes, dependence on water for fertilization, organization of the sporophyte into roots and leafy shoot systems, sporangia, abundance in warm and moist climates. Seed plants: fern descendants; ultimate plant adaptation to land life; the ferns' incomplete mastery of conditions of land life (vulnerability of gametophyte to desiccation); the seed as evolutionary adaptation to that condition; retention of female gametophyte in (sporangial) tissues of parent sporophyte; growth of male gametophyte and of zygote also *within* sporophyte tissue; seed as old sporangium containing embryonic sporophyte and food reserves; further evolution of root and shoot system in seed plants.

Gymnosperms—seed plants with seeds borne naked on the supporting sporophyll—their extensive radiation in the Paleozoic and their subsequent decline; conifers—the only common surviving gymnosperms, predominant today in unfavorable situations—needle- or scale-like leaves, evergreens, male and female cones, nonmotile sperms, wind dispersal of pollen and seeds, various modern conifers.

Angiosperms—flowering seed plants, with sporophylls encasing young seeds in an ovary; the most successful land plants today; their importance in human economy; their first appearance in the early Mesozoic and their dominance by the end of the Mesozoic; their abundance and diversity in size, appearance, and habitats; monocots and dicots.

MAJOR GROUPS

OF ANIMALS

What is an Animal?

This chapter starts with a question that everyone thinks he can answer, but one that is often answered incorrectly. The best answer to "What is an animal?" is not in terms of description at all. It is this: An animal is an organism that belongs by descent and common ancestry to any of the phyla that biologists agree to call "animals." It is, however, possible to make descriptive generalizations about characteristics found more often in animals than in plants. Resemblances and differences between animals and plants have been mentioned frequently in preceding chapters. Now we need only to summarize and review some of the more important and widespread areas of contrast.

1. *Metabolism.* Most plants are photosynthetic. All those that are not were probably derived from photosynthetic ancestors. Animals probably also had photosynthetic ancestors among the protists, but no animals, as such, are photosynthetic. All derive food from other organisms.

2. *Mobility.* Most plants are attached (sessile) and nonmotile as developed organisms and are dispersed in specialized reproductive phases, such as spores or seeds. Many animals are also attached as adults, but most are mobile throughout life, and all have at least a mobile phase in development.

3. *Structure and organization.* Most animals have fixed structures to which new elements are added only at limited, usually early, phases of development. Most plants have less fixed patterns, with new elements added at almost any time or periodically throughout life. Tissue and organ differentiation in animals is often more definite and more complex than in plants. Individual plant cells usually have rigid walls;

animal cells usually do not. Plant cells usually are vacuolated when mature; animal cells usually are not.

4. *Maintenance.* In most animals the cells are either surrounded by sea water or are in a fairly constant internal environment that resembles sea water in being rich in sodium chloride (common salt). Devices for the maintenance of a constant internal environment are less evident in plants, and the internal fluids are usually low in sodium chloride.

5. *Responsiveness.* Most animals are far more responsive than any plants. With relatively few exceptions, animals have nerve and muscle tissue, markedly unlike any plant tissues. Almost all plants lack special receptors, and the rare special receptors that do occur are few and simple. Most animals have special receptors, and these are usually numerous and complex.

6. *Reproductive cycles.* Most plants have a sexual cycle that includes some development of the haplophase between meiosis and fertilization. In animals, development of the haplophase is highly exceptional.

Major Animal Phyla

The classification in the appendix places animals in 18 phyla, not counting the more animal-like protists, which are often considered another phylum under the name "Protozoa." However, some systematists recognize more phyla, and some, fewer.

The best way, and indeed the only adequate way, to learn the characteristics of the various phyla of animals is not from books. As far as possible you

FIG. 17-1   Porifera. 1. The gross structure of a simple sponge like *Olynthus.* Water, laden with microorganisms that are captured as food, enters minute pores (a) all over the body surface. Passing through c, the body cavity, it leaves by the mouth, or osculum, at b. 2. A portion of the wall of the sponge enlarged to show cellular detail: a, entrance pore formed by a single cell that lines the channel all the way into the body cavity (c); b, pore, surface view; d, collar cells that line the body cavity; e, skeletal spicule; f, external covering cell; g, amebocyte (an ameba-like cell) embedded in the jellylike matrix (h) that fills most of the space between the external covering cells and the collar cells. The flow of water into the pores, through the body cavity, and out the osculum is maintained by the beating of the flagella of the collar cells, which trap and ingest microorganisms in the water (cf. Fig. 19-5). Some of the food is transported elsewhere in the sponge by the amebocytes constantly moving about the jelly matrix. Since all the water passing through the sponge enters by many pores but leaves by the one osculum, it is under considerable pressure, and its velocity carries it (depleted of food and oxygen and therefore useless to the sponge) far away from the animal. 3, 4. Progressively more complex sponges and parts of their body walls. Sponge evolution has consisted primarily of adding complications to the body wall such that the incoming current of water passes through a succession of chambers lined with collar cells. The functional significance is that the modern sponge is able to handle more water and provide greater pressures for the exhalant current than its ancestors.

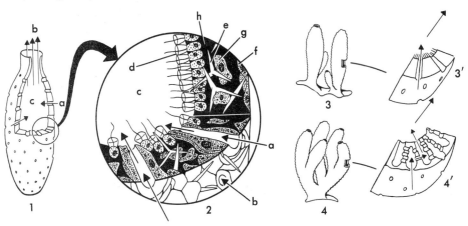

should first see them alive in their natural surroundings or, failing that, in aquariums and zoos. You should then examine preserved specimens, models, and dissections in museums or classroom collections and should dissect some examples yourself. This is not a textbook of zoology or anatomy, and we do not propose to describe the various phyla in detail. Concrete examples are provided by the accompanying illustrations. Beyond that, you need at this point only such brief characterization of the more important phyla as will help to fit them into the broad biological scheme of things.

PORIFERA (SPONGES)

Sponges (Figure 17-1) resemble protistan colonies in that the separate cells seem to lead semi-independent lives within the organization as a whole.

Nevertheless, the cells are of a few well-differentiated kinds with different functions, and there is some coordination of their activities. All sponges are aquatic, and most are marine. Their way of life is not very exciting; they are sessile and do little more than maintain a current of water inflowing through many small pores around their sides and outflowing through a larger opening, usually at the top. They feed on microscopic particles carried by the current.

COELENTERATA

Coelenterates are characterized by a saclike digestive cavity with a single opening, which is

FIG. 17-2 **The basic organization of Coelenterata.** 1. The simple type of polyp present in hydroids: a, ectoderm; b, jellylike layer between the ectoderm and the endoderm (c); d, mouth; e, tentacle; f, digestive cavity. 2. The more advanced type of polyp present in sea anemones, with a gullet (g) leading to the digestive cavity. 3. A medusa, the predominant body form in jellyfishes and present as a motile sexual phase in hydroids: h, circulatory canal that passes along the perimeter; i, extension of the circulatory canal into the tentacle. Both h and i are continuous with the digestive cavity, whose water content is circulated through them. The medusa is essentially an inverted polyp in which the jellylike layer is extensive and the mouth is much drawn out; 3 shows it inverted to facilitate comparison with the polyp, and 3′ shows it as actually oriented. 4. A stinging cell, or nematocyte, before discharge: j, nucleus; k, receptor bristle that, when touched, relays a stimulus to the capsule (1), which contracts, everting the long, coiled filament (m). 5. The nematocyte after discharge: m′, filament; n, barb at the base of the filament. The nematocyte is a self-contained stimulus and response system. Its function is to impale and poison prey, which is then gradually forced into the mouth by other means.

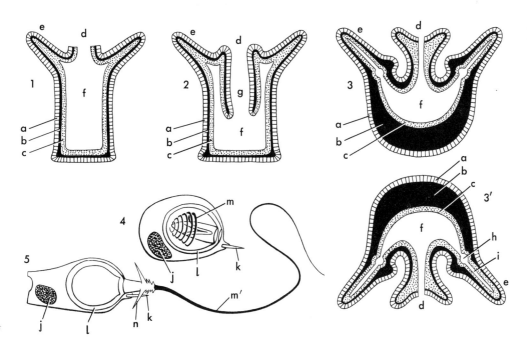

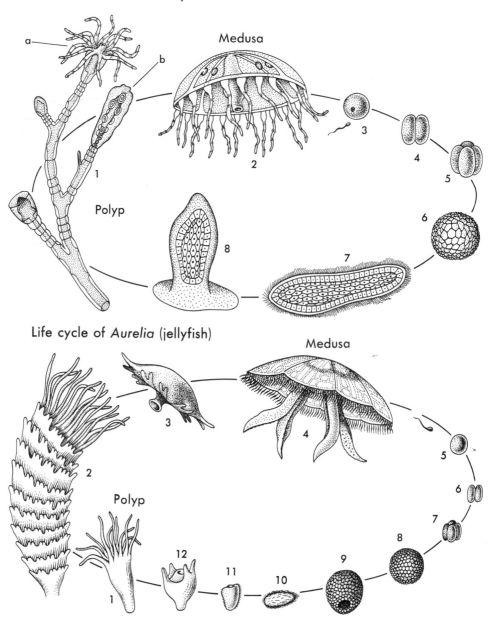

Life cycle of *Obelia* (hydroid)

Medusa

Polyp

Life cycle of *Aurelia* (jellyfish)

Medusa

Polyp

FIG. 17-3 The polyp and the medusa in the life cycle of coelenterates. In *Obelia*, a hydroid, the principal stage is the polyp, which, by asexual budding, becomes a branched colony (1). Some members (a) of the polyp colony are feeding units equipped with tentacles. Others (b) are reproductive units, which continuously bud off medusas (2). The free-swimming medusa serves to disperse the species; it is sexual, producing gametes (3). 4–6. Successive stages in the development of the ciliated larva (7), which ultimately settles (8) to initiate a new polyp colony. In *Aurelia*, a jellyfish, the medusa is the dominant body form. The polyp (1) is a small transient stage that actively buds off (2) young medusas (3), which when fully developed (4) are quite large animals (6 inches in diameter). 5. Gametes liberated by the medusa. 6–9. Successive stages in the development of a ciliated larva (10), which becomes (11–12) a polyp.

surrounded by tentacles with stinging cells. All are carnivorous and snare food in their tentacles. The prey ranges from microscopic animals of many sorts to relatively large crustaceans, worms, or fishes. Like sponges, coelenterates are exclusively aquatic, and they are even more predominantly marine, although there are a few fresh-water types, such as *Hydra*.

The coelenterate's body may assume one of two basic forms: the *polyp* and the *medusa*. There are several variations on a basically similar pattern (Figure 17-2), related to different modes of life.

Coelenterates are highly diverse. Among the different sorts are the following:

Hydroids: Hydra and Obelia are both hydroids (Figure 17-3).
Siphonophores: the Portuguese man-of-war (Figure 17-4).
Jellyfishes: (Figures 17-3 and 17-5).
Sea anemones: (Figure 17-5).
"Corals": (Figure 17-5).

PLATYHELMINTHES

The Platyhelminthes (Figure 17-6), or flatworms, are, as the name implies, flattened from top to bottom, which makes many of them somewhat ribbon- or tapelike. Indeed, tapeworms are platyhelminths, and so are flukes, which are also common parasites. Like many other internal parasites, these have lost organs and tissues that occurred in their ancestry.

NEMATODA

Nematodes, or roundworms, differ superficially from flatworms in being literally rounder and less flattened, and they differ more fundamentally in

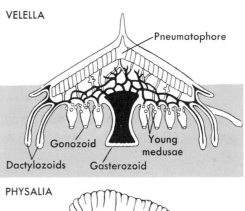

VELELLA

Pneumatophore

Gonozoid
Dactylozoids
Gasterozoid
Young medusae

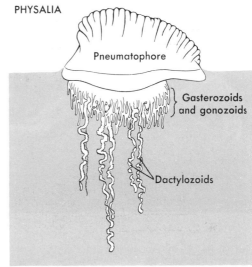

PHYSALIA

Pneumatophore

Gasterozoids and gonozoids

Dactylozoids

FIG. 17-4   Siphonophores. These are highly evolved coelenterates whose bodies are essentially colonies of polyps that have undergone extensive specialization or division of labor. All siphonophores are floating marine organisms. A large polyp forms a float (pneumatophore) to buoy up the rest of the colony. Another polyp (in *Velella*) or several other polyps (in *Physalia*) specialize as feeding units, a gasterozoid. Other polyps, gonozoids, are devoted entirely to reproductive activity. Finally, some are very long fingerlike processes (dactylozoids) devoted entirely to attack; they are heavily endowed with nematocysts. The two drawings represent schematically the organization in two genera of siphonophores, *Velella* and *Physalia*. The photograph shows the Portuguese man-of-war (*Physalia*) with a fish it has captured in its dactylozoids. (Photo, © Douglas P. Wilson)

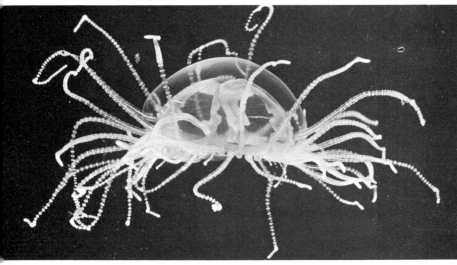

FIG. 17-5 Jellyfishes, sea anemones, and corals. Left, top, the white coral *Madrepora oculata*, from the Bay of Biscay; bottom, the jellyfish *Gonionemus murbachi*. Note on the tentacles the knobs, which are clusters of nematocytes. (All photos, © Douglas P. Wilson, except *Dahlia*, F. Schensky)

Below, left to right, the sea anemone *Dahlia* (note the mouth in the center of the tentacles); the jellyfish *Chrysaora*; the sea anemone *Metridium sessile*.

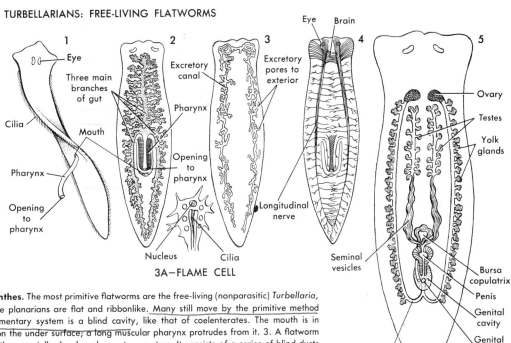

3A—FLAME CELL

FIG. 17-6 **Platyhelminthes.** The most primitive flatworms are the free-living (nonparasitic) *Turbellaria*, the planarians. 1, 2. The planarians are flat and ribbonlike. Many still move by the primitive method of beating cilia. The alimentary system is a blind cavity, like that of coelenterates. The mouth is in the middle of the body on the under surface; a long muscular pharynx protrudes from it. 3. A flatworm is the simplest animal with a specially developed excretory system. It consists of a series of blind ducts connecting with a pair of principal excretory canals running the length of the body. These canals vent to the outside through excretory pores. At the blind end of each excretory duct is a specialized cell (a "flame cell," 3A), which is evidently the active secretor of nitrogenous wastes into the duct. It is ciliated, and its cilia beat actively within the cavity of the duct. 4. The nervous system consists of a simple "brain," two longitudinal nerves and a network of other fibers. 5. The reproductive system is extremely complex and one of the most interesting features of the phylum. The phylum as a whole is hermaphroditic: individual animals carry both male and female organs. This is undoubtedly a major reason the flatworms have been so successful in exploiting the parasitic way of life (all the trematodes and cestodes are parasites). Eggs, formed in the ovaries, pass down the long oviducts to the common genital cavity; on their way they receive yolk material (nutrients) from the extensive yolk glands. The multiple testes shed their sperm into the large seminal vesicles, where they are stored before copulation. Like the hermaphroditic flowering plants, flatworms rarely, if ever, self-fertilize; copulation involves an exchange of sperm between individuals. The muscular penis of each animal inserts sperm into the partner's bursa copulatrix. When eggs are later laid, they are fertilized with sperm released by the bursa copulatrix—not sperm from the animal's own seminal vesicles.

having a digestive tube with two openings—a mouth as the entrance and an anus as the exit (Figure 17-7). Nematodes are incredibly numerous and occur practically everywhere there is any life at all, from the equator to the arctic and from mountaintops to the deep sea. An acre of soil often contains three billion or more nematodes, and you are likely to turn up a million at a time with a spade in your garden. Moreover, nematodes live as parasites in innumerable other animals and also in many plants. Fifty or so species parasitize man; you have probably been a host to them at some time and may well be right now.

Some are practically harmless and others, such as hookworm and trichina, cause serious diseases. *Ascaris*, the most common nematode parasitic in man, is often unpleasant but seldom disabling or fatal.

ANNELIDA

The *annelids* are another group of worms (Figure 17-8), very different indeed from the flatworms or roundworms. Annelids are also literally round worms, built on a cylindrical, tubular plan, with a mouth at one end and an anus at the other.

The cylindrical surface is, however, modified by rows of bristles and often also by more complex appendages. Most strikingly, these worms are made up of numerous segments, visible externally as ringlike bulges and separated internally by partitions. The digestive tube and principal lengthwise blood vessels and nerve cords run right through many or all segments. Other organs, such as nerve ganglia, circular blood vessels, and excretory tubes, are repeated in several or many segments. Earthworms (of which there are many species) are the annelids best known to most of us. Specialized for life in moist soil, they literally eat their way through the ground, passing the dirt through the alimentary canal. Organic matter is digested from the soil, and the residue is ejected from the anus in the form of the familiar worm casting. Their reworking of the soil is so extensive that Darwin doubted whether "there are any other animals which have played such an important part in the history of the world." Do you agree? If not, what animals do you think have played a more important part?

Although earthworms are so readily obtained that they are the usual examples of annelids in biology courses, most of the annelids are marine and look and live quite differently from earthworms. They live almost everywhere in the sea, sometimes free-swimming but often in burrows or tubes. A few annelids are true parasites, and one group, the leeches (class Hirudinea), is semiparasitic, living on the blood of vertebrates, including man. Parasitism is, however, less common among annelids than among other worms. You need not be such a worm fancier as Darwin to agree that some of the plumed, brilliantly colored marine annelids (the polychaetes) are handsome and fascinating.

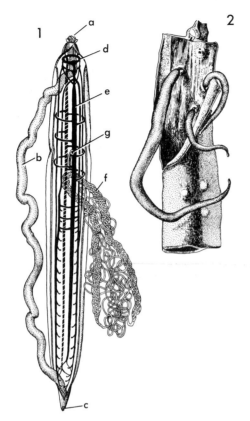
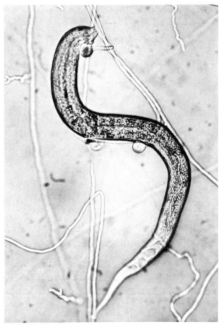

FIG. 17-7 **Nematoda.** Top, 1. Schematic representation of a dissected *Ascaris* (female), the threadworm parasitic in human intestines. The internal organs are few and simple: a, mouth; b, alimentary canal; c, anus; d, nerve ring around the pharynx; e, major ventral nerve cord—a dorsal nerve (crosshatched) is also visible; f, ovary; g, genital pore. 2. The threadworm *Gigantorhynchus gigas* on the gut wall of a pig. (*Gigantorhynchus* is nowadays placed in a closely related though separate phylum, the *Acanthocephala*. However, the group is, for convenience, presented here with the nematodes, of which it was once considered a class.) Bottom, Nematode capture by the predaceous fungus *Dactylella dreschleri*. ($\times$ approximately 560) (Photo, David Pramer)

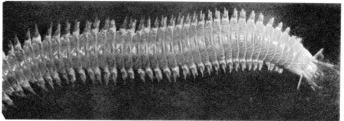

FIG. 17-8 The polychaete annelids. Above, many polychaetes, including the peacock worms, *Sabella favonina*, are sedentary animals that live in tubelike cases they themselves secrete. They set up currents of sea water along elaborate tentacles that lead to their mouths; and from the sea water they extract microorganisms and debris as food. Below, although the annelids are likely to be most familiar through the common earthworm, the group to which the earthworm belongs (*Oligochaeta*) is much less abundant and typical of the phylum Annelida than the marine *Polychaeta*. The simplest and most typical polychaetes are free-swimming, like *Nereis*, shown here. They are carnivorous, possessing stout jaws. Their most characteristic feature is the bristle-bearing, paddle-like parapodia ("feet equivalents") borne on each segment. Used principally for locomotion, the parapodia are also excellent respiratory structures, combining a large surface area and a rich blood supply. (Photos, above, ⓒ Douglas P. Wilson; below, Ralph Buchsbaum)

Arthropods

No one knows how many species of arthropods there are in the world. The number is at least a million, and estimates run as high as 10 million. Arthropods have been brought up from the deepest sea bottoms that have been dredged. They have been encountered by airplanes flying miles above the earth. They are everywhere that life exists at all. They fly, swim, hop, crawl, and just sit still. There is probably no species of organism that is not on occasion eaten by one arthropod or another. Arthropods are, in turn, eaten by many other animals. They are man's chief competitors for food and all sorts of organic materials. They include the worst of pests, but they are also essential links in maintaining the verdure-clad world as it is.

In basic structure the arthropods are somewhat like annelids, and there is no doubt that the two phyla had a common origin something over 600 million years ago.

Among the more important differences are the following:

1. The external coating or *cuticle* of arthropods is harder and serves mechanically as an external skeleton.

2. Arthropods have legs divided into distinct, movable segments or joints (hence the name of the phylum, which means "jointed feet").

3. Arthropods have muscles in definite groups mechanically related to specific movable parts. The muscles of annelids form relatively simple sheets throughout the body.

4. Arthropods generally have fewer segments, and there is a tendency for the segments of some regions, notably in the head, to fuse and become strongly differentiated in structure.

5. Arthropods have distinctly developed jaws. These open from side to side instead of up and down as our and other vertebrate jaws do.

6. Their nervous system is usually more highly developed than in annelids and is accompanied by elaborate sensory receptors, including those in the antennae and eyes.

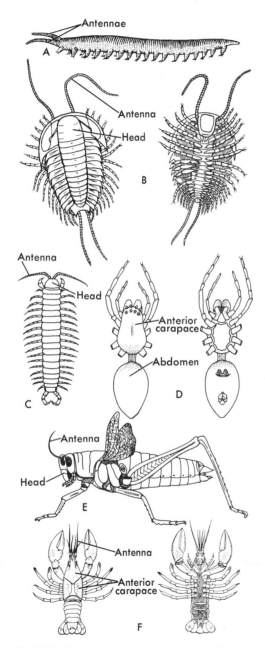

FIG. 17-9 Principal classes of arthropods. A. Onychophora (*Peripatus*), left lateral view. B. Trilobita (extinct; *Olenoides*), dorsal and ventral views. C. Myriapoda (chilopod; Diplopoda are similar), dorsal view. D. Arachnida (spider, with posterior three pairs of legs off), dorsal and ventral views. E. Insecta (grasshopper), left lateral view. F. Crustacea (crayfish), dorsal and ventral views.

Most of these arthropod characteristics improve or elaborate their reactions to stimuli in the environment. Their advantage over other invertebrates is largely in the efficiency and adaptability of their behavior. The vertebrates, and notably man, also owe their dominance in great part to their adaptable and efficient behavior. In arthropods the behavior is relatively inflexible in a given species, but is modified genetically in the course of evolution. Vertebrate behavior has, as a rule, a larger element of flexibility in the individual. We are likely to consider our own kind of behavioral adaptation as "better" or "higher." Arthropods are, however, from 10 to 100 times more numerous than vertebrates in species, incomparably more abundant in individuals, and divergently adapted to an even wider range of environments and habits. They easily hold their own against all the attacks of man and of other animals. Which is the more successful phylum?

The outstanding classes are those of the crustaceans, the spiders (and relatives), and, above all, the insects (Figure 17-9).

Crustaceans

All of us are familiar with some crustaceans, if only because we eat them with pleasure: lobsters (Figure 17-10), crabs, shrimps, crayfish, prawns. We have only those five common names for them, but there are literally thousands of species of these larger, free-living crustaceans, many of them edible by humans. They are the decapods or "ten-legs" among the crustaceans in general. Most of them are marine, but they are also numerous in fresh water, and some crabs can survive considerable periods in the air as long as they do not dry out. All are carnivores or scavengers, eating a wide variety of small living animals and any sort of dead animal matter.

Arachnids

The arachnids (Figure 17-11) are another group, like the octopuses, that have been given a largely undeserved bad name. It is true that most spiders and ticks are poisonous, but only a few are dangerous to man, and most of us are rarely under the slightest menace from them. Most spiders are beneficial to man because they prey on insects considered undesirable with better cause. Mites and ticks, also arachnids, do deserve a bad name from our point of view, for they

FIG. 17-10 Crustaceans. Left, a decapod, the common prawn *Leander serratus* ($\times \frac{2}{3}$). Center, the sow bug or wood louse, *Armadillaria vulgare*, one of the few crustaceans that have become terrestrial. Right, another decapod, the crab *Cancer magister*, from Alaska. (All photos, ⓒ Douglas P. Wilson, except crab, U.S. Fish and Wildlife Service, and sowbug, U.S. Department of Agriculture)

Below, top, a copepod, *Acartia clausi* ($\times 88$); bottom, the goose barnacle, *Lepas fascicularis* ($\times \frac{1}{2}$)

Below, left, Barnacles, *Balanus perforatus* (approximately natural size); right, *Caprella aequilibra*, a delicate, slender-bodied crustacean living among seaweeds in the tidal zone ($\times 6$).

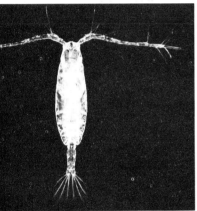

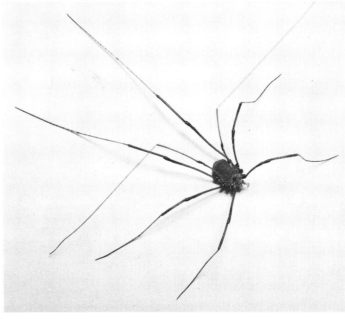

FIG. 17-11 **Arachnids.** Above, left, the house spider *Theridion* with egg sacs on the back of a leaf; right, the harvestman, or daddy longlegs, which feeds on small insects. Below, ventral (*left*) and dorsal (*right*) views of the king crab, *Limulus polyphemus*. (All photos, Hugh Spencer, except king crab, American Museum of Natural History)

Below, top, the dog tick, *Dermacentor*, which transmits the organism causing Rocky Mountain spotted fever in man; bottom, a scorpion.

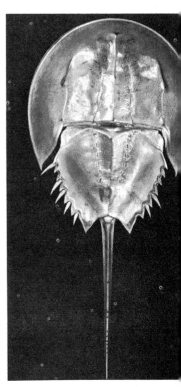

include unpleasant and dangerous external parasites of man and domestic animals and are intermediate hosts for organisms producing some serious diseases. Daddy longlegs or harvestmen are another group of arachnids, entirely harmless and indeed helpful to man.

Most people think of arachnids as insects or bugs (which are, strictly speaking, a group of insects). Arachnids are really quite different and are easily distinguished by the fact that they have four or five pairs of legs, while insects have three pairs. This is what systematists call a diagnostic or key character. It is a handy way to spot whether a particular animal is an arachnid or an insect.

Another living arachnid looks offhand completely unlike a spider, scorpion, or tick. It is the horeshoe or king "crab," genus *Limulus*. The broad protective dorsal shield (carapace) appears rather crablike, but examination of the legs (five pairs) and internal anatomy reveals indubitable phylogenetic resemblances to spiders and differences from crabs.

Insects

No one needs to be told that insects are the most successful and diverse of invertebrates. In fact, no other group of organisms of any kind, protists, plants, or animals, can begin to compare with them in diversity. At least half, and probably a much larger proportion, of all the species of all organic kingdoms living in the world today belong to this one class. What we have said about the importance and dominance of the phylum Arthropoda is true mostly because it includes the class Insecta.

There is just one strong restriction on the distribution of insects. If we lived in the sea, we would be much impressed with their fellow arthropods the crustaceans, but we would consider insects a rare and unimportant group. Insects arose as terrestrial animals. That was the most fundamental adaptive feature in the origin of the class. Many of them have subsequently adapted to life in fresh water, commonly in the larval stages only. A few pass their larval stage or even their whole lives along the shore between tides and in salty pools.

One other restriction on the adaptive range of insects is a matter of size. Multicellular organisms cannot function below a minimum size which is extremely small to our eyes, to be sure, but which

looks large in comparison with a bacterium or many other protists. The smallest insects (which are parasites in the eggs of other insects) are about 0.2 millimeter (that is, only about 1/125th of an inch) in length. Most insects are at least 2 millimeters long. On the other hand, there is a mechanical and physiological upper limit for the size of insects. The weight and the stress of muscles and motions are borne by an external skeleton. There is a limit to the total weight a given kind of skeleton can support. At the limit the skeleton itself either becomes too heavy to move or too light to stand up without collapsing under the weight of the rest of the body. This limit is very much higher for an internal than for an external skeleton; that is one of the advantages that mammals and other vertebrates have over insects. The respiratory and vascular systems also impose limits on the size of insects. They are very efficient for small animals but probably could not adapt to any considerable increase in bulk. Few insects are more than about 40 millimeters long, and the upper limit is around 275 millimeters (less than a foot) for body length. Some moths have a slightly greater wingspread, up to about 1 foot.

Most insects have some features in common, which must have been involved in the evolutionary origin of the class. Most of these may be seen in a common grasshopper (Figure 17-12). Among the most striking characteristics are these:

1. The head consists of six segments, thoroughly fused and practically inseparable in the adult. Appendages of one segment have become sensory antennae. Other appendages have become complex mouth parts.

2. The thorax, the central section of the body, is distinctly separate from the head and the abdomen and consists of three segments, each with a pair of legs.

3. The abdomen has 11 or fewer segments, (usually) without appendages, and the posterior segments are specialized for reproduction.

4. Respiration is by tracheae; the circulatory system is open, without capillaries or veins; oxygen

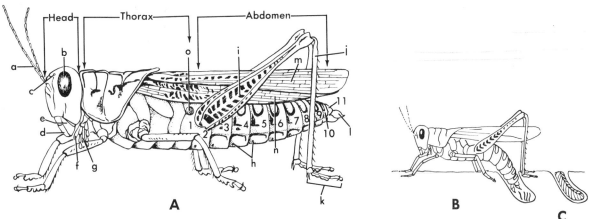

FIG. 17-12 A grasshopper as an example of insect organization. A. The external anatomy of a female grasshopper: a, antenna; b, compound eye; c, ocelli (supplementary light-sensitive organs); d, labrum (upper lip); e, mandible; f, maxilla; g, labium (lower lip); h, spiracles (breathing apertures for the entry of air into the tracheal system); i, femur of the third leg; j, tibia of the leg; k, tarsal segments of the leg; l, ovipositor; m, forewing; n, hind wing; o, tympanum (organ of hearing). Note the division of the body into three major parts—head, thorax, and abdomen. The eleven abdominal segments are numbered. B. A female laying eggs (ovipositing) in the ground. C. the egg mass.

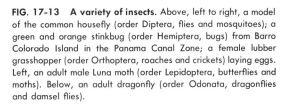

FIG. 17-13 A variety of insects. Above, left to right, a model of the common housefly (order Diptera, flies and mosquitoes); a green and orange stinkbug (order Hemiptera, bugs) from Barro Colorado Island in the Panama Canal Zone; a female lubber grasshopper (order Orthoptera, roaches and crickets) laying eggs. Left, an adult male Luna moth (order Lepidoptera, butterflies and moths). Below, an adult dragonfly (order Odonata, dragonflies and damsel flies).

Left, a bumblebee (order Hymenoptera), with pollen packed into special pollen baskets on its hind legs. Right, top, an adult female mosquito (order Diptera) sucking blood; bottom, mosquito larvae respiring at the surface of a pond.

Left, a cicada wasp (order Hymenoptera, bees, wasps, and ants), with a cicada it has stung. Right, a boll weevil (order Coleoptera, beetles).

Below, left, a human body louse (order Anoplura, lice), carrier of typhus fever; right, adult worker ants (order Hymenoptera) and pupae.

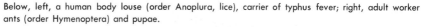

transport by blood is unimportant because the tracheal branches carry oxygen directly to nearly every cell in the body.

(5.) Simple and compound eyes occur, as well as many other receptors in antennae and elsewhere. The nervous system is complex, with two large ganglia or "brains" in the head and a double ventral cord.

Most insects have wings, and most of the wingless forms (lice, fleas, wingless ants, etc.) had flying ancestors. Insects commonly have two approximately equal pairs of wings, and this condition was probably primitive. In many insects, notably the beetles, the front pair has become a protective cover. In flies (order Diptera, or "two-wings," on this account) the hind pair is greatly reduced in size and is a balancing, not flying, organ. Another characteristic that is widespread but not universal in insects is the occurrence of wormlike feeding larvae, with gradual or sudden metamorphosis into adults.

Specialists on insects (entomologists) divide the class into about 25 living orders, the number being variable because it is a matter of taste and opinion whether some related groups should be considered separate orders or suborders of one order. A dozen

or more wholly extinct orders are also known. Some faint idea of the stunning diversity of insects is suggested by Figure 17-13. Among the more numerous and familiar groups of insects are these: roaches and grasshoppers; termites (or "white ants," but they belong to a different order from true ants); dragonflies; May flies; lice; bugs and aphids; caddis flies, moths and butterflies; true flies; fleas; beetles; and ants, wasps, and bees.

MOLLUSCA

Mollusks are especially characterized by the development of a muscular region or organ behind the mouth. This serves for crawling locomotion in many mollusks and is called the *foot*. Above it is the soft mass of viscera. Practically all the organ systems found in any animals are present in most mollusks: digestive (sometimes with a unique rasping device, the *radula*), circulatory (with a heart), respiratory (usually with complex gills, *ctenidia*), excretory, nervous (often with brainlike ganglia and sometimes with well-developed eyes and other sense organs), muscular, and reproductive. Above and surrounding the viscera is a *mantle* of specialized tissue, usually including glands that secrete one or more shells.

The most important groups of mollusks are the classes (Figure 17-14) Gastropoda (snails and their relatives), Pelecypoda (clams and relatives), and

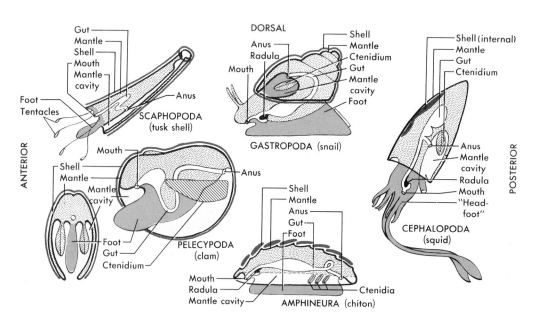

FIG. 17-14   **The main classes of mollusks.**

Cephalopoda (squids, octopuses, the chambered nautilus, and relatives). Each of these groups has great diversity of specific adaptations evolved from a basic ancestral adaptation that is different in each class. The three other classes, equally distinctive but less diverse and relatively unimportant, are the Amphineura, Monoplacophora, and the Scaphopoda, or tusk shells.

Gastropods

The deliberateness of a snail's gait is notorious. Nevertheless, snails are motile, and their slow crawling in search of food is an essential part of their way of life. Also characteristic is protection by a single shell with one opening. The early larva is bilateral, but in metamorphosis the viscera are twisted in a loop. This brings the anus from its original position behind mouth and foot to a point above the mouth.

Gastropods (like all mollusks) were originally marine, and most of them still are. Some, however, have become almost fully terrestrial, although sensitive to dry air and commonly found only in moist locations. The terrestrial gastropods have lost their gills and have instead a lunglike cavity in the mantle that enables them to extract oxygen from air. Among the numerous fresh-water snails some have gills and some "lungs."

Gastropods have evolved into a tremendous array of different forms, usually beautiful and often bizarre (Figure 17-15). Wherever you live, you are familiar with some of them, especially if you have had opportunity to collect sea shells. A museum display of gastropods is one of the most impressive evidences of the diversity of life. One curiosity is that some gastropods have lost their shells. Among them are the unlovely garden slugs and the marine nudibranchs, some of which are really beautiful.

Pelecypods

Pelecypods have retained bilateral symmetry and have two shells or valves, usually nearly symmetrical, one on each side of the body; hence the name "bivalve" is often applied to them. They were primitively motile, and most of them still are, but they usually lead rather sedentary lives and are even less speedy than snails. They seldom move far from where the larva settles down, and some, like oysters, become permanently attached.

In diversity of forms (Figure 17-16), pelecypods

are less spectacular than gastropods, but still they are extremely varied and abundant. Most are marine, although some occur in fresh water (fresh-water clams or river mussels). None are terrestrial. A few swim fairly well; scallops (*Pecten*) swim by clapping their shells together. Burrowing is a more common specialty. Many species of marine clams burrow in mud or sand, as do our common edible clams (*Venus* and *Mya*). Others (like *Teredo*) burrow in wood and cause serious damage to wooden boats and pilings. Some (like *Pholas*) burrow in solid rock. The astonishing giant clams (*Tridacna*) of the South Pacific, which may reach 6 feet in diameter, burrow in living coral reefs.

Cephalopods

It is a literary tradition to play up the horror and menace of octopuses. This is a bit hard on shy creatures that have seldom if ever seriously harmed a man. They, and even more particularly their relatives the squids, are also among the most complex and in almost any sense highest products of evolution (Figure 17-17).

"Active" is the keyword for the cephalopods. They are all free-living and, on occasion, fast-moving forms. A squid has a large mantle cavity with muscular walls and a funnel-like tube (the siphon) through which water can be ejected rapidly by contraction of the walls. The animal moves swiftly by the principle of jet propulsion. If the tube is turned backward, a squid darts forward in pursuit of prey. When it is the pursued rather than the pursuer (which seems to be the more frequent situation), it turns the tube forward and darts backward. In conjunction with its active life, a squid has a remarkably large and complex brain, as brains go among the invertebrates. It also has elaborate image-forming eyes, which work on just the same principles as our own eyes but certainly evolved entirely independently, providing a classic example of evolutionary convergence. Another remarkable convergence between squids and vertebrates is that a squid, alone among invertebrates, has developed a cartilaginous internal skeleton, including a skull-like protective case around the brain. Only

FIG. 17-15 Gastropods. Left, the sea hare, *Tethys,* a herbivorous tidal-zone gastropod. The foot region is developed into two large ''parapodia'' that enable it to swim. Below, garden snails, *Helix,* on a twig. (Photos, left, Willis T. Hammond; below, Hugh Spencer)

Below, left to right, limpets, *Patella,* on a soft slaty rock, which shows scars left by limpets that have died; the whelk, *Buccinum,* a predatory marine gastropod; the shell-less garden slug, *Arion,* with freshly laid eggs. (Photos, © Douglas P. Wilson, except right, American Museum of Natural History)

FIG. 17-16 Pelecypods. Below, the queen scallop, *Chlamys*, escaping from a starfish buried in the sand. Scallops swim by opening and closing the valves, producing a jet-propulsion effect. Right, the giant clam, *Tridacna*, of coral reefs, with coral growing on one side of the valves. (All photos, © Douglas P. Wilson, except giant clam, American Museum of Natural History)

Below, mussels, *Mytilus*, attached to rock by the byssal threads they secrete. They are being attacked by the predatory gastropod *Ocenetra*, which drills through the mussel shells with its radula. Right, *Pholas*, a pelecypod that burrows into solid rock, using the edges of its valves as a drill. Far right, *Solen*, the razor shell, with its foot extended.

traces of the ancestral molluscan external shell remain.

The fact that cephalopods have tentacles with suction discs is familiar to everyone. In octopuses the tentacles serve for slower clambering about (octopuses have jet propulsion, too), and in all cephalopods the tentacles seize prey and convey it to the sharp, shearing jaws. Cephalopods are predacious; they actively pursue, kill, and devour other animals such as fishes or crabs (but not humans). Have you ever meditated on the fact that characteristics we admire, such as brain development, keen senses, and skillful coordination, are more likely than not to be best developed in predacious animals, whereas animals that lead quiet, respectable lives seem to have little else to recommend them?

Besides squids and octopuses, there is just one surviving genus of a markedly different group of cephalopods. This is the genus *Nautilus*. The nautilus lives in a coiled shell divided into chambers by partitions. From time to time as the animal grows, it moves to a new chamber and seals off the old one. The nautilus is a relic of the past, the remaining member of formerly very abundant groups of animals that played major roles in the history of life for tens and hundreds of millions of years.

ECHINODERMATA

The *echinoderms* are relatively complex animals (Figures 17-18 and 17-19) with a (usually) complete digestive tube, coelom, and specialized excretory, reproductive, nervous, and circulatory systems, although the last two are simpler than in most animals otherwise so complex. In spite of belonging in these respects among the "higher" phyla, they resemble the coelenterates in being radially symmetrical. At least, most adult echinoderms seem to be so. In fact, their larvae are bilaterally symmetrical, and there are traces of bilateral symmetry even

FIG. 17-17 Cephalopods. Top, the cuttlefish, *Sepia*, a very active swimmer. Note the large eyes. Center, the common octopus, *Octopus vulgaris.* Note the suction discs on its tentacles. Bottom, the chambered nautilus, *Nautilus pompilius*, with its shell cut away to show the animal in the last, largest chamber. (Photos, above two, © Douglas P. Wilson; below, American Museum of Natural History)

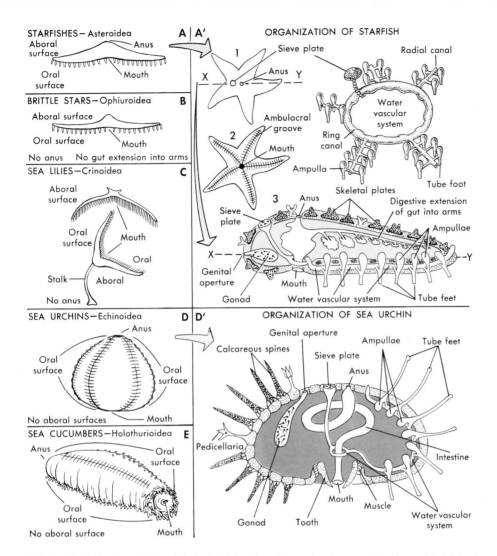

FIG. 17-18 Echinodermata. A, A′. A starfish, Asteroidea. The true dorsal and ventral surfaces of the bilateral larva are completely obscured in the adult, and it is convenient to recognize oral (1) and aboral (2) surfaces instead. The arms lie on five axes radiating from the mouth; these five axes are recognizable in all the echinoderms. Along the oral surface of each arm runs an ambulacral groove, in which the tube feet lie. The tube feet are extensions of the water-vascular system that connects with the external sea water via the sieve plate. The sieve plate is joined by a duct to a tube (the ring canal) encircling the alimentary canal; from this circular vessel ducts lead along each arm, with pairs of tube feet penetrating the body wall. The tube feet are effective walking organs (ambulatory, hence the name of the groove in which they lie) insofar as they are kept inflated by pressure on the sea water within; this pressure is maintained by the ampullae. B. Side view of a brittle star. There is no anus, and the gut is entirely restricted to the central mass; it does not enter the five arms, as in a starfish. C. Side views of a free-swimming sea lily and a stalked, sedentary sea lily. D, D′, E. Side views of a sea urchin and a sea cucumber. As in A′2 the ambulacral grooves bearing the tube feet are shown as crosshatches along the axes radiating from the mouth. In both these groups aboral surfaces are entirely wanting; their organization may be visualized by imagining the tips of the five arms in a starfish drawn backward (away from the mouth) and brought to a point. Note in D′ how the arm of the water-vascular system that bears the tube feet is curled upward to the anus. Compare D′ with A′3. Around the mouth a sea urchin has strong calcareous teeth moved by muscles. The pedicellaria are jointed jawlike structures.

FIG. 17-19 Sea lilies, starfishes, brittle stars, sea urchins, and sea cucumbers. Above, the sea cucumber *Cucumaria frondosa*. Far left, the brittle star *Ophiothrix fragilis*. Left, the sea urchin *Echinus esculentus* crawling on an aquarium wall. Note the tube feet at lower left corner. (Photos, top, F. Schensky, Helgoland; far left and left, © Douglas P. Wilson)

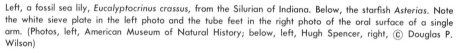

Left, a fossil sea lily, *Eucalyptocrinus crassus*, from the Silurian of Indiana. Below, the starfish *Asterias*. Note the white sieve plate in the left photo and the tube feet in the right photo of the oral surface of a single arm. (Photos, left, American Museum of Natural History; below, left, Hugh Spencer, right, © Douglas P. Wilson)

in adults, but the over-all shape of most adults is radial, usually with five rays, as in common starfishes. Another unique feature of echinoderms, in addition to the true circulatory system (which is poorly developed), is a well-developed water-vascular system. This contains sea water filtered through a special sieve plate. In many echinoderms the water-circulatory system is connected to numerous "tube feet," operated by hydraulic pressure and used in slow locomotion and for grasping. Almost all echinoderms have hard, limy plates in the skin, and in some, such as the sea urchins, these may be immovably united into a hard, protective box. (Sea urchins also have movable spines jointed to the outside of the box.) All echinoderms are marine.

CHORDATA

Most of the chordates are vertebrates—the fishes, amphibians, reptiles, birds, and mammals. Three major groups of chordates (Figure 17-20) are not vertebrates. The Hemichordata ("half-chorded") or "acorn worms" are indeed fully wormlike in body form, and yet they have what seems to be a short equivalent of a notochord and also some other chordate characteristics such as dorsal nerve cords and gill slits. The Urochordata ("tail-chorded," because the notochord is confined to the tail), or tunicates, look even less like vertebrates as adults, in which stage most of them are sessile, superficially spongelike creatures and some are colonial. Even the adults do have some vertebrate characteristics, however, and some of the larvae pass through a stage in which they are very much like tiny fishes. The Cephalochordata ("head-corded," because the notochord extends to the extreme tip of the head, which it does not in vertebrates), or lancelets, are quite fishlike in appearance throughout life. They have most of the basic vertebrate characters but lack vertebrae as well as a true brain and some other vertebrate features.

Vertebrates

The Vertebrata ("with vertebrae"), are another of the great culminations of the evolutionary processes. They are in many respects the most important and most progressive of all groups of organisms. Vertebrates are much less diverse and less abundant than

insects. Their role in the total metabolic turnover of the living world is far less than the parts played by several groups of plants and also less than those of some other animals. The vertebrates are, nevertheless, highly diverse and abundant, and they do have important ecological roles. Moreover, as a whole they are characterized by the highest development of reception of environmental stimuli and the greatest flexibility and widest repertory of reactions. The vertebrates include man, who is in those respects and some others incomparably the most progressive of all organisms and who is, even from the point of view of other organisms, far the most potent force on earth today. While regarding ourselves as the supreme animals, however, we should remember that the vertebrates include other groups that are also dominant and are evolutionary culminations in their own ways and in different adaptive spheres, notably the bony fishes, the perching birds, and the rodents.

The vertebrates may be arranged in eight classes (Figure 17-21), the first four of which are aquatic and are popularly known as fishes: Agnatha, Placodermi (the only extinct class), Chondrichthyes, and Osteichthyes. The four mainly nonaquatic classes are the Amphibia, Reptilia, Aves, and Mammalia.

AGNATHS AND PLACODERMS

The first vertebrates were *agnaths* (jawless fishes), which occurred in a multitude of specific forms. They were abundant and highly diversified in the early days of vertebrate history and then dominated the realm of fishes for a relatively short time (although, even so, for some tens of millions of years). The early jawless fishes were soon replaced by fishes with jaws.

The earliest fishes with jaws are classified as *placoderms* (plate-skin). The placoderms early became extinct and were replaced by more modern sorts of fishes, with more complex and still more efficient jaws. We shall have occasion to mention placoderms again in connection with the history of life in the sea.

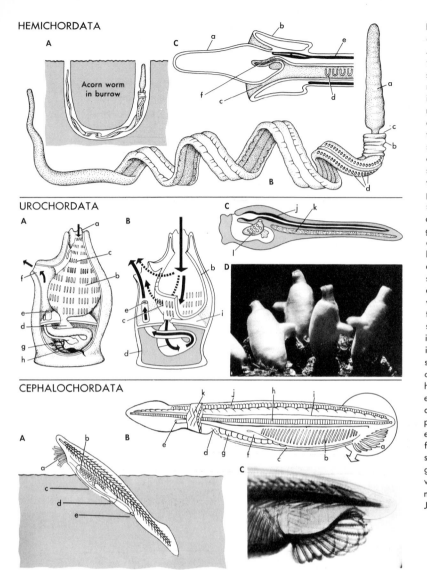

HEMICHORDATA

UROCHORDATA

CEPHALOCHORDATA

FIG. 17-20 The invertebrate chordates. Top, hemichordata. *Balanoglossus*, the acorn—or tongue—worm. A. A whole animal in its U-shaped burrow in the sand. B. External features: a, burrowing proboscis; b, collar; c, mouth; d, gill slits. C. Detail of the head region: e, dorsal nerve cord; f, notochord, extending forward from the roof of the pharynx into the proboscis. The animal is a filter feeder; water and mud enter the mouth and are filtered of food at the gills; excess water passes out of the gills and oxygenates them at the same time. Center, Urochordata (Tunicata). *Ciona*, a sea squirt or tunicate. A. A whole animal with its body wall cut away to show its internal organization: a, mouth (or inhalant siphon), through which the feeding and respiratory current of water (see arrows) enters; b, wall of the much-enlarged pharynx, which is perforated by numerous gill slits (c); d, stomach; e, anus; f, exhalant siphon, by which the water current leaves the animal; g, gonad; h, heart. B. The pharyngeal region of the alimentary system. The inhalant and exhalant siphons are walled off by a membrane (i) from the body cavity proper (stippled). The cavity so formed (unstippled, above i) is the atrium. The feeding current entering the inhalant siphon is filtered through the pharynx wall; the food passes on (solid arrows) into the alimentary system, and the filtered water passes (broken arrows) into the atrium and leaves by the exhalant siphon. C. A sea-squirt larva. It is bilaterally symmetrical, elongate, and free-swimming. It is mainly interesting because of its bearing on the origin of vertebrates. Note its dorsal nerve cord (j), notochord (k), and pharynx with gill slits (1). D. A photograph of sea squirts. Bottom, Cephalochordata. *Branchiostoma*, or amphioxus. A. A whole animal half-buried in sand or gravel, where it lives a semisedentary existence as a filter feeder like the other invertebrate chordates: a, cirri surrounding the mouth; b, gill slits in the pharynx; c, atrium; d, opening from the atrium to the outside; e, anus. B. The animal as though dissected from the side; f, liver; g, gonad; h, notochord; i, nerve chord; j, fin rays, supporting the dorsal fin; k, segmental muscles. The pharyngeal gill slits, as in the tunicates, open into an atrium that vents to the outside. C. A photograph of the head and mouth region. (Photos, upper, © Douglas P. Wilson; lower, J. E. Webb)

CHONDRICHTHYANS

The principal chondrichthyans are the sharks and the rays (with their relatives, the skates) (Figure 17-22). Their original physiological adaptation is seen in the way they meet the problem of osmosis in salty water—a way markedly different from and more efficient than that of the osteichthyans (bony fishes, discussed below). In the osteichthyans the internal osmotic pressure is less than that of sea water, and much metabolic energy is required to keep enough water in the body (Chapter 3). Chondrichthyans retain large amounts of dissolved urea in the body fluids—a peculiar specialization, for such concentrations of urea would be fatal to most animals. Together with the inorganic salts usual in such fluids, the dissolved urea raises the internal osmotic pressure to approximately that of sea water, so that marine chondrichthyans, unlike other marine fishes, are in osmotic equilibrium with their environment. In discussing the adaptations of various groups of organisms, we are likely to emphasize anatomical characteristics, because these are easy to observe. Osmotic regulation in the chondrich-

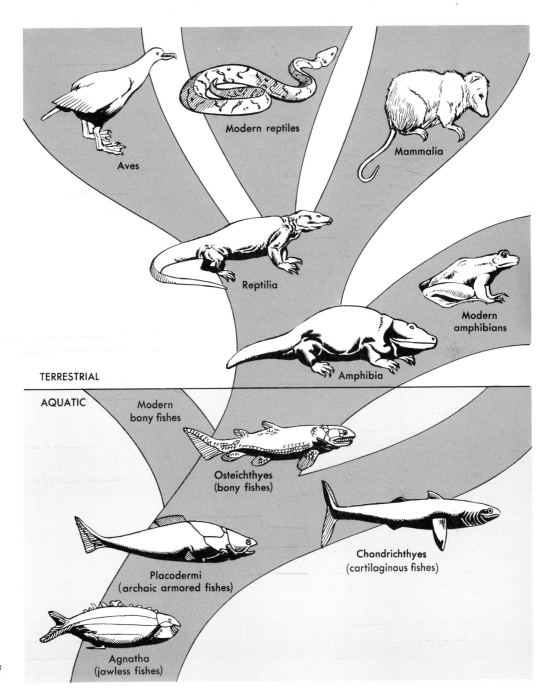

TERRESTRIAL

AQUATIC

Modern
bony fishes

Aves

Modern reptiles

Mammalia

Reptilia

Modern
amphibians

Amphibia

Osteichthyes
(bony fishes)

Chondrichthyes
(cartilaginous fishes)

Placodermi
(archaic armored fishes)

Agnatha
(jawless fishes)

FIG. 17-21 The classes of vertebrates.

thyans is a good example of the fact that *physiological adaptations* are just as numerous and may be even more important than structural ones.

Of course, the chondrichthyans do also have characteristic anatomical features. The most obvious

and universal is the one they are named for—the completely cartilaginous skeleton of recent forms. This is a specialization. Another specialization is that the eggs have heavy, leathery shells and that fertilization is internal. The males have modified posterior

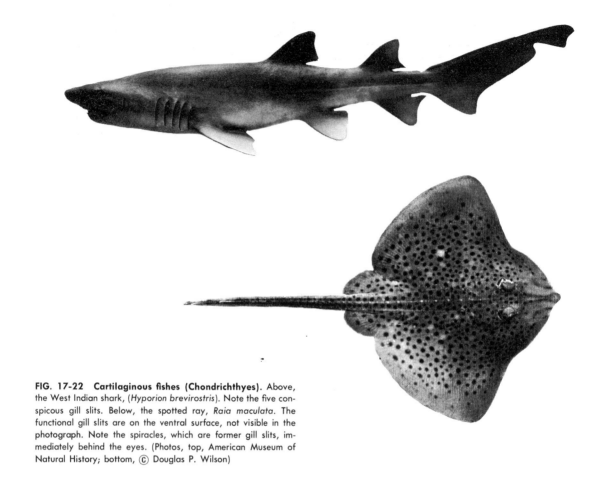

FIG. 17-22 Cartilaginous fishes (Chondrichthyes). Above, the West Indian shark, (*Hyporion brevirostris*). Note the five conspicous gill slits. Below, the spotted ray, *Raia maculata*. The functional gill slits are on the ventral surface, not visible in the photograph. Note the spiracles, which are former gill slits, immediately behind the eyes. (Photos, top, American Museum of Natural History; bottom, © Douglas P. Wilson)

paired (pelvic) fins with structures called *claspers* that aid in injecting sperms into the females. A feature that may be primitive in comparison with osteichthyans is the absence of lungs or swim bladders.

The oldest chondrichthyans are sharks, and of course sharks are still common today, changed in many details but still of the same adaptive type: elongated, streamlined, swift-swimming predators. These and other characteristics of the group are well seen in the so-called dogfishes, usual laboratory animals, which are small sharks. Later in origin and now also abundant are the skates and rays—broad, flattened forms, most of which live on the sea bottom, where they devour various invertebrates.

OSTEICHTHYANS

The osteichthyans (Figure 17-23), and especially the great group (usually classed as a superorder) called *teleosts* ("perfect bones"), are the dominant aquatic animals today. They have become adapted to almost every aquatic environment, from the unchanging cold darkness of the deep sea to dashing mountain streams. One species or another eats practically everything that is edible by any aquatic animal. Some are sluggish, but some are the most swiftly moving of all animals. Their diversity in form is really astonishing; Figure 17-24 gives just a hint of the

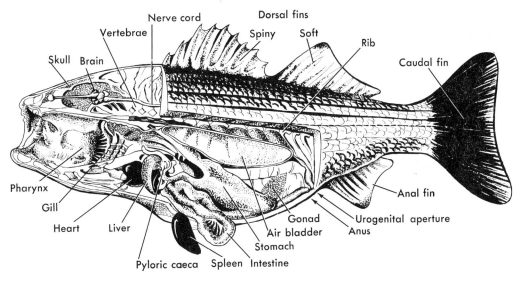

FIG. 17-23 **The organization of a bony fish (Osteichthyes).** (The pyloric caeca are digestive pouches of the gut.)

extraordinary shapes among them. More than 20,000 species are known. The individual abundance of some single species is also remarkable. It is estimated that there are at least a trillion (1,000,000,000,000) herrings in the Atlantic Ocean.

AMPHIBIANS

Among modern amphibians (Figure 17-25), the salamanders, although specialized or degenerate

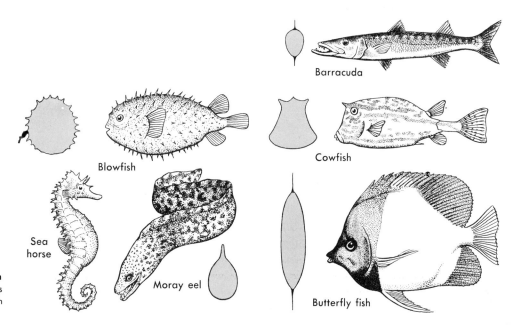

FIG. 17-24 **Some body forms in bony fishes.** The stippled silhouettes represent transverse sections through the various fishes.

FIG. 17-25 **Modern amphibians.** Left, the tree frog or "spring peeper," *Hyla crucifer*. The animal is small (up to 2 inches) but possesses a loud voice amplified by the distended vocal pouch acting as a resonator. Above, top, adult green frog, *Rana clamitans;* bottom, the common tiger salamander, *Ambystoma tigrinum*. The adult is about 8 inches long, an inhabitant of moist woodlands and streams. (Photos, left and above top, Huge Spencer; above bottom, Isabelle Hunt Conant)

Below, left, the mud puppy, *Necturus maculosus*, an inhabitant of streams. The adult, attaining a length of 12 to 17 inches, retains bushy external gills. Right, late larva of the green frog, *Rana clamitans*. (Photos, left, Isabelle Hunt Conant; right, Hugh Spencer)

in many respects, have most nearly retained the ancestral habits, fishlike body form, and even fishlike undulatory movement of the body as a whole. They go through a larval stage in which they resemble adults rather closely except that, among a few other details, they have gills that are lost when metamorphosis occurs. The larvae of frogs and toads, familiar to everyone as tadpoles, are also fishlike, perhaps even more so than salamander larvae, because in early stages they lack legs. Their metamorphosis is more drastic, and an adult frog or toad is completely unlike a fish, and indeed unlike anything on earth, except a frog or toad. The adult anurans (frogs and toads) are among the most distinctive and specialized of all the vertebrates. The most obvious specializations are that they have no tails (that is one of our most obvious specializations, too, but of course we did not get it from the anurans) and that their hind legs are tremendous leaping mechanisms. In addition to these more obvious points, anuran anatomy, physiology, and habits are replete with other aberrant features. In particular, anurans are radically unlike the amphibians that were ancestral to the fully terrestrial vertebrates and therefore can show us little about that ancestry. On the other hand, their very aberrancy gives them a way of life in which they have few serious competitors and which makes them the only group of amphibians that was successful in the long run.

REPTILES

Even though a few kinds of amphibians came to occupy ecological positions in which they continue to have modest success, amphibians are anomalous animals. During parts of their lives they are ecologically or adaptively fishes. They are superior to true fishes only in being less rigidly and permanently confined to the water. They have succeeded and survived only because ability to leave the water when occasion demands has survival value. But as land animals they are still tied to the water. As a rule, they must return to the water to breed, and water is still the obligatory habitat of the young of most amphibians. On land, then, Amphibia are usually at a disadvantage in comparison with animals able to live their whole lives there. It was inevitable that most amphibians would become extinct, given the

evolutionary possibility of the rise of fully terrestrial vertebrates or, more objectively, given the fact that such vertebrates did evolve.

It was the reptiles that became the first fully terrestrial vertebrates. The eggs, laid on land, have leathery or limy shells that impede fatal loss of water by the embryos. Fertilization is internal (the male and female copulate). The eggs contain a large amount of food (yolk), and full development, with no larval stage, occurs before the young hatch. The newly hatched young are already essentially like adults in form and activities, although of course they later grow and, as a rule, change in proportions.

In several respects the respiratory mechanism of reptiles shows a marked advance over that of Amphibia. The lungs are more efficiently ventilated through the movement of the ribs by muscles, inflating and emptying the lungs like a bellows. Other improvements in respiration hinge on structural changes in the respiratory system, especially the heart. A partition (incomplete and still therefore "imperfect") arose in the ventricle of the heart, separating nonoxygenated blood from other blood, freshly oxygenated, returning from the lungs.

The reptiles expanded and diversified into many different habitats throughout the land (except in its coldest climates), and some even returned to the sea and competed with (and also consumed) fishes. Systematists recognize about 15 orders of the class Reptilia, living and extinct. Only four now survive (Figure 17-26). Even among these four, one is on the verge of extinction, represented only by a few individuals of a single species, *Sphenodon punctatum*, on islands off the coast of New Zealand. The other three living orders are still fairly abundant and are familiar to everyone: turtles and tortoises (Chelonia), crocodiles and alligators (Crocodilia), and lizards and snakes (Squamata). Lizards and snakes are the most abundant living reptiles. Different as the swift-running lizard and the crawling snake seem, they are closely related. There are about 2 thousand living species of each, and they occur in many habitats from the high seas (sea snakes) to the desert.

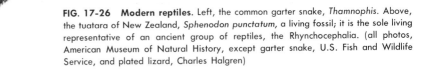

FIG. 17-26 Modern reptiles. Left, the common garter snake, *Thamnophis*. Above, the tuatara of New Zealand, *Sphenodon punctatum*, a living fossil; it is the sole living representative of an ancient group of reptiles, the Rhynchocephalia. (all photos, American Museum of Natural History, except garter snake, U.S. Fish and Wildlife Service, and plated lizard, Charles Halgren)

Above, left, musk turtles, *Aromochelys odoratus* (about 5 inches long), which inhabit rivers and lakes. Note their webbed feet; right, the American plated lizard, *Gerrhonotus*, with its eggs. This lizard (about a foot long) lives in fallen timber. Below, the salt-marsh crocodile, *Crocodilus palustris*, of southern Asia. It reaches a length of 12 feet.

The two latest and most progressive classes of land vertebrates both (but entirely separately) evolved from early reptiles. The birds, class Aves, are a group in which one key characteristic opened up a whole new realm of life. This characteristic is, of course, flight. The oldest known fossil birds (*Archaeopteryx,* "ancient wing") were still almost reptilian except in one respect: they had feathered wings. If the change had stopped there, however, birds would never have reached the great diversity and wide success that make them one of the great climaxes of evolution and that are reflected in their classification as a class.

Along with and after their acquisition of wings, birds evolved other characteristics associated with intense and sustained activity, keen perception, and rapid and varied reactions. They have high and steady metabolic rates, with precise control of the internal environment. Along with the mammals, they are the only organisms that maintain a constant temperature (that is, are homeothermous). Feathers serve not only for flight but also as insulation. As in mammals, the heart is four-chambered; it is completely divided into what are essentially two separate hearts. This represents the final step in efficient plumbing of the circulatory system in relation to lung respiration. Bird senses, especially those of vision, equilibrium, and hearing, are particularly acute. Their brains are large and are peculiarly specialized. Their behavior, although in considerable part stereotyped or instinctive, is often very complicated.

Today when there is nothing scarcer than hen's teeth, no bird has had teeth for tens of millions of years. Instead, the birds have beaks of bone covered with horn. Beaks serve not only for obtaining food, but as instruments for many purposes, from knot tying to wood boring. In their basic anatomy birds are remarkably alike. If there were no other reasons, the stringent mechanical necessities of flight would keep them so. But within the limits of the basic stereotype, they are fascinatingly diverse. The many forms of their beaks, most of which are clearly adaptive, illustrate this fact (Figure 17-27). The feet,

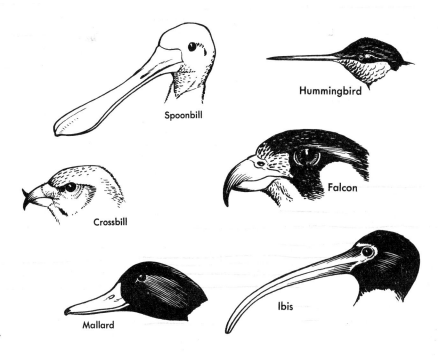

Spoonbill

Hummingbird

Crossbill

Falcon

Mallard

Ibis

FIG. 17-27 A diversity of bird beaks.

too, have numerous adaptive patterns. And everyone knows and enjoys something of the diversity of bird colors and patterns, which are in some cases protective, blending a bird into its background, and in others social, serving for recognition by other members of the group or as a stimulus to the opposite sex.

The systematics of recent birds has been worked out in better detail than that of any other animal group of comparable scope—not that all is yet well understood about this group that is so attractive to both amateur and professional zoologists. There are some 8600 living species, about half of them belonging to the single order of perching birds, which includes among many others the kingbirds, larks, swallows, crows, wrens, thrashers, thrushes (among which is the American robin), vireos, warblers, blackbirds, and sparrows. Other large and familiar orders are those of the herons and their allies; ducks, geese, and swans; the predacious birds such as the hawks; partridges, turkeys, and their many allies; gulls and their kin; owls; and woodpeckers (Figure 17-28). Modern classifications recognize 25 to 30 different orders of living birds.

As you might expect, the birds most unusual in anatomy and physiology are those that no longer have the ancestral adaptation to flight, kinds like the penguins (which still do "fly," but under water) or the ostriches. Since flight is the key characteristic of the class, how would you explain the fact that some birds cannot fly? This is a very difficult question indeed, although it is possible to find a reasonable answer.

MAMMALS

The final and (to us, at least) the supreme class of vertebrates arose from the reptiles not with the appearance of any key characteristic, such as flight, but through long-continued gradual changes in many directions. On the whole, the changes made for greater mechanical, physiological, and reproductive effectiveness in diverse ways of life. Mammals (named for the presence in the females of milk glands or *mammae*)

now occupy much of the range that was once the domain of the reptiles, although they have gone further than the reptiles ever did and although a few special kinds of reptiles still live successfully along with the mammals. Thus the mammals contrast with the birds, which by a new key adaptation entered and exploited a whole new realm of life.

Among the characters that came to stamp the mammals and that underlie their great success in the world are these:

1. Warmbloodedness (homeothermy), as in birds, and external insulation, also as in birds but by hair rather than feathers. Both characters (independently developed in the two classes) are, again, related to higher metabolism and more precise and sustained internal regulation.

2. Complex differentiation of teeth and the development of a new joint between the lower jaw and the skull. These two characters seem to be related and together to involve greater efficiency in the utilization of food. Whatever may have been the factors in their origin, they did certainly lead to remarkable later diversity and efficiency of feeding in mammals. Reptiles (and indeed all vertebrates except mammals) have several different bones in the lower jaw. Mammals have only one. In the changeover, some of the reptilian bones were incorporated in the ear, which thus also became markedly different in mammals.

3. Limbs more upright, more beneath the body, which thus comes to be carried higher off the ground. Changes in the limbs tended in general to make for more rapid and efficient locomotion. Associated were changes in the joints, with increased mechanical precision, and in the manner of growth of the long bones.

4. Increased (although still not complete) separation of the respiratory and alimentary passages; complete separation of the chambers of the heart; and the acquisition of a diaphragm. All three features improve the continuity and efficiency of respiration and thus are other concomitants of sustained metabolic maintenance.

5. Increased protection and sustenance of the young, both before and after birth, and hence greater reproductive efficiency. Fertilization and embryonic

FIG. 17-28 A variety of modern birds.
Above, left, a female marsh hawk (order Falconiformes) is about to alight. Like all its relatives, it is a bird of prey. Above, right, the great blue heron (order Ciconiiformes), a relative of the storks and ibises, feeds on fish, frogs, and small animals. Right, terns (order Charadriiformes) are marine birds that dive for their fish food.

Below, left to right, the kiwi (order Apterygiformes), a flightless bird of New Zealand, has hairlike feathers that do not form a useful vane, and its sternum lacks a well-developed keel; the blue jay (order Passeriformes), a relative of the crows, is an inverterate egg robber; a female Canada goose (order Anseriformes) sits on its eggs in a nest of reeds.

development are internal, and the embryo is nourished by the mother, through a placenta in most mammals. After birth the young continue to receive parental care and are fed on the mother's milk.

6. Greater individual modifiability of behavior, or wider behavioral reaction ranges. Increased comparative size of the brain and especially of its cerebral cortex. In the earliest mammals, and even in some of the stupider living mammals, the brain is not notably better than in some reptiles. Nevertheless, most mammals did eventually evolve brains much larger than in any other organisms.

The marsupials and placentals are clearly groups of common origin among the mammals. It was formerly believed that the marsupials were an older group and ancestral to the placentals, but on present evidence this is highly improbable. They simply diverged from a common ancestry, and many of the peculiarities of the marsupials probably are specializations that evolved in that group and not characters

formerly present in the ancestry of the placentals. The most striking of such peculiarities is that the developing embryo receives little or no nourishment from the mother while in the uterus. It is born in very immature form, crawls into a pouch on the mother's belly, hangs onto a nipple, and there completes development. You probably know that marsupials include kangaroos, wombats, and other exotic mammals of Australia, "land of marsupials" (Figure 17-29). Marsupials, mostly opossums, are, however, also abundant in North and South America and were formerly even more abundant, especially in the southern continent.

Placentals are the mammals in which the fetus is nourished (through a placenta, hence the name) within the maternal uterus until development is far advanced. Although not as diverse as they were a few million years ago, placentals (Figure 17-30) are still the dominant land vertebrates and have been throughout the Age of Mammals. A modern classification divides them into 28 orders, of which, however, only 16 have living representatives. Some species belonging to the more abundant of these orders are already quite familiar to you and well illustrate the remarkable adaptive radiation that has occurred

FIG. 17-29 Australian mammals: marsupials. Left, a kangaroo with young in its pouch. Right, A wombat, with a way of life and gross appearance similar to those of the American woodchuck. (Photos, Australian News and Information Bureau)

FIG. 17-30 Some modern placental mammals. Left, the African leopard, *Felis pardus* (order Carnivora). Right, a bat (order Chiroptera, the only true flying mammals). Flying squirrels (order Rodentia) do not really fly; they glide. (Photos, left, Charles Halgren; right, H. E. Edgerton from National Audubon Society)

Left, the porpoise *Phocaena* (order Cetacea), a relative of the whale found in all oceans of the world. Right, top, a deermouse, *Peromyscus* sp. (order Rodentia); bottom, a South American anteater, *Myrmecophaga* (order Edentata). Note the elongate snout. (Photos, left, Miami News Bureau; right, top, Charles Halgren; bottom, Ewing Galloway)

FIG. 17-31 Some modern primates. Top, left, the tarsier, *Tarsius tarsier,* the only surviving member of an ancient and primitive group of prosimian primates. Note the large eyes directed forward. Top, right, the capuchin monkey, *Cebus apella,* of South American forests. Note the long tail, which in some South American monkeys is prehensile. Bottom, left, the mandrill, *Mandrillus sphinx,* an African monkey. Like its relatives the baboons, it lives on the ground and walks four-footed like a dog. Bottom, right, the crab-eating macaque, *Macaca irus,* a South Asiatic monkey. (Photos, New York Zoological Society)

among placentals in the last 70 million years or so: shrews and moles; bats; armadillos; rabbits; squirrels, porcupines, mice, and a host of other rodents; whales; cats and dogs; elephants; horses; and pigs, camels, sheep, and cows. Placentals burrow, fly, climb, run, and swim. They eat worms, fruit, insects, grass, seaweed, squids, crustaceans, bark, coctail canapés, and each other. They live in the open sea, in tropical treetops, on Arctic ice floes, in apartment houses, and in sandy deserts.

In terms of numbers, both of species and of individuals, the outstanding placentals are the rodents. On land they swarm practically everywhere, and some are amphibious (although none are completely aquatic or marine—the only possibility they seem to have overlooked). In only one respect do they really fall short of being the dominant mammals and the climax of vertebrate evolution, but that is an important respect: they are not as smart as we are.

This is our excuse for calling the order to which we ourselves belong Primates (Latin for "the tops"). Not that all primates (Figure 17-31) are particularly intelligent. Some living primates are below the average intelligence for mammals and so, judging by the outer form of the brain known for a few of them, were the oldest primates. The order arose among the most primitive of placentals, from early Insectivora, and seems at first to have had little to distinguish it beyond the use of the forefeet as hands and an increasing coordination of visual perception and manual response. Yet somehow these primitive creatures had the potentiality to evolve the highest intelligence ever reached by any organisms. "Potentiality" in this application is not explanatory. We only know, after the fact, that they could because they did. Just what there was about them at the time that made possible that later development is not fully clear.

The earliest primates, which were abundant and lived pretty much all over the world except in Australia and South America, were prosimians ("pre-monkeys"). Some prosimians (lemurs, bush babies, tarsiers, etc.) still survive in modified and more or less specialized form in Africa, Madagascar, and southeastern Asia. From early prosimians three other major groups evolved. The New World monkeys, Ceboidea, or ceboids in the vernacular, arose in and are still confined to Central and South America. The name "ceboid" means "cebuslike." *Cebus* is the genus of common South American capuchin monkeys. Marmosets, howlers, and others also belong to this group. Throughout the warmer parts of the Eastern Hemisphere (except Australia) lived and still live the Old World monkeys, Cercopithecoidea. This name for the whole group of Old World monkeys derives from the generic name (*Cercopithecus*) of some common African monkeys. Rhesus monkeys (much used in experimentation), baboons, mandrills, and others belong to this group. Originating somewhere in that vast area of the Old World and soon spreading throughout it was the climax group of the primates, the Hominoidea ("manlike"). Formerly much more diverse, this group now includes the gibbons, great apes (orangutan, chimpanzee, and gorilla), and man.

Basic Characteristics of the Animal Phyla

You now have a passing acquaintance with the more important phyla, taken individually. For a broader understanding of animals and their diversity, the next step is to acquire an over-all view of the differences and resemblances among the phyla. Then, on this basis, something may be said about the origins and relationships of these major groups of animals.

Since the characteristics of the phyla are related to their ways of life, it might be supposed that they reflect adaptation to widely different physical environments. For instance, some phyla might be marine in origin, others fresh-water, and still others terrestrial. This is not the case. Most of the animal phyla certainly arose in the sea, and all of them may have.

TABLE 17-1   Some Characteristics of the Major Animal Phyla

Phylum	Embryonic cell layers	Digestive system	Coelom	Circulatory system	Segmentation	Symmetry	Other features of adults probably primitive for phylum
Porifera	Indistinct	No special organ	None	Absent	Absent	Radial	Sessile. Microscopic food ingested from flagella-produced currents.
Coelenterata	Two	Pouchlike; one opening	None	Absent	Absent	Radial	Sessile. Food captured by tentacles with stinging cells.
Platy-helminthes	Three	Tubular; two openings		Absent	Absent	Bilateral	Motile. Flattened, wormlike. Passive or immobilized animal food.
Nematoda	Three	Tubular; two openings	Pseudocoel	Absent	Absent	Bilateral	Motile. Cylindrical, wormlike. Early becoming parasitic or including some parasites.
Bryozoa	Three	Tubular; two openings	True coelom	Absent	Absent	Bilateral	Sessile but bilateral. External skeleton. Flagellated tentacles. Early becoming colonial.
Brachiopoda	Three	Tubular; two openings	True coelom	Absent	Absent	Bilateral	Sessile but bilateral. Dorsal and ventral shells. Flagellated tentacles inside shells. Noncolonial.
Mollusca	Three	Tubular; two openings	True coelom	Present	Absent	Bilateral	Motile, creeping on a ventral foot. Shelled (but primitive form of shell uncertain).
Annelida	Three	Tubular; two openings	True coelom	Present	Present and similar in the two phyla	Bilateral	Motile. Cylindrical, wormlike. Bristle appendages.
Arthropoda	Three	Tubular; two openings	True coelom	Present	Present and similar in the two phyla	Bilateral	Highly motile. Jointed legs. External skeleton.
Echino-dermata	Three	Tubular; two openings	True coelom	Present	Absent	Secondarily radial	Sessile or sedentary. Heavy protective skeleton. Noncolonial.
Chordata	Three	Tubular; two openings	True coelom	Present	Present, different from that in annelids and arthropods	Bilateral	Highly motile. Internal skeleton aiding propulsion.

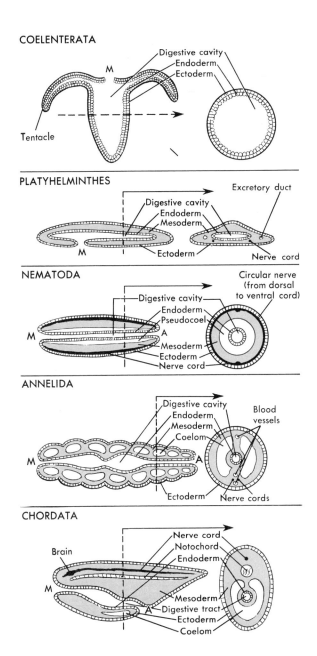

COELENTERATA

Tentacle
M
Digestive cavity
Endoderm
Ectoderm

PLATYHELMINTHES

Excretory duct
Digestive cavity
Endoderm
Mesoderm
M
Ectoderm
Nerve cord

NEMATODA

Circular nerve
(from dorsal
to ventral cord)
Digestive cavity
Endoderm
Pseudocoel
A
M
Mesoderm
Ectoderm
Nerve cord

ANNELIDA

Digestive cavity
Endoderm
Mesoderm
Coelom
Blood
vessels
M
A
Ectoderm
Nerve cords

CHORDATA

Brain
Nerve cord
Notochord
Endoderm
M
Mesoderm
A
Digestive tract
Ectoderm
Coelom

FIG. 17-32 Characteristics of some animal phyla. M, mouth; A, anus.

Most phyla include both marine and fresh-water species. Although both environments are aquatic, they may involve radically different physiological adaptations. Several groups, notably the nematodes and annelids, are abundant in damp soil, an environment not greatly different from fresh water in its physiological restrictions. Only three phyla include strictly terrestrial groups, animals capable of carrying on all their life activities in the open air: Mollusca (the fully terrestrial forms are the land snails), Arthropoda (insects, spiders, and some others), and Chordata (reptiles, birds, and mammals). These, too, include many marine and freshwater animals, and they are evidently of marine origin. Some of their lines of evolution became adapted to the most stringent of all physical environments, the land, where life is so difficult that no other phyla have been able to cope with it. Yet the groups that did become terrestrial underwent no major changes; no new phyla emerged. It is significant that the three phyla that did conquer the terrestrial environment are also extremely successful in aquatic environments and are much the most varied and, in many respects, the most progressive of all the phyla.

The basic differences among phyla are striking anatomical features concerned with such processes as nutrition, internal transportation and maintenance, organ differentiation, coordination, and locomotion. All these features are closely interrelated. They add up to a distinct over-all structural and functional pattern for each phylum. Table 17-1 and Figure 17-32 summarize some of the outstanding characteristics of the major phyla. The characteristics listed are not necessarily present in all the living members of each phylum but are believed to be primitive for the phylum, to have occurred in its earliest and ancestral members.

Summary

What is an animal? The difficulty of definition in protists; major animal characteristics—metabolism (nonphotosynthetic), mobility, definite adult form with complex tissue and organ differentiation and a general absence of rigid cell walls and cell vacuoles, maintenance of an internal environment (with high sodium chloride content), high sensitivity and responsiveness (associated with nervous tissue), an absence of development in the haplophase of the reproductive cycle.

Major animal phyla:

Porifera (sponges): colonies of semi-independent cells, aquatic and sessile; feeding-current mechanism.

Coelenterata (polyps and medusas): single opening to digestive cavity; tentacles and carnivorus nature; polyp and medusa; hydroids, siphonophores, jellyfishes, sea anemones, corals.

Platyhelminthes (flatworms): flat body with one opening to digestive cavity; common parasitism.

Nematoda (threadworms): anus present; parasitism and abundance.

Annelida (segmented worms): earthworms and their soil-eating habits; marine annelids; free-swimming and tube-living forms; leeches, annelids.

Arthropods: immense numbers, diversity, and ubiquity; characters: the seven classes.
  Crustacea: the familiarity of the decapods; the diversity of other crustacean types.
  Arachnids: the undeserved bad reputation, since there are more useful than harmful species; the four or five pairs of appendages; diagnostic characters.
  Insects: their success and diversity (at least one-half of all living organisms, but no marine types); primarily terrestrial habitat; factors responsible for size restriction; the exoskeleton and the respiratory and circulatory systems; organization, as exemplified by the grasshopper; winged and wingless insects.

Mollusks: the classes.
  Gastropods: slow gait; shell; marine origin; terrestrial forms with lungs; adaptive diversity.
  Pelecypods: bivalves; mostly sedentary habit; adaptive diversity.
  Cephalopods: organization; fast movement, with jet propulsion; complex brain and image-forming eyes; predatory nature; history and diversity.
  Echinodermata: sea lilies, starfishes, brittle stars, sea urchins, sea cucumbers; radial symmetry; water-vascular system; tube feet; skeleton; marine habitat.
  Chordata (animals "with a chord," the notochord); Hemichordata (acorn worms); Urochordata (tunicates); Cephalochordata (amphioxus); possession of a notochord, dorsal nerve cord, and pharyngeal gill slits.

Vertebrates: a subphylum of the Chordata; the most progressive and important of all animal groups; their awareness of their environment and their complexity of behavior; the eight classes; agnathus and Placoderms.
  Chondrichthyans: the cartilaginous fishes; a marine group, exemplified by sharks and rays; urea and osmotic regulation; internal fertilization.
  Osteichthyans: the bony fishes; both fresh-water and marine.
  Amphibians: their origin from early osteichthyans; the role of lungs and limbs in their origin; modern amphibians—their locomotion, larvae, metamorphosis, specialization, and divergence from early forms.

Reptiles: the restriction of amphibians to watery environments; reptiles as their descendants and the first true land vertebrates; key adaptation: shelled eggs and internal fertilization; lung ventilation and the partitioning of the ventricle; the four surviving orders.

Birds: descendants of the early reptiles; bird adaptations to land life, permitting sustained high activity; the development of body-temperature control; improved respiration and circulation; the development of the brain and sense organs; the loss of teeth; the specialization of beaks; the classification of modern birds; flightless birds.

Mammals: descendants of the early reptiles; the supreme class of vertebrates; major mammalian characters, contrasted with those of reptiles—body-temperature control, more complex teeth, more upright limbs and more rapid locomotion, improved respiration and circulation, protection and sustenance of the young (including the evolution of placenta and milk glands), the elaboration of the nervous system and behavior; marsupials, with primitive or aberrant reproduction; placentals—represented by 28 orders; the primates of special interest because of their relation to man—their origin from insectivores, coordination of the hands and eyes as creating the potentiality for evolution of higher intelligence, their diversity.

PART SEVEN

THE LIFE OF POPULATIONS
AND COMMUNITIES

The forest in this photograph is a community made up of many species. Each species, such as the pine trees, exists as a population of individuals. Associated with the pines will be populations of other species—aspen trees, grasses, insects, mice, hawks, and the rest—which collectively form the integrated forest community. One of the most striking facts of life is that individual organisms do not, because they cannot, live a wholly solitary existence. They are bound together by one cause or another—by sex, by social ties, by sharing common needs satisfied only by a particular habitat, and, above all, by dependence on one another for shelter and food. This interdependence of organisms dominates the entire subject of ecology, the study of organism-environment relationships; it raises problems and demands explanatory principles of its own, which are the topics of Part 7.

Throughout this section of the book we shall be examining communities and their constituent populations as unit living systems much as in some earlier parts we considered the individual organism as a unit living system. But this approach—of treating populations as units of life—is of course not new to you; in Part 5 on the mechanism of evolution we had to begin (Chapter 12) with a population as an entity whose genetic constitution (genetic pool) is the fundamental unit subject to evolutionary change.

Chapter 18 reviews biologically important features of the environment and some relationships to them of populations and communities. The cyclic flows of materials and the one-way transfers of energy constitute a sort of over-all metabolism of communities and their environments.

Chapter 19 considers some specific features of community organization, especially the lines of transfer of energy and materials and their consequences. Interspecific relationships within communities include consumption, competition, and the more intimately individual associations collectively known as symbiosis. Changes within communities include especially, within the human time scale, successions leading to climaxes. The dynamics of communities also involve the growth, decline, and cyclic or periodic changes in population size and the intraspecific interactions involved in population organization. These include cooperative aggregations culminating in societies.

In Chapter 20 the human species is treated as a biological population from a systematic and ecological point of view. The impact and dependence of this extraordinary society on natural communities are reviewed.

Chapter 21 notes that the distribution of any species of organism is ultimately limited by the distribution of suitable environments. The distribution of cacti within the Americas is limited by climate; the absence of cacti from the wet floors of American rain forests is explained by the ecological fact that they are not adapted to conditions of high moisture and low sunlight. The principle applies to all species, although the limiting environmental conditions are rarely so clearly defined as they are for cacti. However, the distributions of organisms are only partially explained by the limited distributions of their appropriate environments. Deserts occur in Africa, but cacti do not. Full explanation of such cases demands introduction of strictly historical principles. Species arise in a particular region, and in the course of time they disperse, expanding into suitable environments elsewhere. Their dispersal is, of course, contingent on some continuity of suitable habitats.

ENVIRONMENTS, POPULATIONS, AND COMMUNITIES

No organism is ever for even an instant independent of the requirements and advantages of the environment in which it lives. None lives without constantly influencing its surroundings. You cannot possibly think of an organism to which both these generalizations do not apply, and you need only to look around you to find examples of them. You would dress and feel differently if the temperature of your environment were other than it happens to be at the moment. You would not continue to live at all if the medium around you were not air but water, as it is for so many other organisms. As with every other living thing, your life depends strictly on conditions of the physical environment. Your environment also includes other people, the whole of the population of which you are a part. It, too, profoundly influences your life, and, again, interaction with the population as part of the environment normally occurs in all organisms. Moreover, you are completely dependent on other populations, other species of organisms, for many of the materials that make up your body and all of the energy that keeps you going. Like you, all organisms live in communities of numerous different species and participate in the flow of materials and energy through the various specific populations.

Within a few hours or less you will be hungry, a signal that the energy and materials of your tissues need to be renewed. Perhaps you will eat a hamburger and thus transfer to yourself energy and materials previously acquired, transformed, and stored by another animal. That animal got them from plants, perhaps from grass. The grass, in its turn, acquired materials from the air and from water and solutions in the soil. The energy used in syntheses in the grass and stored in the products came from the sun. The substance of your body has come, mostly through the medium of other organisms, from the air, water, and watery solutions of the earth. All your energy was derived, through the same intermediaries, from atomic energy generated in nuclear reactions some 93 million miles away, which, incidentally, is an excellent distance at which to be from nuclear reactions. (Are there any substances in your body that were not derived from other organisms? Is there any of your energy that was not?)

Many other factors influenced the passage of materials and energy from earth and sun to you. The grass was rooted in soil. The properties of the soil that determined the possibility and the amount of growth of grass depended on many things: composition of rocks in the crust of the earth; weathering, erosion, and deposition; climate; movement of ground water; activities of earthworms, bacteria, and innumerable other organisms within the soil; effects, past and present, of plants at the given locality; and so on, through a list too long to make complete. And not only the soil affected the grass. Its growth was also directly influenced by sun, wind, rain, temperatures, insects, rodents, grazing animals, and many other things. The presence of the grass also depended on a long sequence of prior events, such as the development and growth of seeds through generation after generation, the origin of this species of grass and the long evolution of its ancestry back to the beginning of life, and indeed the still older origin of the planet on which life could and did arise.

There is nothing particularly new to you in all this, although you have perhaps not looked at it in just this way before. In turning to discussion of communities in which numerous organisms live together, we find, again, that we are not taking up a completely new and separate topic, but are simply looking more closely at a particular aspect of the living world, all aspects of which are inseparably related to all others. Everyone has some idea of the existence of communities in nature and of relationships of populations and environments, and up to this point such general knowledge has been assumed. To organize and extend such common knowledge, we shall now consider first the environment, basic relationships between populations and environments, and some consequent fundamentals of material and energy transfers in communities.

Environment

The word "environment" has been used repeatedly in previous chapters without being defined. As good a definition as any is that environment is the totality of extrinsic things and conditions affecting an organism. In this broad sense the environment includes several distinct but simultaneous and (of course) interacting phases. It includes, first, the nonliving aspects of the place where an organism lives—its *physical environment*. It includes, too, all the living things that affect the organism—its *biotic environment*.

THE PHYSICAL ENVIRONMENT

All organisms live in water or in air. (Even those that live within the soil are effectively surrounded either by water or by air.) That is the most fundamental feature of the physical environment. The conditions of life are very different in water and in air, and most organisms are confined to one or the other.

Radiation and Climate

Organisms that live in air are profoundly affected by weather and climate, and aquatic animals are similarly affected by such factors as temperature. One of the most important factors in such conditions is *radiation*. Radiation important to living things is mainly in the form of electromagnetic waves from the sun. Radiation that we call "light," because our eyes (and those of most other animals) are sensitive to it, is most intense. (Do you think that is a coincidence?) Organisms are also sensitive in other ways to solar radiation of shorter (ultraviolet) and longer (infrared, or heat rays) wavelengths.

The importance of solar radiation cannot be overstressed because (with insignificant exceptions) it supplies all the energy available for all the processes of life in all organisms. This is the income from which all the life activity on earth must be budgeted. The influence of radiation in any particular local environment follows from this basic fact. Green plants, primary converters of solar energy into vital energy, grow only where solar radiation is received. The amount of their activity is limited by, and is roughly proportional to, the average amount of radiation in a given environment. The activities of other organisms are, in turn, limited by those of the green plants from which, directly or indirectly, practically all their energy and materials must come.

Environments with little or no solar radiation have no green plants. They are inhabited only by animals, some nongreen plants (mostly fungi), and certain protists (especially among the bacteria). These organisms in lightless environments necessarily depend on organic foods that are somehow brought in from elsewhere, from environments that do receive solar radiation. Offhand you might think that environments without solar radiation would be quite limited: caves, for instance, which do have an interesting, sparse population but are of no great importance. Actually, however, such environments are more extensive than any others. They include the soil, below its most superficial layer, and the vast reaches of the sea below the depths to which daylight penetrates.

TABLE 18-1 *Expenditure of Solar Energy at Lake Mendota*

Expenditure	Per cent of solar energy received
Reflected or otherwise lost	49.5
Absorbed in evaporation of water	25.0
Raising temperatures in the lake	21.7
Melting ice in the spring	3.0
Directly used by organisms	0.8

Where does the food of soil organisms come from? Of deep-sea organisms?

Less solar energy is converted directly into vital energy than is expended in changing and maintaining the *temperature* of the environment. Expenditures of solar energy have been calculated (by C. Juday) for Lake Mendota in southern Wisconsin, as shown in Table 18-1.

The figures are quite different in other environments, but everywhere only a small fraction of radiation is used directly by green plants, and a much

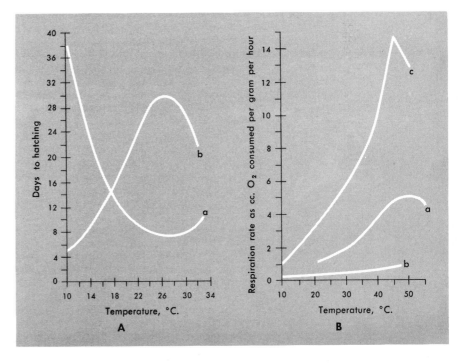

FIG. 18-1 **Temperature and the rate of metabolism.** A. The effect of temperature on the rate of development in the insect *Sitona*: a, the number of days required to complete egg development at different temperatures: b, the reciprocal of curve a, representing the velocity of development. Note how the velocity increases with rising temperature up to about 29°C and decreases at higher temperatures; 29°C is the optimum temperature. B. The effect of temperature on the rate of respiration in a species of fly: a, in the larval stage; b, in the pupal stage; c, in the adult. The rates of metabolism, as measured by the rates of oxygen consumption, are very different for the three stages of the life cycle, but in all of them metabolic rate increases with rising temperature. The curves for the larval and adult stages again show the existence of an optimum temperature; above the optimum the rate of metabolism decreases again. How would you expect the optimum temperature to relate to the distribution of the species in nature?

larger part goes to warm the water or air. (In the example of the lake most of the energy tabulated as lost heats the air above the lake.) Maintenance of environmental temperature is another necessity for life as we know it, which can exist only in the range of temperatures that is, in fact, maintained on earth by solar radiation. Metabolic activities are very strongly influenced by the temperatures of organisms (Figure 18-1), and in all plants and most animals the internal temperature depends largely on that of the environment. (What are the exceptions?) Specific adaptations of plants and animals are also related to the averages and ranges of temperatures in particular environments. You know, for instance, that orange trees require sustained warmth but apple trees thrive in regions with low winter temperatures, and that polar bears live only in the cold north and boa constrictors only in the tropics.

Evaporation maintains the *humidity* of the atmosphere and is the power-input phase in the *water cycle* (Figure 18-2). Involved are *rainfall* by condensation of evaporated water in the atmosphere and consequent maintenance of streams, lakes, and water beneath the

surface of the ground (ground water). The cycle thus provides the whole of the fresh-water environment and also the enormous quantities of water required by land organisms. No farmer needs to be told that water supply is a crucial factor in the activity of plant life, and the contrast (in both plants and animals) between a well-watered New England hillside and a dry Arizona desert is well known.

Movement of water or air is another feature of the physical environment. All these factors ramify and interlock; both in water and in air movement helps to determine the distribution of temperatures, and air movement is a crucial element for rainfall. Winds and currents also influence organisms more directly in many ways. Innumerable land plants, among them the conifers and many grasses, are wind-pollinated.

Microclimates and Niches

The weather, and hence the climate, of our immediate surroundings may be quite different from that recorded by the Weather Bureau. For an organism a few inches under the soil the temperature is usually different and always less variable than for one on the surface. The climate on the floor of a forest is decidedly cooler, less sunny, more humid, and less windy than the climate in the tops of the trees (Figure 18-3). Organisms generally have small climates,

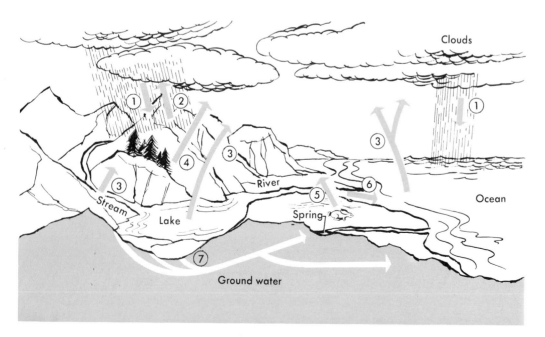

FIG. 18-2 The water cycle.
1. Precipitation as rain or snow.
2. Immediate return to the atmosphere through evaporation. 3. Evaporation from bodies of water—streams, lakes, ocean. 4. Transpiration from plants. 5. Transpiration from animals. 6, 7. Drainage from streams and ground water, ultimately to the ocean.

A STRATUM OF "EXPOSURE" SPECIES

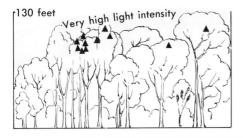

B STRATUM OF "SUN" SPECIES

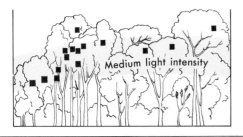

C STRATUM OF "SHADE" SPECIES

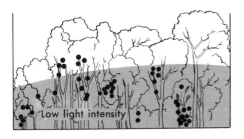

FIG. 18-3 The stratification of forest microclimates. The existence and ecological significance of differences in microclimates is well illustrated by the vertical distribution in a forest of epiphytic ferns, orchids, and bromeliads that grow on the trees' branches. Each epiphytic species has its particular requirements for temperature, moisture, and light. The marked vertical gradients in these environmental factors result in an equally pronounced stratification in the distribution of the various epiphytic species. The figure shows the vertical distribution of three groups of bromeliad species in a South American rain forest: one of the groups (A) occurs only in the highest levels of the forest, where its demand for extremely high light intensities is met; another (B) demands moderate light intensity; and the third (C) requires shade and high humidity.

microclimates, of their own, which are quite diverse and more or less different from the idealized regional climate.

Similarly, particular organisms do not really live in a regional environment, such as a "forest environment," but in small environments of their own. Animals burrowing in the mold, running along the

ground, lurking under bark, or flitting through branches certainly have very different personal environments, both physical and biotic. The microenvironment of a particular species is one aspect of its *niche* (pronounced "nitch"). Every regional environment has a large number of different niches.

The Chemical Environment: Air and Soil

Thanks to its constant and often rapid and turbulent motion, the composition of dry air is much the same almost everywhere: by volume about 78 per cent nitrogen, 21 per cent oxygen, and 0.03 per cent carbon dioxide. Variations affecting organisms are those of water content, already mentioned, and local concentrations of gases, mostly due to human activities.

Soils have a special interest because the lives of nearly all land organisms, including man, depend largely on soil. The bulk of a soil is composed of grains of minerals, especially a mixture of silica (the mineral of common sand) and clays. The mixture is formed by disintegration and decomposition of underlying rocks, or from silts and other sediments washed in by streams or blown by the wind. Among the particles of the soil are spaces, generally from a third to a half of the volume of the soil, occupied by air or water. Water in the interstices of soil is the source of most of the great amounts of water required by land plants. It is also a complex solution from which are drawn many of the other materials incorporated in all sorts of land organisms.

Soils well illustrate the fact that the contrast between physical and biotic environments is not absolute. These aspects of the environment also interact. Soil is penetrated by roots, which change it both physically (for instance, by loosening up its packed particles) and chemically (for instance, by withdrawing mineral salts from it). As plants die, parts of their organic materials are incorporated in the soil. Those organic materials, as well as parts of living plants in the soil, provide food for incredibly huge numbers of bacteria, algae, fungi, nematodes, earthworms, and other organisms. These soil organisms further modify the physical and chemical characteristics of the soil and add their excretions and dead bodies to its contents. Soil is thus itself a populous and complex community in which the inorganic and the organic interact endlessly and inextricably.

THE BIOTIC ENVIRONMENT

By definition, the biotic environment of an organism includes all the living things that affect it. Here at the outset one major distinction may be made among the various members of a community viewed as the biotic environment of any particular organism in it. There is a fundamental difference between the environmental relationships of members of different species and those among members of the same species. The members of different species have different roles; they occupy different niches. They, therefore, constitute an *interspecific* ("among species") *environment*. Members of the same species have, if not quite the same, at least more closely similar roles and niches. For any individual of the species they are its *intraspecific* ("within species") *environment*.

Population and Environment

We have repeatedly noted that different kinds of organisms have different environmental needs or, to put it in a converse way, that different environments (or different niches) provide opportunities for different kinds of organisms. Many such relationships are indeed obvious to anyone who stops to think about them. Here we shall mention some of the principles that emerge in this new context. They arise from facts already becoming familiar to you, and some of them will be further developed in later chapters from different points of view. The subject we are starting to consider in this chapter is broadly called *ecology*.

RANGE, LIMITS, AND OPTIMUM

There is no such thing as a constant environment. The deep sea is the most nearly constant major environment, but even there some changes occur. The deep sea is also the most difficult major environment, for it is characterized by low temperature, great pressure, no light, and hence no production of food within the community. It is perhaps the fact that these conditions, although stringent, are relatively unvarying that has made adaptation to them possible at all. Elsewhere change is frequent and striking: summer and winter in temperate and frigid zones; rainy and dry seasons in the tropics; daily temperature changes, rain and drought, strong and feeble sunlight, and other changes everywhere.

Every individual and every species must be able to live under not one, fixed environmental circumstance but a whole *range* of environmental circumstances. Nevertheless, the range within which life can continue indefinitely always has *limits*. No plant and only the relatively few homeothermous animals can long remain active in environmental temperatures below their own freezing points, and hence no species lives continuously in environments constantly much below about 0°C. All organisms die from heat at temperatures well below 100°C, the boiling point of water. Different species differ markedly as to both the extents of their temperature ranges and the positions of those ranges on the temperature scale. Pine trees survive both greater cold and greater heat than bananas; their total range is wider. The algae of warm springs cannot live at all in the range of arctic algae; the positions of the ranges are different. Similar differences in range exist for all environmental conditions—salinity of water, acidity or alkalinity of soil, light intensity, and the rest.

Within its range, each organism and each species generally has a point or a much more limited range where it does best, its *optimum*. Optima exist for all environmental factors and all vital processes. This is another reason why every species has a range, and not merely an optimum, for each environmental condition under which it lives. It would be a rare coincidence if the optimum for one condition, say temperature, were invariably accompanied by the optimum for another, such as humidity. The existence of optima and the unlikelihood of different optima in a single environment stress again the importance of homeothermy and other controls of the internal environment. Such controls keep the cells and organs of a body within their ranges and near their optima. Thereby the ranges of external environmental conditions within which an organism can survive are widened.

TOLERATION AND PREFERENCES

We say that a plant or animal *tolerates* the range of environments within which it can live and that it *prefers* environments in all respects nearest its optima. Although the words "tolerance" and "preference" are scientifically acceptable in this connection, they are dangerously anthropomorphic: we can never for plants and rarely if ever for animals assume that they mean at all the same as when we apply them to ourselves. Yet we can accept them as vivid metaphors applicable to ranges and optima. It was noted in Chapter 1 that ponderosa pines are intolerant of shade, and horticulturalists often classify trees as tolerant or intolerant, accordingly. Cacti are tolerant of dry, sandy soil; irises are not. Clams are tolerant of cool, brackish, muddy water; corals are not. Additional examples are so numerous that you can supply hundreds for yourself.

ADAPTATION AND ADAPTABILITY

The means by which species meet their needs in different environments and by which environmental niches are parceled out among different species are almost incredibly varied. Some of them have already been discussed in Chapter 13, in connection with their evolutionary explanations and implications, and others will be discussed in Chapter 19. We mention them here only to emphasize their ecological pertinence, thus tying up another of the many interconnections that unify the whole widely branching subject of biology. You will recall that the ability of a species to tolerate particular ranges of environmental conditions is achieved in the course of evolution by three processes: (1) genetic adaptation of a whole population to develop normally and reproduce in a certain environment; (2) genetic

variability within a population, giving demes and individuals different tolerances and optima and thus permitting the population as a whole to maintain itself in changing environments; and (3) individual adaptation (in genetically determined reaction ranges), permitting adjustment to changed conditions even within an individual lifetime.

COMMUNITY AND ENVIRONMENT

For the rest of this chapter and most of the next we shall consider another phase of organism-environment interaction—that involving entire, integrated communities and relationships among rather than within populations. In Chapter 1 the traffic in materials and energy in living things was introduced as a theme to be followed up later. We now turn to a detailed consideration of that traffic in communities.

CYCLES OF MATERIALS

The Carbon Cycle

The flow of carbon in communities is one of the most essential features of their metabolism of organic compounds. The great reservoir of carbon in nonorganic form and the source of almost all the carbon incorporated in organisms is the CO_2 in the atmosphere and dissolved in the waters of the earth. The usual first step in the utilization of carbon as a material in living things is photosynthesis by green plants (Chapter 4). The carbon thus becomes part of simple carbohydrates, and later syntheses in the same plants transfer part of it into polysaccharides, proteins, lipids, and other complex organic compounds. Animals eat plants, and the organic compounds are digested and resynthesized (Chapter 4). Other animals eat the meat-eating animals, with still more digestions and resyntheses. Thus carbon is transferred from one organism to another through a shorter or longer, sometimes very long, sequence. In the course of the sequence, and even within any one organism of the series, the carbon atoms are constantly shifted from one kind of molecule to another. But as long as it is a vital part of an organism the carbon is in some organic compound of greater or less complexity.

Eventually most of the organic carbon becomes a part of CO_2 again and is returned to the inorganic realm of water and air. This return phase is an essential part of the cycle that has kept life going since early in its history, as the available carbon has continuously circled from air and water through plants and animals and back to air and water again. Some of the return is fairly direct. CO_2 is an end product of respiration in both plants and animals, and the respired CO_2 passes at once into the water or air of the organism's immediate environment, where it is available to start the cycle all over again.

Much carbon remains in the tissues of organisms when they die, or is eliminated by animals in waste products that are still fairly complex organic compounds, not usable as a carbon source in photosynthesis. If this carbon were not somehow converted into CO_2, life would have come to an end by now. All the available carbon would be locked up in organic but nonliving form. Here is the role of the organisms of decay or putrefaction, most of which are bacteria or fungi. They attack and digest the organic materials of dead plants and animals and of excretions, reducing them to the simpler and energy-poor compounds with which the various cycles of materials and energy begin. After their work is completed, most of the carbon of organic compounds has become CO_2 again.

Some carbon is withdrawn from the cycle for long periods, if not permanently. Not all the organic compounds of dead organisms have decayed; some have been incorporated in the crust of the earth as coal, petroleum, and natural gas. By burning these, man makes their carbon again available for the organic cycle. Before man, there was little return of this stored carbon, even though some of it was liberated by combustion and by bacteria. An even larger amount of carbon is locked up in limestone, the principal mineral of which has the composition $CaCO_3$. Much, but by no means all, limestone is

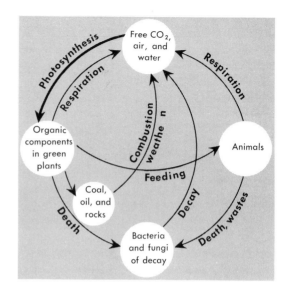

FIG. 18-4   The carbon cycle.

a result of the activities of life. Coral reefs provide a clear example of life-made limestone. The carbon of limestone may be released as CO_2 by natural processes, such as the action of weathering and natural acids, but much limestone is now deep in the earth, where its carbon will not be available for a very long time, if ever.

The most striking features of the whole carbon cycle are summed up in Figure 18-4.

The Nitrogen Cycle

Nitrogen is no less essential to life than carbon. It is, as you know, part of all amino acids, proteins, and nucleic acids. Its cycle is similar to that of carbon and goes on at the same time, but there are some distinctive features.

As we have seen (Chapter 2), nitrogen makes up the greatest part of the atmosphere, but green plants can use little or no atmospheric nitrogen (N_2) in their syntheses—a marked contrast with carbon, which (as CO_2) is mainly derived from the air by green plants. Green plants require nitrogen as ammonia (NH_3) or in the form of nitrates (salts containing NO_3), and these are obtained from the nitrogen-fixing bacteria of soil, which can utilize N_2 directly in the synthesis of their own amino acids and proteins (Chapter 2). Some nitrogen-fixing bacteria live independently in the soil, and some live in nodules in roots of other plants, especially the legumes, members of the pea family. In either location, their death frees nitrogen compounds, which can be utilized by other plants, and particularly green plants. The nitrogen of green plants, thus acquired either from ammonia and nitrates in the soil or from nitrogen-fixing bacteria, may be passed on to animals that eat plants, and then from animal to animal, as carbon is.

As with carbon, too, nitrogen is excreted by animals (in urea, for instance) and also remains in the tissues of dead organisms. Again, it is mainly bacteria that return this locked-up nitrogen to the cycle. Bacteria of decay produce ammonia from proteins and other

nitrogenous compounds. Other bacteria, *nitrifying bacteria,* oxidize ammonia to nitrites, and still others perform further oxidation to nitrates. Thus inorganic nitrogen compounds directly utilizable by green plants are restored to the soil.

It may be a little misleading to speak of *the* carbon cycle and *the* nitrogen cycle. You can see that the pattern of flow, even simplified as it is in Figures 18-4 and 18-5, does not have a single, circular course that carbon or nitrogen necessarily follows. The

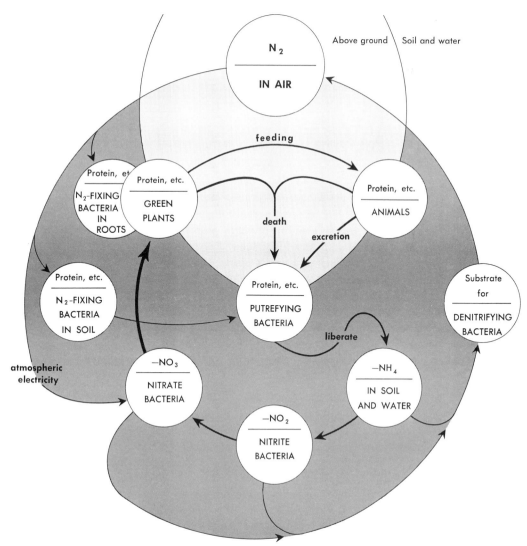

FIG. 18-5 The nitrogen cycle.

patterns are more complex, each with a number of different paths that the two elements may follow in a cyclic manner. The simplest course for nitrogen is soil → plants → bacteria → soil, and so around again and again. What is the simplest cycle for carbon?

Consideration of all the organic cycles shows that green plants and putrefactive bacteria *must* be present if life is to continue indefinitely with a cyclic flow of materials and energy. Animals are unnecessary. In the total metabolism of life they are a side issue or an extra step that complicates the process without really contributing to it.

Mineral Cycles

Analogy with the carbon and nitrogen cycles and what you have learned elsewhere in this and previous chapters are sufficient for you to work out the essentials of the water and oxygen cycles. (The water cycle is also summarized in Figure 18-2.) The mineral cycles have some features of special interest and merit a diagram (Figure 18-6) and some additional comments. Before reading these comments, review Chapter 2, on the inorganic materials of life.

With few and unimportant exceptions, the inorganic sources of all the mineral elements necessary to organisms are salts in solution in water, whether in the soil or in bodies of water. (Even so-called fresh water is in fact a dilute solution of many mineral salts, among other things.) The salt-solution phase is a part of two great cycles in nature, cycles that interlock through this phase. One, the *rock cycle,* is inorganic in essence, although it is strongly influenced by organisms, and organisms may even have direct parts in it. The mineral salts of the earth came originally, and more are still coming, from the crust of the earth. They are formed and liberated from rocks of the crust mainly by processes summed up as weathering: disintegration, and decomposition under the influence of air, water, and organisms. The soluble salts arising among the products of these processes then enter the *water cycle.* With the water, they move through soil, streams, and lakes and eventually into the sea. As they pass through this cycle, perhaps with

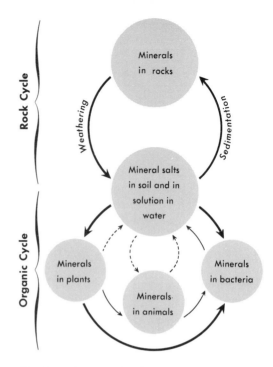

FIG. 18-6   The mineral cycle.

long stops during the trip, they are available to organisms in all the environments of life. Most of them eventually reach the oceans, where much salt remains indefinitely. Some of the mineral salts do complete a cycle and return to the crust of the earth through the processes of sedimentation. Trace through each of the cycles in Figure 18-6.

TRANSFERS OF ENERGY

We learned in Chapters 2 and 4 that all the activities of the living organism—running a race, moving a hand, the heartbeat, even thinking—require an expenditure of energy. Even a plant standing motionless in a field is continually using energy in the syntheses within its living cells. The utilization and transfer of energy as fundamental features of the living world were stressed in these early chapters, where our emphasis was on the cell and the individual organism. Here we are concerned with energy transfers again—this time in relation to whole populations and communities of organisms.

Two generalizations about energy—the capacity

to perform work—may be recalled from Chapter 2. (1) Energy may be potential or kinetic. A boulder on a hilltop has potential energy that becomes kinetic ("pertaining to motion") when it rolls downhill. (2) Energy assumes many different forms [mechanical, chemical, electrical, radiant (light), thermal (heat)] and may be transformed from one kind to another.

Transfers and transformations of energy are governed by the laws of thermodynamics (Chapter 2). The first law, as we recall, relates to the conservation of energy. Whenever transfers or transformations of energy occur, there is neither gain nor loss in the total energy involved in the transaction. The significance of the first law of thermodynamics for living things lies in their capacity to release the potential energy within the structures of organic molecules or, conversely, to capture energy (such as that of sunlight) by transforming it into the potential energy of chemical structure. You are already familiar with the main metabolic processes that make these energy transfers possible: the exergonic reactions of carbohydrate metabolism and oxidative phosphorylation and the endergonic reactions of photosynthesis.

The second law of thermodynamics is equally important in the processes of life. It tells us that as energy is transferred from one substance to another or transformed from one form to another, less and less of the total energy is utilizable in further transfers and transformations. Although the *total* amount cannot change, the amount that is available to perform work of any sort, chemical, mechanical, or other, becomes steadily smaller. The *usable* energy in a sequence of transfers tends to run down, and the whole process will come to a stop unless there is a continuing input of energy from somewhere.

We reintroduce the laws of thermodynamics simply to emphasize again their significance for the activities of living things. In the cycles of *materials,* such as carbon or nitrogen, nothing is lost or necessarily becomes unusable. All the materials that start the cycle are (or, at least, can be) returned to their original

form after going through the cycle, and then they are ready to start around again. There is no reason why the process should not go on forever without addition of anything from outside. *This is not true of energy.* The energy received by an organism cannot be destroyed (that would violate the first law), but it is *dissipated,* scattered in such forms (mainly as heat transferred to the environment) that it can no longer be used by that organism or by others.

Thus organisms pass on to others less energy than they received. When a herbivore eats a plant, it receives chemical energy, but the energy received is much less than the energy that the plant received from the sun. A carnivore, in turn, acquires chemical energy by eating a herbivore, but it receives from the herbivore much less energy than the latter received from the plants it ate. When, finally, the organisms of decay end the sequence, they pass on the materials of life in forms that are utilizable by other organisms, but they practically complete the dissipation of energy in the community. In fact, the flow of *energy* in a community is not a cycle at all. It is a one-way sequence in which vital energy, like all energy, follows the second law and becomes continuously less available.

Since communities do keep going, and have for billions of years, energy is obviously coming in to them continually from an outside source to compensate for what has been lost. The source is the sun, and it, too, is subject to the second law. Some day all its energy will no longer be in usable form. Then life on earth will no longer be possible, but the event is billions of years in the future, so far away that some other catastrophe may wipe out the earth's life long before then. As to where the energy of the sun came from to begin with, the only honest *scientific* answer at present is, "We do not know."

Summary

Environment: extrinsic things and conditions affecting an organism; physical and biotic environments; the physical environment—solar radiation, the water cycle, the movement of air and water, microclimates and niches, the chemical environment, the air, the soil; the biotic environment—all living things affecting the organism, inter- and intraspecific environments.

Population and environment: the ranges of environmental conditions; limits at the ranges; differences in the ranges as to extent and position on the scale; optima and their relationship to range and to internal regulation; toleration and preference and their effects on the occurrence of species; adaptation and adaptability.

Community and environment: cycles of transfer of material and energy; the carbon cycle; the nitrogen cycle; mineral cycles; transfers of energy; the first law of thermodynamics—conservation of total energy; the second law of thermodynamics—dissipation of usable energy; the flow of energy in communities, one-way only, with continual renewal from solar energy necessary.

ORGANIZATION AND CHANGE
IN COMMUNITIES
AND POPULATIONS

The Web of Life

A contemporary of Darwin's suggested that the glory of England was due to its old maids. This is the argument: The sturdy Britons were nourished by roast beef from cows, which ate clover, which was pollinated by bumblebees, which were attacked in their nests by mice, which were kept under control by cats, which were raised by old maids. The argument has become quaint with the passage of time, and perhaps it was always a little farfetched. It is, however, still valid in pointing out that the different species in a community are linked in many and curious ways. The sequence clover $\rightarrow$ cows $\rightarrow$ Briton is part of a chain by which materials and energy are transferred in a community. Another chain is present in bumblebees $\rightarrow$ mice $\rightarrow$ cats, which also involves the interspecific relationship of predation. The relationship between cats and old maids is a somewhat odd but legitimate example of what is called symbiosis. Each stage influences the numbers of individuals in other stages. These and many other relationships unite all living things into a single fabric, the web of life. Since not all can be discussed at once, we shall start with the first-mentioned: food chains and some of their consequences.

Chains and Pyramids

FOOD CHAINS

In the last chapter we saw that a community as a whole is a dynamic system with flow of materials and energy, cyclic for materials and one-way for energy. This is *the* basic feature of a community as an organized association of different, interacting species. Any one sequence of species through which materials and energy pass is a *food chain.* With unimportant exceptions, all food chains start with *producers,* the photosynthetic plants that acquire energy from nonorganic forces and fix it in organic chemical form. All end with *reducers,* the organisms of decay, including fungi and expecially bacteria.

The simplest chain is producer → reducer, but even so simple a sequence normally includes several species of reducers. Commonly one or many *consumers* intervene between producers and reducers. Almost all consumers are animals. (Why? What exceptions are there?) There are different levels of consumers; for example,

willow → deer → puma → bacteria

In a natural community the flow of materials and energy is much more complicated than is suggested by any one food chain. Practically all species of organisms may be consumed by more than one other species; and although some consumers and reducers obtain food from a single species, most consume numerous species. One species of plant may provide food for many species each of insects, birds, rodents, ungulates, worms, fungi, and bacteria; and one of the species of, say, rodents living on those plants may in turn be consumed by any of a dozen or more species of carnivorous snakes, birds, and mammals. Thus chains both converge and branch. There are so many branchings and cross-connections among the food chains of a whole community that the pattern of transfer is actually a *food web* rather than a series of readily distinguishable chains (Figure 19-1).

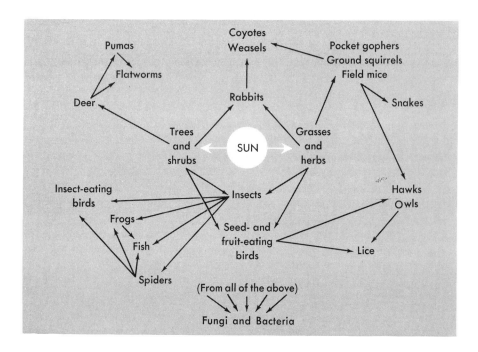

FIG. 19-1 A food web in an American woodland community. The arrows indicate the flow of energy and materials (consumption of food). This diagram is suggestive only and is very incomplete. In a real community there are many more groups of organisms and many more levels and directions of consumption.

In spite of the tremendous complexity of a food web, the partial chain producer $\rightarrow$ level 1 consumer $\rightarrow$ level 2 consumer, or plant $\rightarrow$ herbivore $\rightarrow$ carnivore, does sum up major aspects of food flow in any community. Reducers, although essential parts of all food chains and material cycles, complicate the picture because they derive food from *all* links in all chains and not only (in fact, least of all) from the last consumer link. They are therefore mostly omitted from this discussion of *pyramids*.

Each link in the partial chain has less available energy than the previous link, as follows from the second law of thermodynamics. The total energy of the plants in a community is greater than that of the herbivores, which in turn is greater than that of the carnivores. The total energy of the reducers is less than that of all the rest of the organisms put together, but not necessarily less than that of any one link. The total bulk—the mass—of living substance also tends to decrease from one link to the next. This reduction is not a necessary result of physical law, as is the reduction in available energy, but it is an extremely probable result and seems to occur in all communities except those temporarily under unusual circumstances. If, for instance, you raised sheep for food and had nothing else to eat, your mass would be greater than that of the sheep if you ate the last one, but then you would starve to death. To keep going, you would have to have a flock of sheep with mass continuously much greater than yours. This is about the simplest possible illustration of the generalization that in a continuing community the total mass of later links in food chains is less than that in earlier links.

Thus each successive step in food utilization is smaller than the last, and the over-all pattern is like a pyramid, largest at the bottom (producer level) and progressively smaller toward the top (consumer levels), as shown in Figure 19-2.

THE PYRAMID OF NUMBERS

A concept related to the pyramids of mass and energy and sometimes confused with them (although it is quite distinct) is what animal ecologists call "the pyramid of numbers." If a census is taken of animals of different sizes, smaller animals are generally found to be more numerous than larger ones (Figure 19-2, bottom). You can probably verify this from your own experience. In any natural community known to you, what is the comparative abundance of animals of the sizes of insects, mice, and racoons?

BUDGETS: THE LIMITATION OF LIFE

The principles of cycles of materials, of energy transfers, of food chains, and of mass and energy pyramids have important implications for the abundance and activity of the life of the earth as a whole and of living things at any one place and time. It has been shown that practically all the energy and a great part of the materials in all living things must pass through green plants. They are the basic source of foods, but they are also the bottleneck of life's activities. The total activity of life, the flow of energy through all living organisms, can proceed no faster than the fixing of that energy by photosynthesis. Photosynthesis can proceed no faster than the inflow of radiant energy from the sun. As a matter of fact, photosynthesis is very much slower. Only a small fraction of sunlight that reaches the surface of the earth is transformed into chemical energy by photosynthesis. The available data are highly inexact, but the figure must be well under 1 per cent (see Table 18-1). Whatever the precise figure may be, it represents all the energy available for all the living things on earth.

Limitations of vital activity by the budget of available materials are also strong and may be more obvious in particular localities. On land the most apparent limitation is often in the water budget, as water supply is highly variable and water is the material needed in largest quantities by all living communities. The comparative scarcity of life in the sun-drenched desert is obviously not due to deficiency of solar energy but to limitation of water. The most common budget limitation in the soil is in nitrates (principal source of nitrogen) and phosphates (essential mineral salts). Agriculturalists well know that

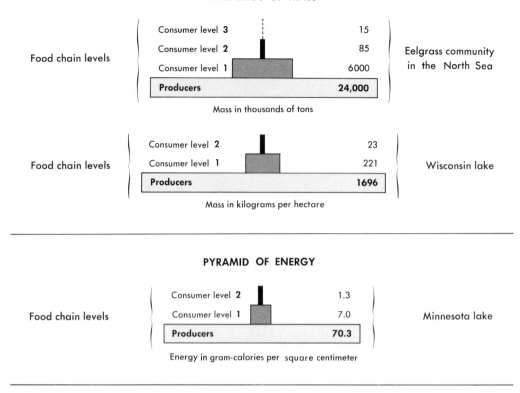

PYRAMIDS OF MASS

Food chain levels
- Consumer level **3** — 15
- Consumer level **2** — 85
- Consumer level **1** — 6000
- **Producers** — **24,000**

Eelgrass community in the North Sea

Mass in thousands of tons

Food chain levels
- Consumer level **2** — 23
- Consumer level **1** — 221
- **Producers** — **1696**

Wisconsin lake

Mass in kilograms per hectare

PYRAMID OF ENERGY

Food chain levels
- Consumer level **2** — 1.3
- Consumer level **1** — 7.0
- **Producers** — **70.3**

Minnesota lake

Energy in gram-calories per square centimeter

PYRAMIDS OF NUMBERS OF INDIVIDUALS

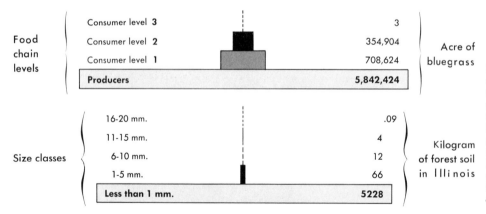

Food chain levels
- Consumer level **3** — 3
- Consumer level **2** — 354,904
- Consumer level **1** — 708,624
- **Producers** — **5,842,424**

Acre of bluegrass

Size classes
- 16-20 mm. — .09
- 11-15 mm. — 4
- 6-10 mm. — 12
- 1-5 mm. — 66
- **Less than 1 mm.** — **5228**

Kilogram of forest soil in Illinois

FIG. 19-2 **Pyramids of mass, energy, and numbers of organisms in a community.** Producers are the green plants, primary converters of environmental resources into living material. Consumers are animals. The levels represent the sequence in a food chain: consumer level 3 feeds on consumer level 2; consumer level 2 feeds on consumer level 1; and consumer level 1 feeds directly on the producers. (Reducers are omitted in these pyramids.)

on heavily farmed land these are the principal materials that have to be renewed by fertilization. Differences in natural supplies of these materials are also reflected in different abundances of land life.

In aquatic environments there is practically no limitation of water budget, but other materials, especially, again, nitrates and phosphates, may be stringently limited. Great quantities of these materials are washed into the sea from the land, which is why marine life is particularly abundant along shores and off the mouths of rivers. Farther out to sea, nitrates and phosphates are rapidly used in upper levels of the water, where photosynthesis occurs. The return of nitrates and phosphates to the cycle by decay is more active at deeper levels, as dead organisms sink through the water and are decomposed by bacteria.

They may be returned to the sunlit surface waters by the upwelling of deep currents along coasts. Combined limitations of energy and material budgets are particularly well illustrated by fluctuations in the abundance of diatoms in the North Atlantic (see Figure 19-3). Since the diatoms, in spite of their small size, are the most important photosynthetic

Niches and Competition

The food web is the most pervasive feature binding a community into an organized system. There are, however, many other interrelationships within that system. One involves the various ways of life, ecological niches, and how they are parceled out by competition. Others involve special associations, both helpful and harmful, between particular species. These further interrelationships will now be discussed in sequence.

organisms of the open sea, the whole life of the ocean community changes with fluctuations in their numbers.

RELATIONSHIPS AMONG NICHES

In some of the driest deserts of Arizona grows the gigantic cactus *Cereus giganteus,* commonly called "saguaro" (or "sahuaro," in either case pronounced sah-*wah*-roh). Although it is not a widespread plant and is absent from most American deserts, it is so striking and picturesque that paintings, decorations, and cartoons have made it the recognized symbol of the Southwest. There are two birds, a flicker (*Colaptes chrysoides*) and a woodpecker (*Centurus uropygialis*), that cut round openings in the spiny, ridged stems of saguaros and excavate recesses for nests in the softer internal tissues. They make more holes than they keep in use, and often an unused flicker or woodpecker hole is occupied by elf owls (*Micropallas whitneyi*), dainty little creatures no longer than sparrows. An elf owl rarely nests anywhere else.

The saguaros, living only in deserts and only in particular parts of them, have their special niche among plants. They provide, in turn, one aspect of

FIG. 19-3 Seasonal fluctuations in diatom abundance in the North Atlantic. Solid black line, diatoms; dashed line, nitrates and phosphates; solid white line, light intensity. Winter, surface waters are cold and poorly illuminated. Under these conditions diatom growth is inhibited, and, as a consequence, the concentration of nitrates and phosphates in the surface waters increases (during diatom growth nitrates and phosphates are incorporated into protoplasm). Spring, surface waters warm up, and light intensity increases. These optimum conditions for photosynthesis, combined with a high concentration of nitrates and phosphates, lead to a spectacular spring pulse of diatom growth. Summer, the diatom population declines for two reasons: (1) diatoms are consumed in huge numbers by herbivorous animals; and (2) the concentration of necessary nitrates and phosphates decreases. This limitation of essential minerals itself has two causes: (1) the nitrates and phosphates have been subject to removal through the earlier diatom growth; and (2) they have not been renewed from the depths of the ocean. The main source of nitrates and phosphates is the dark, deep ocean bottom where bacteria-caused decay is high and photosynthesis is nonexistent. Actual return of the minerals to the main zone of life—the surface—depends on their upward movement by upward currents. The complex distribution of temperature conditions in the summer ocean interferes with the upward movement and thus temporarily contributes to a nitrate–phosphate deficiency that in turn contributes to a fall in the diatom population. Autumn, the temperature conditions of the ocean change, leading to a renewal of nitrates and phosphates at the surface and an upsurge in diatom growth. This autumn pulse in the diatom population is, however, never as great as the spring pulse because temperature and light intensity have dropped, thus limiting the rate of photosynthesis. Winter, growth slackens because of the light and temperature conditions, and consequently the nitrates and phosphates accumulate to the high concentration that will again make possible a spring pulse.

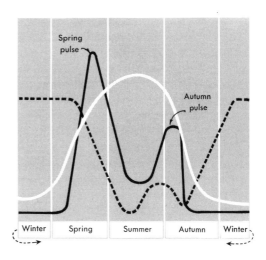

the niches of desert flickers and woodpeckers. These birds, in their turn, excavate the homes of elf owls, and these homes are one of the defining characteristics of the elf-owl niche. The interdependence of all these organisms is evident, and so is the fact that their roles in the community are quite different; they have, in fact, different niches.

Another owl, slightly larger than an elf owl but still small as owls go, also nests in woodpecker holes in saguaros: the saguaro screech owl (*Otus asio gilmani*). A saguaro screech owl and an elf owl may be found in adjacent holes on the same cactus plant. Here, you would be inclined to say, are two species occupying the same niche, but it is not so. The elf owl feeds mainly on small insects, such as beetles, ants, or crickets. The screech owl likewise eats some insects, especially the larger grasshoppers and locusts, as well as scorpions, but also includes in its food mice and other rodents that are seldom attacked by elf owls. There are other differences in their activities, such as the fact that the screech owls raise their young earlier in the year than do elf owls. In short, despite the identity of their homes and the similarity of their habits, these two species of owls do have distinctly different total relationships to their environment or different roles in their community, which is a way of saying that they occupy different niches.

The desert scene illustrates two principles that operate equally in any community: each species in an established community has a distinctly different niche, and two species do not long live together if one of them can fully utilize an aspect of the environment necessary to both of them. Competition need not extend to all environmental necessities, and it seldom does. Elf owls and screech owls do not seriously compete for woodpecker holes. Different species of fishes in the sea do not compete for water. There is plenty to go around, and there are plenty of woodpecker holes in the desert. Species may compete for only one crucial thing and share everything else quite amicably. Still they cannot long exist together if they continue to compete for *anything* that is vitally essential to them. Birds may share the abundant foods of late summer, and then, when the

supply dwindles and competition really begins to tell, they will eat different foods or will migrate to different regions. There are many such escapes from lethal competition. What others can you think of?

NATURE OF COMPETITION

Almost anything needed from the environment may be the object of competition. Plants compete for water or sunshine, sometimes for mineral salts—whatever is in shortest supply at a given time and place. In the desert each mesquite bush is surrounded by a zone of completely bare soil from which it has ousted competitors for water. In the forest a dense growth of seedlings thins out progressively as a few more vigorous trees preempt the sunshine, and others die in their shade. In the sea one species of photosynthetic organisms may locally drive out another as it wins in competition for nutrient nitrates or phosphates.

Among animals food is the usual object of competition. This lies back of the fact that the food habits of animals are so extremely diverse and frequently so specific, characteristics that reduce competition for food between different species. Animals may, however, compete for things other than food. They may also compete for water in a dry environment, or for desirable nesting places or shelters.

We are inclined to think of competition in terms of athletic events or of struggles in which one side goes after the other and tries to beat it. Such events do occur in nature. When a coyote chases a rabbit, there is a race, with food as a prize if the coyote wins and life if the rabbit does. Ants stage epic struggles, real pitched battles between large opposing forces. Jays drive other birds away from food. But such face-to-face combat is decidedly *not* characteristic of competition in nature. The usual competition is a passive process in which each separately seeks to utilize what the other also needs. A plant in getting its water supply does not necessarily attack other plants, and a deer eating foliage may not have any contact with the other herbivores with which it is in fact competing. In this, the usual biological sense of the word, are coyote and rabbit really competing?

Competition frequently occurs among organisms similar to each other, with overlapping niches, and often phylogenetically related. It may, however, occur just as frequently between species that have some one requirement in common but that otherwise lead completely different lives. Man's most severe competitors for food are the insects. Competition between rabbits and sheep caused a crisis in wool growing in Australia.

COMPETITION AND EVOLUTION

If two species compete strongly, the frequent but not inevitable outcome is that one of them becomes extinct. This is not the only cause of extinction, but it has been a widespread cause during the long history of life. A large-scale example occurred when North and South America became reunited from one to several million years ago. Each of the previously separated continents had its own distinctive species of mammals, including rodents, carnivores, and herbivorous ungulates (hoofed mammals). North American species invaded South America, and in the ensuing competition all the ungulates, all the carnivores, and a great many of the rodents native to South America became extinct. (The native South American carnivores were marsupials.)

It is easy to see how competition works as an evolutionary force both to change species and to prevent their changing (Figure 19-4). If two similar species compete strongly, the tendency of natural selection will be to increase the differences between them. Variants in each species least like the other species will have least competition and hence are likely to be most successful in rearing offspring. Over the generations, the species will come to occupy more distinctly separate niches. On the other hand, in a well-integrated community with numerous occupied niches, variants of any species farthest from the usual or modal adaptation to its niche are most likely to encounter competition from the occupants of other

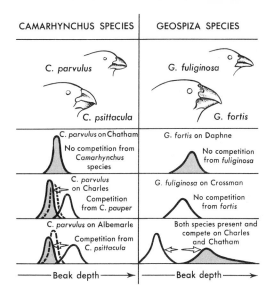

FIG. 19-4 **Evolutionary effects of interspecific competition.** The adaptive radiation of the tree finches (*Camarhynchus* spp.) and ground finches (*Geospiza* spp.) of the Galápagos Islands has been discussed in Chapter 13. The finches also provide excellent examples of the evolutionary effects of competition between ecologically similar forms. *C. parvulus*, *C. pauper*, and *C. psittacula* are closely related insect-eating tree finches. Their beak size reflects the size of insects they eat. *C. parvulus* has the smallest beak. Variations in its size are plotted here as frequency distributions. The *parvulus* graph on all three islands is stippled; the graph for a competing species is unstippled; in the figures for the islands of Charles and Albemarle the broken-line graph is a representation of the *parvulus* graph for Chatham, given for comparison. On Chatham *C. parvulus* is the only species of the three that is present. On Charles it is in competition with *C. pauper*, which feeds on slightly larger insects than *parvulus* does. Competition has caused a specialization on still smaller insects by *parvulus*, minimizing the competition, and a concomitant local evolutionary decrease in the size of the *parvulus* beak. On Albemarle competition is from *C. psittacula*. The evolutionary effects of interspecific competition between *G. fuliginosa* and *G. forits* on Charles and Chatham are clear.

niches. The trend of selection will be adverse to these variants and will favor maintenance of the status quo.

Interspecific Interactions: Symbiosis

All the members of a community live together—this is part of the definition of a community. Two universal kinds of interactions involved in living together have now been considered: consumption (including predation) and competition. There are other relationships, more specific, less universal, but also widespread. A barnacle on a whale, a hermit crab in and a sea anemone on a snail shell, or a dog and its fleas exemplify particularly intimate ways of living together. Such special and closer associations of individuals of different species, within the looser association of the community as a whole, are given a special name, *symbiosis* (Figure 19-5), which simply means "living together."

The three examples given in the last paragraph embody different relationships between the symbiotic animals. Presumably a whale does not mind a few barnacles on its hide and is neither helped nor harmed by their presence. The barnacle, for its part, gets nothing out of the association except a free ride. Whale and barnacle are simply messmates who run around together, eat perhaps at the same table, but take nothing from and give nothing to each other. This is *commensalism* ("being at table together"). Hermit crab and sea anemone, without taking thought or having altruistic motives, are nevertheless helpful to each other. The sea anemone, with its many stinging cells, protects the crab. Sometimes it also obviates the necessity for the growing crab to leave its protective shell and seek another to fit by actually remodeling the shell. The crab seeks out food and tears it to shreds, and the sea anemone lives on such bits as come its way.

FIG. 19-5   A variety of symbiotic relationships. 1. *Organic mutualism:* a lichen, consisting of nonphotosynthetic fungal hyphae and photosynthetic algal cells. Neither member of this mutualistic union ever grows separately in nature. 2. *Mutualism:* photosynthetic protists in cells of *Hydra;* the *Hydra* gains carbohydrates, and the protists gain water, nutrients, and shelter, 3. *Commensalism:* a, a staphylinid beetle, which lives in a termite colony as a tolerated scavenger; b, the beetle riding on the head of a termite. It scavenges food fragments as they are passed from one worker to another. 4. *Social mutualism:* a beetle that is not only tolerated but actually reared and protected by ants for the sake of its secretions. 5. *Parasitism:* a, the larva of a crustacean, *Sacculina,* a relative of the barnacles; b, the adult *Sacculina,* a parasite of crabs, reduced to a mere pouch of reproductive tissue, which bulges out between the abdominal segments of its host, and cellular extensions throughout the body of the host, which digest the host's tissues and leave it a hollow shell.

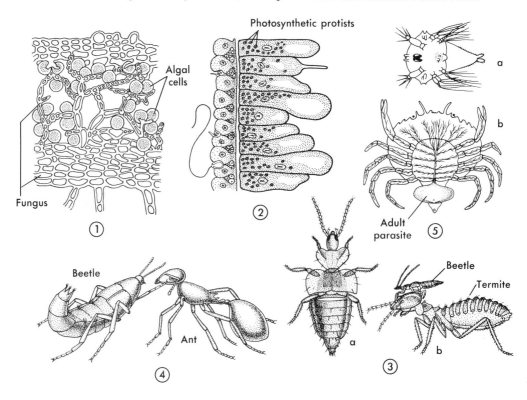

The relationship is mutually beneficial, and so it is called *mutualism.* The dog's fleas benefit; the pup is their food as well as their home. But their unwilling host receives only annoyance or disease in return. That sort of symbiosis is *parasitism* ("eating beside (at the expense of) another").

Distinctions between mere association in a community, commensalism, mutualism, and parasitism are not clear-cut. All sorts of intermediate relationships occur, and it is evident that one sort of relationship has often evolved into another. All the closer associations probably evolved from looser communal rela-

tionships. When commensalism occurs, one of the associates usually does derive some benefit. Whether the partnership is completely unimportant to the other (making it commensal), more or less helpful (therefore mutualistic), or harmful (parasitic) may be a question that is practically impossible to determine or may be a matter of definition or point of view.

Change in Communities

Communities are dynamic systems living in and forming parts of environments that are also dynamic. They change from hour to hour, season to season, year to year, and epoch to epoch. The rhythm of day and night is reflected in the activities of all communities, and many organisms have "internal clocks" adjusted to such biologically significant environmental rhythms. In the Temperate Zone we are all familiar with the dramatic cycle of the seasons and with its effects on not only the activities but also the compositions of local communities. This cycle tends to return annually to the same condition, but it does not do so exactly. Although one rare day in June may be much like another a year later, as the years pass they bring gradual changes.

The gardener finds tent caterpillars or other pests more abundant some years than others. The New

Englander sees the pastures of his boyhood overgrown with shrubs or merging into surrounding woods. The old swimming hole in the Midwest becomes a marsh or a prairie. The sod of the high plains, turned by courageous but injudicious pioneers, gives way to tumbleweeds and to desolate dust bowls, which yet, with renewed rain and rational treatment, may slowly recover their verdure. In the Southwest, the ruins of prehistoric Indian dwellings show that thousands of men once lived in wooded, fertile, watered valleys where now is a desert. The student who traces the longer history of the earth finds that still greater changes have taken place. Turtles, alligators, and fishes once swarmed where now extend the dry sagebrush flats of New Mexico, and the sands of barren dunes lie buried beneath fertile fields in the Mississippi Valley.

Succession

Rhythms corresponding with daily, yearly, or other environmental cycles exemplify the dynamic aspects of communities but do not, in themselves, alter the over-all characteristics of the communities. Anyone old enough to read this book has nevertheless seen a community change in character, perhaps with breathtaking speed where man was involved, more slowly but still quite perceptibly without human intervention. A striking feature of such change is that it is not so much a modification of a single com-

munity as a *succession* of more or less different communities in one area.

EXAMPLES OF COMMUNITY SUCCESSION

Consider what is likely to happen to a lake in the northeastern United States (Figure 19-6). The open waters of the lake have a community including protists, algae, small aquatic animals, and fishes, among other things. In shallower water near shore

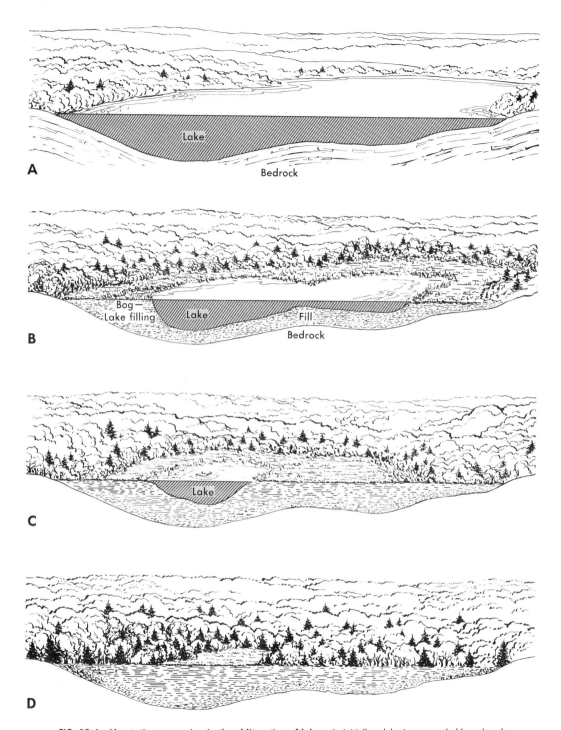

FIG. 19-6   Vegetation succession in the obliteration of lakes. A. Initially a lake is surrounded by a beech and maple (hardwood) forest; a few conifers, like tamarack, stand near the edge of the lake (bog forest). B, C. Accumulation of humus from lake plants (water lilies, cattails, pickerelweed, etc.) forms a marginal marsh or bog invaded by sedges and sphagnum moss; then by blueberry, wintergreen, and similar plants; then by willows, poplars, and other trees; and later by tamarack, yew, dogwood, and maple. This succession, as the lake fills with humus, ends when the surrounding beech and maple forest takes over entirely. D. The lake is filled but still surrounded by the tamaracks and other plants of the bog forest, which are ultimately succeeded by the hardwoods.

are pond lilies, cattails, and other comparatively large plants that grow (so to speak) with their feet in the water and their heads in the air. Silt and soil wash in and are piled up by waves, and dead vegetable matter accumulates. The lake becomes shallower, with marshy margins. The former shoreward rim of the lake becomes damp land on which grasses, herbs, and willows take root. The filling and the succession of new communities progress toward the center of the lake until finally open water and the aquatic community disappear entirely. In the meantime the marshy marginal soil continues to build up as humus and silt accumulate. Eventually oaks begin to grow there, and finally the whole site of the vanished lake is occupied by a beech and maple forest, which follows the oaks.

Similar successions where lakes once were can often be followed over periods of thousands, even tens of thousands, of years. Changes are recorded in layers of silt, peat, and humus that fill the lake basin and in the different kinds of pollen deposited in the various layers.

Community succession is not confined to lakes or to the Temperate Zone. It occurs wherever physiographic or climatic changes take place. A coral reef grows toward the surface, its rich community changing as the species of shallower water immigrate and become more populous. Waves grind coral rock to sand and pile the sand up in shifting dunes barely above the tides. Vines take root, bind the sand in place, and contribute to it the humus of their dead tissues. Low trees, resistant to winds and spray, grow in the accumulating soil, to which they contribute in turn. Finally a copse of tall trees develops in the richer soil, and a more protected land environment is thus gradually formed. Or perhaps the climate becomes progressively drier in a region where a pine forest flourishes. The pines, starved for water, die, and scrubby junipers grow in their place. Still drier conditions see the junipers replaced by sagebrush and greasewood. Finally there may be a cactus and thorn-bush desert where once a forest stood.

In all these examples, plants are stressed because they are in most instances the clearest indicators and the biological keys of the situation. In each situation, however, the association of plants is accompanied by a characteristic association of animals, and the two together make up the community.

CONVERGENCE AND CLIMAX

Let us return to northeastern United States and consider what happens to a bare rock exposed near the lake where we followed a community succession. The first living things to get a foothold on the rocks are small, scaly lichens. The lichens hasten the mechanical decomposition and chemical disintegration of the rock surface. In them dust lodges and humus begins to develop. More luxuriant lichens arise, and then moss and ferns. Soil develops along with increasing vegetation, and shrubs spring up. As the process continues, trees begin to grow, perhaps pines first while the soil is still rather rocky and comparatively poor in organic matter. Oaks follow, and in their shade appear seedlings of beech and maple, which grow up to overshade the early trees. Finally a beech and maple forest flourishes where once was bare rock, and it spreads and joins the beech and maple forest that grew up where a lake was earlier.

Different beginnings and different community successions led to the same result: the beech and maple forest community. The two successions *converged* and gave rise to the same kinds of community, or even to parts of identically the same community. Successions in the same region starting, say, on bare silt left by a flooding stream or on a cut clay bank would involve different sequences of communities, but would also tend to converge, culminating in beech and maple forest. That forest is the usual culmination or *climax* of community succession in the region. Once it is established, there is little tendency for further progressive change in the community. With the usual and incessant fluctuation of populations, the forest community persists until some further physiographic or climatic change or some interference by man starts a new community succession.

Most regions have a type of *climax community* with which all the community successions of the region usually end and which then tends to persist there. Of course, the climax is not always a beech and maple forest (although that is a common climax over much of northeastern United States), or even a forest of any kind. In many mountains the climax is a spruce and fir forest. A frequent climax on Western plateaus and other uplands is ponderosa pine forest. Mesquite communities are the climax in many more arid regions. (Mesquite is a thorny shrub belonging to the pea family.) The climax over most of the high plains east of the Rockies is grassy prairie. The nature of the climax is ultimately determined more by climate than by any other factor. Local differences in climate are fairly common even within a single region, so that regions often have more than one climax in different, more limited localities. Both grassland and forest climaxes are common in some regions.

What is the usual climax community in your part of the country? Has man disturbed or destroyed that community in places? If so, has the disturbance started a new community succession? Is there a tendency for abandoned fields and clearings to follow a succession back to the original climax?

CLIMAX AND CHANGE

Here is a question that probably arose in your mind as you read about climax communities: If the community in each locality tends toward a fixed climax in time and if this has been going on for millions of years, why are there any further changes in communities? Why are not all communities everywhere set and static at their climaxes?

A climax community tends to persist, it is true, but it tends to persist only as long as no internal or external disturbance affects the community and there is no essential physiographic or climatic change in its environment. In fact, such disturbances and changes are frequent, and in the long run they are sure to happen. Inevitably, always and everywhere, the climax community does eventually change. New successions lead to new climaxes, or change is so continual that a stable climax can hardly be designated. These facts have raised some doubts as to the general validity and usefulness of the concepts of convergence and climaxes. The doubts are not very serious if we remember that convergence and climaxes are not defined as universal and eternal. Convergence is a frequent tendency, and climaxes often do plainly exist and tend to persist for periods long in terms of human life, even though they always do change finally. The concept of climax as a stable condition in nature does have validity, but only in a limited and short-range way, because nature is not static.

Moreover, communities evolve by the extinction of species in them, the incursions of new species, and evolution within their populations. The species of which a community is composed are not themselves static units. Over the generations each one changes, and so does the community of which it is a part.

Rise and Fall of Populations

Communities are composed of local populations of numerous different species. The community as a whole, as we have now seen, is a dynamic system with many and diverse interrelationships among the species that compose it. Each specific population is also a system, understandable only in the context of its community, but with its own dynamics and interrelationships. Population growth and decline have special importance both in themselves and in their effects on the community as a whole. We shall now consider population changes and then turn to some particular intraspecific interactions culminating in the evolution of societies and leading to the study of the human species and biological aspects of human society in the following chapter.

BIRTH, DEATH, AND SURVIVAL

The size of a population is apparently determined by quite simple facts of life, birth, and death. If more organisms are born than die, the net result is an increase, and if more die than are born, a net decrease occurs. The factors that determine birth and death rates are not so simple; in fact, they are very intricate. The situation is also complicated and made more interesting by the fact that the size and composition of the population is not determined by birth and death rates alone but also by how long individuals survive, that is, by *when* death occurs. A simple problem will demonstrate that fact. Suppose that in some species 1000 individuals were born and the same number died each year. Would there be a change in population from one year to another? What would be the size of the population at any one time if each individual died at the age of 1 year? If each died at the age of 10 years? In the latter population, what percentage of individuals would be 7 years old?

The problem is, of course, oversimplified by the assumption that all individuals die at the same age. This is not really true of any species. Some individuals drop out at all ages from birth to death. The percentage of individuals that die at a given age—the death rate for that age—also changes markedly through the life span. Usually the death rate is high among the very young and the very old and reaches a low point somewhere in between. This is as true of man as it is of most other organisms. The human death rate is high in the first year, drops to a low in the early teens, and then rises slowly at first (until about 60) and then with increasing rapidity. That fact of life as it is really lived contrasts with the fact that all normal organisms of the same species are usually *capable* of living for about the same length of time, a life span characteristic of the species. There is, as would be expected, some hereditary variation in potential life span. Early death, which is more the rule than the exception in nature, is a premature failure due to an environmental incident such as competition, infection, predation, or accident.

A clear and convenient way to represent the incidence of death in a population is by a *survivorship curve* (Figure 19-7), which shows the percentage of individuals still living at various times after birth. If most individuals live out the potential life span, the curve is nearly horizontal until that span is reached and then drops precipitously (Figure 19-7A). If, on the other hand, most individuals die early in life and the survivors of that critical period have comparatively low death rates, the curve drops rapidly at first and then levels off (Figure 19-7B). The first situation, practically speaking, does not occur in nature. The second seems to be fairly common. Probably more

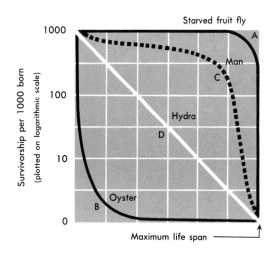

FIG. 19-7 Survivorship curves. (The survivorship curve for fruit flies (A) applies only to their life spans under the unnatural conditions of starvation in the laboratory.)

common, however, are situations intermediate between the two extremes (Figure 19-7C, D).

Human survivorship curves are of the intermediate type but differ greatly in precise form in accordance with nutrition, sanitation, and medical care in a particular population. Where the level of public health is high, there is an approach to type A, and where it is low, the approach is to type B. There is little evidence that any of the great advances in public health and medicine have increased the *potential* life span. They have greatly improved the chances that individual lives will more nearly achieve their potential span. One of the effects is to increase the percentage of older people in the population. In the United States and most other Western countries the last 50 years have been generally characterized by a declining birth rate. The net result of these two factors has been that the percentage of Americans aged 20 to 45 (hence in the ages when most reproduction occurs and in the ages of most productive work) has remained fairly steady, while the percentage of younger people, under 20, has decreased and that of older people, over 45, has correspondingly increased. What influence of this change can you see in your

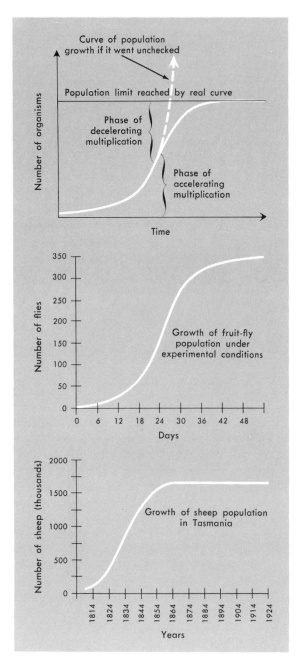

FIG. 19-8 Curves of population growth. Top, a generalized growth curve showing how multiplication ultimately decelerates to reach a population limit. Center, a growth curve for fruit flies in bottles. Bottom, a growth curve for sheep in Tasmania.

own community? In the national political and economic scene?

MALTHUS AND THE GROWTH OF POPULATIONS

All populations have tremendous capacity for increase. Elephants are notoriously slow in reproduction, but it is certainly conservative to estimate that, if all their young survived, the population would more than double every 50 years. A single couple that lived 100,000 years ago (and this is a short time in the history of natural populations) thus *could* have an astronomically enormous number of descendants today—a number represented, *at the very least,* by 4 followed by 602 zeros. That many elephants would fill the visible universe, and so we are obviously leaving something out when we say that so large a number of descendants is possible. It would be possible if all elephants reproduced at the stated rate and all offspring reached their potential life span. The result, in itself, forcefully demonstrates that such survival is absolutely impossible. Yet the example supposes that the population merely doubled in 50 years. In numerous invertebrate species one female may lay more than 2 million eggs per year. If all eggs developed and survived, the population would increase a millionfold every year—and would fill the universe during the lifetime of one generation of elephants.

If unchecked, the size of any population would increase at a fantastic rate. Its numbers would literally multiply each year, and the population growth in absolute census figures would be a curve that rapidly shot up skyhigh (Figure 19-8). The increase must be and is always checked. The environment can contain and support only so many individuals of a given species. When a population starts to grow from a few individuals in an environment favorable to it, its size shoots up at first, but then it begins to run against the barrier of the capacity of the environment. Population increase then slows down, and finally the population size is stabilized at a figure at or below environmental capacity. An increase in the carrying capacity of the environment may be quickly countered by further population growth. A decrease in the carrying capacity leads to higher death rates and so to a decline in population. The result is a tendency for populations to be as large as possible under existing conditions or, you might say, to live up to their income. Yet organisms usually keep on reproducing at rates that would rapidly raise their populations above capacity level if all the offspring survived and bred. The obvious corollary is that all offspring do not survive and breed. Only a small fraction of them do under ordinary conditions. The others necessarily are eliminated by competitors, within or outside their species, and hence by starvation, or by enemies, diseases, and other factors.

An English clergyman and economist named Thomas Robert Malthus pointed out these grim facts of population limitation in 1798. Malthus applied the principle to man and concluded that famine, pestilence, and war are inevitable brakes on the increase of human populations. Darwin noted that the Malthusian principle applies even more clearly to most organisms other than man. He saw that the inevitable decimation of offspring is a possible mechanism for evolution by natural selection. There is no serious doubt that Darwin was right on this point and that Malthusian or Darwinian selection is an important process in evolution, although we now consider that other mechanisms of selection occur and may be at least equally important, as we have stressed before.

Malthus' conclusions as applied to man were decidedly unpleasant. We all have an ingrained human (but not scientifically sound) tendency to disbelieve what is unpleasant to us. It is not surprising, then, that it has become an article of faith for many, including some politicians, theologians, economists, and even a few biologists, that the Malthusian principle does not really apply to man. Indeed, events during the last 150 years in some progressive countries have seemed to give the lie to Malthus. In those

countries, of which the United States is an outstanding example, populations have increased greatly because birth rate exceeds death rate and survival has been lengthened. Yet the standard of living, instead of dropping to minimum subsistence level, has risen notably. The explanation is of course that the extent and efficiency of production have been raised and that population growth, although large, has lagged behind increase in production. In other words, for some human populations the capacity of the environment has enlarged faster than the population. This has encouraged belief that the solution to human population problems is simply to go on increasing production as fast as possible. Unfortunately for so optimistic an outlook, it is a biological fact that this solution can work only temporarily and locally.

There are physical limits to the amount of food that the earth can possibly produce for any one species, including man. No matter how much of the earth's surface is brought into production for human use and how efficiently it is managed, the limit of environmental capacity is still there and cannot be removed. We are only temporizing with the Malthusian principle, not evading it. Eventually population must be balanced, and birth rate cannot continue to exceed death rate. That is the inevitable conclusion from biological principles. Whether the balance is to be by decrease of birth rate or increase of death rate, and at what level of subsistence and crowding the balance is to be achieved, are economic and political problems of great magnitude and urgency. They concern the biologist not so much as a biologist but, like everyone else, as a citizen.

Limiting and Balancing Factors

Apart from its controversial aspects, the Malthusian principle is certainly correct to the extent that for every species there are factors that limit population growth and determine population size by a balance of reproduction, death, and survivorship. Most of these factors are inherent in the interactions studied in this and the preceding chapter. Here they can be reviewed briefly from this different point of view.

MATERIALS AND ENERGY

All life is ultimately limited by the usable energy received from the sun. Remember that the percentage that can be directly used by life is always small. This is true not only because of the low efficiency of photosynthesis, but also because still larger amounts of energy go to keep the earth livable, especially to maintain the temperatures of its surface, water, and air and to run the water cycle on which all land organisms are dependent. If the energy now used in these ways were to decrease significantly, living populations would automatically decrease. Materials available for organisms in any community are also limited, and no population can live beyond its budget.

FOOD CHAINS

Each link in a food chain is dependent on the links before it. Population size at any point in a food chain is therefore limited by the sizes of populations in all previous links. The connection is particularly evident when, as often happens, fluctuations of population size in one species are accompanied by fluctuations in another that feeds on the first. An example will be given when we discuss periodic changes in populations later in this chapter.

Predation

Population size in food chains is influenced in two directions. The population of a food species limits the population that feeds on it, and at the same time the fact of being eaten affects the population of the food species. In parasitism there is necessarily a balance between the numbers of parasites and the damage done to the hosts. The plant–herbivore balance is closely analogous to that of host-parasite, as the herbivore does not necessarily kill the plant on which it feeds. Reciprocal balance of populations is especially evident in the relationship called predation, in which the individual used as food is killed. The predator population necessarily has less bulk than the prey population (except in very temporary instances) and usually is much less numerous. An increase in the prey population generally increases the number of predators, but an increase in the number of predators tends in turn to decrease the prey population. The

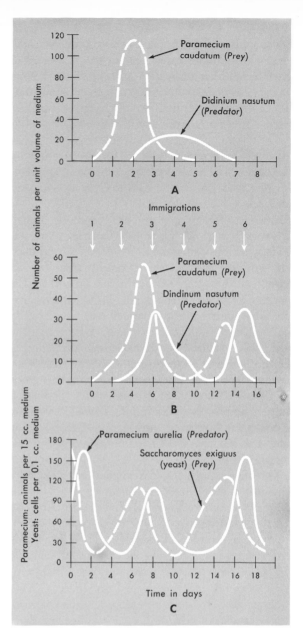

FIG. 19-9 Prey–predator relationships. A. The simpler case. The prey population, *Paramecium*, grows until predation by the ciliate, *Didinium*, commences. The predator population grows until the prey is exterminated. Then the predator population—now without resources—itself declines to extinction. B, C. Two cases of prey–predator oscillations. The relationship here is in general the same as in A; however, the decline of the prey population causes a simultaneous decline of the predator population and thus relieves pressure on the prey before it reaches extinction. The prey population, under temporary reprieve, again begins to grow; but as it does so, the predator population—now with renewed resources—grows also. The system can persist for many cycles in this oscillatory state. [In B the prey population is protected against extinction by the regular addition ("immigrations" 1 through 6) of small groups of individuals.] (G. F. Gause's data)

interaction can produce very complex results in the populations, but one of three reactions or a combination of them ordinarily ensues. Two of the three are illustrated in Figure 19-9. Increasing predation may wipe out the prey population, after which the predator population either also becomes extinct or turns to other prey. This is obviously a short-range reaction that cannot persist in a balanced community. Increased predation and decrease of prey may be followed so promptly by decrease of predators that the prey survives and becomes more abundant with lessened predation, and then predators and predation increase again, and so on. This cyclic relationship can persist indefinitely, but it is delicately balanced and may lead to extinction of the prey or to a more stable situation. In a stable balance, certainly common in nature and probably the rule in established communities, predators consume just about as many of the prey as to keep the prey population at or below the limit of environmental capacity. It can be said that predators are simply cropping excess production of the prey.

In stably balanced prey–predator populations,

predation is often actually beneficial to the prey as a group, even though it destroys individuals. This fact and the unforeseen and disastrous possibilities of ignorant interference in natural communities are dramatically illustrated by the history of deer on the Kaibab Plateau in Arizona (Figure 19-10). Before 1907 the plateau had a healthy deer herd with a stable population kept well below the capacity of the vegetation (which thus also was healthy and stabilized) by heavy predation by pumas, wolves, and coyotes. With the idea of benefiting the deer by removal of their "enemies," a campaign of extermination was waged against the predators. The deer population did, indeed, increase enormously, from about 4000 in 1907 to some 100,000 in 1924. The peak population was far beyond the capacity of the range, and in the next 2 years more than half the deer starved to death. Thereafter the deer population

FIG. 19-10   The history of the Kaibab deer. The white line represents numbers of deer.

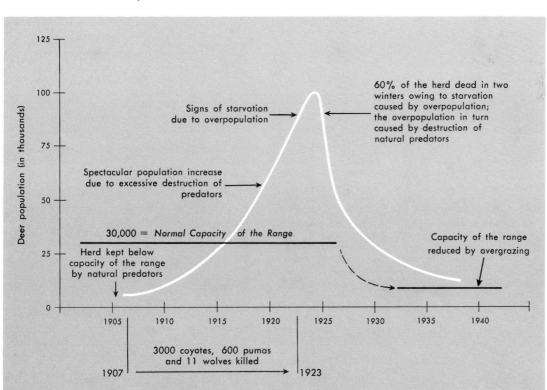

continued to decline more slowly and by 1939 was down to 10,000, living up to the capacity of the range, now seriously damaged by overcropping. With the range still deteriorating, starvation continued to kill more deer than the predators had.

COMPETITION

The immediate cause of death of most of the Kaibab deer after the removal of predators was starvation, but the starvation resulted from excessive *intraspecific* competition for a limited food supply. The frequent result of close *interspecific* competition is the decline and ultimate extinction of one of two competing populations. Experiments have shown patterns of population change that underlie such events in nature (Figure 19-11). Population growth of the successful competitor is slowed down, but eventually the population reaches the size it would have had without competition. The losing competitor's population starts to grow normally but soon slows down and then gradually declines to extinction.

POPULATION PERIODICITY

Fluctuation in Population Size

Change in population size is rarely a simple matter of smooth increase up to the capacity of the environment or decrease to extinction. There are always fluctuations, sometimes violent ones, even when the end result is indeed either maximum or minimum (zero) population size. Many of these fluctuations

FIG. 19-11   An experimental study of interspecific competition. The experiments concern competition between two species of *Paramecium*—*P. aurelia* and *P. caudatum*—grown in the same culture vessels. They compete for food and other requirements. A. The growth of both species when grown separately under conditions similar to those in which they later compete. Note that *aurelia*'s growth is more rapid; its stable population size (about 100 units) is greater than that (about 60 units) of *caudatum*. B. The history of the two species in competition. C, D. Comparison of each species, grown alone and in competition. *P. caudatum* is eliminated by the competition from *aurelia*; competition slows the population growth of *aurelia*, but it eventually attains its normal population size (about 100 units). (G. F. Gause's data)

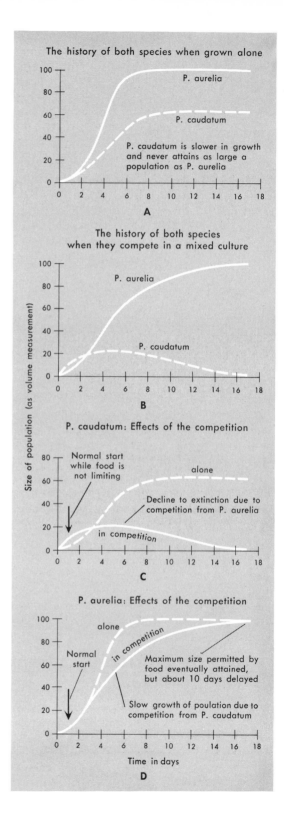

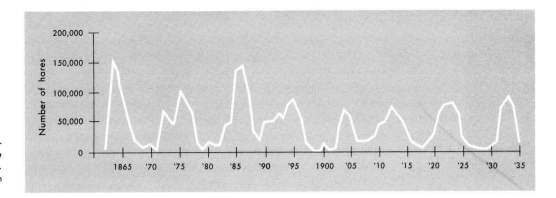

FIG. 19-12 Population periodicity in the varying hare of Canada and Labrador. The cycle reaches its maximum about every 10 years.

are irregular and episodic, caused by environmental events (such as unusual weather conditions) so intricate or themselves so unpredictable that the population changes cannot be predicted. At present, most changes in wild populations are of this type.

It is a matter of common observation that there are good years and bad years for different species of plants and animals. Populations of lynxes have a cycle closely following that of the hares (Figure 19-12). This suggests the previously noted experimental cycle in prey–predator relationships (see Figure 19-9), and it undoubtedly has a related cause: the lynxes prey on the hares. In this case, however, the decline in hare population is believed not to be due to predation but to overpopulation and epidemics. In the ensuing underpopulation reproduction is rapid and builds up anew to overpopulation in a few years. The lynx cycle is a secondary effect of the hare cycle, caused by changes in the food supply for the predators.

Many attempts have been made to correlate cyclic population changes with climatic or other physical cycles (of sunspots, for instance), but without success up to now. It is probable that the principal causes of regular population cycles are biological reactions within the communities themselves, as in the example of the hares and lynxes. Irregular fluctuations, on the other hand, can often be directly ascribed to environmental causes. The great reduction in the house-sparrow population of the Shetland Islands in 1926–1928 is known to have resulted from epidemic disease, and the periodic decreases in the populations of a species of British sea urchins in 1917 and 1929 followed cold winters.

Other Periodic Population Phenomena

Numerous activities in populations are periodic and sometimes cyclic. Insofar as they are long-term characteristics of the organisms and do not lead to definite population changes, they do not particularly concern us here. Examples of rhythmic, environment-correlated breeding activity involve daily, tidal, and seasonal cycles (Figure 19-13). Such rhythms, varying in regularity and correlated with many different environmental factors, are almost universal, and they influence abundances of species and other population phenomena markedly at given places and times. What bearing do they have, for instance, on summer and winter bird populations in your area?

Intraspecific Interactions

The dynamics of populations of course include much more than increase and decrease in population size. Each population also has some degree of internal organization, involved in interactions among its individuals. It is to some of these interactions that we now turn.

Members of the same species living together in a community necessarily affect each other. Relationships corresponding with food chains (for example, predator-prey) and with parasite–host interactions between species are slight or absent within species. Competition, aggregation (more or less analogous

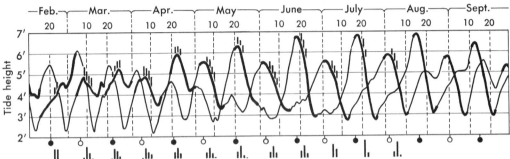

FIG. 19-13 Tidal and lunar periodicity. Top, a photograph (by flash) of a remarkable phenomenon exhibited by the grunion (*Leureshes tenuis*) on the southern coasts of California. The grunion wriggle out of the waves at the highest points during the highest (night) high tides of the lunar cycle. Momentarily stranded on the wet beach between waves, the females wriggle down into the sand tail-first. (Note the females with only their heads protruding from the sand.) In this position the female lays her eggs while the male, curled around her body, ejaculates sperms, which travel over the female's wet flank to reach the eggs. Both male and female return to sea with the next wave that covers them. The entire grunion population's egg laying is thus synchronized, being restricted to the two periods of highest tides in the lunar cycle. Furthermore, although there are two high tides each 24 hours, the grunion limit their activity to the night high tide. The eggs, buried in the sand, hatch as young fish in time to go to sea with the next set of very high tides about 2 weeks later. Bottom, a chart showing the occurrence of grunion egg laying in relation to tidal and lunar cycles at La Jolla, California. The heights of high tides (in feet) about 24 hours apart have been connected by smooth lines. The two tides each day yield the two series of curves; the night tide is indicated by the heavier line. Grunion activity is represented by short vertical bars above the curves. Moon phases are given below (the black circles indicate new moon, and the white circles full moon). The vertical bars under each set of high tides show the relative intensities of individual runs on successive nights. Graph, Boyd Walker; photo, Moody Institute of Science)

with commensalism between species), and cooperation (analogous with mutualism) are at least as common within as between species, but they tend to take different forms and have different evolutionary results in the two cases.

COMPETITION

Species in the same community compete if their niches overlap in some essential and exhaustible environmental requirement. The result is that each species in a stable community has its own niche, and vital overlapping tends to be eliminated. All members of a single species live (approximately) within the same niche. Obviously, intraspecific competition may be particularly strong, but it is equally obvious that its effect is not to move each individual into a separate niche. Each niche has a number, usually large, of places that may be occupied by individuals without lethal interference among them. Competition is for these individual places in the specific niche. The winners are, as a rule, those individuals most precisely and efficiently adapted to the niche. Competition is one of the processes that lead to natural selection. It is the one most stressed by Darwin, but in the modern concept it is only one of many selective forces. (What are some of the others?)

In its simplest form, the net effect of intraspecific competition in the community is merely to eliminate surplus population and to assign to each survivor its own place, or what the Germans call *Lebensraum* ("living space"). This minimal effect is universal. A gardener thins out seedlings as they grow. You have only to watch the annual growth of herbs in a field or the slower growth of trees in a forest to see the same process in nature. The same sort of process occurs among all groups of animals. Even fully mobile species are thinned out to the numbers that can be supported by available materials and energy.

Among animals with more complex behavior, especially arthropods and vertebrates, *territoriality* is common. Each animal has a smaller or larger territory that is somehow home to it. Often the territory centers around a literal home, such as a hive, nest, or burrow. The animal may spend all its time there; if it does stray far afield, it returns periodically to its home territory. The competitive background of such behavior is particularly evident in the many species in which the home territory is actively defended. You must have seen birds or chipmunks aggressively driving away trespassers on their preserves. Not only some birds and mammals but also some lizards, fishes, crabs, and others defend territory. This is one of the many deep-seated biological tendencies that are still present, even in their primitive forms, in man, although in him they are integrated into a far more complex network of intraspecific interactions. "An Englishman's home is his castle"—it is defended territory.

AGGREGATION AND COOPERATION

Group defense of territory introduces, in relatively complicated form, other widespread kinds of relationships among members of a species. "Birds of a feather flock together." Members of a species usually tend to occur together, to be *aggregated,* and within such groups complex interactions in addition to competition may develop. In plants and in many animals, especially those with comparatively simple

behavior, the aggregation is passive. Individuals do not seek out each other's company, and there is little or no differentiation of roles within the group. Even so, the aggregation as such has biological significance and survival value for the species. If nothing else, it facilitates interbreeding in sexually reproducing species.

The formation of mutually tolerant and cooperative groups has been not a universal, but nevertheless a frequent and a highly successful, trend in evolution. The widespread occurence of the trend should be strongly emphasized. It flatly contradicts the idea that the process of evolution is one of unbounded individual competition in "nature red in tooth and claw." It is particularly important for a true understanding of the evolution of man, the biological basis of human society, and the possible future of our species.

DIVISION OF ROLES
AND THE RISE OF SOCIETIES

In species with individually separate sexes (some plants and most animals), the sexes have different roles in reproduction, at least. That difference is often accompanied by marked differences in size, color, pattern, physiology, and behavior, especially in higher animals, with corresponding differences in roles even beyond the essentials of reproduction. Males and females may even belong to quite different food chains, as in mosquitoes, with males eating the juices of green plants and females eating mammalian blood. In groups that defend territory, defense is usually by the male, even though the territory may be shared with a female.

In cooperative groups there is a further evolutionary tendency for differentiation of roles, not necessarily on a sexual basis. Even in loosely organized animal aggregations, there is often an order of dominance or a "social scale" in which each individual has its place. The more dominant animals often take the lead in group activities; they are likely to have first whack at food; the more dominant among the males may monopolize the more desirable females. This dominance sequence is called the "pecking order," because it is readily seen in who pecks whom in a flock of fowls, in which dominance has been extensively studied. If you observe a flock of hens, you will almost surely find that there is one hen that pecks all the others and one hen that is pecked by all the others but never pecks back. Throughout the pecking order, each hen pecks those of lower status and is pecked by those higher in the order. Such dominance is established competitively, but once it is established it reduces competition and tension in the group. After the group is organized into a pecking order, less pecking goes on. Each hen, or each member of the sequence of whatever species, learns to know its place and gives way to its "betters" without further fuss.

Not all groups are organized into pecking orders.

For instance, ants, which live in very rigidly organized groups, have none. There may, nevertheless, be a distinct division of roles. Sometimes the division is temporary. In a prairie-dog town or in a roving band of baboons, some individuals generally act as sentinels while the others go about their business, but sentinel duty rotates. Army ants on the march follow a leader, but the leadership shifts rapidly, each leader remaining at the head of the column for perhaps only an inch of the advance. On the other hand, there is often also a more or less permanent division of labor. When army ants are moving their base, the workers always carry the young, and the soldiers always protect the line. When a grazing herd is attacked, in most species it is the mature males that wheel into the first line of defense.

Differentiation of roles in its many forms makes a group more than merely an aggregation. It introduces organization within the group and makes it a *society*.

Societies

Both human and insect societies are groups of individuals living together and reacting more or less as a unit toward other groups and with respect to many of the forces of evolution. There is some complexity of organization within each group, and different individuals have different roles. Beyond those broad resemblances, the two kinds of societies are fundamentally different, and the parallel so often drawn between them should be viewed with reserve or even suspicion. The biological basis of human society is of course to be sought among human ancestors and relatives, especially the mammals, and not among animals like the insects, which have been evolving in a strongly different direction for hundreds of millions of years. Individual roles and behavior in insect societies are rigidly determined by genetic mechanisms, while mammalian social relationships are characteristically more flexible and involve learning. Human social organization is varied and malleable.

HUMAN SOCIETIES

A mammalian society is not an expanded family, but rather is an aggregation of adults (with their children in the persisting but subordinate family units) with some differentiation of roles other than that of male and female in their reproductive capacities. In mammals other than man, the differentiation of roles seldom goes beyond dominance or leadership of some individuals over others. In civilized human societies, with their butcher, baker, and candlestick maker, the differentiation may become almost incredibly complex. An official classification of occupations in the United States lists 40,023 different occupations—and this list is clearly not a complete one.

The flexibility of human societies in contrast with the rigidity of insect societies reflects and depends on the similar contrast in the behavioral patterns of the individuals involved. This is an example of alternative solutions of evolutionary problems. Both kinds of societies are biological adaptations with high survival value, and both have been outstandingly successful in their quite different ways. Institutions and organizations within the framework of human societies may also be viewed as biological adaptations meeting, by different and generally more complex means, the same broad kinds of basic needs as are met within insect societies. Typically human organization depends on the biologically versatile, all-purpose human individual; ant organization depends on the biologically restricted, specialized, and almost depersonalized insect individual. Sociology has a biological basis and can be studied from a biological point of view, but it is a complex and highly special subject

beyond the scope of general biology. Biological aspects of human populations and society are discussed in the next chapter.

Summary

Food chains: producer → consumer → reducer; the pyramids of energy, of mass, of numbers; budgets of materials and energy.

Niches and competition: differences in niches; the principle that all species in any one community have different niches; the universality of competition, which is generally passive; competition leading to extinction; competition leading to the differentiation of competing forms.

Interspecific reactions: consumption, competition, symbiosis; symbiosis—commensalism, mutualism, parasitism.

Changes in communities: a succession of communities in one area leading to a climax; the concept of climax limited in spatial and temporal application; climaxes also going through successions in longer periods of time.

Rise and fall of populations: population size and changes in it determined by birth rate, death rate, and survivorship; survivorship curves.

The Malthusian principle that the potential reproductive rate of any species is enormously greater than the capacity of the environment: elephants, slow-breeding, as examples; the inevitable result that only a small fraction of offspring, or potential offspring, can possibly survive and breed in turn; the apparent exception in human populations only apparent and temporary.

Limiting and balancing factors in population growth: budgets of materials and energy; food chains, with later links on smaller budgets; predation, requiring fewer predators than prey and limiting both; mistaken interference with predation balance and the example of the Kaibab deer; competition, intraspecific and interspecific.

Population periodicity: cyclic fluctuation, due to biological reactions within communities; the example of varying hares and lynxes; noncyclical, episodic changes from environmental incidents; rhythmic patterns, especially of breeding seasons.

Intraspecific interactions: intraspecific competition, lessened by territoriality; aggregations of organisms; cooperation; the importance of noncompetitive and mutually helpful aggregation in evolution; division of roles, leading to societies; pecking order.

Insect societies, with roles not learned and subject to little modification.

Human societies: not evolved from a family but from a mammalian aggregation of adults; the enormous number of roles, many potentially available to any individual and all learned and subject to extensive modification; the basis of a human society in a flexible determination of behavior; familial insect and associative human societies as alternative solutions of similar biological problems.

CHAPTER TWENTY

THE HUMAN SPECIES
AND COMMUNITIES

Man and Nature; Man in Nature

Let us take a quick tour of the world, beginning at home. You are reading these lines in a human community, probably in a town or city where little or nothing remains of the natural community that existed there before man came. Somewhere nearby are fields where the original communities have also been eradicated and replaced by rich, new communities partly (only partly) of man's choice. From those fields and from other communities, near and far, even from the opposite side of the world, ships, trains, trucks, and planes bring foods and other materials into your community. Power, fuel, and water are also poured into the community from nearer or more distant sources.

A first hop to a rain forest in the Amazon Basin offers a major contrast. Here you may find small, naked, reddish-brown people, quite different in appearance from your neighbors at home. Some of them hack out small clearings along the edge of the forest where they plant cassava, corn, or other crops. Some gather wild fruits and vegetables and hunt the birds, mammals, and other animals of the forest. They use no power but their own; they find fuel and water where they may be. But even they are almost certain to have beads, knives, fishhooks, and other things that originally came from distant lands unknown and unimaginable to them. Another great hop may take you to central Asia, where squat, powerful, weather-beaten brown nomads live in felt houses, travel on horseback, and tend flocks of sheep. In southern Asia and its islands yellowish or tan farmers slosh through their wet rice fields. In African savannahs you may see magnificent, tall, shining black people, living in well-organized villages and owning large herds of cattle. At a village perched on the Norwegian coast you may see blond fishermen setting out to gather a crop from the sea.

430

Nowadays, even if we have never left home, all of us are familiar with these scenes and a thousand others over the varied surface of our planet. Taken together, they illustrate biological facts and principles of profound human significance. Human interest is likely to center on the people in the scenes and to notice their differences first. The human species is endlessly varied, and among its variations are sets of characteristics by which we distinguish local groups and races, analogous to the demes and subspecies of plants and animals. Next, however, is the fact of unity in that diversity. All men are more alike than different, biologically. All groups intergrade and all can interbreed. Mankind is one species.

Each human community is found to be intimately associated with, indeed really to be a part of, a broader biological community in which there are also many other species of animals and plants. The biological communities differ in different places, and the human communities are adjusted to those differences. The human communities, too, reflect environmental conditions and have local adaptations. Yet, now that we are in the second half of the twentieth century, human communities everywhere interact in ways more extensive and intensive than was usual in earlier biological communities, and they have drawn the biological communities also into a worldwide network of interactions. Everywhere we see that man has changed the environment. He has modified all the biological communities in which he lives. The effects seem slight in the Amazonian forest and are tremendous in your home town, but they exist everywhere that man is or has been. Many of the changes are constructive, from the human point of view at least. They have oriented nature for the benefit of its dominant species. Other changes are decidedly destructive from almost any point of view. They have reduced the capacity of the environment to support our own or other species, and they constitute a serious man-made problem for man.

In taking up these themes of the present chapter, we are drawing together threads that have run through what has been said before. The science of biology is integral, and all of it has a bearing on human life. Moreover, logical compartmenting of different biological "subjects" or distinction between the biology of man and that of nature is neither possible nor desirable.

Systematics of Homo sapiens

After what has been said, it is unnecessary to stress again the fact that man is an organism, subject to all the principles that apply to other living things. Man is the most widespread of all species and has an unusually high degree of what was originally local differentiation. He is the most mobile of all species, and that mobility has always blurred and has now thoroughly mixed the regional differences usual in a widespread species. On top of that, man's more strictly biological characteristics are not only overlaid by but also inextricably interwoven with cultural factors wholly absent in most species and only barely incipient in any other species of animal.

ORIGIN AND NATURE OF RACES

It is entirely obvious that mankind includes numerous groups that are physically different (Figure 20-1). Chinese, American Indians, and Scandinavians are groups within which there is great variation, but there are also consistent differences between any two of these groups. A member of one can almost always be distinguished from a member of another. Interbreeding can and does take place between the groups, but it is far less common than breeding within one group. If, however, the whole sequence of peoples through Europe and Asia and over into the Americas is taken into consideration, it is impossible to draw a fixed line, either geographically or between populations, and say, "Here, precisely, is where the Scandinavian physical type leaves off and the Chinese begins, or the Chinese ends and the Indian starts."

That kind of situation is common in species other than *Homo sapiens*. It is, indeed, the rule for populous, widespread species of either animals or plants. There is every reason to believe that the biological phenom-

FIG. 20-1   Some races of living man. Top left to right, American Indian (Assiniboin); Australian aborigine; European (Portugal); African (Kenya). Bottom, Asiatic (China). (Photos, top left to right, American Museum of Natural History, Australian Information Office, Socony Mobile Oil Company, Kenya Information Office; bottom, American Museum of Natural History)

enon is exactly the same in man as in any other species. Small local populations, demes, tend to have gene frequencies somewhat different from those of adjacent demes, partly as a random result of mutation and sexual reproduction and partly as a result of natural selection under local conditions. Nevertheless, there is gene exchange among demes, and groups of demes tend to have genetic features in common that distinguish them, on the average, from other, more distant groups.

The major races of mankind as usually designated, such as the Mongolian or Caucasian race, are exactly like the subspecies of other species of animals. They have all the characteristics of subspecies. In fact, they are subspecies, or perhaps (for reasons soon to be mentioned) it might be better to say that they *were* subspecies. The word "race" has been so abused for political and ideological reasons that some well-intentioned persons have denied the fact that such subdivisions really occur. Of course they do, and perhaps it would avoid unscientific emotionalism if we called them "subspecies" instead of "races." That

would emphasize the biological facts that races or subspecies are not fixed and separate units but are arbitrary and shifting subdivisions of the species and that there is no rational way to designate them as "higher" or "lower," "primitive" or "advanced." They are simply regional populations all with the same status within the species.

Even now it is evident that the various races evolved by differentiation of populations in different parts of the earth. In the early days of human history populations were sparse. Family units and demes of a few interbreeding families were widely scattered and comparatively isolated. Even with occasional interbreeding among all intervening demes, passage of a gene by inheritance from a deme in, say, South Africa to one in China would take a great many generations. It might well not occur at all, especially if, as would be likely, the gene had less selective value elsewhere than in South Africa. Under such conditions genetic differentiation of populations in different regions would be sure to occur, and there is no doubt that the human races did arise in that way.

If mankind had continued to live under the primitive conditions of race differentiation, it is entirely possible that speciation would have occurred and that there would have been, for instance, separate African and European species of men. That did not happen, and now it cannot happen. The partial isolation and regional divergence among groups of primitive men that *might* have made them separate species came to an end. Expanding populations reduced isolation. Human mobility, constantly increasing, practically wiped out any effectiveness of geographic barriers. There is now no place on earth where the population consists entirely of a race, or any other subdivision of the species, originally differentiated there. Effects of the prehistoric subspecies are still apparent enough, but biologically the subspecies really no longer exist as such. There is no chance at all that the same sort of geographic divergence will continue or will be resumed.

There are still barriers to interbreeding, but now they are mainly cultural or social and only secondarily, or in minor degree, geographic. In part they follow the lines of the old geographic subspecies, as in the case of the cultural barrier in some countries between interbreeding of descendants of the prehistoric African and European subspecies. Many of the cultural barriers, however, follow quite different lines. Just now there is little interbreeding between Communists and non-Communists, and there has long been comparatively little between members of conflicting religions. In some European countries generations passed with little interbreeding between the hereditarily (but not genetically) wealthy and the hereditarily poor, but that barrier is fast dissolving.

RACIAL CHARACTERS

"How many races are there?" is a question that does not make biological sense. In order to answer that, races would have to be fixed or sharply definable units, and they are not. It is purely a matter of convenience how many and what groups of men are to be called "races." Adaptation is so universal in nature and is so clearly involved in differences between subspecies that it is a reasonable conclusion that many differences between human races were originally adaptive. (This does not exclude the probability that some arose from random fluctuations of

gene frequencies in small groups of primitive men.) That has been hard to check, however, one way or another. There is good but inconclusive evidence that differences in skin color were adaptive when and where they arose. The color of the earliest men, doubtless variable as color is in all races, probably ranged through shades of brown. Darker or black skin was perhaps an adaptation in regions of damaging ultraviolet solar radiation, and lighter or white skin an adaptation to regions where that radiation (which is beneficial in *small* amounts) was deficient. Such genetic changes under the influence of selection take long periods of time. Whites have not been in Africa or Negroes in America nearly long enough for selection to have made a perceptible difference in their skin color. Is white or black skin more "primitive"? Which is "better"? Neither is more primitive than the other. Each was adaptively better under different conditions when and where it arose. Neither one seems to have a biological advantage under present conditions.

Skin color is so obvious that we are inclined to think of it as the main indication of race. It is, however, superficial, both literally and figuratively. It would be more interesting and more important if we could measure hereditary differences in intelligence and personality between races, but so far all attempts have failed. The difficulty is that what can be measured under the names of "intelligence" and "personality" is so strongly influenced by learning that genetic differences (although they surely exist) are obscured. Groups of American Negroes usually average lower than whites from the same region on the scoring of standard intelligence tests. It is, however, known that these tests are strongly influenced by education and cultural background and that on an average Negroes do not now have equal educational and cultural opportunities with whites of the same region anywhere in the United States. The suspicion that it is *that* difference, and not a genetic difference, is confirmed by the fact that Negroes test higher than whites when they have a cultural advantage, for instance, in comparisons of urban northern Negroes with rural southern whites.

About all that can be said now is that genetic racial differences in average intelligence and personality are so small in comparison with cultural differences and with genetic variation *within* each race as to have doubtful importance. There is also a theoretical biological reason for expecting this result when measuring intelligence, at least. During the prehistoric period of racial differentiation, it is inconceivable that intelligence was not at a premium everywhere. It would, then, be expected that natural selection would favor intelligence in all races, although the response might not be precisely the same everywhere. (This selective trend may no longer operate in modern societies.)

Recently a more direct approach to the investigation of genetic racial differences has been begun.

Study is made particularly of the blood groups, the genetics of which are known and simple and which can easily be determined in individuals. The best-known of many different blood groups (O, A, B, AB) are dependent on three alleles, the frequencies of which have been measured in many populations (Figure 20-2). In combination with similar data on other human genes, this study provides a more rational and meaningful basis for the biological classification of mankind than older studies based on such things as skin color or head shape.

UNITY AND DIVERSITY

Man exemplifies in high degree the interplay of unity and diversity evident in the whole realm of life. Living men constitute a single species, *Homo sapiens,* by all criteria of modern definitions of species. They share a rich genetic heritage, and all are parts of an interbreeding, worldwide population. Specific

FIG. 20-2   Distribution of the I^B blood group allele in world populations. The three degrees of shading indicate the percentage frequencies of the I^B allele. It is clear that the gene controlling the B blood group is not uniformly distributed among human populations; it is relatively abundant in Asiatic populations and virtually absent in American Indians. (Note that the data apply to original populations in the areas concerned; B blood groups are now common in North and South America among populations that have come from Eurasia.) Of course, the same inhomogeneous distribution applies to the other blood group alleles: I^O is relatively abundant in the Western Hemisphere and less common in Eurasia.

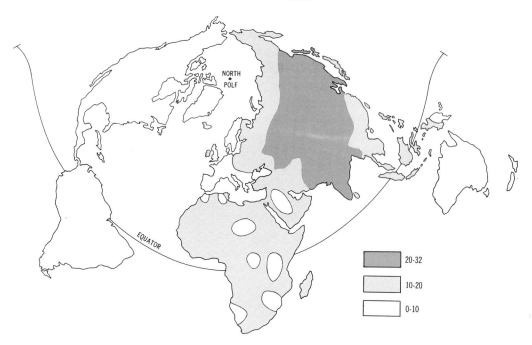

unity makes it possible for desirable hereditary traits to be combined and spread, whatever their source. It makes all men fundamentally alike, with incomparably more biological resemblances than differences. The cultural apparatus has stopped or reversed primitive trends toward divergence. Mobility and communication are cultural reinforcements of the unity rooted in biological facts.

On the other hand, within the species there are innumerable differences among individuals and between groups, and both biological and cultural factors maintain diversity. Extensive variation within the bounds of one species is biologically favorable both because it extends the immediate range of adaptation and because it is the indispensable material for any progressive change. There is absolutely no evidence that any race or other group is inherently, biologically, better than another. Originally racial differences probably made *each* race better fitted biologically to the particular place where it lived, but cultural changes have largely or wholly eliminated even this local superiority of any race over any other.

Basic Ecology of Homo sapiens

The diversity of human demes and races was originally related to the diversity of the natural communities in which men lived. It still is to some extent, but with great changes involved in man's cultural evolution, an evolution arising from and interacting closely with his biological evolution.

Man everywhere lives in interspecific animal and plant communities, and he depends on his environment no less than any other organism. It is part of his cultural development that he reacts on the environment more widely and more strongly than any other species—a fact that would require special attention to this particular species in any book on general biology, even if it were written by a squirrel or an oyster.

PRIMITIVE MAN AND ENVIRONMENTS

Man's primitive position in natural communities was that of a particularly large, vicious, land animal with an unusually wide range of foods. We are *omnivorous* ("eating everything") structurally, physiologically, and psychologically. That does not mean that men do or can eat literally everything, but that they eat almost any kind of animal food large enough to be worth the trouble and also a great variety of concentrated plant foods, especially fruits, seeds, and tubers or starchy roots. Biological consequences of this breadth of adaptation were that man could find food in almost any of the endlessly diverse natural communities of the earth and that in each community his status was complex. He became part of almost all food chains that could include a large animal.

Even before the clear establishment of civilization, the human species had spread into almost all land communities. Extension into the Americas was slowest, but it occurred thousands of years ago and before the rise of civilizations anywhere. Noncivilized man lived practically everywhere on land except on the highest mountains, on some of the smallest and most barren islands, and in Antarctica. Civilization has greatly increased the density but has not appreciably changed the extension of man's distribution. Noncivilized cultures coped with a tremendous variety of environments, and they now survive (although everywhere with some impingement of civilization) precisely in the environments most difficult for man, those that are very cold, very dry, or very warm and humid.

The immediate factors to which primitive man became adapted in each community are, by and large, the same environmental factors that affect all natural communities. They are still important, although the interactions are profoundly modified in modern civilized human communities. Climate, soils, water supply, and the biotic environment consisting of protists, plants, and animals still strongly affect your own life, and you can see how much more direct and decisive the effect was on primitive man. Climate and soils determined, and still do to large extent, the growth of green plants on which the whole community depends. Animals interacted, and still interact, with man as foods, as competitors, and as antagonists (parasites and predators on man, for instance). Although he is decisively a land animal, man also early developed shore communities that derived most of their food from the sea and its shore. Fishing in inland waters was also among the earliest sources of human food.

Civilization brought other environmental relationships not found in primitive cultures or in organisms other than man, and yet with an element of primitive, direct environment–organism reaction. Industry requires power and raw materials (other than food), and this has environmental relations of no significance to nonindustrial organisms. The distribution and nature of human communities is influenced by the natural distribution of water power, mineral fuels, ores, and other industrial resources. In this, however, as in all his relationships with nature, civilized man has greatly modified the directness of his interaction with the environment.

CULTURAL MODIFICATION
OF HUMAN ECOLOGY

Cultural changes have probably been greatest as regards food. The gathering of wild foods, sole resource of the earliest men and of almost all other organisms, has become comparatively unimportant.

It affects civilized communities on a large scale only in the form of commercial sea fishing, which is an enormous industry but yet accounts for only a small fraction of the food of mankind.

Food gathering has, as everyone knows, been almost entirely supplanted by agriculture and animal husbandry, both of which go far back in history to the dim days even before the definitive rise of early civilizations. This is one of the two most radical changes of man's relationships with environments. It is decidedly a reciprocal interaction. On the side of the organism, the food supply of *Homo sapiens* has been enormously increased and made more dependable. On the side of the environment, everywhere that cultivated plants are grown or domestic animals are raised the biotic environment has been profoundly changed. There have also been repercussions in the physical environment, for instance in the composition of soils or the localization of erosion.

The worldwide interlocking of human supply, commerce, and industry is thoroughly familiar to you, perhaps so familiar that you do not think about it enough. We need not belabor the point beyond emphasizing that this is a biological phenomenon. Local environmental interactions have by no means been eradicated and are as important as ever, but they are caught up into a worldwide network of interactions. It is becoming increasingly true that a reaction anywhere affects the human environment in some way and degree everywhere. *Homo sapiens* is rapidly becoming a species (the only one) in which an individual's environment is not only his own surroundings but the whole earth.

Modification of Environment

The results of man's cultural changes in his relationship to the environment have not affected man alone. They have reverberated through the whole world of life and have affected the environments of countless other organisms. If a state of nature is defined as one uninfluenced, directly or indirectly, by man, then you would search far to find a state of nature anywhere on earth today. It is certainly not to be found anywhere that man lives or travels, not in the remotest Amazonian jungle or the most barren desert. Perhaps it still exists on some unscaled

Himalayan height or unplumbed oceanic deep, but even in these regions, far removed from any contact with "civilization," some remote effect of human activity is likely to be felt.

All organisms influence their environments, and many have some small measure of active control over parts of their environments. The fact is obvious when a beaver builds a dam, and it is no less true when a tree sheds its leaves. Man, however, controls and modifies environments more extensively than any other organism.

LAND USE

Here in the United States and in many other of the most intensely developed parts of the world the most obvious widespread changes have been produced by man's destruction of natural communities to convert them and the space they occupied to his own uses. Indians had already considerably modified their environments in North America, but the changes they made were insignificant in comparison with what has happened since Europeans settled here. In 1492 almost the whole eastern half of North America was covered with vast forests. About 300 million acres of forests have since been destroyed. Most of the early clearing was for farmland; that is to say, biologically its purpose was to remove native communities with low supporting capacity for *Homo sapiens* and to replace them with controlled communities more productive of human food. Clearing has now become a negligible activity, simply because most of the good agricultural land was long ago cleared. Forests now remain mainly where they are themselves more productive for human use than would be farming where they stand. They are now cut for forest products, mostly lumber. Destruction of forests still goes on, although in the national forests and those controlled by the more enlightened private owners the cutting is so managed as to crop surplus growth and keep the forest healthy. Even in that situation, the controlled crop forest is a community unlike that of virgin forest. The same is true of extensive tracts early cut for farmland and now gone back to forest by natural succession or deliberate reforestation. We are not, at this point, concerned with whether this is a "good thing" or a "bad thing" but only with making the biological observation that the natural communities have been destroyed or profoundly altered. It should be added that destruction of forests still goes on extensively by fires, many of which are of human origin.

Besides replacing native vegetation with introduced plants, man has also drained environments too wet for his crops and put water on those too dry. In the United States enormous areas have been drained, mostly in Florida, the Mississippi Valley, and the North Central states. The mere fact of draining radically changes the environment, and of course its usual purpose is to introduce new communities. Other immense areas, mostly west of the 100th meridian (about the longitude of Kansas), have been irrigated and their native vegetation (for none of the reclaimed "desert" land was bare) again replaced by cultivated plants and introduced weeds.

Land not used to produce food or raw materials is still not free from human disturbance. Cities, industrial plants, airfields, roads, and other such constructions wipe out the natural environment wherever they are built, and in the aggregate they cover a considerable and rapidly increasing fraction of the surface of the land. Even areas not permanently inhabited, such as the high mountain country, or those deliberately kept "natural," such as the national parks and parts of the national forests, are intensively used by man for recreation, if nothing else. No biologically minded person who joins the traffic jam in, say, Yellowstone Park can imagine for a minute that he is seeing a community natural in the sense of absence of radical human disturbance.

Even now—and intensity of use increases yearly—it is unlikely that there is an acre of land in the United States that is not sometimes and in some way used by man for his specific purposes and that has not been changed by that use. The same is true almost everywhere on earth, true to even greater extent where man's occupation has been longer, as in Europe, and true to less extent where exploitation has been less intense, as in the Amazon Basin, but nevertheless true. If you would like to return to nature, you were born too late.

DISTURBANCE OF COMMUNITIES

The most radical result of human activities is that a community is destroyed as such and another put in its place. This is by no means a simple occurrence. When grassland is plowed up and planted in corn, the result is not simply that we have corn instead of grass. The grass and other associated green plants were, as you know, only a first link in innumerable food chains and one element in a populous community. Some of the food chains are cut off at the bottom when the grass is destroyed. The organisms in those chains die out or move elsewhere. It is man's intention that corn shall start food chains leading only to himself, but with all his controls he is unable to carry out those intentions. Some members of the destroyed community happily switch to corn, and some of the old food chains continue. Other organisms that eat corn (any part of the plant) move in, and their populations increase. New food chains develop. A whole community organization is rapidly resumed on the new basis.

It seems a fairly obvious fact that interference in a food chain or in a predator–prey balance is going to react on the whole chain or on both sides of the balance. Yet men have often deliberately interfered in such situations without foreseeing the results. The destruction of predators in the Kaibab forest is a good example (p. 423). Another along the same lines

happens when coyotes are eliminated because they occasionally prey on sheep. The main food supply of the coyotes is rabbits, which may increase so in numbers when the coyotes are removed that the sheep are starved by competition with the rabbits for food. Or again, widespread use of insecticides to control mosquitoes and other insect pests in some areas has led to the death of desirable fishes and birds. Experimentation with the "wonder drugs" has also developed strains of bacteria immune to the drug, and even some that require the drug in order to thrive.

Man has wiped out numerous species single-handedly, such as the passenger pigeon and the dodo, and he reduced others, such as our bison and pronghorn antelope, to the verge of extinction before deciding to save a few for his own pleasure. On the other hand, he has greatly increased the populations of some species, even aside from his domestic animals. House rats should be grateful to man who, although unwillingly, made possible their worldwide expansion. More pleasantly, some native quail find cultivated fields a fine addition to their environment and thrive in community with man.

Depletion and Conservation

All organisms derive materials and energy from their environments. All tend to increase in population and to spread in areas as greatly as is permitted by the capacity of the environment and their capacity to utilize the environment (including, of course, the biotic environment). All are checked, ultimately, by limitations of the environment and by such factors as competition and predation, which do not, as a rule, reduce the utilization of the environment but only determine the proportions of its resources that go to support each of the various species present. There is a tendency for each species to monopolize as much as possible of the supporting capacity of the environment. Man is no exception to any of these biological principles. Quite the contrary, it is precisely these principles that underlie and explain man's spread over the earth and the consequent disturbance of natural communities everywhere. That the disturbance is so incomparably greater than results of the same tendencies in any other species is merely a measure of the complexities of man's

demands on the environment and of his success in enforcing them.

UTILIZATION VERSUS PRESERVATION

A first reaction to the widespread destruction of natural communities is often a wish that they could be preserved. Many sentimentalists understand "conservation" as opposition to any disturbance of nature. Certainly biologists, above all other people, are sensitive to the interest and beauty of nature, but they must recognize that the attitude of purely sentimental conservation—that is, a desire for the preservation of untrammeled nature—is as unsound biologically as it is impossible politically or socially. As a practical matter, and regardless of whether such action would be desirable, it would now be absolutely impossible to find a natural community of any great extent completely uninfluenced by man and to keep it so. If it could be done, what benefit would arise?

Any visit to such a refuge or any study of it would immediately end its pristine nature.

Man is an organism, and all organisms utilize their environments. Man will do so no matter what anyone says or does. Even his destruction of nature is biologically natural. His utilization of the whole of his environment is biologically inevitable and is desirable from the viewpoint of his own species. Surely for a human being to take any other viewpoint would be monstrous. It is, however, evident that such utilization may be either wise or foolish. Wisdom in this sense also has a biological significance. Utilization is wise if it does really, both immediately and in the long run, produce maximum benefit for our species. That is the practically and biologically sound definition of conservation.

Wise utilization for production is that which increases, or at any rate does not decrease, the capacity of the environment to meet human needs. Increase in capacity, although it can be spectacular, is inherently limited. It has, indeed, been found that rapid increase may actually lead to ultimate decrease, as has happened in agricultural areas too intensively farmed. The ideal would be to put production on a cyclic basis, turning to the use of man such cycles as have kept all life going continuously for some 2 billion years. That involves a thorough understanding of biological cycles, with emphasis on the facts that you cannot get more out of a cycle than goes into it and that disturbance of any part upsets the whole.

Resources that can be operated in cycles are *renewable*. The possible rate of use is limited by the rate of the cycle as a whole and by the rate of input of energy, a resource that is *not* renewable because of the second law of thermodynamics. To the extent that energy is available and that use of resources is limited to the capacity of the cycle and the cycle is kept in operation, renewable resources are inexhaustible. This *possibility* applies particularly to biological resources, to food and to raw materials derived from plants and animals. Man need never lack food or organic raw materials if his consumption of them is kept to the rate of their production by continuously balanced cycles. Unfortunately, consumption does have a tendency to run ahead of the capacity of the cycles, and some efforts to increase their capacity have actually ended in decreasing it.

Other resources are *nonrenewable*. Their production

cannot be made cyclic, not, at least, as man produces them and at rates even modestly sufficient for his demands. Our present major sources of power, fuel, and light are nonrenewable. Petroleum (and its products, such as gasoline), natural gas, and coal are organic in origin, and hence theoretically renewable, but we are rapidly using up the accumulations of several hundred million years, and the rate of renewal is so extremely slow as to have no practical significance. Naturally fissionable elements, such as uranium, are a future source of power, but they are also ultimately limited in amount and are nonrenewable. Most of our intensively used mineral products, notably the metals such as iron, copper, and many others, are nonrenewable. Their atoms are not destroyed by use, but they are eventually so scattered as to be unrecoverable by any process economically possible now or in the foreseeable future. An economy as dependent on nonrenewable environmental resources as ours is cannot be permanent in the really long run. Wise utilization of nonrenewable resources is evidently the slowest possible utilization with the least possible waste. When such resources will run out is not primarily a biological problem. It does concern biology that the best chance of an indefinite future for civilization recognizably similar to ours seems to be the eventual substitution of nonrenewable materials by renewable materials, that is, in the main, of mineral production by organic production.

It is possible to foresee consequences of continuous increase in the world population, consequences that few will consider pleasant. The absolute limit to otherwise unchecked population increase would be imposed (as it already has been in some countries) by food production. Since each link in a food chain dissipates energy and some materials, a maximum population would have to live as near the beginning of a food chain as possible; human food would consist solely of green plants. Because nongreen plants and all animals compete with man for food, all would be exterminated as far as possible. Pressure for food production would be such that renewable production for any other use would be minimized. Nonrenewable resources would soon be gone, and industry, along with all the products of civilization as we know it, would be reduced to a minimum. What steps will be necessary to obviate this dismal prospect?

Even on a basis of greatest production, it can be shown that wise utilization often involves as little disturbance of natural communities as is practically feasible. The natural cycles may be as productive as any that man can substitute for them. That is probably particularly true of forests, of much semiarid and arid land, and of the seas. Forests over wide areas of poor soils and hilly or mountainous country in the Temperate Zone are more productive of useful organic materials than any method yet devised for farming the same land. That is particularly true of the vast tropical forests, the productivity of which is probably the largest natural resource not yet extensively utilized by man. Cutting down those forests to clear farmland, in the way traditional to us in the Temperate Zone, has so far almost invariably failed. The hopeful new trend is the devising of techniques for cropping the exuberant production of the forests themselves. As for regions with too little rainfall for farming, irrigation is not the full answer to their utilization. There is not enough available water to irrigate them all. Many of the desert and semidesert soils do not repay irrigation even when water can be put on them. In fact, where soils were good they have sometimes been ruined by irrigation through accumulation of salts from the evaporating water. But the natural communities of such areas, adapted to their low water supply, are as productive as the environment permits. In the sea the natural communities are extremely productive, and cropping of the natural food cycles by man is more effective than any other utilization in prospect.

Hitherto we have spoken of utilization in terms of material production. If the human population does reach the maximum capacity of the environment, no other utilization will have much significance. That point is not yet reached, and some may well hope it never is. In the meantime, we can afford and profit by nonproductive utilization of some of the surface of the earth. Space for recreation, or a silent place in which to think, or simply room to draw a clear breath—most of us think that, too, is good utilization

of part of our environment. It is also of value, and practical in the fullest sense, to reserve what space we can for natural communities as little disturbed as possible, where biologists and everyone else can observe and learn more about the processes of nature by which we live and of which we are a part.

MAN AND SOIL

Conservationists are greatly concerned with soil utilization, and for good reasons. We depend on natural soils for most of our food, whether more directly as plant food or less directly as animal food. It is possible to make excellent artificial soils or soil substitutes, but so far, at least, that is so expensive that is has little promise as a possible source of the bulk of human food. It is also unlikely that the aquatic environments, rich as they are, could economically be made the main source of plants and animals usable as human food; they are not so now, at any rate. The soil, then, is the basic factor in supplying man's most basic need, a double "basic" that makes soil fundamental indeed.

It has been carefully estimated that the United States once had 1517 million acres of economically usable farm and grazing land. By the same estimate, 282 million acres had been ruined by use up to 1947 and had become essentially unusable for the predictable future. It was estimated that continued use by traditional methods would soon ruin 775 million acres more. Only 460 million acres were considered in reasonably good shape and not seriously threatened.

Soil is theoretically a renewable resource. All soils are formed, at some time, from bare rock, sands, silts, or barren clays, and soils are continuously being formed now. The process is slow. Under the best of conditions, formation of a good agricultural soil takes centuries, and it may take thousands of years. Agricultural practices that result in loss of soil are therefore essentially mining it, using it up as a nonrenewable resource. These statements are only partly modified by the fact that silts spread by floods may be immediately highly fertile and have their fertility renewed each year, as in the Nile Valley. The fertile silts are soils eroded from areas upstream, and so the process robs Peter to pay Paul.

When a farmer removes a crop from a field, he also removes material that came from the soil and

FIG. 20-3 Erosion. Left, gully erosion in Guilford County, North Carolina. Right, a result of wind erosion: sand blown from eroded fields and piled up on a farm in Cimarron County, Oklahoma, April, 1936. (Photos, left, Soil Conservation Service; right, Farm Security Administration)

that would, under natural conditions, have returned to it. Harvesting cuts off part of the cycle of materials and depletes the soil. The cycle can be kept going by interspersing harvested crops with planting that enriches the soil and by making good the losses by adding fertilizers. More serious and practically impossible to compensate for its actual physical loss of the soil by wind and water erosion after the protective natural plant cover is removed. A windstorm on May 12, 1934, swept up 300 million tons of soil from the plains east of the Rockies and began the "dust bowl" devastation that brought on an economic crisis and the migration of thousands of homeless "Okies," farmers whose farms had blown away (Figure 20-3). In 1900 drip from a barn in Georgia started a gully in surrounding bare soil that has since spread to 3000 acres and washed away whole farms. The millions of acres of soil already lost in such ways cannot be recovered, but further losses are being slowed down, at least, by contour plowing, terracing, and more care in maintaining a vegetation cover (Figure 20-4). On grazing land, heavy overgrazing has also laid bare the

FIG. 20-4 Contour farming in the Elm Creek watershed, Bell County, Texas. By running his plowing and planting lines along the contours of the land, a farmer can minimize water, and therefore topsoil, runoff. The practice must often, as in this case, be a cooperative venture between adjacent landowners. (Photo, Soil Conservation Service)

soil and promoted erosion, besides having damaged the grass community and having permitted invasion by undesirable weeds. The remedy is obvious although not easy: replanting of hardy grasses and reduced grazing (Figure 20-5).

FLOODS AND FLOOD CONTROL

Soil kept porous and covered with vegetation absorbs much rainfall. On cleared land the soil tends to pack, and more rain runs off over the surface. This is of course the immediate cause of accelerated erosion on cleared land, and it is also an interference with the water cycle that has extensive repercussions on living communities. Uplands from which forests have been cleared no longer retain water effectively, and the ground water below them is also less steadily maintained. Organic productivity is thus decreased by a lack of steady water supply. The runoff also tends to produce floods more severe than those that would occur without human disturbance. A return to natural water conditions is generally desirable and can be achieved only by restoring vegetation on the uplands. Even natural flooding, without intensification by human activity, is a serious problem to those who live and farm along such rivers as the Mississippi and its main tributaries.

Flood-control projects represent one of the most heroic efforts of man to control the natural environment and the intensification of natural forces resulting from man's own activities. Some attempt is made to control floods where they come from, in the runoff in the uplands, but most of the effort goes into delaying the floodwaters downstream by holding them behind storage dams. The water so impounded may also be used for generating power and for irrigation. The geologist notes that the expedient is temporary, for all the storage reservoirs will fill up with silt in a few generations at most and then be useless. (Some have filled in a dozen years. See Figure 20-6.) Extension of their usefulness demands that silting be reduced by the control of erosion above them. The biologist may add that the adjustment of human utilization to the natural cycles of earth and life is the only *permanent* solution.

RENEWING RENEWABLE RESOURCES

When the whole situation is reviewed, it seems that man's troubles in the utilization of his environment are rooted in biological principles. Life has kept going throughout its tremedously long history by the inpouring of energy from the sun and by interlocking inorganic and organic cycles and sequences of materials and energy on the earth. Man's manipulation of his environment has resulted in its deterioration, from his point of view, whenever he has ignored these natural processes instead of utilizing them. He accelerates the water cycle and erosion, both of which are going to continue, man willing or not. Then he becomes alarmed, but instead of recognizing the nature of the cycles and working with them, he tries to stop them. Intensifying floods by clearing the uplands and then trying to stop them with dams is rather like whipping a horse and then shooting it when it runs away.

Similarly, man ignores food chains and tries to control them by removing the one link that seems

FIG. 20-5 Overgrazing on a Texas range. To the left of the fence, where cattle have been kept out, there is still a good growth of grasses; to the right the land has been reduced to a minimum cover of sagebrush. (Photo, Soil Conservation Service)

FIG. 20-6 Mono Dam and Reservoir, Los Padres National Forest, California. Note that the reservoir is filled with silt. Dams are only temporary solutions to flood-control problems. (Photo, U.S. Forest Service)

to him, often erroneously, to be responsible for trouble, as when he kills coyotes only to have the more damaging rabbits increase. He tries to get out of a cycle more than goes into it, as in the many projects that are pumping down the water table without concern for the fact that no more water is continuously available from the ground than comes into it from rainfall. Also, he nets fish without remembering that next year's population depends on the reproductive capacity of those he leaves behind this year.

Even more serious than man's living beyond his biological income—his depletion of natural re-sources—is his unchecked population growth. This has already resulted in untold misery and an unbalanced biological economy over much of the earth. If no effective corrective measures are taken, this will eventually occur everywhere. Material deficiencies are to some extent staved off by biological improvements in production, agricultural advances; and power shortages may be alleviated for a time, perhaps a long time, by the development of new sources, especially from atomic energy. Nevertheless, population limitation is inevitable, and the only questions are whether it will be voluntary and at what level it will occur.

Summary

Man in nature: the human environment in the modern Western world—mechanization, communication, the interdependence of communities—contrasted with that of primitive peoples; mankind as one species with diverse local cultures; the interaction between man and his environment.

The species *Homo sapiens:* the unusually wide distribution of the species; local differentiation, of both biological and cultural characteristics; origin and nature of human races; population evolution in man as in other animals; the existence of subspecies, usually designated "races"; political and emotional overtones of the word "race"; the impermanence of subspecies as units; the breaking down of human subspecies because of human mobility, with cultural and social factors the only remaining barriers to breakdown and intermixing; racial characters: skin color and other racial differences as adaptive, at least in part; no evidence for racial differences in intelligence; the use of blood-group frequencies as objective characterizations of races; no race inherently "better" in any biological sense.

Basic ecology of *Homo sapiens:* primitive man and environments; man as omnivorous and as part of all food chains open to large animals, thus permitting the success and wide dispersal of human culture; culture as, in part, adaptive; the environmental impact on human culture; the cultural modification of primitive human ecology—clothing, shelter, the human influence on environment, the transition from food gathering to agriculture, the complex interdependence of modern communities in commerce.

Modification of the environment: land use and disturbance of natural communities; in North America, the removal of forests and the development of arable land; the eradication of natural communities of animals; the introduction of foreign plants and animals; dangers in disturbing community balance.

Depletion and conservation: the severity of man's demands on environment; problems raised and the possibility of solving them with foresight; utilization versus preservation—conservation's sentimental form and its wise form, as the planned exploitation of environment to the maximum *long-term* benefit of human species; renewable and nonrenewable resources and the problems posed by the latter (exemplified by fuel and mineral resources); erosion and flooding; the prime significance of soils in food production; the destruction of soils and factors involved in soil destruction (overfarming, wind erosion, gully erosion, etc.); flood control; the need for understanding ecological processes, to live within biological income, and eventually to limit population.

CHAPTER TWENTY-ONE

BIOGEOGRAPHY

Bases of Biogeography

A visit to the country is a pleasure that is greatly increased by an understanding of biological principles. One thing that cannot have failed to impress you in the countryside is that different associations of plants and animals occur even quite near each other. The living things in a stream or lake are decidedly different from those on land along the shore. Farther back on a hillside or a drier meadow other local communities will appear, plainly unlike those of the shore.

Thus at one locality a walk of a few feet can take you from one community into another. If you take a longer trip you soon see that there are broader regional differences in communities. Suppose you drive from New York to Tucson. For the first couple of days you will be in regions where the predominant natural regional community, among the many different more localized communities, is usually a deciduous forest. In the flatter areas most of the forest has been artificially replaced by farmland, but it is still evident that the deciduous forest represents the usual natural climax. Farther along, west of the Mississippi, you will be in a region also extensively plowed into fields but with a natural predominance of open grassland communities. This extends onto the high plains of eastern Colorado and New Mexico, with a change in species of grass apparent if you examine the communities closely and with a botanist's eye. Then you may, depending on your route, have an interlude in mountain forests. Eventually, however, you will see the grassland grading into brush communities, dominated by such plants as sagebrush and greasewood. Finally these communities will grade into others, typical of the true desert, in which cacti, mesquite, and ocotillo are conspicuous.

We have mentioned only plants by way of example because they are fundamental in all communities and are easy to observe. The animals in the communities tend to have similar resemblances and differences on local, regional, and intercontinental scales. Many of their geographic distinctions are common knowledge. Everyone knows that you have to go up north to see a polar bear or out west to see a grizzly bear in their native haunts. You must go to Asia to see a wild tiger and to Australia to see a wild kangaroo.

These common observations show that communities are not everywhere the same. Living things have a geography of their own, which, because it relates to life, is called *biogeography*. The observations further show that biogeographic relationships require the use of an expanding scale. Some involve a few square meters, others large regions, others whole continents, and others the entire earth. At the narrow end of the scale it is obvious that the geographic positions of living things depend primarily on the environment. The fish is in the stream; the squirrel is on the hillside. As the scale broadens, that factor continues to be evident. A deciduous forest community in Pennsylvania and one in Missouri are similar because the climate, soil, and other environmental conditions are similar. They differ to the extent that the environ-ments are not exactly the same. Farther west on the high plains the climate is different, particularly in having less average annual rainfall. In the drier climate the forest community gives way to the grasslands community, and in the still drier Southwest the grasslands give way to the desert communities.

Such resemblances and differences in communities are ecological, and their study is *ecological biogeography*. In this aspect the distribution of plants and animals and their associations in communities with different geographic positions are functional. They are adaptive. That is our first geographical subject. Before proceeding with it, however, we should note that there is more to biogeography than that. Ecological conditions in an Australian desert can be closely matched with one in Africa, or those in a Malayan jungle with one in South America. Ecology always and everywhere affects the geography of living things, but evidently it cannot provide the whole explanation of that geography. The puzzling differences among regional *biotas* (a biota is the totality of organisms of a given place or region, its flora plus its fauna) that are not due primarily to ecology are due to differences in the histories of the regions. Their organisms came to them at different times and from different places; they also evolved differently once they were there. That will be our second geographical subject. Our discussion of both will necessarily be limited. We will deal only with land communities and thus will not cover fresh water and the oceans.

Some Principles
of Ecological Biogeography

Ecological biogeography depends fundamentally on some broad principles with which you are already familiar. Environments differ from place to place. Every organism is adapted to the environment at the particular place where it lives. Every organism is also a member of a community and is adapted to living with other members of the community, which are, in fact, part of the organism's environment. Interrelations in the community as a whole are, further, adaptive among themselves and are also such as to adapt the whole community to the conditions prevailing in its geographic position. You have been familiarized with these principles and with examples of their operation in previous chapters.

IMPORTANCE OF PLANTS
IN BIOGEOGRAPHY

Plants play a predominant role in the geography of biotas, especially of those on the land. Green plants are at the beginning of all food chains. Their nature in a given place strongly influences the nature of later links in the chains and therefore of the whole biota. Plants are also particularly sensitive to variations in the physical environment, especially climate and soil. Although animals are also influenced by such variations, their dependence on a given set of physical factors is usually less narrowly circumscribed. Apparent dependence of animals on climate may in reality be a dependence on a given vegetation type, which is in turn primarily dependent on climate.

On land the kinds of plant communities are so varied, so well defined, and so basic for the whole biota that a map of vegetative provinces generally serves to indicate the ecological differentiation of biotas as a whole. A map of broad types of plant communities is given in Figure 21-1. To the extent that it is ecologically determined, the distribution of animals tends to follow the same pattern.

HORIZONTAL AND VERTICAL CONTROLS

Temperature, solar radiation, and precipitation are the main climatic controls of the plant communities. Each of these factors affects the vegetation directly or indirectly through effect on soil. Important for each of them is not only average intensity but also distribution through the year. Temperature and radiation have a familiar north–south gradient.

There is also, especially through the Temperate Zone, an east–west differentiation that is due mainly to changes in precipitation and subsequent evaporation. Rainfall follows a somewhat erratic pattern influenced particularly by usual air movements, by distance from the coast, and by topography. Precipitation is high on our northwest coast and in the mountains of California. Air moving eastward from there has lost moisture, and the result is an arid belt of deserts and semideserts. The Rocky Mountains

again catch moisture, and the plains immediately eastward are semideserts of high, dry grassland. From there on to the Atlantic coast the general tendency, with many local irregularities, is for increase in rainfall, largely because of moist air that periodically moves northeastward from the Gulf of Mexico. Similar irregular zoning of rainfall occurs on all the continents and in all of the north–south climatic zones of temperature and radiation. Deserts as well as lush rain forests occur in the tropics, and indeed one may occur right next to the other.

Besides these horizontal zonings of climates and of biotas along with them, there is a vertical zoning. If you climb any mountain of considerable height, the climate and the life perceptibly change as you go up. The most obvious climatic change is that it gets colder. This change is similar to one that occurs if you do not climb but simply travel north or south from the equator. Conditions on a mountain are similar to those at sea level farther north. The tops of mountains on the equator have a considerable ecological resemblance to arctic lowlands. Timberline, above which trees do not grow, becomes lower from the southern Rockies into Alaska and finally reaches sea level at the northern tree line. These relationships between horizontal and vertical climatic zones are shown diagrammatically in Figure 21-2. The correspondence of an "arctic zone" on a high southern mountain and in the actual Arctic is not, however, exact. Other factors than average temperature—such as lengths of day and night, extreme temperatures, and atmospheric pressures—are quite different in the two areas, and these may have a distinct ecological effect.

Terrestrial Communities

Ecological geographic consideration of communities is like those nested Chinese boxes or wooden eggs that some of us played with in childhood; when you opened one there was always a smaller one inside. The biggest box is the whole of life on earth. Next smaller are the whole of the land communities

on one hand, and of the aquatic communities on the other. So it goes on down until we are considering the life of one thicket, one meadow, or one pool. What we are now going to consider, by way of example and to bring out further biogeographic principles, is something between the extremes of the

WORLD — ORIGINAL NATIVE VEGETATION

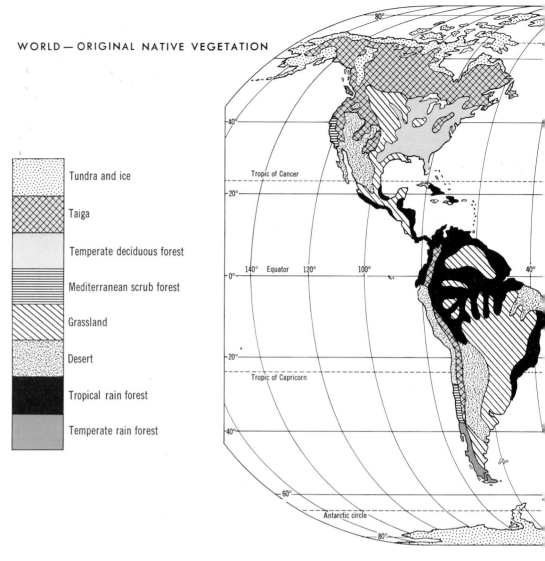

Tundra and ice

Taiga

Temperate deciduous forest

Mediterranean scrub forest

Grassland

Desert

Tropical rain forest

Temperate rain forest

FIG. 21-1   The distribution of original native vegetation in the world. The categories of vegetation on a map of this scale are necessarily broadly conceived. Thus many of them—like taiga, temperate deciduous forest, and tropical rain forest—include within them a diversity of recognizably distinct subtypes. Within any one wide region there may also be quite different types of vegetation in patches too small to show on this scale.

series. It concerns broadly regional kinds of communities, each of which is of course quite variable and includes many different, more local communities. The most important and widespread of them will be reviewed, but our list is not exhaustive. There are, for instance, highly distinctive kinds of geographically definable communities in salt lakes, marshes, or subterranean environments, but they are not considered here. You might consider them on your own. In each community you should especially try to answer two questions, as we shall do in the examples we discuss. The questions are: What are the special conditions of life here? How are they met by adaptations of and within the community?

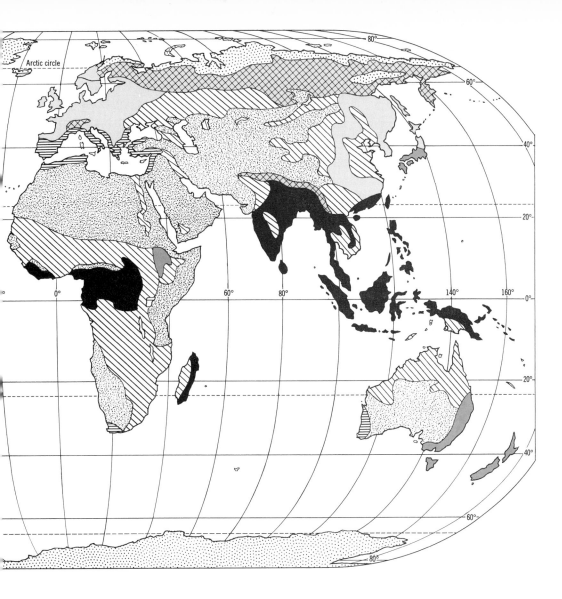

TUNDRA AND ALPINE COMMUNITIES

In North America, Europe, and Asia a vast northern zone encircling the Arctic Ocean is known as the *tundra,* a word borrowed from the Russians. No similar extensive zone occurs in the Southern Hemisphere, because the south has little land in corresponding latitudes. The tundra (Figure 21-3) has the arctic climate, cold on an average, with a long, dark winter and long or even continuous summer daylight. Frost may occur at any time of the year, and the ground is permanently frozen a few feet below

the surface. During summer thaws the region is extremely wet, with saturated soils and innumerable bogs, ponds, and streams.

There are no upstanding trees in the tundra, but dwarf, shrubby alders, birches, willows, and conifers are common. Mosses, especially sphagnum, and lichens, especially "reindeer moss" (not a true moss), cover large areas. Herbs with large, brilliantly colored flowers are conspicuous and beautiful during the brief growing season. Temperatures for growth are minimal, and surviving plants must mature without becoming large. They must resist frequent frost. Many of them can be frozen solid at any phase of life, even

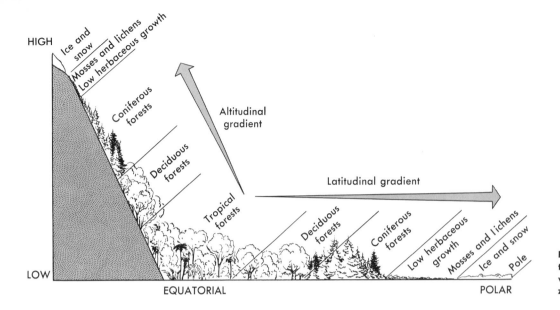

HIGH

Ice and snow
Mosses and lichens
Low herbaceous growth
Coniferous forests
Deciduous forests
Tropical forests

Altitudinal gradient

Latitudinal gradient

Deciduous forests
Coniferous forests
Low herbaceous growth
Mosses and lichens
Ice and snow
Pole

LOW

EQUATORIAL

POLAR

FIG. 21-2 The parallel between the horizontal and vertical distributions of life zones.

when in flower, and survive to resume activity when another thaw comes along. Tundra plants spend most of their lives in a state of suspended animation, active only in brief periods of warming sunshine.

Vast hordes of birds, especially waterfowl, nest in the tundra in summer, but most of them desert it in winter. Permanent residents include a few birds and mammals, warmblooded and well protected by feathers or fur. Some of the resident birds, like the ptarmigan, and mammals, like the snowshoe hare, turn white in winter. White is protective coloration

in a snowy environment and also minimizes heat loss by radiation. Musk oxen and caribou (wild reindeer) are large herbivores, dependent mainly on the abundant moss and lichens. Arctic hares and lemmings (small, ratlike rodents) are numerous and are preyed on by arctic foxes. Polar bears are amphibious; they frequent coasts and ice floes, but also wander inland on the tundra. Insects, especially flies, are so numerous as to be one of the major drawbacks of the tundra from the human point of view. Their eggs and larvae are particularly cold-resistant, and the adults appear

FIG. 21-3 Tundra. Left, a general view of the tundra at Dumb Bell Bay on Ellesmere Island, Canada. Right, "Reindeer moss" (a lichen) and other tundra vegetation in Finland. (Photos, left, Royal Canadian Navy; right, Finnish National Travel Office)

by the billions on warmer summer days. There is no lack of life on a warm day in the tundra, but the numbers of species permanently resident there are smaller than in almost any other sort of community, even the deserts.

TAIGA

The *taiga* (another word we owe to the Russians) occurs in a still broader zone just south of the tundra across northern North America, Europe, and Asia (Figures 21-1 and 21-4). Like the tundra, and for the same reason, it is practically absent in the Southern Hemisphere. Winter temperatures may be as severe as in the tundra, but there is a well-defined summer growing season of 3 to 6 months. It suffices for a heavy growth of hardy trees, and the taiga as a whole is a tremendous forest. In the typical taiga the forests are coniferous, especially spruce, although several other species of conifers occur. Alder, birch, and juniper thickets are also common. Burned areas of the coniferous forest are invaded by aspens and birches, which later are succeeded by conifers again.

The moose (called an "elk" in Eurasia) occurs throughout the whole taiga, where not exterminated by man, and is its most conspicuous animal. Smaller mammals are much more varied than in the tundra. Black bears, wolves, and martens are more common in this zone than elsewhere. Fishers, wolverines, and lynxes are practically confined to it. So are some rodents, such as the northern vole, although most of the abundant rodents are races or subspecies of groups also occurring farther south. Squirrels thrive

in these rich coniferous forests. So do many birds, most of which, however, are here summer breeders and migrate southward in the fall. The many insects and other invertebrates are of species that lie dormant during the severe winters.

The coniferous forests of our western mountains have some distinctive characters of their own but are essentially extensions of the taiga, occurring at increasingly high altitudes the farther south they are. Many of their species, both of plants and animals, are the same as in the typical taiga. The hemlock–hardwood forest of southern Canada and down into the Appalachians is also an extension of the taiga.

TEMPERATE DECIDUOUS FORESTS

Regions with moderate, well-distributed precipitation, with cold winters and warm summers, tend to develop communities in which deciduous trees dominate or climax the natural succession. These conditions occur in the Temperate Zones where the average annual precipitation is somewhere around 40 inches, without very well-defined dry and rainy seasons. In the United States, most of the eastern half of the country has such a climate and was formerly covered by a deciduous forest (Figure 21-5). Northward it graded into the taiga, through the hemlock–hardwood forest, and southward into the southeastern pine forests, a special local group of

FIG. 21-4 Taiga. A Northern spruce forest along the Alaska Highway in Canada. (Photo, National Film Board of Canada)

FIG. 21-5 Temperate deciduous forest. (Photo, Helen Faye)

communities with peculiarities of soils and drainage. The British Isles and practically all of central Europe were also formerly occupied by temperate deciduous forests, and so was a large region in China and southeastern Siberia. There are similar forests in the Temperate Zone of South America, but they are not so widespread there because the precipitation is not suitable over such large areas.

The word "deciduous" implies the most obvious characteristic of this climate and the most obvious adaptation to it. Half the year or somewhat more is the growing season, when perennial plants put on their leaves and are active, while annual plants go through the whole cycle from seed to seed. The rest of the year is a period of nearly suspended animation, with trees and fields bare.

Common trees of the deciduous forest are beech, tulip, sycamore, maple, oak, hickory, elm, poplar, and birch. Chestnuts were formerly common but now have been almost eradicated in the United States by blight. The taiga and other coniferous forests include fewer species of trees, and locally a coniferous forest tends to be dominated by a single species. The deciduous forests have more varied local groupings, each of which commonly includes two or more species, as in the beech–maple climax and oak–hickory, elm–ash–maple, or willow–cottonwood–sycamore communities. The complex distribution of these and other communities within the broader deciduous forest zone is governed by local conditions of climate, soil, and drainage.

The most striking herbivores of the deciduous forests are the browsing deer, mainly the white-tailed or Virginia deer in North America and other species in Eurasia and South America. In Eurasia wild pigs (or boars) are also characteristic of this group of communities, but they do not occur native in America. The principal predators on the larger herbivores are large cats. Our variously named puma, mountain lion, cougar, or panther (all one species, *Felis concolor*) ranges into most of the environments of North and South America. It is now extinct in the eastern forests but was originally their commonest large carnivore. Wolves, although more characteristic of the taiga, also formerly ranged widely into these forests, both in Eurasia and in North America. Foxes are still common in them. The arboreal martens are locally as common here as in the taiga, and the raccoon (absent in Eurasia) is especially abundant in our deciduous forests. These forests throughout the world are also rich in tree squirrels. Among mammals of the North American deciduous forests, over a third of the species are mainly arboreal. Tree-nesting birds are also abundant, and woodpeckers have the most obvious connection with the forest environment. The leaf- and mold-covered forest floor is a world in itself, swarming with fungi and invertebrates.

RAIN FORESTS

The lushest and most complex forest communities develop where there is an abundant and continuous water supply and a long growing season, which may be continuous through the whole year. Such *rain forests* occur in the Temperate Zone, for instance, on our north-west Pacific coast, where they have their own special characteristics and species. They are, however, most widespread and impressive in the tropics (Figure 21-6) and subtropics. They cover most of Central America and northern South America, central Africa, southern Asia from India eastward, the East Indies and South Pacific islands from Sumatra through New Guinea, and small parts of northeastern Australia (see Figure 21-1).

Nowhere is life more exuberant than in the tropical rain forests. A temperate or cold climate forest frequently consists of one species of trees and rarely has a dozen. A tropical rain forest generally includes a hundred or more species of trees, and as many as 500 have been counted in one such forest. Two trees of the same species seldom stand near each other. Having noted a tree of a given species, you may have to travel for miles through the jungle before you find another. The actual species present may be totally different in different rain forests, and are sure to be if the forests compared are in widely separated regions of the earth. Always, however, there is this peculiar abundance of species in each forest, and the general aspect or structure, the ecological make-up, of a tropical rain forest is remarkably uniform wherever it may be and whatever species may compose it.

Microenvironmental conditions change continuously and radically through various levels below the canopy, down to and into the forest floor. The floor is dark even at noon, and among green plants only a few with the most modest photosynthetic requirements manage to grow there. Direct rain is cut off by the umbrella of the canopy, but the lower levels have constantly high humidity.

Apart from the forest trees themselves, two habits of vegetation are especially characteristic of tropical rain forests: lianas and epiphytes. *Lianas* (a word of French origin) are climbing vines. Rooted in the dark forest floor, they use the standing trees as supports up which they climb toward the canopy, where they spread their leaves in the light. The rain forest is a tangle of lianas, slender or big and strong as bridge cables, looped and festooned around and among the trunks and branches of the trees.

Epiphytes are plants that grow on other plants

FIG. 21-6 Epiphytic bromeliads in Trinidad, West Indies. Top, a large clump of *Gravisia aquilega.* A group of plants this size holds many gallons of water and supports a pond fauna high in the trees. Bottom, part of the same clump brought to ground and with the leaves cut away, showing how the leaf bases overlap to form cups in which water collects (the water has spilled out from this specimen). Note the humus (dead leaves, etc.) that has accumulated; it is the plant's substitute for a soil. (Photo, Karl Weidmann)

without parasitizing them or deriving from them anything but a base on which to grow. Growing especially in the upper levels and canopy of the rain forest, they are well above the dark floor and are bathed in light, even though their own height is small. Orchids, ferns, and many other epiphytes form veritable aerial gardens among the high branches of the trees of the rain forests. Without roots reaching to a water supply in the soil, the epiphytes of a rain forest are paradoxically adapted to a dry climate (see Figure 21-6).

Most of us think of the jungle, which is simply an overpopularized name for rain forest, as teeming with animals. At first visit to a rain forest is disappointing in that respect, for animals are rarely seen there. Closer study reveals that animals are indeed common in those forests, although probably no more so than in our familiar Temperate Zone forests and grasslands. They are inconspicuous in the rain forest because many are nocturnal and most of those active during the day live high up in the canopy, where they are practically invisible from the ground. During the day the forest is oppressively silent, a silence likely to be broken only by the chattering or howling of monkeys (most of which are diurnal) or the squawking of parrots overhead. At dusk an ear-shattering chorus breaks out. Birds, mainly diurnal but foraging more quietly during the day, sound off as they settle for the night. Grasshoppers and allied insects make a din. They are joined most vociferously by tree frogs.

Ants, termites, flies, butterflies, beetles, and other insects are abundant in rain forests and are especially numerous in species there. Frogs also reach a sort of climax in this environment. Snakes are present but may be rather rare, contrary to accounts written more to astonish than to instruct. Mammals are less abundant in the forest than in adjacent (or, for that matter, Temperate Zone) grasslands, but they are still quite numerous. Arboreal forms include monkeys and rodents, especially squirrels. In the Old World rain forests, ground-dwelling herbivores include musk deer, small forest antelopes, and forest pigs. In South America similar ways of life are represented mainly

by terrestrial rodents and peccaries. In both hemispheres the herbivores are stalked by partly arboreal carnivores, especially cats, such as the Old World leopard and the New World jaguar. Here is an illustration of the fact that the same ecological roles exist in geographically widely separated environments, but that the roles may be filled by distinct species or even by animals of different families, orders, or classes in different regions.

GRASSLANDS

In drier parts of the tropics, forests may still extend in narrow zones along watercourses where there is a good underground supply of water. These are the *gallery forests*. A similar forest formation can be seen in the United States and elsewhere in the Temperate Zone, where galleries of these may border a stream far out into a region otherwise treeless. Away from the stream galleries are vast areas in both Tropical and Temperate Zones where the water supply does not suffice for tree growth but does permit a heavy growth of grasses and other small herbs. These areas are variously called prairies, steppes, savannahs,

FIG. 21-7   Grasslands, in the National Bison Range, Moiese, Montana. (Photo, U.S. Fish and Wildlife Service)

pampas, or velds in different parts of the earth. All are ecologically similar and may be classed as *grasslands* (Figure 21-7).

The major North American grassland was the region of the high plains east of the Rocky Mountains. Most of it has now been plowed under to make way for crops. It has, however, been discovered that the drier parts of the region are more permanently productive as they were than as we have made them, and an effort is being made to return some of them to grass. Grasslands are even more extensive on other continents.

The dominant environmental restriction of the grasslands is a low, intermittent water supply. Rainfall may be only 12 to 20 inches per year. It is more than that, even up to 40 inches or thereabouts, on some grasslands but is unevenly distributed through the year. The irregularity of rain, porosity and drainage of the soil, or both factors together prevent a continuous or ample supply of water to plant roots. Other environmental conditions vary greatly in grasslands and help to give each its special characteristics. A savannah in the midst of a Venezuelan rain forest and a high prairie in Alberta have little in common except this: the water supply for plants is unreliable in both places. This one common feature has led to the dominance of grasses adapted to survival through unpredictable alternations of drought and downpour.

Within the grasslands different species and habits of grasses are adapted to special conditions of soil, precipitation, evaporation, and other environmental factors. The eastern, wetter parts of our North American grasslands had tall grasses, attaining heights up to 3 meters: bluestems, Indian grasses, slough grasses. The tall-grass prairie did repay plowing under; it is now our richest agricultural area, including the corn belt. In the arid western prairies short grasses predominated, especially grama and buffalo grasses, often growing among sagebrush. Between the extremes were mixed grasses, sod and bunch grasses, including needle grass, little blue stem, and wheat grass.

The grasslands swarm with animals, which are certainly more conspicuous and probably really more numerous in these communities than in any others on land. Primary consumers are the large grazing mammals. Countless millions of bisons and pronghorns roamed our prairies. Even now the African

grasslands support large herds of zebras and of several species of grazing antelopes. Living in open country, these grassland ungulates are all fleet of foot; they are cursorial. Hares and rodents are also common primary consumers in the grasslands. Some, like the hares, are likewise cursorial. Many rodents, like the prairie dogs and other ground squirrels or the pocket gophers, are burrowing animals. Australian grasslands have herbivores very different in appearance and relationships but ecologically similar: large, grazing, cursorial kangaroos and small, burrowing, rodentlike pouched "mice." Predators are adapted to the herbivore prey: wild dogs, lions, and the like preying on the ungulates; weasels, snakes, and others on the smaller herbivores. Herbivorous insects, such as locusts and grasshoppers, are also incredibly numerous. So are birds. What are some of our characteristic herbivorous and predacious birds in the grasslands?

DESERTS

With increasing aridity, grasslands grade into deserts (Figure 21-8) without any sharp line of demarcation. Deserts are marked by low precipitation, generally 10 inches per year or less, which is likely to fall during a few heavy showers at erratic intervals. Deserts are also characterized by intense sunshine and very hot days, 35 to 40°C and upward, at least during summer; and the evaporation rate is very high. Nights are generally cold, even in summer, and daily variations in temperature reach extremes found in no other environment.

Most annual plants in the desert are small. When a shower falls, they grow rapidly, bloom, and produce seed all within a few days. Among the most astonishing and beautiful sights on earth is one of our southwestern deserts carpeted with brilliant and many-hued flowers a few days after a spring rain. After another few days the desert is drab again, but scattered in it are millions of seeds waiting to perform the miracle anew.

Many perennial desert plants have small leaves or none at all, characters that decrease loss of water. Some have tremendously long roots, reaching deeply buried

FIG. 21-8 Desert, in the Cerbat Mountain Range, Arizona. Joshua trees dominate the scene. Note the abundance of vegetation in this true desert. Animal life is also abundant. (Photo, Trans World Airlines)

water. Others, notably the cacti in our deserts, absorb water rapidly after a rain and store it in spongy internal tissues. Can you think of any adaptive or selective explanation for the fact that most of the desert perennials are spiny or thorny?

Desert animals are also adapted to the scarcity of water and extremes of temperature. Large mammals are rare in deserts, although some Old World antelopes are adapted to extreme desert conditions. Small rodents are numerous. Almost all are burrowers, and many in different parts of the world have independently evolved bipedal, leaping locomotion. The kangaroo rat is an example in our deserts. Snakes and lizards are common in deserts, which nevertheless put sharp limitations on their activities. They are sluggish in the cold desert nights, and yet they quickly die of heat prostration in the sun. Consequently, they are usually active only for short periods in the morning and evening and spend the rest of the time in burrows or crannies.

Historical Biogeography

Ecological biogeography goes far toward explaining why plants and animals live where they do. That explanation, however, is clearly incomplete. Ecology gives a satisfactory answer to such questions as why monkeys occur in the forests of South and Central America but not in the desert and grassland regions of our West and Southwest. It gives a similarly satisfactory explanation of the distribution of monkeys through Africa and southern Asia. It does not explain why monkeys in apparently identical ecological situations in South America and Africa belong to different species, genera, and families. Still less does it explain why forests in eastern Australia, ecologically similar to those occupied by monkeys in South America, Africa, and Asia, harbor no monkeys at all. Australia does have animals similar to monkeys in habits and habitat, but they are not monkeys and the phylogenetic relationship is distant.

There are innumerable problems of that kind in all habitats. Oysters lead similar lives in the sea on the two sides of the Atlantic, but they are distinct genera. Lungfishes live in a few rivers of South

America, Africa, and Australia, but they are of different genera on the three continents and they are completely absent in many other rivers apparently equally suitable for them. Large, spotted semiarboreal cats occur in both South America and Africa, but the South American jaguar is specifically distinct from the African leopard.

The explanations of all these and many similar problems of biogeography are *historical* in nature. The earth has changed during its long history, and its floras and faunas have changed with it. They have changed not only in evolving into new species, genera, and so on but also geographically, in their distribution over the face of the earth.

Many facts like those exemplified above really present a double problem and require dual historical explanations. Take the jaguar and the leopard, for instance. There is no land connection between South America and Africa today, apparently no way in which the big cats could possibly travel from one to the other. Yet the two species are closely related. At some time not long ago, geologically speaking, they had common ancestors in the same place, and those ancestors must have spread to both continents over practicable routes that no longer exist. That is one aspect of the problem. On the other hand, the jaguar and the leopard are different species, and the communities in which they live are radically different in taxonomic composition. We know that there must have been a way for land animals and plants to spread to the two continents, but how did their differences arise? That is the second aspect of the problem.

Biogeographic Regions

We have referred to the varying scale involved in biogeography. Ecological explanations of the distribution of plants and animals apply, for the most part, to the smaller end of the scale. They explain why a certain kind of community lives in one place and another kind a mile away, why one lives at the foot of a mountain and another on top, or one in northern Canada and another in southern United States. Ecological and historical aspects interact and overlap all along the scale, but on the whole the historical side becomes predominant or most evident at the larger end of the scale. The most purely historical explanations apply to the resemblances and differences of the faunas of large areas, such as whole continents or seas.

FAUNAL REGIONS ON LAND

The first approach to any scientific problem is to recognize that a problem exists. Existing facts must be observed, relationships among them must be inferred, and then an explanation must be sought. The observations from which the science of biogeography arose began in antiquity. They bore on the familiar and even obvious fact that different plants and animals live in different places. With the wide exploration of the earth from the fifteenth century onward, the nature and magnitude of the problems became more evident. Facts of the distribution of organisms over the whole earth were gathered, and broadly regional interrelationships began to appear.

In the nineteenth century it became increasingly clear that there are regional patterns of floras and faunas that cannot be wholly, at least, explained by ecological factors. Such patterns occur in the sea as well as on land, but they are not, as a rule, so clear-cut in the sea, nor are the marine patterns as yet so well known. On land, regional patterns of plants are well marked, and so are those of all groups of animals that have been sufficiently studied from this point of view. Best known, in the combination of present condition and historical explanation, is the biogeography of land mammals. We shall therefore stress the mammals as an example of facts, problems, and derived principles. You should, however, bear in mind that the problems are similar and the principles the same for all groups of organisms.

By the beginning of the twentieth century the essential facts about the over-all distribution of land mammals were known. When these facts were arranged and generalized, there emerged a pattern of *land faunal regions*. Each region has some measure of general faunal resemblance throughout, and each has distinctions from any other region. The arrangement shown in Figure 21-9 is now usual.

Faunas intergrade everywhere, and there are no such sharp lines in nature as on the map. Note, too, that this particular pattern is primarily for mammals and birds; its application to other groups of animals and to plants is also generally valid but less clear. Even for mammals and birds, its application to islands other than those recently connected to continents is misleading. With these provisos the pattern has a real validity that may be briefly demonstrated.

The *Holarctic region* has such animals as the timber wolf, hares, moose (called "elk" in Europe), and stag (called "elk" in America) that range through most of it and only marginally, if at all, elsewhere. The New World and Old World parts are distinctive in a lesser way. For instance, our most common deer are of a genus (*Odocoileus*) absent in Eurasia, and the wild boar of Holarctic Eurasia is absent here. The Holarctic is often separated into *Nearctic* ("new (world) northern") and the Eurasian *Palaearctic* ("old (world) northern") subregions.

The *Oriental region* is the haunt of the tiger, Indian elephant (a different genus from the African elephant), gibbons, and many other mammals nearly or quite

confined to this region. The *Ethiopian region* is especially characterized by the giraffe, zebras, African elephant, and a great abundance of antelopes, some related to Oriental species and others sharply distinct.

The *Neotropical region* is more distinctive than any of those already mentioned. Among the many mammals nearly or entirely confined to this region are the guinea pigs and many related rodents, New World monkeys (ceboids), sloths, true anteaters, and armadillos. Actually, the name "neotropical" is somewhat misleading. An enormous part of this region, in southern South America, is outside the tropics.

The *Australian region* is even more distinctive. Its mammalian fauna consists largely of marsupials, and all belong to families that occur nowhere else. The peculiar monotremes are also confined to this region. There are some native placental mammals—bats, rats, and a dog—but most of them are also of distinct species or genera.

SOME PROBLEMS

A biogeographic map like that of Figure 21-10 sums up many facts, but it is still only a generalized description. A description of things is not much use and indeed is not truly a part of science unless it helps to go further, to require explanations and to find them. The descriptive data of mammalian geographic distribution do require many explanations.

There are problems here of resemblances and

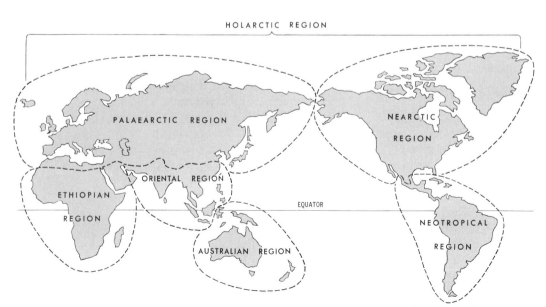

FIG. 21-9 The faunal regions of the world.

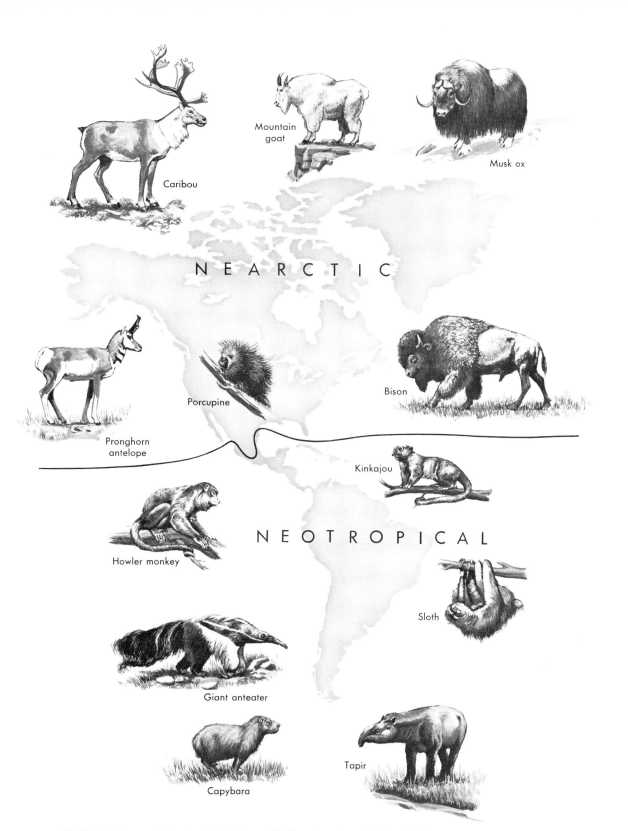

FIG. 21-10 Mammals characteristic of the world's faunal regions. The New World.

Bison

Reindeer

Hedgehog

P A L A E

Polecat

Binturong

Aardvark

ETHIOPIAN

Gorilla

African elephant

Zebra

Gnu

Giraffe

FIG. 21-10 Mammals characteristics of the world's faunal regions (continued). The Old World.

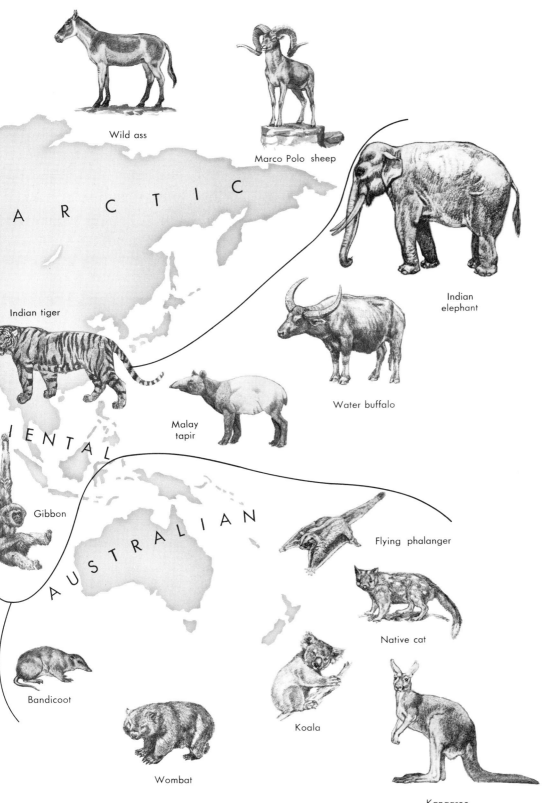

Wild ass

Marco Polo sheep

Indian elephant

A R C T I C

Indian tiger

Water buffalo

Malay tapir

I E N T A L

Gibbon

Flying phalanger

A U S T R A L I A N

Native cat

Bandicoot

Koala

Wombat

Kangaroo

differences. The fauna of North America north of Mexico (that is, of the Nearctic subregion) resembles that of northern Asia much more than that of South America. Yet the Nearctic is connected to South America and not to Asia. Northern Africa, although not connected directly to Europe, has an essentially European fauna. Central and southern Africa are farther from Asia than from northern Africa, but the fauna is more like that of southern Asia.

Then there are problems of apparently conflicting resemblances and origins. One animal abundant throughout the taiga of North America, the porcupine, has its closest relatives in South America. Most of the other animals of the taiga have their closest relatives in Asia. There are a few exceptions. Mule deer and whitetail deer, which do range into the taiga but are somewhat marginal there, are more closely related to some South American deer than to any in Asia. The geographic relationships seem anomalous in themselves, and they also suggest further questions as to places of origin. Did the taiga fauna as a whole come from Asia and a few members, such as porcupines and deer, spread into South America? Or are the forms with South American affinities, the porcupine and the deer, of South American origin? (We shall give you the answer: historical evidence proves that the first explanation is correct for the deer and the second for the porcupine.)

Many of the classic problems of biogeography, including some that have never been satisfactorily solved, arise from what are called *disjunctive* (that is, unconnected) *distributions*. It rather frequently happens that two closely related groups of organisms occur in widely separated regions but that there are no equally closely related forms in between. Because the disjunctive groups are closely related, they must have had a common ancestry not long ago, geologically speaking. Therefore, ancestors of the existing groups must have spread from one region to the other, or to both regions from a third. The problem is to determine what route they followed and how. Famous examples among mammals are the tapirs, which live only in Central and South America and in southeastern Asia, and the camels, which live (as wild animals)

only in South America and Asia. (Both those problems have been solved, as you will see later.) Still more puzzling examples occur among other groups of animals and among plants.

Such problems can be solved only by historical methods. Yet historical study soon raises other problems of its own. It sometimes shows that earlier faunal relationships were quite different from those of today. Thus further explanations are required. The fauna of Honduras (Central America, north of the Panama constriction) now is South American in predominant affinities. But we know from fossils that a few million years ago the mammals of Honduras had nothing to do with those of South America and were all of northern affinities. They were, in fact, more nearly related to mammals of Eurasia, even of Africa, then to those of next-door South America. At about the same time southern Europe, now part of the Holarctic region, had a fauna more closely related to that of the present Oriental region.

FAUNAL CHANGE
AND EARTH CHANGE

Evidently faunas and faunal regions have not stayed put. A biogeographic map of the present world may be true enough as of now, but it is a static picture and does not convey anything of dynamic, historical processes. Those processes are the real story of biogeography. Confining attention to the static map is like looking at one frame of a motion picture instead of running through the whole film.

Organisms have developed on a constantly changing earth. Climates have changed. Mountains have arisen and been worn down. Shallow seas have advanced and retreated where now is land. Most important of all, from our present point of view, seas now separated by land have been united, lands now separated have also been united, and both seas and lands now united have at times been separated. During the latter part of geological history at least, the last hundred million years or more, major seas and lands, the oceans and continents, have substantially maintained their present identity. Their outlines and detailed features have changed considerably, but they have existed continuously as geographic units. The connections among them have changed, however. That has had most profound effects on the distribution of organisms seen on such a large scale as in the biogeographic regions.

Historical changes in any given biotic region and indeed within any community are of four kinds: (1) Evolutionary change takes place within each of the species present in region or community. (2) The proportionate numbers of individuals of the various species change; some become more and some less abundant. (3) Some species disappear, either locally or by total extinction; this is a special case of (2), the reduction of proportionate numbers to zero. (4) New species spread into the region or community from elsewhere.

The last-mentioned kind of change is the one that is most directly geographic. Historical biogeography is concerned primarily with the spread of species and of whole biotas—their dispersal. It is this that is so intimately bound up with the earth changes we have mentioned, because the earth changes open and close routes of dispersal. The geographic changes cannot, however, be wholly separate from the other kinds of change in regions and communities. This geographic spread of species is a cause of numerical changes, including extinction, in invaded communities. Such spreads are generally accompanied by adaptive changes in the species involved, because as these species reach new environments selection tends to modify adaptation accordingly. Evolution may also be speeded up within the invaded communities, if there is an intensification of selection and change in its trend.

Basic to all these aspects of biogeography are the means of dispersal and the things that facilitate, hinder, or prevent it.

Dispersal and Isolation

MEANS OF DISPERSAL

All organisms have some means of dispersal. That is a necessity for living things. Can you imagine an organism that did not have any way of getting from one place to another? What would the consequences be for such a species?

The means of dispersal are most obvious in the many animals that go places under their own power. They fly, walk, crawl, or swim and so constantly change their precise geographic localities. Included in this category are most of the vertebrates, insects and other arthropods, many worms, some mollusks (such as the squids), and some coelenterates (in the medusa form, although their locomotion is not so directive as in the other groups named). Most land animals (above microscopic size) and the actively swimming aquatic animals belong to these groups.

Even among actively and directively motile organisms dispersal is not a simple matter of packing up and going somewhere else. It is to be distinguished from migrations, in which a whole population moves periodically to another region. That is a geographic movement, but only among regions already occupied on occasion and hence not an actual spread or dispersal of the species. Most animals have a strong attachment to the community into which they are born, whether that community is fixed at a single geographic locality or is mobile or migratory. Dispersal usually takes place through a sequence of generations. As the population becomes more dense, marginal individuals have a better chance if some of them move out from the center of density. Any one individual may move only a few centimeters, meters, or kilometers from where it was born. Continued over many generations, the sum of such movements may spread the species, or others derived from it, over a whole continent or ocean, or more than one.

The dispersal of protists, plants, and many animals is passive as far as the organisms themselves are concerned. Planktonic organisms are dispersed by currents in which they float. Sessile animals, such as corals, have floating larvae that are in effect temporarily planktonic and are similarly dispersed. (All sessile animals are aquatic.) Most plants have spores or seeds that are air-borne or are dispersed by animals and in other ways involving intricate adaptations.

Insects, spiders, and other light animals are often blown for long distances by wind, and this may facilitate their dispersal. Fallen trees and mats of vegetation and debris are often floated long distances down rivers or carried for hundreds, even thousands, of kilometers by ocean currents. With them may go not only seeds but also eggs and adult animals. Violent winds, especially tornadoes, occasionally pick up salamanders, toads, frogs, and even fishes and drop them elsewhere, still living. Flying birds frequently carry live seeds for great distances. Eggs and larvae of many small aquatic animals become attached to the feet or feathers of swimming and wading birds and are carried away and deposited elsewhere in the aerial wanderings of the birds.

In the world as we see it today and not as it was in a true state of nature, man is one of the most effective agencies of dispersal. He has purposely taken domesticated animals and cultivated plants wherever he himself dispersed. He has also purposely introduced many wild animals and plants in regions where they are not native. Mice, rats, and other small animals, especially insects, have hitchhiked with man, against his own intention, in boats, wagons, automobiles, and now airplanes. As a result, there is now no region on earth where all the plants and animals are native, none introduced purposely or accidentally by man.

ROUTES OF DISPERSAL

There are so many means of dispersal for organisms that it is somewhat surprising that there are few worldwide species. For a group with completely effective dispersal the final control would, after all, be purely ecological. That is, the group would soon occur wherever the environment provided an ecological role for which it was well adapted. This is true of man and of some of his commensals and parasites, but man and the organisms most closely associated with him are special cases. Few other species are literally worldwide even in suitable environments.

Dispersal depends not only on means but also on route. An analogy is that where you drive depends not only on having an automobile, the means, but also on where a road goes, the route. Nature has many routes, from broad turnpikes to bumpy back roads. It also has many barriers, roads that are closed for one species or another and regions where, for a given species, no roads exist.

For many animals of the open sea, the whole ocean is a highway. They tend to spread widely until they encounter an environmental or ecological barrier. Distribution is strongly affected by the great ocean currents. The over-all pattern of these currents is fairly constant now, although it must have had some radical regional changes in earlier geological times. A current from the Gulf of Mexico once flowed through what is now Central America into the Pacific, instead of doubling back into the Atlantic as the Gulf Stream. Thus routes may change in the sea as on land, but wherever they go, the ocean currents are main dispersal routes for plankton spreading downstream.

The winds, turbulent and erratic as they are locally, have an over-all pattern of air movement that has probably changed little through later geological time. For plants and animals with an air-borne dispersal phase, the zones of prevailing westerly winds, for instance, are and long have been major routes for dispersal from west to east.

Physical and climatic maps of Eurasia show that there is a pathway from western Europe clear across to northern China which could readily be traversed in all its parts by many land plants and animals. That dispersal route has been extensively followed, as is evident from the fact that some natural communities in Europe are remarkably like others in China, thousands of kilometers away. Yet they are not exactly the same in the two regions. A dispersal route, no matter how open it may be, like the Eurasian corridor or the Atlantic equatorial current, is never 100 per cent effective.

For any given group of organisms there are dispersal routes that differ in the probability of dispersal. The scale of probabilities is continuous. At one extreme are routes along which dispersal is prompt and nearly certain. At the other extreme are routes so unsuitable that dispersal along them is so unlikely as to be effectively impossible. Of course, for the group in question such an extremely low-probability route is more likely to be a barrier to spread than a dispersal route.

For whole biotas there is also a continuous scale of probabilities of dispersal or of migration. If chances are good for the spread of many or most species of a biota (although chances may still be poor or practically nil for some species), the route is a *corridor*. The Eurasian route previously mentioned has been a corridor for Holarctic floras and faunas. Other routes are more and more selective. Some species migrate readily along them, whereas others do not. The route may then be considered a *filter,* because it passes parts of biotas and holds others back. There is no sharp distinction between a corridor, which is still a filter for some individual species, and a filter, which is still a corridor for certain species. It is merely a matter of what percentage of a whole biota follows the route. A good example of a filter route is the Middle American connection between North and South America discussed later in this chapter.

BARRIERS

In a sense a barrier can be thought of as a dispersal route looked at from the other end of the scale of probability. Probabilities of dispersal for a given species along a given route may be anything from near 100 per cent to near 0. (Whether the chances are ever *exactly* 100 per cent or 0 is a moot point.) If the chances are low, the route is a barrier. In consideration of whole biotas, almost any route may be a corridor for some species and a barrier for others. A filter route is, of course, a barrier for the species that are filtered out.

A barrier is any zone physically or ecologically unsuited for the organisms impeded by it. A mountain range is a barrier to species better adapted to lowland conditions on each side of it, and the lowlands are barriers between mountain ranges. Grassland is a barrier for forest animals, and forests are barriers for plains animals. A cold ocean current is a barrier for warm-water species.

Faunal regions are delimited by major barriers. The change from the Nearctic to the Neotropical across Middle America is gradual, but it tends to center along the barrier formed by the change from temperate grassland and desert to tropical forests in Mexico. The Sahara and other deserts separate the Palaearctic and Ethiopian regions in Africa. The Himalayas and other mountains are the barrier between Palaearctic and Oriental in Asia. These barriers are not absolute. They are filters, but strong ones.

They have not always been there, and faunal regions have not always been delimited as they are now.

A special kind of barrier that is one of the strongest limitations on dispersal of organisms is purely ecological. Plant seeds may be wafted for hundreds of kilometers, perhaps even across an ocean. If they land on bare soil of suitable composition and in a suitable climate, the seeds will grow. Dispersal has occurred, and the species has spread geographically to a new region. But there is a catch in the word "bare." There is practically no evironment that is not already occupied by plants adapted to it. There is little chance, indeed, that the new types of seeds will land on suitable bare soil. They will land in an established community where they must compete with species already fully established there, well adapted to the community's ecology and to the environment. Exceptional invaders can overcome this tremendous handicap, but the chances are usually slim.

Strong Barriers and Sweepstakes Dispersal

A plains animal is not likely to cross a mountain range, but it could do so in some instances and might find food and other necessities of life on the way. The animal might be neither more nor less likely to cross an arm of the sea of equal width, but the character of the barrier is quite different. The sea is an environment in which a land animal cannot possibly carry on its normal activities. Similarly for seed plants, the sea is an area where they cannot possibly grow. As still another example, an isthmus is a barrier for marine animals where they cannot possibly colonize or sustain active life.

Barriers that represent not merely difficult but downright impossible habitats for the organisms in question are of the very strongest kind. Populations cannot spread across them by the usual processes of expansion or migration. If the barrier is crossed at all, it must be by individuals and in one jump, so to speak, not by the gradual expansion of a population. Even the strongest barriers of this kind can be crossed by many organisms and have been crossed repeatedly in the long history of life. This is *waif* or *sweepstakes dispersal,* "sweepstakes" because the individual chances of dispersal over such barriers are small, as are the chances of winning a sweepstakes, and yet the event does occur (Figure 21-11).

A great natural experiment in sweepstakes dispersal occurred when the island volcano Krakatoa, near Java in the East Indies, blew up in 1883. Every trace of life on the island was destroyed. The nearest island not destroyed by the eruption is over 18 kilometers distant, and yet in only 3 years there were 11 species of ferns and 15 of flowering plants on Krakatoa. Animals soon followed, and within 25 years there were 263 species of animals resident on the island. Most of them were insects, but there were 4 species of land snails, 2 of reptiles, and 16 of birds. In 1928, 45 years after the explosion, there were 47 species of vertebrates on the island, mostly flying forms (birds and bats), but including two kinds of rats.

The Hawaiian Islands are surrounded by a tremendous oceanic barrier and have never been connected to other land, but they had a luxuriant native land biota. All the ancestors of the thousands of species of Hawaiian plants and animals reached there by sweepstakes dispersal.

One reason the historical biogeography of land mammals has been studied more extensively than that of any other group is that they are little subject to sweepstakes dispersal. It can usually be assumed that their migration routes were on continuous land connections. Their geographic history thus is crucial in determining when and where variable earlier land connections existed. Nevertheless, it is practically certain that a few land mammals have had sweepstakes dispersal. Although exceptional, those instances have influenced mammalian biogeography markedly in some regions. Their recognition has cleared up some classic problems that seemed insoluble when it was supposed that land mammals *always* spread over continuous land.

FIG. 21-11 Sweepstakes dispersal. A group of weevils (Cryptorhynchinae) has island-hopped from west to east. The height of the vertical bar is proportional to the diversity (number of genera) of the group at each place. Clearly the group has been sifted out, fewer and fewer managing to follow each successive sweepstakes route. These insects are, even so, particularly good at sweepstakes dispersal.

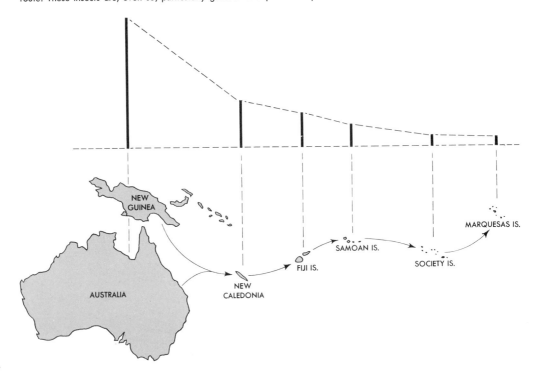

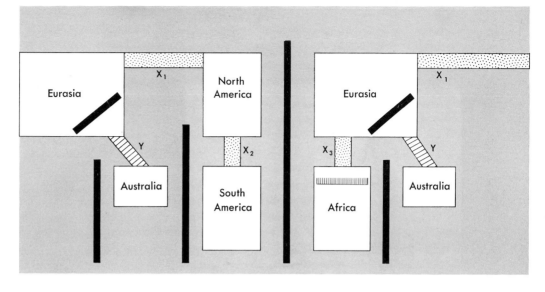

FIG. 21-12 **World dispersal routes: barriers, filters, and corridors.** Major features of the geographic history of faunas, especially mammals, are best accounted for by considering the continental blocks and the main sea barriers as constants and the three main filter bridges or corridors and one main sweepstakes route as variables. X_1, X_2, X_3, variable filter bridges or corridors; Y, variable sweepstakes route; ||||||||||||||, constant barrier during the Age of Mammals; //////, somewhat variable land barrier.

Changing Biotas and Geography

THE WORLD CONTINENT

We have noted that the Neotropical and Australian regions are more distinctive than the Holarctic, Ethiopian, and Oriental regions. We have also mentioned that the fauna of northern North America is more like that of Asia, to which it is not connected by land, than that of South America, to which it is connected. The historical reasons for these facts may now be stated, and the general geographic background is illustrated in Figure 21-12. Australia is now and has long been an island continent. South America is not now but was during most of the Age of Mammals, the last 70 million years or so, an island continent. Africa, Europe, Asia, and North America were separated from each other for various shorter times, but they were also connected periodically during the Age of Mammals.

As far as the mammals are concerned—and other groups of land organisms have also frequently tended to follow this pattern—Africa, Europe, Asia, and North America were long essentially one big land unit, a supercontinent or World Continent. There have been repeated regional isolation and differentiation from time to time, but by and large the history of land faunas has followed along the same broad lines on the World Continent. There has been frequent although always incomplete (filtered) intermigration of faunas among its different parts, the continents as we have them today.

With the aid of fossils it is possible to measure the relative intensities of intermigrations on the World Continent during the past 60 million years or so. The varying extent of dispersal of land mammals in either direction between Eurasia and North America is shown in Figure 21-13. In general, it is reasonable to conclude that when dispersal was comparatively high there was a land connection between the continents and that when it was low there was a sea barrier. Other evidence indicates that the connection, when it existed, was between Alaska and northeastern Asia.

The connection or connections within the Old World kept the World Continent faunas sufficiently mixed so that they retained a broad similarity. The connections were filters, however, and other filters developed within the continents. As might be expected, relatively few animals especially adapted to warm climates managed to cross the northern bridge between Asia and North America, in spite of the fact that Alaska was a good deal warmer during most of the Age of Mammals than it is now. Contrary to some popularizations of the subject, there is no

to isolate what had been more nearly uniform faunas and finally resulted in the distinction we recognize now between the Ethiopian and Oriental regions.

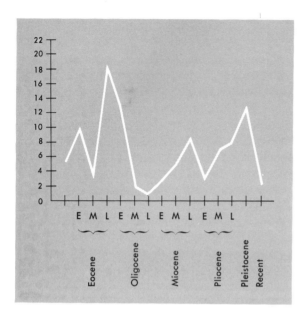

FIG. 21-13   Interchange in the mammalian faunas of North America and Eurasia through the Cenozoic. The graph plots the numbers of items of evidence for the interchange. The intensity of the actual interchange doubtless followed rather closely the ups and downs shown here. Evidence indicates that the land connection, when it existed, was between Alaska and northeastern Asia. E, early; M, middle; L, late. For the time scale see Chapter 22.

good evidence that Alaska was ever tropical in climate.

Regional differentiations of faunas thus could and did occur in spite of repeated mixing by intermigration. The World Continent did not develop a really uniform fauna, even where environmental conditions were closely similar. The alternating filter and barrier between Asia and North America gave a degree of isolation reflected now in considerable distinction of their faunas. In the Old World the east–west desert filter in Africa and the mountain filter in Asia developed during the age of Mammals. Northern and southern faunas then became more sharply separated than they otherwise would have been, or than they were earlier in the Age of Mammals. Narrowing of the land connection between Africa and Asia and extension of the desert filter in south-western Asia also tended

ISLAND CONTINENTS

Similarities between the faunas of two regions naturally tend to be in proportion to the amount of intermigration that has occurred between them. Regions long connected by corridors have faunas of much the same composition, differentiated moderately on a local, largely ecological basis. Isolation, the interposition of barriers, leads to more radical differences on a regional, more historical than purely ecological, basis. The longer the period of isolation, the greater the differences. Australia and South America, long island continents, illustrate this principle, which explains the regional peculiarities of their floras and faunas.

In Australia most of the ecological roles (or ways of life) of land mammals are filled by marsupials. That is in itself a radical difference from the World Continent, where practically all such roles are filled by placentals. If there had been a land migration route between the World Continent and Australia during the Age of Mammals, it seems certain that there would have been early mixture of placentals and marsupials there. Evidently, Australia started the Age of Mammals with marsupials only and has been isolated by a strong barrier ever since.

Spreading over a whole continent with highly varied environments, the Australian marsupials early speciated profusely. Different lines rapidly became specialized in adaptation to the many possible ecological roles. They underwent, in short, an adaptive radiation on a grand scale. The roles assumed were generally similar to those of the phylogenetically distinct placentals of the World Continent. The result, as we have already mentioned in another connection (Chapter 15), was convergence between many Australian marsupials and World Continent placentals.

Later, rats, placental rodents that had evolved on the World Continent, also reached Australia. They are now numerous there and have evolved into many species and genera peculiar to the region. This is one of the facts of biogeography that can be explained only by sweepstakes dispersal. If the rats came in over a land connection, it is incredible that no other placentals accompanied them. Rats are also known to be particularly good at oversea dispersal or island-hopping. The only other native placentals of Australia are bats, dispersed by flight and winds; a wild dog, probably introduced by the aborigines; and the aborigines themselves, who came by boat.

South America must have been connected with the World Continent, undoubtedly with its North American part, early in the Age of Mammals. It started out with a far more varied stock of land mammals than did Australia, including primitive marsupials and several groups of primitive placentals. Then the connection with North America was broken, and the mammals evolved in isolation in South America for tens of millions of years. Here, too, adaptive radiation occurred on a continental scale and here, too, there was extensive convergence toward World Continent mammals. Placentals, evolving into families and orders peculiar to South America, took over most roles. The marsupials, however, became much more diverse than they ever were on the World Continent and took over various roles. Most striking is the fact that all the predacious carnivores of island South America were marsupials. Only placental mammals evolved into predators on the World Continent.

Later on, some 30 or 35 million years ago and thus just about the middle of the Age of Mammals, two new groups appeared in South America as the

rats did in Australia. The most reasonable explanation is the same: the newcomers probably got there by sweepstakes dispersal, island-hopping down from Central America, which was not then attached to South America. The newcomers were New World monkeys and rodents resembling guinea pigs; both types expanded greatly in South America and are still characteristic of that continent.

FAUNAL INTERCHANGE

In the later part of the Age of Mammals, a few million years ago, the mammalian fauna of South America was far more distinctive than it is now. It had almost nothing in common with North America or the rest of the World Continent. Then movements of the earth's crust heaved up a land connection between the two continents. The result was first a trickle and later a flood of mammals from each continent onto the other. Such mixtures of faunas after the disappearance of a barrier have often occurred, both on land and in the sea, but this is at present the clearest and most fully analyzed example (Figure 21-14).

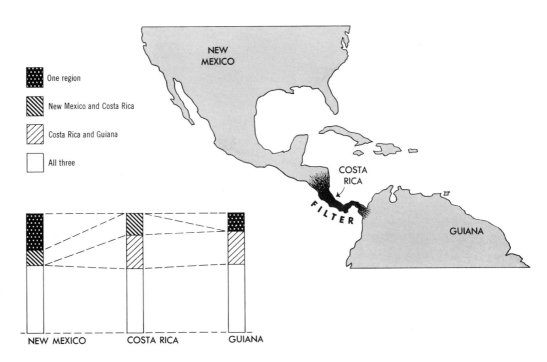

FIG. 21-14 The Isthmus of Panama, a major filter route. The filter action of the isthmus is well illustrated by the graphs, which show the high proportion of families of mammals in both New Mexico and Guiana that either have entirely failed to cross the isthmus (black with white stippling) or have only gotten halfway across (diagonal lines). The total height of the column for each of the three zones represents 100 per cent of the local mammalian fauna.

One region

New Mexico and Costa Rica

Costa Rica and Guiana

All three

NEW MEXICO

COSTA RICA

FILTER

GUIANA

NEW MEXICO   COSTA RICA   GUIANA

The filtering action of the connection was striking. Wild dogs, raccoons, cats, weasels, field mice, peccaries, deer, tapirs, and many others eventually passed the filter in great numbers from north to south. But other common North American mammals, such as beavers, pronghorns, and bison, did not. (Why do you suppose these animals were filtered out?) From South America into North America came porcupines, capybaras (large, amphibious rodents, extinct here now but still present in South America), armadillos, glyptodonts (large extinct relatives of the armadillos), giant sloths (large extinct relatives of the living tree sloths), and perhaps opossums, although they may have been in North America all along. Most of the South American mammals, however, failed to get completely through the filter. Among others, the peculiar native ungulates, the monkeys, and the marsupial predators did not.

Animals spread in both directions between North and South America, as is usual on most dispersal routes. North American animals were, however, more successful than those of South America in making their way into the communities of the other continent. Both continents became temporarily richer in land mammals than they had been. Before the interchange North America had 27 families of land mammals and South America 23. At the height of the interchange the figures were 34 and 36, respectively.

The increase in diversity involved some duplication of ecological roles. Animals that had evolved convergently on the two separate continents now came into direct contact and competition. Such a situation cannot last indefinitely. Ultimately one of the competing forms wins out, and one becomes extinct. The interchange was followed by the widespread extinction of species, genera, and whole families. At present North America (north of Mexico) has only 23 families of land mammals—actually fewer than before the interchange—and South America has 30. The mammals of North American origin were more successful; fewer of them became extinct. The only mammals of known or probable southern origin still present in our fauna are the porcupine, armadillo, and opossum, and they do not loom very large in the fauna. In present-day South America about half the mammals are descendants of comparatively recent invaders from North America. All its native hoofed mammals and all the marsupial predators became extinct.

FAUNAL STRATIFICATION

Wide dispersal of plants and animals has been frequent through the geological past, but it has been scattered and episodic as new dispersal routes appeared or old ones disappeared. Moreover, it has seldom if ever happened that a *whole* biota, a complete and integrated community, was dispersed all at once.

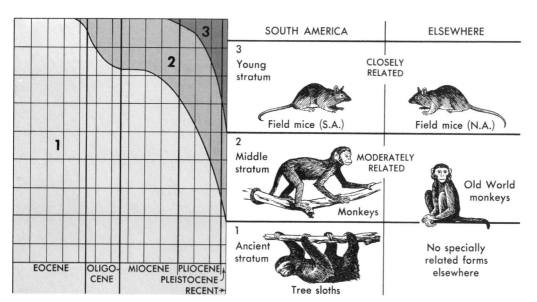

FIG. 21-15 **Stratification of the South American fauna.** Three strata can be recognized. 1. Ancient, in South America since before the Eocene; no closely related forms elsewhere; sloths, anteaters, etc. 2. Middle, in South America since the late Eocene or Oligocene; arrived by sweepstakes dispersal; New World monkeys, guinea pigs, etc. 3. Youngest, in South America since the late Miocene and mostly after the still later reunion of North and South America; field mice, cats, dogs, deer, etc.

There is always some filtering. Thus it happens that the regional communities we have today consist of species whose ancestors spread into that region at different times. For example, in our now decimated grasslands fauna the bison (or "buffalo") and pronghorn (or "antelope") were the prominent large herbivores, both equally at home on the high plains. But the ancestors of the bison came here from Asia quite recently, geologically speaking—a matter of some 500,000 years. The ancestors of the pronghorn, on the other hand, have been here for tens of millions of years.

The division of a fauna into different *strata,* depending on how long the various groups have been in the region, is particularly clear among the land mammals of South America. There are three readily distinguished major faunal strata there. The oldest consists of descendants of animals dispersed to South America when it was connected with the World Continent around the beginning of the Age of Mammals. Armadillos, sloths, and anteaters are prominent surviving members of that stratum. The next stratum descends from animals that reached South America by sweepstakes dispersal around the middle of the Age of Mammals: monkeys and many native rodents such as the guinea pig. The youngest stratum consists of groups that invaded from North America when the continents were reunited toward the end of the Age of Mammals: field mice, dogs, cats, deer, and many others.

As a rule, with some exceptions, older faunal strata are more distinctive and peculiar to their region than younger strata. In other words, the longer a group has been in a particular region, the more likely it is to evolve along lines different from those of its relatives elsewhere. This is eminently true of the South American strata. There is nothing like a tree sloth anywhere else on earth. South American monkeys do resemble their relatives in Africa and Asia, but they belong to a distinct superfamily. South American field mice are, on the whole, barely distinguishable from their North American relatives (Figure 21-15).

DISJUNCTION

We are now ready to review briefly the problems of disjunctive distribution mentioned earlier in this chapter (Figure 21-16).

Some disjunctive distributions are simply explained by the fact that a climatic or other environmental change has restricted a formerly widespread group to scattered parts of its previous range. For instance, pikas (small-eared, tailless relatives of the rabbit) occur disjunctively on various western mountain ranges and in the Yukon and adjacent parts of Alaska. They are cold-climate animals that became widely distributed during the Ice Age and now occur only where the climate is still like that of the Ice Age. *Glacial relicts,* as they are sometimes called, which are plants or animals widespread in the Ice Age and now scattered disjunctively in the far north and on mountains, are common in North America and Eurasia.

Pikas also occur on the cold northern steppes of Eurasia, which is not surprising for such a glacial relict. Disjunction between Old World and New World pikas is clearly accounted for by the sinking of the former land bridge between Asia and Alaska. It is not unusual for a barrier to arise where a migration route used to be, producing disjunction. Many closely related pairs of marine species are disjunctively distributed on the Atlantic and Pacific coasts of Central America. This at once suggests that there was a marine migration route across the region where the isthmian land barrier now stands. The suggestion is confirmed by geological studies. What connection do these facts have with the history of the South American land fauna?

The most striking and disputed instances of disjunctive distribution involve southern land areas. The examples of the tapirs and camels have already been mentioned. Others include the marsupials in Australia and South America (absent in Eurasia), the southern beeches (*Nothofagus*) and pines (*Araucaria*) in Australia and adjacent islands and in South America (but not in Africa or the northern continents), and a group of strictly fresh-water fishes in South America and Africa (and nowhere in the north). Many others exist among both plants and animals.

We know from fossil evidence that many of these now disjunctive groups formerly occurred in northern lands. There is no reasonable doubt that they spread between the Old World and the New across the

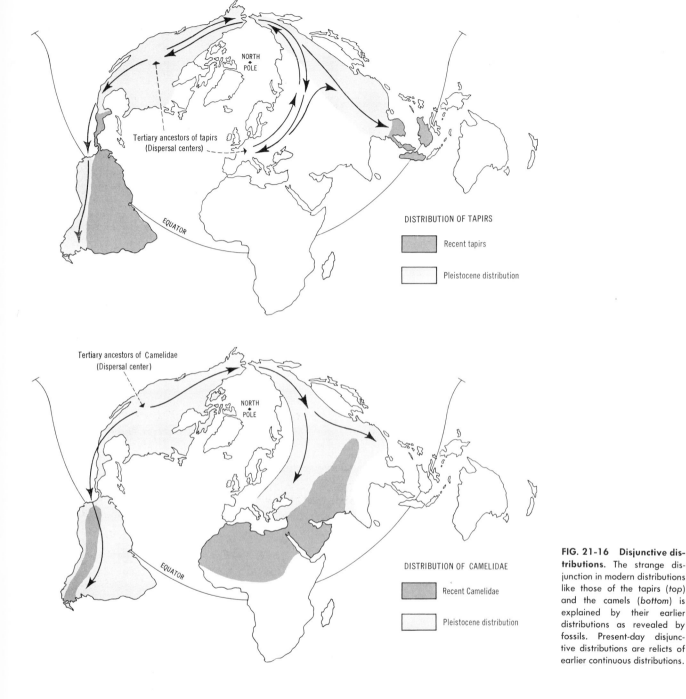

DISTRIBUTION OF TAPIRS

Recent tapirs

Pleistocene distribution

NORTH POLE

EQUATOR

Tertiary ancestors of tapirs
(Dispersal centers)

Tertiary ancestors of Camelidae
(Dispersal center)

NORTH POLE

EQUATOR

DISTRIBUTION OF CAMELIDAE

Recent Camelidae

Pleistocene distribution

FIG. 21-16 Disjunctive distributions. The strange disjunction in modern distributions like those of the tapirs (*top*) and the camels (*bottom*) is explained by their earlier distributions as revealed by fossils. Present-day disjunctive distributions are relicts of earlier continuous distributions.

Asia–Alaska land connection. Change in climate reasonably explains their present survival only in the southern parts of the two hemispheres. It is known that the northern lands now have much more severe climates than they had during most of geological time. They are only now emerging from an Ice Age. That explanation clearly applies to the tapirs, which formerly ranged all over the Holarctic region and thence spread southward into the Oriental and Neotropical regions. It also applies to the camels, which lived only in North America during most of the Age of Mammals and thence finally spread to Asia and to South America.

So many examples are established by the evidence of fossils that it can be stated as a general rule that land plants and animals now disjunctively distributed in the south were formerly northern and migrated between Asia and North America. For many groups there is no adequate fossil evidence, but it is usually reasonable to assume that they followed the rule. It is, however, by no means established that *all* of them did and that the rule has no exceptions. It seems probable that some southern disjunctive groups of plants, and perhaps a few animals, were really dispersed across regions now oceanic, through the tropics and farther south.

There are two ways in which such dispersal might have happened: by former land connections across what are now tropical and southern areas; or by sweepstakes dispersal across those seas. The existence of former land connections variously placed among Africa, Australia, Antarctica, and South America was formerly a popular theory. It is still sustained, in one form or another, by some biogeographers. Most, however, now believe that that theory is neither necessary nor adequate to explain why the floras and faunas of the southern continents are most decidedly distinct in spite of the presence of some disjunctive groups on two or more of them. Probably whatever migration did take place directly between tropical and southern lands was by sweepstakes dispersal over sea barriers. It may have been facilitated by island chains no longer in existence and by milder climates, so that land plants may have spread along Antarctica.

Summary

Bases of biogeography: the diversity of vegetation types in the world; associated diverse faunas; regional distribution as the subject matter of biogeography; ecological versus historical biogeography.

Principles of ecological biogeography: the importance of plants; plant distribution, especially sensitive to physical environment, and its role in determining animal distributions; horizontal and vertical controls; temperature, solar radiation, and precipitation as dominant factors controlling plant distribution; the consequent parallelism between altitudinal and latitudinal distributions of plant communities (exemplified by North American communities).

Terrestrial communities: major types—tundra and alpine communities, taiga, temperate deciduous forests, rain forests with vertical stratification, grasslands and gallery forests, deserts.

Biogeographic problems for which ecological explanation fails (exemplified by the absence of monkeys in Australia); the need for historical explanations.

Biogeographic regions: faunal regions on land—Holarctic (Palaearctic and Nearctic), Oriental, Ethiopian, Neotropical, and Australian, and typical animals; sample problems of historical biogeography, including resemblances and differences among faunas, conflicting resemblances and origins, disjunctive distributions; faunal change and earth change—changing climates, changing connections between land masses, consequent (historical) change in faunal distributions, the four categories of historical change in a biotic region, only one of which (the regional spread or dispersal of animals) is directly geographic.

Dispersal and isolation: means of dispersal; the long-term nature of dispersal, involving successive generations; dispersal, distinguished from migrations; the passive dispersal of protists and other small organisms, the role of sea currents, winds, and severe storms, the role of birds in dispersing seeds and other organisms, the similar role of human migrations; routes of dispersal—the open sea and currents for marine forms, prevailing westerly winds for air-borne organisms, easily traversed land routes; the probability scale for dispersal of a biota; corridors, filters, and barriers; barriers as obstacles to dispersal set up by physical or ecological conditions; physical barriers—mountain ranges, deserts, oceans; ecological barriers; chance crossings of nearly absolute barriers; the idea of sweepstakes dispersal (exemplified by the histories of Krakatoa, the Hawaiian Islands, etc.).

Changing biotas and geography: the World Continent—Africa, Europe, Asia, and North America—a supercontinent with parts only intermittently isolated during Age of Mammals; relatively free dispersal within the World Continent as an explanation of broad faunal similarities, especially of the paradox provided by greater similarity between North American and Asian faunas than between North and South American faunas; South America like Australia as an island continent during most of the Age of Mammals; filters leading to the development of regional differentiation within the World Continent—Palaearctic, Nearctic, Ethiopian, and Oriental.

The island continents, South America and Australia: the marsupial fauna of Australia; the absence of placentals in Australia at the beginning of the Age of Mammals; their subsequent exclusion by a strong sea barrier; the adaptive radiation of Australian marsupials; their convergence with placental adaptive types; Australian rats' arrival by sweepstakes dispersal; marsupials and primitive placentals in the early South American fauna; their isolation on the island continent; their adaptive radiation; the late arrival of rodents and monkeys by sweepstakes dispersal; faunal interchange, exemplified by the faunas of South and North America; the development of a land connection between South and North America; interchange across it; the success of North American forms in South America; the relative failure of South American forms in North America; the analysis of fauna before and after interchange; faunal stratification, exemplified by South America; the occurrence of three strata in the fauna, each stratum entering South America at a different time; disjunction, exemplified by certain animals and plants; the two explanations—(1) some disjunctive distributions as relics of formerly continuous distributions and (2) others as results of sweepstakes dispersal.

The possibilities of adaptive changes in color and form are illustrated by great variations in the orchid family. (George G. Simpson)

Opuntia mezacantha are cultivated in Mexico. (Edith Reichmann)

A mutualistic relationship exists between protists and the coral animals in which they live. The protists are responsible for the colors of the reef. (Lanks from Monkmeyer)

A shark and the remora fishes that travel with it provide a good example of commensalism. These fishes have their dorsal fins modified into suction discs by means of which they attach to the underside of the shark. They ride along with the shark and occasionally detach themselves long enough to collect fragments of food from the shark's meal. (Russ Kinne from Photo Researchers)

White egrets often perch on the back of an elephant and feed on ticks and other ectoparasites which have fastened themselves to its skin. (Dick Hufnagle from Monkmeyer)

A flock of flamingos gathers in a common nesting area. Each pair builds a nest in a muddy area. The mud is scooped from the bottom and piled in a mound. The mound hardens and one or two eggs are laid on its concave top. (Sandy Sprunt from National Audubon Society)

Fly entombed in amber, the 20 million year old petrified resin of an evergreen tree. The preservation of insects is often so good that even identification of the species is possible. Below, Mioplosus, a fossil perch eating a herring (from the Eocene Period). (Top, David C. Stager; bottom, Donald Baird)

Wood (from the Triassic Period) from the Petrified Forest National Park of northeastern Arizona. The colorful mottled pattern was caused by varying amounts of iron and manganese oxides. (Bill Belknap from Rapho Guillumette)

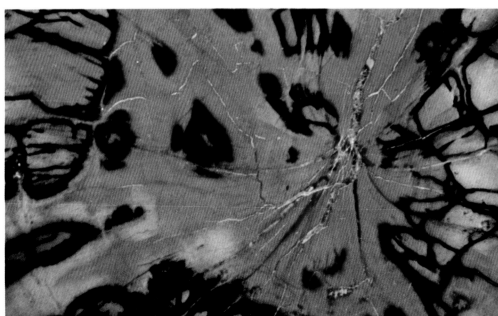

PART EIGHT

THE HISTORY OF LIFE

In the seventeenth century the great French philosopher René Descartes conjectured that we would reach a much deeper understanding of the world we live in if we could only know the processes by which the world had come into being. But it was not until the early nineteenth century that his conjecture was made a reality. Before this time—in Descartes' own day, for instance—science was largely confined to observation and inference about the workings of the contemporary world. In the social sciences the introduction of historical explanations came from French and Italian writers in the eighteenth century; in geology it came from Charles Lyell and his predecessors in the late eighteenth and early nineteenth centuries; and in the life sciences it came from Darwin as late as 1859. Ever since, the scientist has perceived the world as something more than meets his eye; he has seen the present as a product of the past, and the past as something to be known and explained before the present can be understood.

In Part 8 we relate the history of life as a whole. The account begins with the young planet Earth, sterile of life, and ends with the rich diversity of living things that covers its surface today.

Chapter 22 deals mainly with the principles of historical biology, with time scales and earth history, and with the nature of the historical record of life. For the later stages of evolution—for somewhat more than the past half-billion years—life has left, in rocks, a rich record of its history in the form of fossils like the dinosaur eggs in the photograph introducing Part 8. For still earlier stages of evolution the direct fossil record yet discovered is inadequate; but, as we shall demonstrate, the early stages are still not a book wholly closed to us.

Chapters 23 and 24 describe the history of the living world in its better-known later stages as documented in the rocks. The record reveals a long early phase in the ocean, where nearly all the major groups of organisms had their origins, and it shows how life eventually conquered the land. The history of terrestrial life focuses on the vertebrates, which have dominated the scene and have left an excellent record of their past. For a very long period, some 200 million years, reptiles were masters of most of the available ways of life for vertebrates on land. Their spectacular downfall about 70 million years ago was followed by the equally spectacular radiation of long-insignificant forms, the mammals. The final stages in the history of terrestrial life concern the progress of the mammals toward their present modern aspect, and the ultimate emergence of man.

CHAPTER TWENTY-TWO

BACKGROUND, BEGINNINGS, AND TRENDS

"Being" Versus "Becoming"

There are many ways of looking at a tree or at a squirrel in the tree. There is the way of a poet, who projects into the scene a complex of associations with human experiences and emotions. There is a workaday way, which also sees tree and squirrel in human terms but in terms of utility, of board feet or of squirrel pie. Then there is the scientific way, which accepts the tree and the squirrel on their own terms as things existing in the natural world. Quite independently of our reactions to them they have form, composition, and activity of their own. The purpose of science is first to ascertain but then more especially to understand, in terms deeper than mere description, those properties of existing things. Scientific understanding may be sought along many lines, but it generally follows one of two broad approaches. One is the avenue of *being,* and the other is that of *becoming.*

The law of gravitation, for instance, is something that *is;* it has not become something different since yesterday or a million years ago, and it will not become something different tomorrow or a million years hence. Most of the subject matter of the physical sciences is appropriately studied in terms of being rather than of becoming. When organisms are studied, however, it is evident that that approach alone is entirely inadequate for understanding them. Trees and squirrels have not always been what they are now. They have *become* so, and how they became so is essential to understanding what they are. The tree grew from a seed; the squirrel developed from a zygote in its mother's uterus. Understanding cannot stop there. It must follow the seed and the zygote back and back through the generations to times when there were no seeds or zygotes, no trees or squirrels. The long process of becoming—evolution—yields the most profound understanding of the organism that exists today.

That point of view has been kept constantly in mind, and much that we have said about living things has been said in terms of becoming as well as of being. Now we propose to pay even more particular attention to the fact that life as manifested in all living organisms has a *history*. We shall review that history, with special attention to the peculiarly *historical principles* involved in it.

Time and the Earth

IN THE BEGINNING

History is what happens through a span of time. To follow it, we need first of all a time scale on which to orient its events. Where should our scale start? Was there a beginning of time? This is a question that science cannot answer. It is difficult, perhaps impossible, to imagine literally infinite time, but the problem must be left to religion or philosophy. There are good scientific reasons to believe that our solar system, at least, has not always existed in anything like its present form. Since life as we know it is absolutely conditioned by the solar system, the appropriate starting point for a biological time scale might be taken as the formation of the planets more or less in their present condition.

Unfortunately there is as yet no sure and accurate way of knowing how old the solar system is. We do know beyond doubt that it is more than 3 billion years

TABLE 22-1   *The Geological Time Scale*

Approximate time since the beginning of the period, in millions of years	Era	Periods or epochs[a]	Some important events in the history of life
0.01		Recent	
2		Pleistocene	First true men. Ice Age. Mixture and later thinning out of mammalian faunas
10	CENOZOIC	Pliocene	Culmination of mammals. Radiation of apes
25	(The Age	Miocene	
35	of Mammals)	Oligocene	
55		Eocene	Modernization of mammalian faunas
70		Paleocene	Expansion of mammals
135	MESOZOIC	Cretaceous	Last dinosaurs. Great expansion of angiosperms
180	(The Age	Jurassic	First mammals and birds
230	of Reptiles)	Triassic	First dinosaurs
280		Permian	Great expansion of primitive reptiles
345		Carboniferous[b]	First reptiles. Great coal forests
405		Devonian	First amphibians. First insects
425	PALEOZOIC	Silurian	First land plants
500		Ordovician	Earliest known fishes
600		Cambrian	Appearance of abundant marine invertebrates
>3000	PRE-CAMBRIAN	(Period names not well established and not needed for our purposes)	First known fossils

YOUNGER →

OLDER

[a] In technical geological use an epoch is a subdivision of a period, but the distinction is not important for our purposes. The names in this column for the Cenozoic are technically epochs, and those for the Mesozoic and Paleozoic are technically periods.

[b] American geologists often call the early Carboniferous "Mississippian" and the late Carboniferous "Pennsylvanian."

old. Certain astronomical considerations seem to place the probable upper limit at not more than 10 billion years and perhaps around $4\frac{1}{2}$ billion. This is not very precise, but it is better than the old guesses, which ranged from about 6000 years to untold trillions.

We know that the solar system is more than 3 billion years old because there are rocks exposed in the earth's crust that are of about that age. The dating has been done by the study of radioactive minerals.

THE GEOLOGICAL TIME SCALE

The geological time scale designates the *sequence* of rocks (Table 22-1) and events rather than the elapsed time between them. Approximate times in years are also given, but in our discussion of the history of life we shall refer to the names of the eras and periods rather than the admittedly inaccurate year dates.

It is hard to visualize the vast time span involved

and the increasing tempo of the history as time went on. It may help to comprehend the relative durations, at least, if we consider the history of life as if it had all occurred within the 24 hours from one midnight to the next. Let us arbitrarily set the beginning, the first midnight, at 3 billion years ago, now known to be the *minimum* age of life. On that scale fossils did not become abundant until about 7:20 P.M. At 8:40 P.M. the invasion of the land by plants was under way, and by about 9:10 insects and the first amphibians had joined them. The Age of Reptiles began about 10:10. It ended, and the Age of Mammals began at about 11:25 P.M. Modern man appeared at most 3 seconds before midnight, and the whole span of recorded human history occupies less than the last $\frac{1}{5}$ second.

Origin of Life

PROBLEMS

Nothing is *directly* known about the origin of life. There could be only two kinds of direct evidence: fossils of the first organisms or the rise of similar organisms from nonliving matter today. No such fossils are known or are ever likely to be. The first organisms were almost certainly extremely small and could hardly have become fossilized or be found and recognized if they had. Most biologists now agree that the earliest forms of life could and almost certainly did arise from nonliving matter by a natural process. On the basis of what is now known there is, at least, nothing improbable in this view. We shall adopt it as the basis of a hypothesis.

A HYPOTHESIS
ON THE FORERUNNERS OF LIFE

It seems to be a necessary prerequisite for the rise of life that complex organic molecules should first have arisen. Systems of such molecules may become capable of self-reproduction, at least in the sense that, if the environment supplies suitable materials and a source of energy, they can serve as patterns

by which the materials are combined into likenesses of themselves. The likenesses would not always be perfect, and even at that extremely primitive level something akin to mutation would occur and variation would be present in the molecular population. Whether such molecular systems were themselves alive is a matter of definition. If the process really went along in anything like the way outlined by this hypothesis, then there was no exact point where the nonliving became alive. Acquisition of the full panoply of life was gradual.

It seems almost inescapable that life must have arisen in an environment that was *already* rich in rather complex organic compounds. In the world as it is today, the rise of complex organic compounds by nonorganic means must be a rare event indeed, but life did not arise in the world just as it is today. On other grounds it has been inferred that the original atmosphere of the earth contained little or no free oxygen or nitrogen but consisted largely of water vapor, ammonia (NH_3), and methane (CH_4), with small but increasing amounts of carbon dioxide and free nitrogen, plus a variety of other minor constituents. It has further been demonstrated experimentally that the passage of a spark (as from lightning) or of strong ultraviolet radiation (as from the sun)

FIG. 22-1 Early stages in the evolution of life. This represents what we consider the most reasonable hypothesis at present. It is based on some good evidence, and there is no serious doubt that it could have happened. There is, however, no *direct* evidence that it *did* happen, and it is not presented as an established theory. Four major stages are distinguished. A. Stage One: nonorganic synthesis; the creation of conditions necessary for life's origin; the slow accumulation of non-organically synthesized complex molecules such as amino acids, nucleic acids, and simple carbohydrates. Such nonorganic synthesis and accumulation of organic compounds was possible at this unique stage in evolution because of three conditions then prevailing: (1) necessary precursor compounds (NH_3, CH_4) present in the atmosphere; (2) necessary energy available in the form of ultraviolet radiation penetrating the (ozone-free) atmosphere; (3) absence of life and, therefore, exclusion of decay. The first stage ended with the origin in the accumulated organic compounds of a molecular aggregate capable of self-duplication. B. Stage Two: the growth of populations of these aggregates. Their expansion and evolution took place at the expense of the reservoir of complex organic molecules accumulated in Stage One; this reservoir was the source not only of chemical building blocks but also of energy, which doubtless was mobilized for metabolic use through some form of anaerobic respiration that promoted the accumulation of CO_2 in the atmosphere. The first organisms were, in fact, heterotrophs—here termed primary heterotrophs to distinguish them from now-familiar heterotrophs that arose in a different, later evolutionary context (Stage Four). Two points about Stage Two are important: (1) its extent and duration were rigidly limited by the size of the reservoir of nonorganically synthesized resources (Stage One) on which it was dependent; (2) the consumption of this reservoir by the first heterotrophs destroyed the conditions necessary for further spontaneous origins of living systems—from then on biogenesis became the only mode of origin of organisms. C. Stage Three: a continuation of life, dependent on the mutational origin of the capacity to synthesize organic compounds from simple, renewable resources—dependent, in other words, on the origin of autotrophy. Some chemosynthesis may originally have played a role, but the foundation of all later life and its evolution required development of the photosynthetic ability. Photosynthesis was possible in part because of atmospheric CO_2 accumulated in Stage Two. Photosynthesis led to the oxygenation of the atmosphere, which had two principal consequences: (1) an ozone (O_3) layer formed, screening out most of the sun's ultraviolet rays and excluding them as an energy source for synthesis; (2) conditions were established for the evolution of aerobic respiration—thereafter photosynthesis and respiration maintained a more or less steady state of CO_2 and O_2 in the atmosphere. D. Stage Four: the probably often-repeated origin and expansion of populations of secondary heterotrophs. They are descendants of autotrophs, and they have indefinitely renewable resources of energy and materials for their growth in the form of the now well-established autotrophs that mobilize solar energy for the whole world of life. Living systems had probably attained a cellular level of organization before the origin of secondary heterotrophs and therefore in Stage Three or earlier. All still-surviving heterotrophs (with the exception of viruses, which are probably neither primitive nor true organisms) have a cellular organization and have almost certainly inherited it from a common ancestor.

through such a mixture can produce complex organic compounds, including amino acids and nucleotides. These compounds could well have become concentrated in pools, or even in primitive seas, where they could give rise to the giant molecules hypothesized as forerunners of life and then provide a suitable medium for the reproduction and the increasing variety of such molecules. The first reproducing molecules may have been nucleic acids, and in any case nucleic acids must have participated early in the reproductive process. The basic mechanism of heredity thus arose, and natural selection could begin to act and to guide evolution into its subsequent stages.

Another step would be the aggregation of molecules that interacted favorably with each other and with their environment. The association of nucleic acids, proteins, and compounds required for energy transfers (Chapter 2) would thus be among the early steps.

Once such interacting aggregates began to form, they would tend to become more numerous and more distinctly and constantly organized in composition and pattern. A complex aggregate of favorably interacting molecules would have evident and great advantages over any remaining free-lance molecules. Given the existence of variation within molecules

and within increasingly complex aggregates of molecules, natural selection would occur and would favor change in the direction of more effectively and constantly organized aggregates. The result would eventually be a true multimolecular organism, a primitive protist, alive by any definition.

EARLY ORGANISMS

At first sight it might seem logical that the earliest true organisms must have been autotrophs, performing all their necessary organic syntheses from quite simple inorganic materials and using either other inorganic materials or solar radiation as a source of energy. It might even seem absurd to think that the first organisms could have been heterotrophs when there were no other kinds of organisms to feed on. In recent years almost all biologists have come to an opposite conclusion. Autotrophy requires more complex organization and metabolism than heterotrophy. It strains the scientific imagination too far to think that the very first organisms can have been so complex, and no one has succeeded in visualizing in convincing detail how such organisms could originate from molecular forerunners.

As organisms multiplied, they would rapidly

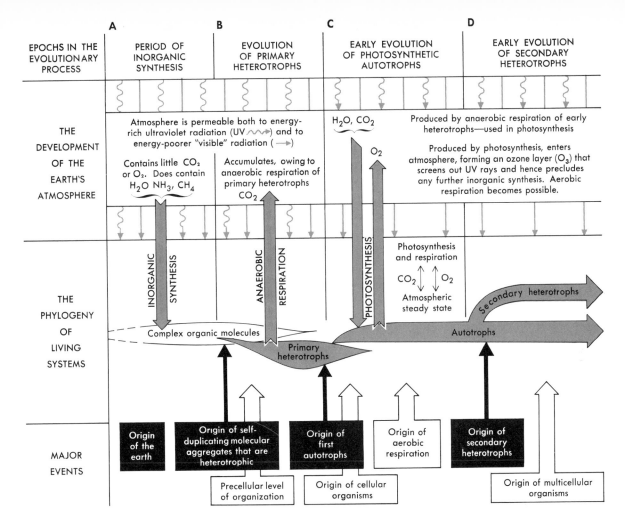

consume all the available organic materials. Synthesis by nonorganic processes would soon tend to lag behind consumption. Moreover, conditions on the earth and especially in its atmosphere were changing. The organisms themselves would cause much of the change. They would, for instance, tend to lock up much of the carbon that formerly was in methane or more complex compounds, or to convert it into CO_2, from which more complex organic molecules are less likely to be formed by nonorganic processes.

Imagine what would happen if, as some needed organic compound were becoming rare in the environment, there appeared a mutant organism that could synthesize that compound from simpler and more widely available materials. The mutant organism would have a tremendous advantage over the others, and its descendants would soon become the dominant, or even the only, remaining organisms. As other compounds became rarer, additional mutations for

their synthesis would be favored by selection. Step by step the trend would be toward greater self-sufficiency, toward more complete autotrophy. The culmination of this stage of evolution would be in organisms that could use CO_2 as their sole external source of carbon and solar radiation as their sole external source of energy. Such organisms would be photosynthetic protists and eventually plants.

When we first began to get a little real light on the scene, the physical conditions of earth and atmosphere were much as they are today, and photosynthetic organisms already existed. Their existence made possible the concomitant and subsequent evolution of other organisms that fed on them and on the materials synthesized by them: plant-eaters, parasites, and organisms of decay. Then there could also evolve still another stage: meat-eaters that fed on plant-eaters. The possible sequence in these early stages of evolution is summarized diagrammatically in Figure 22-1.

Fossils and the Historical Record

PRINCIPLES

The history of life ceases to be hypothesis and inference and becomes direct knowledge when fossils are available. A fossil is a fact: it is a visible trace of some organism that lived in the geological past. That is the fundamental basis of *paleontology,* the study of ancient life (the Greek roots mean exactly that). Science arises from the observation of isolated facts, but it does not become truly science until those facts are seen in relationship to others and are placed in an explanatory context. The paleontological deciphering of the history of life involves, among others, these observations and inferences:

A fossil, an organism with definite characteristics shown by its remains. Further inference concerns characteristics and activities not directly preserved.

The geographic locality at which the fossil was buried and near which it must have lived, another observed fact.

The age of the fossil, an inference based on a wide range of geological and paleontological data.

Association of the fossil with others of the same species, the basis of systematic study of the fossil population.

Association with fossils of other species, part of the basis for the study of the community and the environment (and also of the age).

Characteristics of the rocks in which the fossil occurs and of the position and mode of burial of the fossil in those rocks—further data for the study of environment and age.

Relationships of the fossil population to others, earlier, contemporaneous, and later; comparisons and inferences leading to phylogeny and to classification.

The broader generalizations and principles of the history of life, with which we must be mainly concerned in this summary of an intricate branch of the life sciences, are derived from a vast number of detailed observations and inferences mainly of these kinds.

WHAT FOSSILS ARE

It is a wonderful thing that you can hold in your hand the remains of an organism that lived hundreds of millions of years ago. It is a common observation that dead organisms usually molder and become unrecognizable in a few years at most, sometimes even within hours. "Dust thou art, to dust returnest" is indeed the common lot of living things. The organisms of decay see to this, and it is good for the continuity of the communities of life that they do. Yet there are millions upon millions of ancient organisms that have never wholly decayed.

Fossils are being formed today, but they are only a minutely small fraction of the organisms that die. Moreover, they are being formed where you are most unlikely to see them (for reasons that you will be able to discern for yourself). It has always been true that an exceedingly small fraction of organisms has fossilized. A still smaller fraction by far has been recovered and studied. Nevertheless, the numbers of organisms have been so countless and time so long that even so minute a fraction adds up to a respectable documentation of the history of life.

The usual first condition for preservation as a fossil is burial before decay is complete. Such natural burial occurs when a dead organism sinks into mud or sand or when these and other sediments are swept over its remains by waves or streams, occasionally by winds.

It is a common misapprehension that fossils are petrified, that the organisms have "turned to rock." Such a thing rarely happens, at least in the usual understanding of the words. Preserved hard parts usually consist of the same material as when the organism was alive, perhaps with some recrystallization or slight chemical change. Spaces left by the decay of soft parts, for instance in the marrow of a bone or inside the cell walls of a tree trunk, are often filled with secondary deposits of a mineral, frequently silica (SiO_2 in various forms). After burial and hardening of the surrounding sediments, the hard parts of a fossil may be dissolved by percolating waters. Then a cavity, a mold, may be left, or else mineral-laden waters may precipitate silica or some other mineral in the space, producing a mineral replica of the original fossil (Figures 22-2 and 22-3).

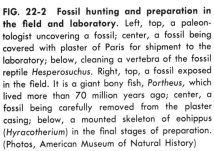

FIG. 22-2 Fossil hunting and preparation in the field and laboratory. Left, top, a paleontologist uncovering a fossil; center, a fossil being covered with plaster of Paris for shipment to the laboratory; below, cleaning a vertebra of the fossil reptile *Hesperosuchus.* Right, top, a fossil exposed in the field. It is a giant bony fish, *Portheus,* which lived more than 70 million years ago; center, a fossil being carefully removed from the plaster casing; below, a mounted skeleton of eohippus (*Hyracotherium*) in the final stages of preparation. (Photos, American Museum of Natural History)

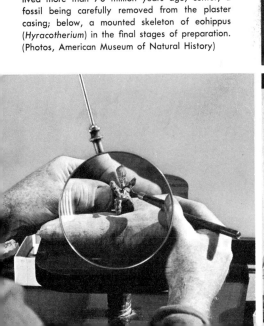

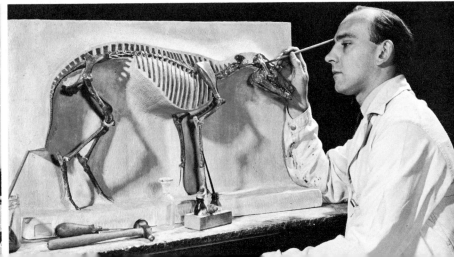

FIG. 22-3 A diversity of fossils. Above, left, fragments of the plant *Otozamites* from the Petrified Forest of Arizona. This cycad lived about 200 million years ago; right, An ammonite from the Jurassic, about 150 million years old. Below, left, fossil dinosaur tracks in Texas; right, detail of the dinosaur *Corythosaurus*, showing muscle and skin on the tail vertebrae. (All photos, American Museum of Natural History, except dinosaur tracks, R. T. Bird)

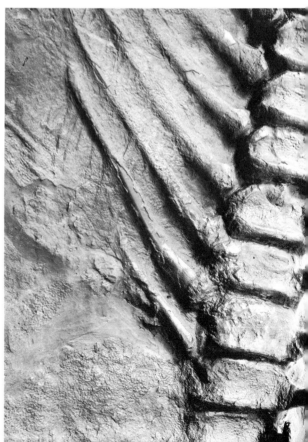

We have already noted that there is no fossil record of the beginnings of life. The whole span of the Pre-Cambrian is poor in fossils but is not an absolute blank. At present the oldest unquestionable fossil remains that we have are microscopic algalike plants from rocks believed to be at least 3 billion years old. In the later Pre-Cambrian, a billion years or less ago, fossils are still rare but more numerous and varied.

OVER-ALL RECORD

With the Cambrian begins a rich, continuous record of the history of life in the form of fossils.

Some Major Tendencies

EXPANSION

The first striking generalization about the over-all tendency of evolution is that life has expanded. The total number of living things has increased. The bulk of matter in living form has increased. The number of different kinds of organisms has increased. Their diversity, in the sense of the extent of differences among them and not only in the number of species, has increased. All of these increases may be viewed as aspects of the expansion of life, although they are quite distinct from each other.

Expansion is seen in Figure 22-4, where it reflects especially the increase in number of kinds of organisms. New structural extremes, new levels of organization, have continually arisen without an equal loss of the old. Divergence has continued. There is far more difference among an ameba, a maple tree, and a man living today than among any organisms that were alive in the Cambrian.

Increase in numbers of individuals and in total bulk of living matter cannot be read directly from the fossil record, yet these expansions must also have occurred. Numbers of individuals tend to be in inverse ratio to their size (Chapter 19). The evolution of large plants may have involved a distinct decrease in the total number of photosynthetic organisms, at least. Among the factors limiting the bulk of living matter, or its total turnover or metabolic activity,

There are some groups that we infer must have been present and important but that are nevertheless rare, although not entirely absent, as fossils. Among these are bacteria and worms. (What basis is there for inferring that they were present and important even when not represented by fossils? Why would they tend to be underrepresented in the fossil record?) On the whole, the record is amazingly good when we consider the infinitesimal chance that any one organism, or even a representative of any one species, has had of winding up on a paleontologist's desk.

are input of solar energy and efficiency of photosynthesis. There is no reason to believe that either radiation input or photosynthetic efficiency has increased significantly since well back in the Pre-Cambrian. Even a few primitive species in the Pre-

FIG. 22-4 **The expansion of life.** The width of the pathway is approximately in proportion to the known diversity of organisms (plant and animal) at various times in the past. Note the constriction of the pathway during the late Permian and Triassic; a time of widespread extinction (Chapter 23).

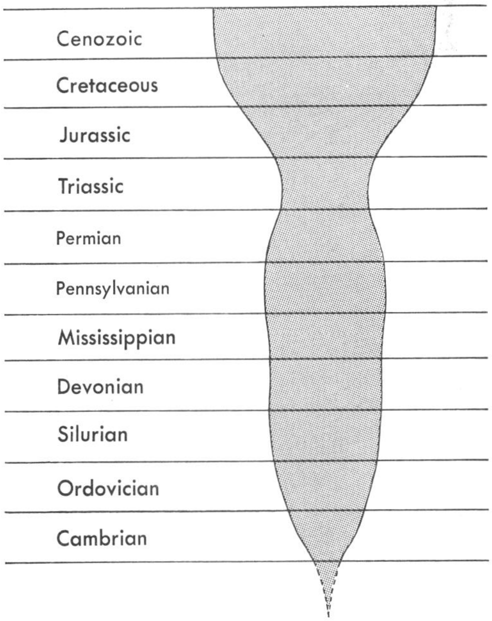

Cenozoic
Cretaceous
Jurassic
Triassic
Permian
Pennsylvanian
Mississippian
Devonian
Silurian
Ordovician
Cambrian

Cambrian might have filled their environment with as great a bulk of living matter and might have had as much metabolic turnover as was possible—and the possibility may not have increased much or at all since then in a particular environment, such as the sea. However, two other factors tend to increase both numbers and total bulk of organisms: invasion of new environments and lengthening of food chains. Both those tendencies were plainly still active long after the Cambrian.

OCCUPATION OF ENVIRONMENTS

The expansion of life has been accompanied by both more extensive and more intensive occupation of the possible environments for life on the earth. In fact the spread in environments has been, in a sense, one of the main reasons for the general expansion. The most spectacular example of extension in environment, spread into great areas hitherto unoccupied, was the invasion of the land by plants and animals. Until Silurian times life was confined to the water, or nearly so. Then started an expansion in land environments not completed until some hundreds of millions of years later. Increasingly intensive occupation of environments is also evident in the fossil record.

CHANGE: PERSISTENCE
AND REPLACEMENT

Another evident over-all aspect of the whole of evolution is its constant state of flux. Nowhere in the fossil record is there any time of static equilibrium. Change has been slower at some times than at others and faster in some groups of organisms than in others, but some change has always been going on. There is not even any evidence that evolution tends to approach an equilibrium or that it has, on an average, slowed down as if it might eventually reach completion. There are, it is true, some biologists who think that such a final state has now been essentially reached. To them we can only say that change has *always* occurred through the past and we

see no reason why it should stop now. The next 10 million years should settle the point, but there may be no biologists around when it is decided.

How can there be change without expansion? The fossil record is replete with examples. Some groups of organisms have persisted for long times without notable change. They get into a comfortable rut, a persisting environment to which they are well adapted, and they remain there. However, there are more examples of the replacement of now extinct organisms by others better adapted to what are essentially the same environments. Environments suitable for seed ferns, cycadeoids, cordaites, and other early land plants exist today, but those plants do not. The flowering plants (and to less extent the conifers) have replaced them.

Expansion and replacement are two of the main factors in the constant change among living things, and, if expansion is limited, replacement has not so far appeared to be.

COMPLICATION
AND IMPROVEMENT

Increasing complication and improvement of biological functioning are the changes most often mentioned in discussions of the overall tendency of evolution. You may be surprised that we have left them till the last. We have done so purposely with the intention of de-emphasizing them, because we believe that they are overemphasized and somewhat misunderstood in much popular thought and teaching. Increasing complication has certainly been an important factor in various phases of the history of life, but it has been far from universal as an evolutionary tendency, and it has not been particularly noticeable in the last few hundred million years of history.

The most important point to stress about improvement, change for the better, or progress in evolution is that it is not inherent. It is not built into the nature of the universe or of life. Improvement has occurred in the course of evolution, not because it is an inherent and general tendency, but where and when it had a natural, immediate cause: selection. This statement could fall into the fallacy of circular reasoning if it were taken for granted that what selection favors is improvement.

Summary

Being versus becoming, two broad approaches to scientific explanation: the explanation of tree and squirrel as entities in the process of becoming; historical principles in the understanding of becoming.

Time and the earth: beginnings—estimates of the age of the solar system; life is more than 3 billion years old; the geological time scale, primarily a scale of sequence only—its approximation to an absolute time scale by radioactivity datings, analogy of the history of life with a 24-hour day.

Origin of life: problems—fossil evidence unavailable, the difficulty of experimental recreation of processes involved, restriction of discussion largely to indirect evidence, the scientific belief in the natural origin of life from nonliving world; a hypothesis on the forerunners of life—the nonorganic synthesis of complex organic molecules from atmospheric constituents energized by lightning and ultraviolet radiation, the slow accumulation of such molecules on sterile earth, the ultimate origin of aggregates of such molecules capable of self-duplication and, therefore, alive; early organisms—the heterotrophic status of the first living systems, their utilization of the accumulation of nonorganically synthesized molecules and thus ultimate destruction of conditions for the further spontaneous origin of life, their production of CO_2 by anaerobic respiration, the origin by mutation of photosynthetic autotrophs utilizing CO_2 and solar energy, the subsequent origin of modern heterotrophs feeding on the autotrophs.

Fossils and the historical record: principles of the paleontological method; fossils as facts; observations and inferences concerning fossils; the definition of fossils; conditions for their preservation and ultimate recovery by man; fossils predominantly of former hard parts of organisms; fossils not usually petrified; Pre-Cambrian fossils; an adequate fossil record spanning only perhaps the last quarter of life's total history; the over-all fossil record.

Some major tendencies in the history of life: life's expansion—an increase in the total number and diversity of living organisms but not at a constant rate, factors involved in the expansion; the occupation of environments; evolution as change—continual flux with no static equilibrium, change as the replacement of one group by another as well as expansion, or the multiplication of groups; complication and improvement of organic structure (usually overemphasized as an aspect of evolution since evolutionary change is never guaranteed to be progressive).

CHAPTER TWENTY-THREE

ANCIENT SEAS
AND CONQUEST OF THE LAND

If you had a time machine, set it for 600,000,000 B.C., and took off, you would have a rude shock when you arrived. Even though you started from a mountaintop, you might find yourself floundering in a sea when you landed. That would be an unpleasant demonstration of the fact that the face of the earth has changed radically. Some of the main ocean basins and continental masses probably already existed in the Cambrian, but their outlines were different. There were mountains, but not where our mountains now stand. Shallow seas, arms of the oceans, flooded far into the interior of the continental blocks, across what is now dry land.

If you had the luck to arrive on land, all would seem well at first. The air would be breathable. Clouds, winds, and rain would be familiar. The climate would probably be better than where, or we should say *when,* you now live—better, at least, if you like it to be rather warm throughout the year, without sharp alternation of hot summers and cold winters. At second glance, the land would seem completely alien to you. It would be alien, not so much because of the unfamiliar topography as because it would be completely bare. No grass, no shrubs, no trees, no buzzing insects, singing birds, or scurrying rodents—no life at all. You would quickly starve unless you could reach the seashore, and even there everything would be unfamiliar. There would be seaweeds, shellfishes, and other marine life in some abundance, but all of kinds you never saw before. There would be no fishes. You might eke out a dreary existence by eating shellfishes, if they proved not to be poisonous to you, but at best you would be deeply impressed with the fact that the earth has not always been the pleasant world you live in now.

488

Cambrian and Ordovician Seas

APPEARANCE OF THE ANIMAL PHYLA

Fossil animals suddenly become abundant with the beginning of the Cambrian, and almost all the phyla appear as fossils during that period. The suddenness of the change from the relatively barren Pre-Cambrian rocks is real enough, but it is not true that all the phyla mysteriously show up at precisely the same time. The Cambrian was a very long period, on the order of 100 million years, and the various major groups of animals straggle into the fossil record throughout that long span. Some, notably the verte-

brates, do not appear until some time in the Ordovician, also a long period of some 75 million years. Many major groups probably were actually originating during the long time represented by the Cambrian and Ordovician. We need not look for the origins of all of them in the Pre-Cambrian. Table 23-1 shows the numbers of phyla and classes of animals (including animal-like protists) definitely known as fossils at the stated times or earlier.

LIFE OF THE LATE ORDOVICIAN

We cannot follow in even a summary way the life of the seas through all of the geological periods. A quick review of the Ordovician life pictured in Figure 23-1 will, however, show characteristic ancient marine floras and faunas.

It is in the Ordovician that the first fossil vertebrates appear, completing the roster of the animal phyla as far as these can readily be preserved as fossils. Strange as it seems to think of a sea without fishes, that was the state of the seas before this time.

The first fishes were the jawless agnaths, primitive, few, and unimpressive. Their appearance is, however, one of the most dramatic events in the history of life. It marked the rise of the phylum that was to become dominant in every sphere that it invaded and that was eventually to produce the writers and the readers of this book.

TABLE 23-1 *Numbers of Classes of Animals Surely Known to Have Existed in Subdivisions of Cambrian and Ordovician Time*

Time	Number of phyla	Number of classes
Cambrian		
Early	8	12
Middle	10	20
Late	11	22
Ordovician		
Early	11	27
Middle	12	32
Late	12	33

The Age of Fishes

The Silurian, next period after the Ordovician, was no exception to the rule of ceaseless change in the history of life. Its most important biological event was the still feeble beginning of the occupation of the land, an event to which we will return.

The next period, the Devonian, was a period of accelerated evolutionary activity in many groups of organisms. Most important (from the human point

of view, at any rate) is the fact that fishes first became common in the Devonian and that their most basic differentiation occurred mainly in that period. For these reasons the Devonian is often called the Age of Fishes.

The scanty Ordovician and Silurian fossil vertebrates are all, or nearly all, jawless fishes, agnaths. They were well represented in the early Devonian,

FIG. 23-1 Some faunas of early Paleozoic seas. Middle Cambrian, western North America: 1, a jelly-fish, (scyphozoan); 2, the spongelike *Archeocyathus*; 3, a trilobite, *Ogygopsis*; 4, an arachnid, *Sidneyia*; 5, a crustacean, *Barella*; 6, an annelid worm; 7, a holothurian (echinoderm); 8, a crustacean, *Hymenocaris*; 9, a trilobite, *Neolenus*.

Middle Ordovician, central North America: 1, a straight-shelled (orthoconic) nautiloid cephalopod; 2, a gastropod; 3, a small trilobite, *Calymene*; 4, a large trilobite, *Isotelus*; 5, massive coral; 6, branching coral; 7, two solitary corals.

FIG. 23-1 (cont.) Middle Silurian, Illinois—a coral-reef community: 1, a stalked (sessile) cystoid echinoderm; 2, a cephalopod mollusk, *Phragmoceras*; 3, honeycomb coral, *Favosites*; 4, tube coral, *Syringopora*; 5, chain coral, *Halysites*; 6, a solitary coral; 7, a nautiloid cephalopod; 8, a trilobite, *Isotelus*; 9, another trilobite, *Actinurus*; 10, brachiopods, *Pentamerus*; 11, brachiopods, *Leptaena*; 12, a cephalopod mollusk, *Cyrtorizoceras*.

Late Silurian, New York: 1, a eurypterid, *Pterygotus*; 2, a snail, *Pycnomphalus*; 3, a eurypterid, *Carcinosoma*; 4, a eurypterid, *Hughmilleria*. (All photos, Field Museum of Natural History)

FIG. 23-2 **The vertebrates conquer the land.** Top left, Devonian lobe-fin fish, *Eusthenopteron*, crawling out of the water. Bottom left, the skeleton of *Eusthenopteron*. Top right, primitive Carboniferous-Permian labyrinthodont amphibians, *Diplovertebron*. Bottom right, the skeleton of *Diplovertebron*. Note that the limb bones of *Diplovertebron* show the same pattern, now familiar, as those of all higher vertebrates; this pattern is not clear in *Eusthenopteron*. (Photos, American Museum of Natural History)

including bottom-living forms with broad, flattened head shields as well as more active swimmers. They declined rapidly thereafter, and by the end of the Devonian they were all extinct except for the unknown lines that led to the living lampreys and hagfishes. Primitive agnaths gave rise to the earliest jawed fishes, the placoderms, which became numerous in the Devonian. The placoderms were quite diversified and included strong predators. The fishes destined to replace the later placoderms arose from early placoderms, just as the placoderms arose from early agnaths and then replaced the later agnaths. The replacing groups, finally successful in that they are the dominant fishes today, are the cartilaginous fishes and the bony fishes. Both groups arose in the Devonian and were becoming abundant by the end of that period.

One group, that of the crossopterygians or crossopts (Figure 23-2), gave rise in the later Devonian to the amphibians and, through them, to all the vertebrates of the land and air. After the amphibians had appeared, other lines of crossopts lingered on in diminishing numbers. They are represented today by the single relict *Latimeria*.

Occupation of the Land

DIFFICULTIES

We have previously had occasion to refer to the difficulties of life on land and to some of the adaptations of plants and animals to terrestrial environ- ments. The outstanding difficulty is that land organisms are no longer surrounded by water, as their ancestors all were. Water must still be obtained from somewhere: by root absorption from the soil, by breathing water vapor from air (a scanty resource in most situations), by drinking liquid water on the surface, by eating plants and animals (which contain water), or by metabolism of carbohydrates and lipids in such a way as to release water. Once acquired, water must be conserved against evaporation. All the fully terrestrial plants and animals have external coverings of one sort or another by which evaporation is controlled and limited. In spite of this needed protection against desiccating air, it is necessary to obtain CO_2 (in the case of plants) and O_2 from the air, and also to discharge waste gases into the air. Land plants have stomata and associated structures. Land animals have lungs, tracheae, or pouches or modified gills that function as lungs. Gravity, no special problem to an organism buoyed up by water, becomes serious for all but the smallest land organisms. Most land animals, excluding only small and wormlike forms, have strong skeletons, external or internal. All true land plants have supportive tissues, especially in the stems, and all of any great size are woody. Extremes of temperature from season to season outside the tropics and from day to night everywhere (including the tropics) are far greater on land than in the water. Land plants and animals have numerous adaptations to these fluctuations. Some have been noted in previous pages, and you can probably think of others.

Only four phyla include organisms that can be considered fully and progressively adapted to land life: Tracheophyta among plants; Mollusca, Arthropoda, and Chordata (Vertebrata) among animals.

EARLIEST LAND PLANTS AND ANIMALS

In the historical sequence of occupation of the land, it seems necessary that plants should have led the way. Animals require accessible plant material

at the beginning of their food chains. This is borne out by the fossil record, in which land plants begin to appear before any land animals. The first certain and fairly common fossils of land plants appear in the middle Silurian, and they are for the most part small psilopsids (Chapter 16). At least one may be a forerunner of the lycopods or transitional between the psilopsids and that group. Basic divergence of the subphyla of vascular plants was probably already under way then, but at this stage it had not yet gone far.

During the Devonian, land plants became common. Some of them reached the size of trees, and the first forests grew on the earth. Psilopsids continued, but they had become scarce by late Devonian. The incoming, replacing groups were the lycopsids, sphenopsids, and ferns (Chapter 16), all of which were abundant by late Devonian. A few primitive gymnosperms (cordaites) had also appeared.

In the Devnoian are found a few animals that were certainly terrestrial. All are arthropods: a mite, several forerunners of the spiders probably not yet advanced enough to be definitely classified as spiders, and a creature that may similarly have been a forerunner of the insects.

By the end of the Devonian some of the crossopts had developed legs and had become amphibians. They still had fishlike tails and were probably still almost as aquatic as fishes. Nevertheless, they were the first vertebrates to walk on land, and their descendants were to rise to dominance in the new environment (see Figure 23-2).

The Permo-Carboniferous

The Carboniferous and Permian, the last two periods of the Paleozoic following the Devonian, had much in common and may be considered together.

COAL FORESTS

The Carboniferous, "carbon-bearing," is so called because many extensive coal deposits are of

that age, including our Appalachian coal fields in Pennsylvania and adjacent states. The coal is the compressed remains of plants that grew in widespread, swampy forests. Deep burial for long periods of time has driven out the more volatile constituents of the plant tissues, and the compacted residue has a higher percentage of carbon than the original plants. It still retains traces of the original structure, however, and

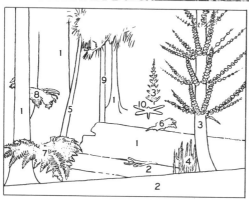

FIG. 23-3 A Carboniferous forest. Lycopsids: 1, various species of *Sigillaria*; 2, two species of *Lepidodendron*. Sphenopsids: 3, *Calamites*; 4, *Sphenophyllum*. Ferns: 5, *Caulopteris*; 6, *Mariopteris*. Gymnosperms: 7, 8, two species of *Neuropteris*; 9, *Cordaites*. Insects: 10, a primitive dragonfly, *Meganeura monyi*. (Photo, Field Museum of Natural History)

associated shales and sandstones are often rich in well-preserved fossil plants. Thus we are well acquainted with the compositions of the forests and the structures of their plants (Figure 23-3).

LAND INVERTEBRATES

Animal life, so rare hitherto, swarmed in Carboniferous forests. Here appeared the first land snails, the only mollusks to complete the great transition from water to air. Undoubtedly terrestrial scorpions were common, and so were relatives and ancestors of the spiders. Centipedes were present. Most striking and most important of the land invertebrates were insects. Most Carboniferous insects were small,

but some were remarkable for their large size. One dragonflylike giant is believed to have had a wingspread of nearly 75 centimeters. No known later insect reaches such dimensions. It is noticeable that the groups of insects now particularly associated with flowers were absent in these early faunas. They begin to appear in the fossil record in the Jurassic and spread greatly during the Cretaceous and early Cenozoic, in close parallel with the fossil record of the flowering plants.

AMPHIBIANS

Amphibians were particularly common during the Carboniferous and scarcely less so in the

Permian. The Permo-Carboniferous is sometimes called the Age of Amphibians, although, as a matter of fact, amphibians were already much outnumbered by reptiles in the Permian. None of the modern groups had yet evolved. Most Permo-Carboniferous amphibians were labyrinthodonts (Figure 23-2). Typically they were clumsy brutes with four short, sprawling legs, big, flattened heads, and stubby tails.

REPTILES

The transition of the vertebrates to land life was completed when the reptiles arose. Since the change was gradual, it is difficult to point to an exact time and say, "Here the reptiles appear," but some of the latest Carboniferous fossils were already true reptiles, and reptiles were abundant in the Permian. Most of the Permian reptiles belonged to only two main groups, neither of which was at all like any reptiles living today. The *root reptiles,* cotylosaurs, were

most primitive. They intergraded with the earlier labyrinthodont amphibians and often looked not unlike those ancestors, although they did develop some more unusual later forms. Even more common were the *mammal-like reptiles.* The earliest of them, the pelycosaurs, included the ancestry of the whole group (hence also of the mammals) (Figure 23-4). The somewhat later and eventually more varied therapsids were the dominant land animals of the late Permian and early Triassic and were the immediate ancestors of the mammals. They are best known from South Africa, where they have been discovered in almost incredible numbers, but some have been found in Russia, China, Brazil, the United States, and elsewhere. They doubtless occurred on all the continental land areas of the Permian and Triassic.

The Age of Reptiles

The Permian was already an age of reptiles, but the term is usually applied to the next three periods, the Triassic, Jurassic, and Cretaceous, composing the Mesozoic. In the Triassic there was a great radiation of new reptilian orders (Figure 23-4). It set the pattern for the great diversity and dominance of reptiles that continued throughout the Mesozoic. Most impressive and famous of the innumerable Mesozoic reptiles were the many kinds of dinosaurs.

DINOSAURS

The animals popularly called *dinosaurs* technically comprise two different orders of reptiles, the Ornithischia and Saurischia. During their heyday, in the Jurassic and Cretaceous, the dinosaurs were extremely numerous and varied. They are known for their huge size, and some of them, *Brontosaurus* and its relatives, were indeed enormous, reaching about 20 meters in length and perhaps 25 metric tons in weight. No larger animals ever walked on land. (But some larger ones still swim the seas.) However, not all dinosaurs were large. They came in many shapes and sizes, some not much bigger than chickens.

In the early Triassic, dinosaurs did not exist as such. Their ancestry was then represented by a primitive group, the thecodonts, that radiated widely. They gave rise not only to the two orders of dinosaurs but also to the crocodiles, the flying reptiles (pterosaurs), and the birds. The earliest true dinosaurs, in the late Triassic, were rather slender, mainly bipedal forms. The later Saurischia include not only the large, herbivorous, quadrupedal, long-necked and long-tailed allies of *Brontosaurus* but also a host of bipedal, mostly carnivorous forms. Some of the latter were tiny, as dinosaurs go, but some, like *Tyrannosaurus,* were very large.

AQUATIC AND MARINE REPTILES

Several groups of reptiles became fully aquatic and marine in the Mesozoic (Figure 23-4). The *plesiosaurs* had a broad, flattened body, four paddles, and a long neck or tail, or both. Someone has likened them to a snake threaded through a turtle. (But they had no turtle-like external armor.) They appeared in the Triassic and were abundant in the Jurassic and through the Cretaceous. The *ichthyosaurs*

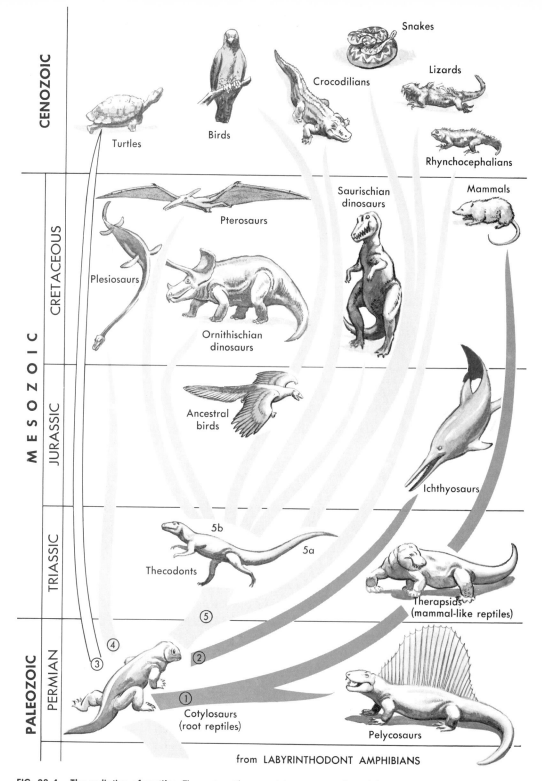

FIG. 23-4 The radiation of reptiles. The root reptiles, or cotylosaurs, were derived from the labyrinthodont amphibians. From the cotylosaurs five major lines of reptilian evolution can be traced: (1) to the mammal-like reptiles and mammals; (2) to the ichthyosaurs; (3) to the turtles; (4) to the plesiosaurs; and (5) to the thecodonts (5b) and the snakes, lizards, and rhynchocephalians (5a). From the Triassic thecodonts another major radiation took place: to the crocodiles, birds, and flying **reptiles** (pterosaurs), as well as the great dinosaur orders, the Ornithischia and the Saurischia.

looked something like sharks and even more like porpoises or dolphins. Both these groups of marine reptiles ate fish, and the ichthyosaurs, at least, also relished active cephalopods. Food habits of extinct animals usually have to be inferred from the tooth and jaw apparatus, but stomach contents have been found in the fossil skeletons of ichthyosaurs.

INTO THE AIR

Once the land was occupied, there remained only one great unoccupied sphere accessible to life on the earth: the atmosphere. Even now there are no completely aerial organisms; none live their whole lives suspended in air. Fully terrestrial animals are, however, already aerial in physiological adaptation. They do live surrounded by air, derive oxygen directly from that medium, and are adequately protected from the perils that air has for animals of aquatic ancestry. To be launched fully into the atmosphere for longer or shorter periods, they require only an additional mechanical adaptation, some structure that can sustain them in air against the pull of gravity.

Flight was already completely achieved by insects

in the Carboniferous and has remained an insect specialty ever since, although there are, of course, a good many nonflying insects.

The first known bird is *Archaeopteryx* ("ancient wing") from the middle Jurassic of Germany (Figure 23-5). It had teeth, a long, jointed tail, and so many other reptilian characters that it might well be considered a reptile if identified only by its bones. By an extremely rare and fortunate chance, however, impressions of feathers, which generally do not fossilize, were preserved. They show that *Archaeopteryx* had a feathered wing attached to its otherwise reptilian forearm and hand. *Archaeopteryx* is about as completely intermediate between a reptile and a bird as one can imagine.

MAMMALS

The once great group of the mammal-like reptiles became steadily more and more mammal-like

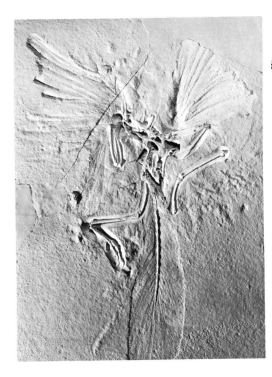

FIG. 23-5 *Archaeopteryx.* Left, a photograph of an actual fossil. Right, a reconstruction of the animal. The feathers (birdlike feature) are clear in the fossil. The animal also possessed teeth and an incompletely specialized forelimb (reptile-like features). (Photos, left, American Museum of Natural History; right, British Museum (Natural History))

through the Permian and the Triassic. In the latest Triassic and early Jurassic a few fragmentary fossils suggest that some of them may then have become mammals by definition. The process was gradual, and the distinction is necessarily arbitrary at first. Remains of unquestionable mammals appear in the middle Jurassic and at intervals thereafter. The mammal-like reptiles, those that did not make the grade and become mammals, declined greatly toward the end of the Triassic and became extinct during the Jurassic.

THE GREAT DYING

The late Cretaceous was a time of widespread extinction. The great marine reptiles, plesiosaurs and ichthyosaurs, became extinct in the Cretaceous. Yet, oddly enough, nothing radical happened to the fishes living along with them and on which they fed. On land, all the dinosaurs became extinct. Of all the hordes of Mesozoic reptiles, only four orders survived (Chapter 17).

Innumerable attempts have been made to explain the great dying, and especially the extinction of the dinosaurs, but none is satisfactory. It is agreed that there was some widespread environmental change, but no one has come up with a really plausible and well-supported theory as to just what the change was. In any attempt to explain this mystery, certain facts should be kept in mind:

1. Groups that became extinct were of many wholly different kinds living in entirely different environments.

2. Other groups living along with them and in the same general environments did not become extinct, and some did not even undergo evident change.

3. It is not logically necessary or probable that any *one* factor caused the extinction.

4. The extinction was not really sudden, although it has been said to be. It went on over millions and tens of millions of years. Many kinds of dinosaurs gradually disappeared, and only a few were left at the very end. Ichthyosaurs were already rare in the early Cretaceous, and they disappeared long before the end of the period.

Whatever may have been its exact causes and sequences, the great dying did occur. It closed an era and opened the world to the Age of Mammals.

Summary

Cambrian and Ordovician seas: the appearance of some major groups and the great expansion of life generally in the Cambrian and Ordovician; life still marine and the land barren; few fresh-water faunas; replacements in the post-Ordovician marine faunas; the first appearance of fishes, the agnaths.

The Age of Fishes: faunal changes in the Silurian: the Devonian as the Age of Fishes; replacement of agnaths by placoderms; the replacement of placoderms by cartilagenous and bony fishes; crossopterygrans as ancestors of land vertebrates.

Occupation of the land: difficulties facing organisms on land, fully overcome by only four plant and animal phyla—Tracheophyta, Mollusca, Arthropoda, and Chordata; earliest land plants—Silurian psilopsids; Devonian land plants abundant—psilopsids, lycopsids, sphenopsids, ferns, and some primitive gymnosperms; Devonian land animals—arthropods; the first appearance of amphibians.

The Permo-Carboniferous, close of the Paleozoic: coal forests; land invertebrates—land snails, scorpions, centipedes, cockroaches, and dragonflies; amphibians—labyrinthodonts, like *Eryops;* reptiles abundant by the Permian—cotylosaurs, mammal-like reptiles, and others.

The Age of Reptiles, the Mesozoic: the emergence of angiosperms; the decline of amphibians; major changes in the reptilian faunas; two dinosaur groups derived from thecodonts, extinct aquatic groups—plesiosaurs, ichthyosaurs; birds; the bearing of *Archaeopteryx* on theories of evolution; rise of mammals; mammal-like reptiles, evolving slowly through Permo-Triassic times and becoming full mammals by late Triassic and early Jurassic; the great dying—widespread extinctions in the Cretaceous; extinction of all the dinosaurs; the problem of explaining the great dying; cautions in its interpretation.

CHAPTER TWENTY-FOUR

MODERNIZATION
OF THE LIVING WORLD

By the end of the Cretaceous we are far along in the history of life, with a mere 70 million years or so to go. What remains chronologically is the Cenozoic era, often popularly designated as the Age of Mammals. Its brief last part is the Age of Man, who is a mammal, too. From our vantage point at the time called "now," the greatest interest of the last 70 million years is that they did eventuate in the modern world. The origin of what is now, the modernization of the earth and its life, thus becomes a main theme in this chapter. Before we concentrate on the mammals and man, the theme involves some considerations of principle and of the more wide-ranging modernization of other groups of organisms.

Modernization in Aquatic Environments

Aquatic environments were the first to be occupied by living things. It might be expected and is on the whole correct that they would have approached their present aspect at earlier times than the land environments. You have seen that even in the late Ordovician, more than 425 million years ago, the seas, at least, swarmed with plants and animals about as diverse as those now living in the same environments. Yet most of the dominant organisms of the Ordovician have become extinct without issue and have been replaced by others whose direct ancestors were few and obscure in the Ordovician.

The fossil record of aquatic plants is inadequate. Most of them are soft-bodied and usually fossilize as a structureless smear of carbon or not at all. Nevertheless, we do know that algae were already common far back in the Pre-Cambrian. It is probable that most of the main groups of algae were present in the Paleozoic. They have never lost their dominance in all aquatic environments. Certainly many new species have evolved more recently, but on the whole the aspect and general composition of aquatic floras seems already to have been modern several hundred million years ago. The most recent important change for which there is good evidence was the appearance of the diatoms, first found as fossils in the Jurassic and increasingly common since then. Now they account for a good fraction of the photosynthesis in most aquatic environments.

A few modern groups of aquatic invertebrates date back without really profound change from the early Paleozoic. Most of them, however, have had extensive replacement since then within groups and adaptive niches. Corals, bryozoans, and clams, for instance, had much the same roles in Paleozoic seas as they do now and did not look very different superficially. Nevertheless, there has been almost complete replacement in these groups, not only of species and genera but of families and superfamilies, even, in some instances, of orders.

Although they got started so much later, the fishes rather closely paralleled the aquatic invertebrates in their modernization. The beginning of dominance of higher bony fishes was evident in the Triassic. By the end of the Cretaceous that group was fully dominant and modern in aspect.

The archaic amphibians mostly disappeared by the Triassic. The rise of the modern groups is poorly documented by fossils, for some unknown reason, but frogs almost modern in appearance are known from the Jurassic. The salamanders may be equally old, but none is yet known before the Cretaceous.

The rise of several groups of aquatic reptiles in the latest Paleozoic and during the Mesozoic introduced a bizarre and unmodern note in the aquatic faunas of those times. The extinction of most of them in the Cretaceous left the turtles and crocodiles (with their allies the alligators) as the common amphibious or aquatic reptiles. Neither group has changed essentially during the Cenozoic.

A striking change in aquatic environments during the Cenozoic, practically the only change of deep significance, was the rise and spread of aquatic mammals, whales, seals, sea cows, and their relatives. They began to appear in the Eocene and were common and essentially modernized in the Miocene.

Modernization in Land Environments

PLANTS

The dominant, archaic vegetation of the Carboniferous vanished, for the most part, by the Triassic. In the Triassic and Jurassic there was a sort of interim dominant floral type composed mainly of ferns, cycadeoids, cycads, ginkgos, and conifers. Most of those groups do survive now, but in greatly diminished numbers. Their dominance and the scarcity of flowering plants gave the plant life of the Triassic and Jurassic a decidedly nonmodern aspect. By late Cretaceous time, however, the aspect was fully modern. No distinctive groups of plants are known from the late Cretaceous that do not survive today. The flowering plants were then already decidedly dominant, and almost all their modern groups date from then or from quite early in the Cenozoic. Changes during the middle and late Cenozoic involved little more than the shifting of established floras as climates changed.

INSECTS

Modernization of insects also began in the Triassic, when most of the archaic groups that had appeared in the Carboniferous had become extinct. No important groups (for instance, no orders) that are now extinct evolved after the Permian. The whole picture of insect evolution during the Mesozoic was one of steady expansion by the evolution of new groups that were to continue onward into the modern world. Expansion in detail went on also through the Cenozoic and is perhaps still going on, but most if not all of the main groups of insects were already present and modern in form in the late Cretaceous.

REPTILES

The modernization of land reptiles was essentially only a matter of extinction of the dinosaurs. That left the lizards, snakes, and tortoises, all of which had nearly reached their modern form while the dinosaurs still lived.

BIRDS

Birds rarely fossilize except under unusual circumstances, so that their fossil record is spotty. Patient accumulation has, however, revealed the essentials of their history. They arose in the Jurassic and became fully birdlike, essentially modern in structure, by the end of the Cretaceous. Some of them then still had teeth, but their scanty remains suffice to show that their skeletons were no longer semi-reptilian but completely avian. They had, moreover, undergone some sharp divergence or adaptive radiation, for, along with normal flying birds, there were large, wingless, swimming birds at that time. Despite the comparatively thin fossil record, birds surely flitted throughout the Cenozoic in great numbers, and it would be as true to call that the Age of Birds as to call it the Age of Mammals.

FIG. 24-1 *Diatryma, a large flightless bird of the Eocene.* (Drawing, American Museum of Natural History)

Large flightless birds evolved on all the larger land areas of the Cenozoic (Figure 24-1). Three groups have survived: ostriches in Africa and Arabia (and formerly over most of Eurasia); rheas in South America; and cassowaries and the closely related emus in Australia and New Guinea. More have become extinct: *Diatryma* in North America, with relatives in Europe; moas in New Zealand; "elephant birds" (*Aepyornis* and relatives) in Madagascar; and several kinds in South America. It is an oddity of evolution that the birds, after acquiring flight and dominating a new environment, repeatedly gave rise to lines in which flight was lost. The large running birds have competed, on the whole quite successfully, with mammals.

History of the Mammals

MESOZOIC MAMMALS

You recall that the mammals evolved from mammal-like reptiles in the late Triassic or earliest Jurassic (Figure 24-2). They are about as old as flowering plants, turtles, or crocodiles, and probably older than teleost fishes, lizards, snakes, or birds. They are by and large the most progressive, by most definitions the very highest, of all organisms. Yet their

modernization and their rise to dominance in their own environments was slower than for most other groups dominant at various times in the history of life. For more than 100 million years after they first appeared, mammals cut a small figure in the world. That duration is considerably longer than the whole era of their later dominance, the Age of Mammals. By the late Jurassic they had some diversity, but even up to the end of the Cretaceous they remained small, mostly about the size of a mouse, and rare.

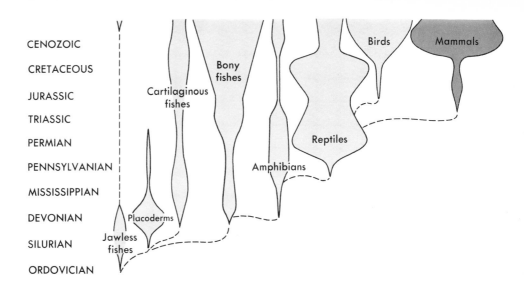

CENOZOIC

CRETACEOUS

JURASSIC

TRIASSIC

PERMIAN

PENNSYLVANIAN

MISSISSIPPIAN

DEVONIAN

SILURIAN

ORDOVICIAN

FIG. 24-2 The historical record of the vertebrates. The widths of the pathways roughly approximate the relative numbers of known genera in the classes.

Why were the mammals so obscure for so long? We do not know, but we can offer a hypothesis. When amphibians arose, they had a new way of life with no competitors. Expansion was rapid, geologically speaking, as you would expect. Early reptiles had to still greater extent access to new ways of life and new environments empty of any possible competitors. They not only expanded rapidly but also eventually all but wiped out the amphibians, whose environments overlapped theirs. When mammals arose, the situation was quite different. Niches or adaptive types accessible to the mammals, where they would much later become dominant, were already extensively occupied by well-adapted reptiles.

BEGINNING OF THE AGE OF MAMMALS

The Cenozoic began at an unfortunate time from the fossil-hunters' point of view. In the long seesaw between the uplift and the wearing down of the continents it was a time of predominant, widespread uplift. A result was that erosion was likewise widespread. Most of the eroded material was reworked and eventually deposited beyond the margins of what is now dry land. Few deposits of sediments were made and left where we can now get at them. Consequently, there are few available deposits of the beginning of the Cenozoic, the early Paleocene, where fossils of land animals can be found. In spite of intensive search, earliest Paleocene mammals have been found in only

one part of the earth: in and near the Rocky Mountains in the United States. Later Paleocene mammals are known from Europe, Asia, and South America, and probably early Paleocene mammals will be found elsewhere eventually. In the meantime we can follow the detailed change from Age of Reptiles to Age of Mammals only in the Rocky Mountain region. Obviously a good deal that we do not know about must have been going on elsewhere.

In the Rocky Mountain region the latest Cretaceous rocks contain dinosaurs in some numbers and also tiny mammals. The mammals included one holdover group from the Jurassic, the old seedeaters, which were to become extinct during the Eocene. The "insectivorous" forms were mostly marsupials, closely similar to our modern opossums, which are still thriving in spite of the fact that they have hardly changed at all since that remote date. With them were a few true insectivores, that is, placental mammals classified in the order Insectivora.

In the earliest Paleocene rocks the dinosaurs are completely absent; they seem to have disappeared with startling suddenness. The fauna is already dominated by mammals, although as yet these are of only a few kinds. The largest in the early Paleocene was about the size of a not-too-robust collie. Strong differentiation among placental mammals had not yet occurred. They were long, rather short-legged, running (probably not very swiftly) on feet with five toes. Tails were long, heavy at the base, and heads were small

FIG. 24-3 *Ectoconus, a Paleocene mammal.* (Drawing, American Museum of Natural History)

in proportion. The teeth suggest that most of these animals were omnivorous, some with a tendency to rely more on plant food and some with a tendency to rely more on animal food (Figure 24-3).

Later faunas in the American Paleocene show marked and relatively rapid expansion and divergence of the placental mammals. By late Paleocene there are many kinds: numerous hoofed herbivores, some of them now well over a meter in height; fairly specialized predacious carnivores of many sizes and kinds; small forerunners of the monkeys; the first, still very rare, rodents; and others. The later Paleocene faunas from Europe and Asia suggest that much the same sort of expansion had been going on there. It was probably shared by the whole World Continent, the intermittently united land masses of Africa, Eurasia, and North America. In South America a great expansion was at least well under way in the late Paleocene, although it was already peculiar to that island continent.

What had happened is fairly clear: the mammals were finally inheriting the earth. Extinction of most of the Mesozoic land reptiles left empty environments which were occupied by the mammals in a worldwide adaptive radiation most active during the Paleocene. The mammals, more efficient and more capable of divergent adaptation, eventually went further than the reptiles ever had in occupation and subdivision of the environmental niches. All this only makes more mysterious and more exasperating the problem of *why* the Mesozoic reptiles became extinct and left the environmental opportunity to the mammals. The

record seems to make it clear that the dinosaurs did not become extinct because the mammals had expanded, but on the contrary that the mammals expanded because the dinosaurs previously had become extinct.

MODERNIZATION OF MAMMALS

Eocene and Oligocene Mammals

On the World Continent, basic modernization occurred most prominently in the Eocene, with a filling in of detail in the Oligocene and later. Probably all the main groups, the orders, of living placental mammals were already in existence in the Eocene. Eocene and Oligocene faunas look strange to us in spite of the rapid modernization that was going on. There are three main reasons for their exotic look: some of the striking and peculiar ancient groups were not yet extinct; some modern groups had different geographic distributions then and occurred in unexpected places; and, as a point of detail, the direct ancestors of our present mammals had not yet reached just their present forms (Figures 24-4 and 24-5).

Startling later changes in geographic distribution are illustrated by the presence of abundant camels and horses in North America through much of the Cenozoic, in spite of the fact that there are no native camels or horses here now.

FIG. 24-4 **The modernization of the mammalian fauna of North America.** The diagram shows the percentages of North American mammals belonging to different groups as they changed through the Age of Mammals. Extensive turnover from archaic to modern groups is especially evident in the Eocene and Oligocene. (The early native primates in North America were all of archaic, prosimian groups; modernization of primates occured, but in the Old World.)

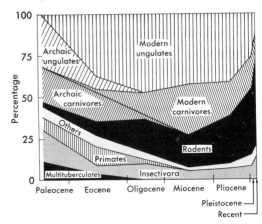

Eohippus

Uintathere

Titanothere

Camel

Oreodont

Oligocene
sabertooth

**FIG. 24-5   Some Eocene and
Oligocene mammals.**

The Horse Family

Changes in modern groups from the Eocene onward are well illustrated by that classic example of evolution, the horse family (Figures 24-6 and 24-7).

Its earliest known member is eohippus (*Hyracotherium*), in the early Eocene (see Figure 24-5). "Little eohippus, no bigger than a fox," generally stood about 45 to 60 centimeters high. It had four toes on the front feet and three on the hind, each toe ending

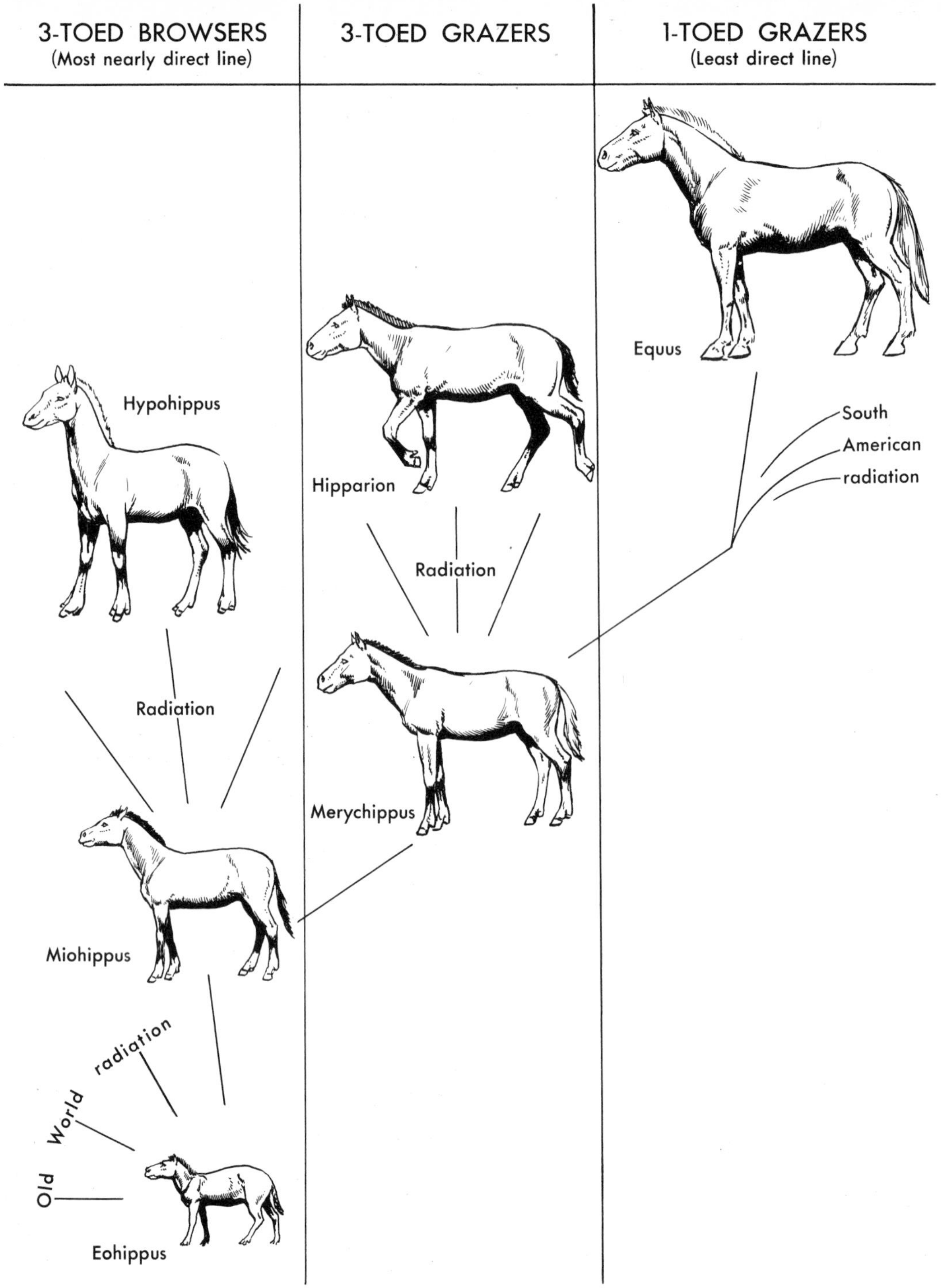

FIG. 24-6 History of the horses. *Miohippus* was only one product of an early radiation from eohippus. It was still three-toed and browsed on trees and bushes. From *Miohippus* many forms arose, some of which remained three-toed browsers; but one of them, *Merychippus*, made the major step to the grazing habit; it began exploiting the extensive grasslands of the Miocene period. The line eventually leading to the one-toed *Equus* from *Merychippus* was, again, only one of many in the adaptive radiation of the three-toed grazers. Thus the lineage from eohippus to *Equus* is the least direct of those that might be traced through the succession of adaptive radiations. This diagram is greatly simplified and shows only a few of the many genera known.

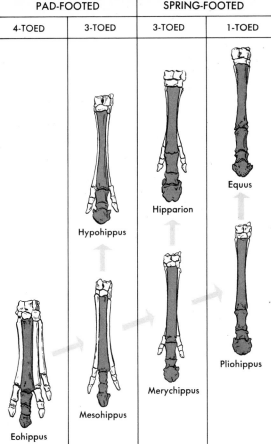

PAD-FOOTED		SPRING-FOOTED	
4-TOED	3-TOED	3-TOED	1-TOED

Equus

Hipparion

Hypohippus

Pliohippus

Merychippus

Mesohippus

Eohippus

FIG. 24-7   The evolution of the forefoot in the horse family. The single toe (gray in the figure) of the modern horse (*Equus*) is the sole survivor of four toes present in the ancestral form eohippus (technically *Hyracotherium*). *Hypohippus* and *Hipparion* show stabilization of the mechanism, without advance toward the condition of *Equus*. The feet, of different sizes, have been reduced to the same length for comparison.

in a tiny hoof. The small head lacked the heavy muzzle of modern horses and had comparatively large eyes that were set near the middle, not far back as in our horses. The teeth of the *Hyracotherium* were simple, not fit for grazing but only for browsing on soft vegetation.

The contrast between little eohippus and the large horses of today is great. Yet almost all the intermediate stages are known, a powerful demonstration not only that evolution is a fact but also of how it has occurred. This group, at least, convincingly demonstrates that progressive change is a process of spread of small mutations and new combinations of genes and chromosomes in variable populations.

It is to be emphasized that the picture of steady, gradual change from eohippus to *Equus,* the modern horses, still commonly given in popular discussions, is quite incorrect. The true history of the horse family does not show a lineage that gradually increased in size, reduced the number of toes, and developed higher, more complex teeth from eohippus to *Equus.* There was not one lineage but, at times, dozens of them. The phylogeny is intricately branched, although all but a few of the branches have now become extinct. Increase in size and change in the feet were not constant but sporadic. The change from eohippus to *Equus* occurred irregularly through the complex phylogeny shown in greatly oversimplified fashion in Figure 24-6.

Forerunners of Man

We may forgive ourselves for being more interested in the evolution of man and his relatives than in that of horses or other nonhuman groups. The fossil record of human origin and of the order Primates in general is now quite extensive. Although it still has gaps, many will doubtless be filled as larger gaps in the past have been filled by new finds of fossils. Some gaps may always remain, because the fossils are simply not preserved or where we can find them, but the main features of the history are already clear (Figure 24-8).

That the primates have not left as complete a fossil record as, for instance, the horses is readily understandable. The greater part of the history of the horse family—its most central and progressive part, at least—took place in one region, a region rich in fossils and well explored by bone diggers: central North America. The history of the primates was more far-flung, with crucial episodes in several different regions. Moreover, central parts of the history occurred in tropical areas, which are, as a rule, neither very rich in fossil deposits nor as yet thoroughly explored

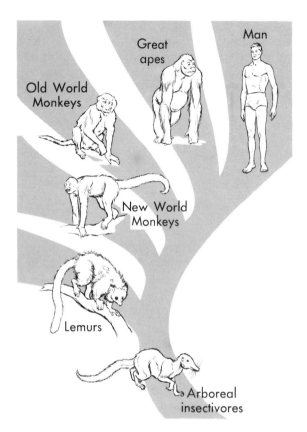

FIG. 24-8 **The phylogeny of the primates.** The figure is not scaled either to size of animal or to time.

for them. The primate way of life also militates against a good fossil record. Most primates are and have been arboreal, and tree dwellers are comparatively unlikely to be buried and to fossilize. It has further been suggested that higher primates were too bright to be fossilized with any great frequency. A shrewd animal has a better chance to avoid being mired down or swept away in a flood, or suffering other accidents that could readily lead to burial and fossilization.

EARLY PROSIMIANS

The main groups of primates were briefly mentioned in Chapter 17. The history starts with the most primitive of these groups, that of the *prosimians*

or premonkeys. Their oldest known fossils are found in the middle Paleocene of the Rocky Mountain region. Prosimians (Figure 24-9) were abundant through the Eocene, not only in North America but also in Eurasia and probably in Africa, where the Eocene fossil record is extremely poor as far as yet discovered.

Primates were probably more widespread and included more species in the Eocene than at any later time. Those primitive early primates had evolved from still more primitive Insectivora. It is, indeed, impossible to draw a sharp line between the orders Insectivora and Primates. Prosimians, even now, have poorly developed brains. Many of them have rather long, pointed snouts, markedly unlike the flattened faces and more localized noses of most monkeys and all apes and men. A basic characteristic of primates present in early prosimians is the retention and further evolution of grasping hands and, often, feet, with apposable thumbs and big toes. In connection with this adaptation, the insectivore claws early began to evolve into nails.

MONKEYS

The Old World monkeys, *ceropithecoids,* and New World monkeys, *ceboids* (Chapter 17), are fully distinct phylogenetic units. They have always had approximately the same geographic distribution that they have now: Old World monkeys in the warmer parts of Africa, Asia, and Europe, and New World monkeys in South and Central America. Both groups evolved from prosimians, probably from closely related prosimians, but they arose separately, on different continents. (Why did not these warm-climate animals migrate in either direction between Eurasia and North America?)

Both groups first appeared in the Oligocene. They differ from prosimians in similar ways. They have larger, more effective brains, with expansion especially of the upper part of the cortex. The brain case correspondingly forms a larger proportion of the head. The snout is reduced, and the flattened monkey face is characteristic. The eyes are pointed more nearly forward, and the fields of vision of the two eyes overlap widely. The shortened muzzle involves a shortening of upper and lower jaws, and the number of teeth is reduced. The molars are squared, but remain

FIG. 24-9 **Prosimians.** Left, an Eocene prosimian, *Notharctus*. Note the grasping hands and feet; the thumb closes over the branch in the opposite direction to the fingers. Right, a living prosimian, *Loris tardigradus* (the slender loris). Note the thumb and the manner in which both eyes are directed forward, permitting stereoscopic vision; the latter is an advanced character in which this particular prosimian has paralleled the higher primates. (Photos, left, American Museum of Natural History; right, New York Zoological Society)

simple. Hands and feet are grasping, but no more so than in some prosimians.

APES

The name "ape" is sometimes applied to a monkey, but strictly it means a member of one particular family of the Primates, the Pongidae (Figure 24-10). Sometimes they are called *anthropoid apes* to make the distinction clear. The living apes are the *gorilla* and *chimpanzee* of central Africa, the *orangutan* of Sumatra and Borneo, and the *gibbons* of southeastern Asia. All are above average size for primates, and gorillas are big brutes, the males becoming heavier and stronger than any men. All lack tails. They have relatively larger brains and brain cases than the monkeys and are in general more intelligent.

All recent apes except the gorilla are highly arboreal, spending most of their lives in trees. Gib-

bons, smallest of the apes, have tremendously long arms and are astonishing acrobats. They swing (*brachiate*) and jump for great distances between branches. When they do come to the ground, they walk on their hind legs, holding up the long arms as balancers. The other apes habitually walk on all fours unless they have been taught to walk clumsily on the hind legs as a circus or vaudeville trick. Gorillas also climb trees, and their immediate ancestors were evidently arboreal, but now they spend much of their time on the ground. Chimpanzees and orangutans do not swing from limb to limb with the abandon of gibbons, but they are agile four-handed climbers and spend most of their time in trees.

Apes have always been confined to the warmer parts of the Old World. The earliest known fossils occur in the Oligocene, along with the first Old World monkeys. Apes and Old World monkeys share some characters present neither in the New World

Gibbon

Chimpanzee

Orangutan

Gorilla

FIG. 24-10 **The great apes, Pongidae.** Note the hands and eyes. The gibbon is brachiating.

monkeys nor in the prosimians. The earliest forms are hard to tell apart. It is apparent that apes either were derived from a branch of the earliest Old World monkeys or that the two groups had an immediate common ancestry among the prosimians.

In the Miocene, apes became more varied than they are today. Their remains are not common, but diligent search has turned up fragments of many species in the Miocene of eastern Africa and the Pliocene of India and a few in the Miocene and Pliocene of Europe. There was a great expansion of the family starting at about the beginning of the Miocene. Some of the members of that late Cenozoic complex were aberrant and became extinct. Others were ancestral to the modern apes and were already becoming specialized in similar ways. Still others, especially in the Miocene, were comparatively light, agile forms not yet strongly specialized for arboreal life and lacking other characters peculiar to the surviving apes. *Proconsul* (Figure 24-11), from the Miocene of Kenya, is the most completely known and is among the less specialized.

Fig. 24-11 *Proconsul, fossil ape from the Miocene of Kenya, Africa.*

The australopithecines now known were quite varied and covered a considerable span of time, from about 2 million to about $\frac{1}{2}$ million years ago. Some of them were seemingly too aberrant (for instance, in great enlargement of the molar teeth and development of a crest on the skull) to figure in the direct ancestry of modern man. There is also evidence that when the later, at least, of them lived, more advanced members of the human family had already evolved. It is, however, now the consensus of competent specialists that early and comparatively unspecialized australopithecines did represent the human ancestry around the beginning of the Pleistocene. The combination of a brain still practically on the ape level with nearly human dentition and posture is remarkable and was not anticipated in earlier speculation about intermediaries between apes and men.

Whether to call the australopithecines "apes," "men," or something else is really a semantic and not a scientific question. Scientifically the consensus now places them as pre-*Homo* hominids, that is, as members of the human family that had not attained the status of the living genus of humans. An important but not necessarily decisive point is whether they made tools. Living chimpanzees frequently use and occasionally make very simple tools, usually sticks or straws, but most anthropologists consider the regular making of special tools a definitely human trait beyond the capacity of the true ape brain. Although stone tools certainly and perhaps others of bones, teeth, and horns have been found associated with australopithecines, it is not yet certain that they manufactured them.

AUSTRALOPITHECINES

In 1925 was discovered the first of a remarkable group of fossil primates known as the *australopithecines* ("southern monkeys (or apes)"). Since then, several nearly complete skulls and numerous teeth, jaw fragments, and other parts of skeletons have been collected (Figures 24-12 and 24-13).

The australopithecine brain was comparable in size and complexity with that of the larger living apes. It was smaller than in any normal modern human. The skull as a whole is apelike in appearance, but it has a number of more manlike anatomical details. Among these is evidence that it was set squarely on top of the backbone, not thrust forward as in the apes. The teeth are more manlike than apelike. The pelvis and limb and vertebral parts suggest that the australopithecines walked upright, or nearly so, a posture decidedly human in contrast with that of the apes.

Man's Place in Nature

HUMAN ORIGINS

Even the pre-evolutionary biologists recognized that man is an animal, fundamentally like other animals but distinguished as a species by higher and

different development of intelligence. In the eighteenth century Linnaeus, an antievolutionist, classified man, *Homo sapiens,* in the order Primates with the prosimians, monkeys, and apes. That classification is still accepted by biologists. Knowledge of evolution makes it evident that man's distinctive characteristics

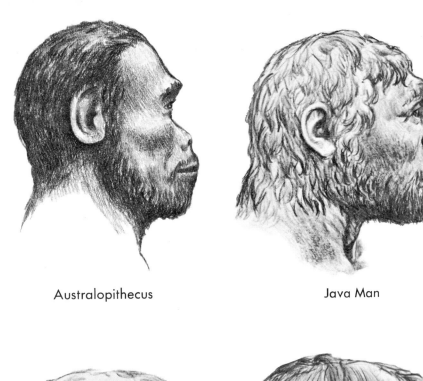

Australopithecus

Java Man

Neandertal Man

Cro-Magnon Man

FIG. 24-12 *Australopithecus and fossil men.*

arose in the same way as those of other species of animals, by more or less gradual change in varying populations. That man's material being evolved from other and (in intelligence, at least) lower animals is about as certain as a scientific conclusion can be.

It is obvious to the most casual visitor to a zoo or circus that the apes are the most manlike of living nonhumans. This has been confirmed by intensive investigation of structure, physiology, and behavior. It is, however, impossible that any living ape represents the human ancestry or is even very closely similar to it. Obviously no animal now living can be literally ancestral to animals of any other living species. Moreover, all the living apes have specializations that surely did not occur in our ancestry. The apes undoubtedly had a common ancestry with us, but since then they have diverged definitely from the line of our later ancestors. It is not impossible and is in fact probable that some of the primitive Miocene members of the ape family were our ancestors. The australopithecines add to the weight of evidence favoring that conclusion.

Modern man's most distinctively human characteristic is his brain. But the origin of man and of his brain was dependent on older features, reflecting earlier primate adaptations. Three of the most important of those prehuman acquisitions, in the order in which they evolved, were grasping hands, binocular, stereoscopic vision, and upright posture.

The earliest primates were arboreal, as so many still are. A fundamental adaptation to arboreal life was the apposable thumb, already present in the oldest known fossil prosimians. With it, the hand was able to grasp the branches of trees. That ancient adaptation now makes possible for us all our most complex manipulations and hence all the tools we make and use as *our* most powerful adaptive equipment.

In the earliest primates and the most primitive of those still surviving, the eyes are directed more laterally, somewhat as in a long-nosed dog. The two fields of vision overlap only slightly, and an object is ordinarily seen with only one eye at a time. In various lines of descent there was an early trend for the eyes to point more forward, so that the fields overlapped more widely. Then an object was generally seen with both eyes at once, with *binocular* ("two-eyed") vision. This, in turn, provided the basis for an actual fusion of the images from both eyes as

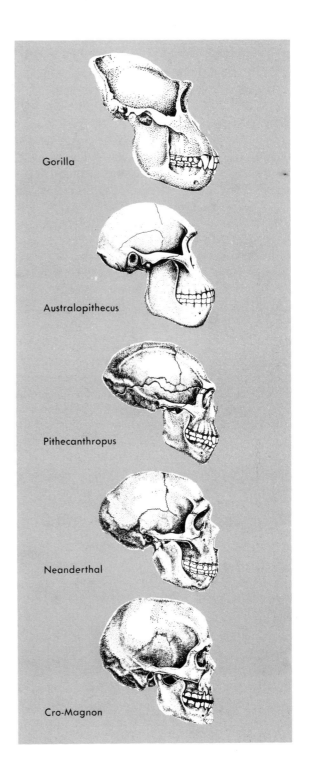

FIG. 24-13 Skulls of an ape and of members of the human family. In comparing apes and men as a group, it is useful to recognize two sets of skull features: one set (called paleanthropic) is more apelike and characterizes earlier members of the human family; the other set (called neanthropic) characterizes modern men. Paleanthropic skull characters include (1) small brain-case volume; (2) brain case shallow relative to length; (3) heavy bony brow ridges over the eyes; (4) jaws protruding forward from a vertical dropped from the eyes; (5) receding lower jaw—no chin. Neanthropic skull characters are the opposite: (1) large brain-case volume; (2) brain case deep relative to length; (3) no brow ridges; (4) jaws not protruding in front of the eyes; (5) chin protruding forward.

perceived in the brain, giving *stereoscopic* ("solid (three-dimensional) viewing") vision. These developments were also probably adaptations to arboreal life, in which acute vision and depth perception have special importance. On the ground there is always something under foot, but an animal moving from branch to branch must know precisely where the next branch is. In man, more than in most other vertebrates, vision has become the dominant sense, the source of our most valuable information about the world around us. And this priceless stereoscopic vision has combined with the earlier grasping hand in *hand–eye coordination,* the basis of tool use.

Primates are basically four-footed in locomotion and posture. In the larger arboreal monkeys and in the apes there was a trend toward brachiation, swinging from tree branches by the arms instead of walking along the branches on four feet. This involved a straightening of the trunk of the body and an adaptive elongation of the arms. Our own ancestors never became extremely specialized brachiators like the modern apes (especially the gibbons), but some advance along this trend may have facilitated the upright posture when our ancestors came down to walk and live on the ground. That posture freed the hands from use in locomotion and permitted efficient specialization of fore and hind limbs–fore (now upper) limbs for manipulation only, hind (now lower) limbs for locomotion only.

Thus our ancient arboreal primate ancestors supplied the basis for becoming human. The australopithecines had grasping hands, stereoscopic vision, and erect posture. After that stage came the final great expansion of the brain—and we were fully human.

FOSSIL MEN

Just when man arose and which fossils should be classed as human are matters of definition. Not one but many "missing links" are known, and it is arbitrary which of them we choose to call "men." Some would confine the designation to populations of *Homo sapiens* just like those now living. Others insist that even the australopithecines should be called

"men." In the present section we are concerned with the members of the human family more advanced than the australopithecines. All are limited to the Pleistocene, and not the earliest Pleistocene as far as is known. None of them is likely to be more than about a million years old, and most of them are probably under 500,000. Dating is still inexact in this range. In any event, man has a respectable antiquity from the viewpoint of human history, but he is a newcomer, a Johnny-come-lately, in comparison with most other species of animals.

Except for the australopithecines, the most primitive fossil men are represented especially by a group of skulls, jaws, and other fragments found in Java and another group found near Peking in China. The most primitive Java men (see Figures 24-12 and 24-13) have been called *Pithecanthropus* ["monkey (or ape) men"], and the Peking men *Sinanthropus* ("China men"). They are, however, so similar that they probably represent merely different demes, or at most different subspecies, of a single specific population. The present consensus is that the species was not generically distinct from modern man, and the name *Homo erectus* is applied to it. Recently, fossil remains of the same general type have been found in northern and central Africa, and members of the species probably occurred throughout most of the Old World. Apparently none of them ever discovered America.

Skulls of this archaic group retained apelike characters that are reduced or lost in all living men. The brain case was small. Brain size varied greatly, from about 775 cubic centimeters to about 1300. The average was about 1000, which is nearly intermediate between living apes (500) and men (1350). There were heavy ridges above the eyes. The jaws and teeth protruded in front, and the chin retreated as in apes.

NEANDERTHAL MEN

Later than the group just discussed there lived another large population, distinctly more advanced than *Homo erectus* but still more primitive than modern man (see Figures 24-12 and 24-13). The scattered finds at many places in Europe, Asia, and Africa show individual and probably racial differences, but they are enough alike for all to be considered as members of one variable population, the *Nean-*

derthals or Neanderthaloids (that is, Neanderthal-like).

The Neanderthals were short, stocky, powerful people with large, heavy-boned heads. Brow ridges were present and the chin was receding, but neither character was as extreme as in the older Java and Peking men. The forehead was sloped and the brain low, but surprisingly enough the total size of the brain was about as great as in modern man. We do not know how we would stack up with Neanderthals in an intelligence test, but we do know that their intelligence was considerable in amount and human in quality. They constructed a large variety of beautifully made tools and were successful hunters. They sometimes buried their dead and put offerings or sacrifices in the graves, which implies that they had a religion and rituals.

EARLY HOMO SAPIENS

Several fossil skulls have been discovered that are somewhat older than the typical Neanderthals but that show greater resemblance to modern man. Among these are the Swanscombe (England) skull, unfortunately only a few fragments, and the more nearly complete Steinheim and Ehringsdorf (Germany) skulls. They are not fully modern in appearance and do have some primitive and Neanderthaloid traits, but they are more like *Homo sapiens* than are the most fully developed later Neanderthals. They suggest that the history of man in the Pleistocene was not a simple line that could be symbolized by Java man → Neanderthal man → modern man.

There are two main possibilities. One is that Pleistocene man constituted a single species but was split up into highly varying demes, some more *Homo sapiens*-like, even at an early date, and others retaining or even accentuating more archaic characters. Selection within the species eventually eliminated archaic variants. This idea is supported by the fact that some

fossil men do seem to represent contemporaneous intermediates between the Neanderthaloid and the more extreme modern types. The other main possibility is that the Neanderthals were a separate branch of mankind, a species that became extinct and was replaced in competition with forerunners of *Homo sapiens*. The contrast between these two theories is not absolutely clear-cut.

True *Homo sapiens,* indistinguishable from modern man, is first known in the last glacial stage of the Pleistocene. Cro-Magnon men, first found in France, lived at least 20,000 and probably not over 50,000 years ago (see Figures 24-12 and 24-13). All discoveries of younger fossil men are also true *Homo sapiens,* with no more variation or regional differentiation than still occurs.

In spite of inevitable doubts as to certain details, the increasing modernization of human populations during the Pleistocene is a fact, and it bears eloquent witness to the rise of *Homo sapiens* by natural evolutionary processes.

EARLY MAN IN AMERICA

No men truly primitive in a biological sense ever reached the Americas as far as is yet known. America was peopled by repeated invasions from Asia, principally although perhaps not exclusively by way of Alaska. The oldest surely dated traces of man in America are not over 30,000 years old. It seems fairly certain that man did not reach America until the closing stage of the Pleistocene. By then *Homo sapiens,* with various racial and lesser distinctions, was universal in the Old World. Only *Homo sapiens,* mainly or entirely mongoloid in origin, ever reached the New World before the European discovery.

And What of the Future?

This brings the biological aspects of the history of life up to date. *Homo sapiens* has evolved and has expanded to nearly all the lands of the earth. He dominates the land environments as no other species or larger group of organisms ever has. He is, so far, the culmination of the whole incredibly long and complex evolutionary process.

It is natural to sit back at this point and to

life and one that seems just now to be highly unpredictable.

The being and the becoming of the universe, its rules and its history, will always limit and condition what can occur. Man, for the first time ever, has conscious knowledge of many of the rules and much of the history. He can use that knowledge to modify and guide his own destiny and the destinies of other organisms. How he will in fact use that awesome power is hidden in the darkness of the future. Perhaps the only safe prediction is that you and your descendants, whether you want to or not, whether indeed you know it or not, will have the most decisive influence on the future history of life.

speculate on the future history of life. The simplest assumption would be that past trends will continue indefinitely. It is, however, one of the lessons of history that trends do not continue indefinitely. They eventually change direction or stop. There is reason to believe that the trend of physical evolution by which man arose has now stopped. Under present conditions man's future biological evolution is more likely to be degenerative than progressive. But man himself is really a new factor in the history of

Summary

The Cenozoic, Age of Mammals: 70 million years duration, with man's appearance toward the end.

Modernization of aquatic environments:
Aquatic plants: very little change; the Jurassic appearance of diatoms the only major event.
Invertebrates: extensive replacement within groups, since the Paleozoic.
Fishes: by the end of the Cretaceous, the full emergence of higher bony fish as the dominant group.
Other aquatic vertebrates: the extinction of archaic amphibians (Triassic); the rise of aquatic reptiles in the Mesozoic and of aquatic mammals in the Cenozoic.

Modernization of land environments:
Plants: the disappearance of the predominantly lycopsid-sphenopsid forests during the Permo-Triassic; forests of the Triassic-Jurassic mostly ferns and gymnosperms (cycadeoids, cycads, ginkgos, and conifers); by the late Cretaceous forests of modern aspect—predominantly angiosperms.
Insects: their modernization during the Mesozoic, essentially complete by the late Cretaceous.
Reptiles: the extinction of dinosaurs, leaving lizards, snakes, and tortoises as the main surviving reptiles.
Birds: their poor fossil record; their Jurassic origin; their modernization nearly complete by the end of the Cretaceous; adaptive radiation in the Cenozoic, including the origin of large flightless forms.

History of the mammals:
Mesozoic mammals: the Triassic-Jurassic origin of mammals; their slow early evolution; their small size and scarcity up to the end of the Cretaceous.
Beginning of the Age of Mammals: the geological factors responsible for the poor early Cenozoic fossil record; faunal changes from the Cretaceous to the Paleocene; the archaic character of early Paleocene mammals; the diversification

of mammals by the late Paleocene; their adaptive radiation, made possible by the evacuation of niches by reptilian extinctions.

Modernization of mammals: their post-Paleocene history; on the World Continent most of the modernization occurring in the Eocene and Oligocene: the complexity of the eohippus–*Equus* lineage.

Forerunners of man: the fossil record of primates; the effect of their arboreal way of life on the quality of the record.

Early prosimians: lemurs; their early distribution; insectivore-primate relationships; primate characteristics.

Monkeys: Old World and New World types.

Apes: the four living types; their large size and predominantly arboreal habit; their restrictions to warm climates and other characteristics; their relationship to Old World monkeys, the Miocene expansion; *Proconsul.*

Australopithecines, a late group of fossil primates from Africa; their manlike features; their position in the human family.

Man's place in nature:

Human origins: man as a primate; evolution from lower forms; the probability of ancestors among Miocene apes; distinctive biological attributes of man—brain, grasping hand, binocular-stereoscopic vision, upright posture; the early evolution of many of these characters as adaptations to aboreal life.

Fossil men: *Homo erectus* group and its skull characters; Neanderthal men—wide distribution, size, skull characters, tools, and other cultural relicts.

Early *Homo sapiens:* the Swanscombe, Steinheim, and Ehringsdorf skulls; the relation of the Neanderthals to modern men; the Cro-Magnon men, the first completely modern type of about 20,000 to 50,000 years ago.

Early man in America: the mongoloid immigration from Asia; the oldest remains fully modern.

The future: man's current dominant biological role; the human evolutionary future: evolution, now including social and cultural evolution, potentially in human power to control.

APPENDIX: A CLASSIFICATION OF ORGANISMS

No two authorities agree on every detail in the classification of organisms. The following arrangement seems reasonable to us. It generally represents either the consensus or a compromise when significant conflict occurs. Most of the names in current use for major groups in protistology, botany, and zoology appear here. The classification may thus serve as a glossary of systematic names as well as an indication of the tremendous basic diversity of living things.

All phyla recognized by us are listed, although some systematists would add several more. A few phyla and subphyla that are *relatively* unimportant in the modern world are named in lightface type. Most of the classes are listed, and these include the groups sometimes considered as phyla. When classes are not designated within a phylum, either the phylum is small and has a single class, or a proposed division into classes is not satisfactory. The symbol † indicates that a group is totally extinct. Of course, virtually all the phyla and classes include known extinct smaller groups.

For each phylum or class at least one genus is named by way of example. As far as possible, the genera given as examples are available for demonstration or dissection and have been mentioned elsewhere in this book.

KINGDOM PROTISTA

PHYLUM SCHIZOPHYTA or **SCHIZOMYCETES,** bacteria: *Bacillus, Escherichia, Azotobacter, Clostridium, Pneumococcus*

PHYLUM CYANOPHYTA, "blue-green algae" (many are not blue-green in color, and none seems to be closely allied to other or true algae): *Anabaena, Nostoc, Oscillatoria*

PHYLUM MASTIGOPHORA, flagellates:

Class Phytomastigina, plantlike flagellates: *Euglena, Volvox, Chlamydomonas, Cryptomonas*

Class Dinoflagellata, dinoflagellates: *Ceratium, Peridinium, Gymnodinium, Gonyaulax, Ceratodinium, Noctiluca*

Class Zoomastigina, animal-like flagellates: *Trypanosoma, Polytoma, Chilomonas, Astasia, Oikomonas, Mastigamoeba, Hexamitus, Calonympha*

PHYLUM SARCODINA or **RHIZOPODA:** rhizopods, *Amoeba;* forams, *Globigerina;* radiolarians, *Lychnaspis*

PHYLUM SPOROZOA: *Plasmodium*

PHYLUM CILIOPHORA

Class Ciliata, ciliates: *Paramecium, Stentor, Stylonichia, Euplotes, Epidinium*

PHYLUM MYXOMYCETES, slime molds: *Lycogala, Physarum*

KINGDOM PLANTAE (PLANTS)

The word *division* is often used for the botanical equivalent of a *phylum.*

Subkingdom Algae (sometimes considered protists and sometimes excluding fungi)

PHYLUM CHLOROPHYTA, green algae

Class Chlorophyceae, grass-green algae: *Ulothrix, Oedogonium, Spirogyra, Closterium*

Class Charophyceae, stoneworts: *Chara, Nitella*

PHYLUM CHRYSOPHYTA

Class Xanthopyceae, yellow-green algae: *Vaucheria, Tribonema, Botrydium*

Class Chrysophyceae, golden-brown algae: *Synura, Dinobryon*

Class Bacillariophyceae, diatoms: *Navicula, Pinnularia, Tabellaria, Actinoptychus*

PHYLUM PHAEOPHYTA, brown algae: *Ectocarpus, Laminaria, Fucus*

PHYLUM RHODOPHYTA, red algae: *Porphyra, Batrachospermum, Nemalion, Lithophyllum, Thamnion, Polysiphonia*

PHYLUM MYCOPHYTA, fungi

Class Phycomycetes, tube fungi: bread molds, *Rhizopus;* water molds, *Saprolegnia;* white rusts and downy mildews, *Albugo;* chytrids, *Chytridium*

Class Ascomycetes, sac fungi: bread molds, *Neurospora;* yeasts, *Saccharomyces;* blue and green molds, *Aspergillus, Penicillium;* powdery mildews, *Microsphaera;* cup fungi, *Sclerotinia;* morels, *Morchella*

Class Basidiomycetes, club fungi: mushrooms, *Psalliota;* toadstools, *Amanita;* bracket fungi, *Fomes;* smuts and rusts, *Puccinia*

(*Fungi imperfecti:* Under this name botanists place a large number of disease-producing fungi, such as those causing athlete's foot or beet leaf spot. They are probably ascomycetes and basidiomycetes in which the sexual cycle has been lost or is unknown. This is not, strictly, a unit of classification but a catchall for fungi that have not been classified.)

(**Lichens:** These composite organisms are obligatory symbiotic associations of a fungus and an alga; in *ascolichens* the fungus is an ascomycete, and in *basidiolichens* it is a basidiomycete.)

Subkingdom Metaphyta

PHYLUM BRYOPHYTA

Class Anthoceropsida or Anthocerotae, hornworts: *Anthoceros*

Class Hepaticopsida or Hepaticae, liverworts: *Marchantia, Riccia, Conocephalum*

Class Bryopsida or Musci, mosses: *Sphagnum, Andreaea, Mnium, Funaria, Pottia*

PHYLUM TRACHEOPHYTA, vascular plants

Subphylum Psilopsida

Class † Psilophytales: † *Rhynia,* † *Psilophyton*

Class Psilotales: *Psilotum, Tmesipteris*

Subphylum Lycopsida: lycopods
† *Lepidodendron,* † *Sigillaria, Lycopodium, Selaginella*

Subphylum Sphenopsida: † *Calamites, Equisetum*

Subphylum Pteropsida, ferns and seed plants

Class Filicineae, ferns: *Ophioglossum, Cyathea, Polypodium, Aspidium, Azolla*

Class Gymnospermae, gymnosperms: † seed ferns, † *Neuropteris;* † cycadeoids, † *Cycadeoidea,* † *Williamsonia;* cycads, *Zamia, Dioon;* ginkgos, *Ginkgo;* † cordaites, † *Cordaites;* conifers, *Pinus, Abies, Tsuga, Taxus, Sequoia, Metasequoia, Araucaria;* joint firs, *Ephedra*

Class Angiospermae, angiosperms, flowering plants

DICOTS: magnolias, *Magnolia;* snake root, *Aristolochia;* eucalypts, *Eucalyptus;* oaks, *Quercus;* elms, *Ulmus;* maples, *Acer;* beeches, *Fagus, Nothofagus;* peaches, *Amygdalus;* cacti, *Cereus;* blackberries, *Rubus;* peas, *Pisum;* nightshades, *Solanum;* sages, *Salvia;* mustards, *Brassica;* dandelions, *Taraxacum;* ragweeds, *Ambrosia*

MONOCOTS: grasses, *Panicum, Stipa;* sedges, *Cyperus;* lilies, *Lilium;* tulips, *Tulipa;* yuccas, *Yucca;* palms, *Sabal;* orchids, *Cypripedium, Ophrys, Cryptostylis*

KINGDOM ANIMALIA (ANIMALS)

Subkingdom Parazoa

PHYLUM PORIFERA, sponges

Class † Pleospongiae: † *Archeocyathus*

Class Calcarea or Calcispongiae, chalky sponges: *Scypha*

Class Hexactinellida or Hyalospongiae, glass sponges: *Hyalonema*

Class Demospongiae, horny sponges; bath sponges, *Spongia*

Subkingdon Metazoa

PHYLUM COELENTERATA or **CNIDARIA,** coelenterates

Class Hydrozoa: *Hydra; Obelia; Gonionemus;* Portuguese man-of-war, *Physalia, Velella*

Class † Stromatoporoidea: † *Clathrodictyon*

Class Scyphozoa, jellyfishes: *Aurelia, Chrysaora*

Class Anthozoa: corals, *Astrangia, Madrepora;* sea anemones, *Metridium, Dahlia*

PHYLUM † GRAPTOLITHINA, † graptolites: † *Didymograptus*

PHYLUM CTENOPHORA, comb jellies: *Cestum*

PHYLUM PLATYHELMINTHES, flatworms

Class Turbellaria, planarians: *Planaria, Dugesia*

Class Trematoda, flukes: *Fasciola, Polystomum, Schistosoma*

Class Cestoda, tapeworms: *Taenia*

PHYLUM MESOZOA: *Rhopalura*

PHYLUM NEMERTINA or NEMERTEA, ribbon worms: *Lineus*

PHYLUM ASCHELMINTHES (classes highly diverse; each is sometimes considered a phylum)

Class Rotifera or Trochelminthes, rotifers or wheel animalcules: *Rotaria, Asplanchna*

Class Gastrotricha: *Chaetonotus*

Class Kinorhyncha or Echinoderida: *Echinoderes.*

Class Nematomorpha or Gordiacea, horsehair worms: *Paragordius, Nectonema*

Class Nematoda, roundworms (much the most important group of Aschelminthes and taken to represent the whole phylum in the discussion of principal phyla in the text): *Ascaris, Trichinella, Turbatrix, Ancylostoma*

PHYLUM ACANTHOCEPHALA, spiny-headed worms: *Gigantorhynchus*

PHYLUM BRYOZOA or **POLYZOA**, bryozoans, sea mosses, or moss animals (each class is often considered a phylum):

     Class Endoprocta: *Urnatella*

     Class Ectoprocta: *Plumatella, Bugula*

PHYLUM BRACHIOPODA, brachiopods or lampshells

     Class Inarticulata: *Lingula*

     Class Articulata: *Laqueus, Terebratulina*

PHYLUM PHORONIDEA: *Phoronis*

PHYLUM CHAETOGNATHA, arrow worms: *Sagitta*

PHYLUM MOLLUSCA, mollusks

     Class Amphineura, chitons: *Chiton, Neomenia*

     Class Monoplacophora: *Neopilina*

     Class Gastropoda, gastropods: snails, *Helix, Lymnaea, Planorbis;* whelks, *Buccinum, Ocenebra;* slugs, *Arion;* limpets, *Patella;* nudibranchs, *Archidoris;* sea hares, *Tethys*

     Class Scaphopoda, tooth-shells: *Dentalium*

     Class Pelecypoda or Lamellibranchia or Bivalvia, pelecypods: clams, mussels, *Venus, Anodonta, Mya, Pecten, Chlamys, Tridacna, Pholas, Teredo, Solen, Mytilus*

     Class Cephalopoda, cephalopods: squids, *Loligo;* octopuses, *Octopus;* nautilus, *Nautilus*

PHYLUM ANNELIDA, annelids, segmented worms

     Class Polychaeta, polychaetes, sandworms: *Neanthes, Nereis, Aphrodite, Chaetopterus*

     Class Oligochaeta, oligochaetes: earthworms, *Lumbricus*

     Class Archiannelida: *Polygordius*

     Class Hirudinea, leeches: *Hirudo*

     Class Gephyrea, sipunculid, echiuroid and priapulid worms (often placed in one, two, or three separate phyla): *Sipunculus, Echiurus, Priapulus*

PHYLUM ARTHROPODA, arthropods (several other small classes are often recognized)

     Class Onychophora: *Peripatus*

     Class † Trilobita, † trilobites: † *Triarthrus,* † *Neolenus,* † *Ogygopsis,* † *Isotelus,* † *Calymene*

     Class Crustacea, crustaceans: brine shrimps, *Artemia;* † *Barrella;* † *Hymenocaris;* water fleas, *Daphnia;* copepods, *Cyclops;* cirripeds (barnacles), *Balanus, Lepas, Sacculina;* wood lice, *Armadillaria, Caprella;* euphausids, *Euphausia;* prawns, *Leander;* lobsters, *Homarus;* crabs, *Cancer*

     Class Arachnida: † eurypterids, † *Pterygotus,* † *Carcinosoma,* † *Hughmilleria;* spiders, *Eurypelma, Theridion;* scorpions, *Vejovis;* king crabs, *Limulus;* ticks, *Dermacentor;* sea spiders, *Pycnogonum*

     Class Chilopoda, centipedes: *Lithobius*

     Class Diplopoda, millipedes: *Julus*

     Class Insecta, insects: cockroaches, *Periplaneta;* grasshoppers, *Melanoplus;* dragonflies, † *Dunbaria, Libellula;* bugs, *Cimex, Halobates;* butterflies, *Papilio, Colias;* flies, *Musca, Drosophila;* beetles, *Calosoma;* ants, *Pogonomyrmex;* bees, wasps, and allies, *Bombus, Vespa, Coccophagus*

PHYLUM ECHINODERMATA, echinoderms

     Class † Cystoidea, † cystoids: † *Caryocrinites*

     Class † Edrioasteroidea, † edrioasteroids: † *Edrioaster*

     Class † Blastoidea, † blastoids † *Pentremites*

     Class Crinoidea, crinoids, sea lilies: *Antedon*

     Class Asteroidea, starfishes: *Asterias*

     Class Ophiuroidea, serpent stars, brittle stars: *Ophiura*

     Class Echinoidea, sea urchins: *Strongylocentrotus, Cidaris*

     Class Holothuroidea, sea cucumbers: *Cucumaria*

Subphylum Hemichordata, tongue worms (acorn worms): *Balanoglossus*

Subphylum Urochordata, or **Tunicata,** tunicates: ascidians, *Ciona*

Subphylum Cephalochordata, lancelets: *Branchiostoma* (amphioxus)

Subphylum Vertebrata, vertebrates

SUPERCLASS PISCES, aquatic vertebrates, fishes

Class Agnatha, agnaths, jawless fishes: † *Cephalaspis,* † *Kieraspis,* † *Pteraspis;* lampreys, *Petromyzon*

Class † Placodermi, † placoderms: † *Climatius,* † *Diplacanthus,* † *Coccosteus,* † *Dinichthys,* † *Pterichthyodes*

Class Chrondrichthyes or Elasmobranchii: sharks, *Squalus;* rays, *Raja; Chimaera*

Class Osteichthyes, bony fishes: † *Cheirolepis;* sturgeon, *Acipenser;* trout, *Salmo;* perch, *Perca;* anglerfish, *Photocorynus;* crossopterygians: † *Eusthenopteron, Latimeria;* lungfishes: † *Dipterus, Epiceratodus, Protopterus*

SUPERCLASS TETRAPODA, land vertebrates, tetrapods

Class Amphibia, amphibians: † labyrinthodonts, † *Diplovertebron,* † *Eryops;* salamanders, *Ambystoma, Necturus;* frogs, *Rana;* toads, *Bufo;* tree toads, *Hyla;* caecilians (Apoda), *Gymnophis*

Class Reptilia, reptiles: † cotylosaurs; turtles and tortoises, *Testudo, Aromochelys;* † ichthyosaurs † *Ichthyosaurus;* † plesiosaurs; rhynchocephalians,

Sphenodon; lizards, *Gerrhonotus, Crotophytus;* snakes, *Thamnophis;* † thecodonts; alligators, *Alligator,* and crocodiles, *Crocodilus;* † pterosaurs, † *Nyctosaurus,* † *Pteranodon;* † dinosaurs, † *Coelophysis,* † *Ornitholestes,* † *Tyrannosaurus,* † *Brontosaurus,* † *Anatosaurus,* † *Stegosaurus,* † *Ankylosaurus,* † *Triceratops;* † mammal-like reptiles, † *Dimetrodon,* † *Cynognathus*

Class Aves, birds: † *Archeopteryx;* † *Aepyornis;* † *Hesperornis;* kiwis, *Apteryx;* † *Diatryma;* pigeons, *Columba;* chickens, *Gallus;* owls, *Micropallus, Otus;* woodpeckers, *Centurus;* flickers, *Colaptes;* flycatchers, *Myiarchus;* finches, *Geospiza, Camarrhynchus, Certhidia*

Class Mammalia, mammals: Monotremes, *Ornithorhynchus.* Marsupials, including opossums, *Didelphis,* and others (see Figure 17-29). † Mesozoic placentals, † *Deltatheridium,* † *Zalambdalestes.* Primates, including: † *Notharctus; Loris;* monkeys, *Cebus, Cercopithecus, Macaca;* apes, *Gorilla* and others; † *Australopithecus;* men, *Homo.* Anteaters, *Myrmecophagus.* Rodents: rats, *Rattus;* mice, *Mus, Peromyscus;* hamsters, *Cricetus.* Carnivores: † Creodonts, † sabertooths; dogs, *Canis;* cats, *Felis;* seals, *Phoca.* Cetaceans: whales, *Orcinus;* porpoises, *Phocaena.* Ungulates: † condylarths, † *Phenacodus;* † uintatheres, † *Uintatherium;* † titanotheres, † *Brontops;* elephants, *Loxodonta;* horses, † *Hyracotherium* ("Eohippus"), † *Miohippus, Equus;* deer, *Cervus, Odocoileus,* † *Megaloceros;* pigs, *Sus;* sheep, *Ovis;* cows, *Bos.*

GLOSSARY

abiogenesis the production of a living thing from nonliving materials.

acid a chemical compound that can liberate a hydrogen ion.

adaptation in individuals, a useful physiological reaction to changes in the environment; in populations or species, evolutionary (genetic) change of survival value to individuals or to the group as a whole, and also the anatomical and physiological results of such change.

adaptive radiation the splitting up of a group of organisms into a number of species or higher groups with different ways of life (adaptations or ecological niches).

adsorption the attachment of molecules, or parts of them, to a surface.

allantois an embryonic membrane involved in excretion and respiration in most nonaquatic vertebrates.

allele (*originally allelomorph*) one of two or more differing forms (or mutants) of the same gene.

amino acid any of about 30 organic acids containing an amino group, —NH$_2$, and uniting with other amino acids to form proteins.

amphoteric said of a chemical that can act both as an acid and as a base.

anabolism the aspects of metabolism tending to build up or synthesize organic molecules.

analogy in comparative anatomy, the relationship of different structures serving similar functions, for example gills and lungs, both means of respiration.

anaphase the period of cell division during which the two sets of chromosomes move apart and separation of daughter cells begins.

anther the sperm or pollen-bearing organ of a plant.

antibiotic an organic compound poisonous to some organisms, especially bacteria.

antibody a protein that reacts specifically with an antigen and neutralizes it.

antigen a substance, usually a protein, that produces a neutralizing reaction (by an antibody) when introduced into an organism.

artery a vessel carrying blood from the heart to capillaries.

atom the smallest unit of a chemical element.

autosome a chromosome not directly involved in determination of sex.

autotroph an organism that can produce its own carbohydrates, and generally also proteins and other organic molecules, from inorganic sources.

auxin a plant hormone, usually involved in growth.

axon a process of a nerve cell (neuron) conducting impulses away from the body of the cell.

bacteriophage a virus that infects and destroys bacteria, extensively used in virus and DNA studies.

base a chemical compound that can combine with the hydrogen ion from an acid.

biogenesis the production of organisms from other, parental organisms.

biota the total of all living things of a specified region or time.

blastula a stage in which an embryo develops a cavity surrounded by a single layer of cells.

blood group any of many different chemical characteristics of blood alternative among the individuals of a population, for example the A, B, O groups in men.

bond a force holding atoms together in a chemical compound; the principal kinds are covalent, ionic, and hydrogen.

cambium a cylinder of meristem in trunks and stalks of vascular plants.

capillary a minute blood vessel between an artery and a vein.

carbohydrate a chemical compound of carbon, hydrogen, and oxygen with the latter two atoms usually in the proportion 2:1.

carpel a leaflike structure or a tissue on or in which seeds develop in advanced plants.

catabolism the aspects of metabolism tending to break down complex organic molecules.

catalyst anything that causes or facilitates a chemical reaction without itself being permanently changed; enzymes are the important organic catalysts.

cell a unit of organized matter in or from a living thing, enclosed in a membrane and usually including a nucleus and surrounding cytoplasm.

cell theory the theory, now universally accepted, that organisms are cells or are composed principally of cells.

cell wall a nonliving stiff layer outside and distinct from the living membrane of a cell.

cellulose a complex carbohydrate present in the cell walls and woody tissues of most plants.

centromere the point on a chromosome to which the spindle is attached in cell division.

centrosome a star-like body at the apex of a spindle in cell division.

chlorophyll any of several pigmented compounds in plants capable of absorbing radiation and involved in photosynthesis.

chloroplast a complex organelle in plant cells containing chlorophyll, seat of photosynthesis.

chorion an embryonic membrane of nonaquatic vertebrates; in mammals part of the placenta.

chromatin the material of chromosomes.

chromosome a generally threadlike or rodlike structure within a cell, composed essentially of protein and nucleic acid, containing the genes.

cilium a movable, hairlike organelle, usually multiple on a single cell.

class the next full step above order in the hierarchy of classification, including one or more orders; man belongs to the class Mammalia.

climax in ecology, the type of community that tends to be the stable end member of a succession.

coelom a body cavity in most animals, developing embryologically within the mesoderm.

coenzyme a nonprotein compound that acts with an enzyme to produce an organic chemical reaction.

colloid a stable suspension, often jelly-like, of minute particles in a liquid.

colony a group of relatively undifferentiated individual cells or multicellular individuals all ultimately derived from a single cell and maintaining organic connection.

commensalism a symbiosis not markedly helpful or harmful to either partner.

community the interacting total of organisms of various species in a given area.

connective tissue any of a great variety of tissues consisting of cells scattered through a matrix of noncellular (hence nonliving) material, such as bone and cartilage.

convergence in evolution, resemblance among organisms brought about by adaptation to similar functions or environments without original genetic similarity; in ecology, a tendency for different successions in the same region to have the same climax.

copulation in animals, the junction of male and female organs leading to internal fertilization.

corridor in biogeography, a route interposing no definite impediment to the dispersal of organisms under discussion.

cotyledon an embryonic leaf-like storage organ in angiosperm seeds.

covalent bond the connection of atoms by their sharing an electron.

crossing over in genetics, the exchange of segments from one member of a chromosome pair to another during meiosis.

cryptic coloration coloration of animals that reduces their visibility in their usual environment.

cycle any more or less regularly recurrent phenomenon; in ecology, the cyclic movement of specified materials from the environment through various species in communities and back to the environment.

cytoplasm the contents of a cell outside of its nucleus.

Darwinism sometimes, but misleadingly, applied to the theory of evolution in general; more correctly, the theory, now generally accepted, that evolution is guided principally by natural selection.

datum (*plural data*) an observation used as a basis for inference or induction.

deciduous said of trees that shed all their leaves in one season of the year.

deme a local population of organisms of the same species.

dendrite a process of a nerve cell (neuron) conducting impulses inward to the body of the cell.

diastole the expanding (dilation) phase of the heart cycle.

differential reproduction or fecundity reproduction within a continuing population such that individuals with certain genetic factors consistently tend to produce more offspring, on an average; this is the basis of natural selection.

diffusion the dispersion of molecules from a region of higher to one of lower concentration.

digestion the reduction of foods to

soluble form; especially the reduction of large organic molecules (for example, proteins) to smaller units capable of entering cells (for example, amino acids).

diploidy the presence in a cell of two sets of chromosomes; such a cell is said to be diploid ($2n$).

diplophase a stage in a succession of generations in which the cells of an organism are diploid.

disjunctive said of more or less closely related animals living in distinctly separate areas, with no equally related forms in the intervening region.

DNA any of the deoxyribonucleic acids, a family of nucleic acids in which the sugar unit is deoxyribose.

dominant said of an allele the effects of which tend to override and conceal effects of another allele (recessive) of the same gene in the same individual.

ecology the study of organisms in relationship to each other and to their environments.

ectoderm the outer layer of cells in early development of an embryo.

effector an organ, such as a muscle, producing a behavioral reaction to a nerve impulse.

electrolyte a compound with ionic bonds, forming ions and capable of transmitting electric currents in solution.

electron a minute, negatively charged particle in an atom.

element a fundamental chemical substance, comprising atoms of a single kind.

embryo an early stage in the development of a plant or animal, when the plant is still incipient and the animal unhatched or unborn; in humans, an individual in the first 2 months of uterine development from the zygote.

endergonic said of a chemical reaction that binds energy.

endocrine gland an organ producing a hormone.

endoderm the inner layer of cells in early development of an embryo.

endoplasmic reticulum an intricately folded membrane-like organelle, site of protein formation and some other syntheses in cells.

energy the capacity to do work; potential energy is at rest, as in a chemical compound; kinetic energy is in any of many forms of motion, such as light radiation or muscular contraction.

enzyme a protein that brings about or facilitates (catalyzes) an organic chemical reaction.

epiphyte a plant that grows on other plants but is not parasitic on them.

epithelium a tissue covering an external or internal surface in animals.

erythrocyte a red blood cell.

estrus cycle in mammals, the periodic production of eggs by females and changes in sex hormones and uterus.

evolution the genetic change of populations of organisms through time.

excretion the elimination of waste or superfluous matter from an organism.

exergonic said of a chemical reaction that releases energy.

F in genetic experimentation, designation of a descendant (filial) generation; F_1 is the first generation bred from the original parents (P), F_2 the second generation, and so on.

family the next full step above a genus in the hierarchy of classification, including one or more genera; man belongs to the family Hominidae.

fauna the total of all animals of a specified region or time.

fetus a mammal, or especially a human, in the later stages of development before birth, after the second month in humans.

filter in biogeography, a dispersal route open to some but not others of organisms under discussion.

flagellum a movable, whiplike organelle projecting from a cell.

flora the total of all plants of a specified region or time.

food chain or web the sequence of species through which nutrients pass in a community.

fossil any trace of ancient organisms.

founder principle the principle that a small population on being cut off from the whole larger specific population does not have a complete representation of the parental gene pool.

gallery forest a border of trees along a watercourse.

gamete a cell involved in sexual reproduction, which involves fusion of two gametes, usually distinguishable as male (sperm) and female (egg).

gametogenesis the origin of a gamete from a germ cell, generally by meiosis.

gametophyte a plant (in haplophase—$1n$) producing gametes.

gastrula a stage in which an embryo differentiates two layers of cells.

gel a relatively set, jelly-like state of a colloid.

gene the functional unit of heredity, also implicated in other aspects of cellular metabolism, forming a segment of a molecule of nucleic acid.

gene migration the introduction of genes into a population through breeding with a neighboring but different population.

genetic pool the sum total of genetic factors (genes, chromosomes) within a species at any one time.

genotype the genetic constitution of an individual, as distinct from the visible characteristics actually developed during its life history (phenotype).

genus (*plural genera*) the next full step above a species in the hierarchy of classification, including one or more species; man belongs to the genus *Homo*.

germ cell a cell in a reproductive organ from which gametes arise.

gland an organ of secretion.

glucose a simple sugar, the most common immediate energy source in organisms.

gonad an organ in which gametes, male or female, are produced.

haploidy the presence in a cell of a single set of chromosomes; such a cell is said to be haploid ($1n$).

haplophase a stage in a succession of generations in which the cells of an organism are haploid.

Hardy-Weinberg law the principle that recombination in a population breeding at random does not change the gene pool.

hemoglobin a combination of a protein (globin) and another group (heme) that readily takes up and gives off oxygen.

hermaphrodite an individual, such as a monoecious plant, in which both sexes occur in a single individual.

heterotroph an organism that must obtain carbohydrates, amino acids, and generally some other organic molecules by consuming other organisms.

heterozygosity the presence of different alleles of a gene on two sets of chromosomes of an individual; the individual is then heterozygous for this gene.

hierarchy a graded system in which each step or category includes all those below it; especially the Linnaean hierarchy used in classification of organisms.

homeostasis the maintenance of a relatively steady state within an organism or a group of interacting organisms; a homeostatic process or mechanism tends to produce that effect by counteracting any wide divergence from an average state.

homeothermy internal control of an animal's temperature, tending to maintain it at a level.

homology resemblance among organisms due to inheritance from a common ancestry; structures related by homology are homologous and are homologues.

homoplasy resemblances among organisms not due to inheritance from a common ancestry (not homologous).

homozygosity the presence of the same alleles of a gene on both sets of chromosomes in an individual; the individual is then homozygous for this gene.

hormone a cell product with specific effects on the activity of other cells.

hybrid offspring from crossing of genetically different parents; generally applied to crossing of parents of different species but in plant and animal breeding also to crossing of different strains or varieties.

hydrogen bond the attraction between molecules due to the attraction between the small positive charge of hydrogen atoms and negative charges.

hypha in fungi, an elongate threadlike structure containing many nuclei not separated by cross walls.

hypothesis a tentative explanation of relationships among observed phenomena.

induction in embryology, the complex of processes by which embryonic cells become differentiated into specific tissues and organs; in scientific method, generalization from a body of data.

interphase the period during which a cell is not dividing or visibly preparing to divide.

ion an electrically charged atom or combination of atoms.

ionic bond the union of charged groups in a molecule by the attraction of opposite electrical charges.

isolating mechanism anything that tends to impede or prevent interbreeding between groups of plants or animals.

isomer a molecule containing the same atoms as another but with the atoms differently arranged.

karyotype designation of the number, sizes, and shapes of chromosomes in an organism.

kingdom the highest step in the hierarchy of classification, including phyla and all lower steps; man belongs to the kingdom Animalia.

Lamarckism the former theory, now disproved, that variant characters acquired by individuals in their lifetimes may be passed on to their descendants and effect genetic evolution; more properly called Neo-Lamarckism.

larva an early feeding and motile, free-living stage in the development of an animal, when this is distinctly different from a final breeding stage, as in the caterpillar stage of a butterfly or the tadpole stage of a frog.

leucocyte a white blood cell.

liana a vine that climbs on trees of a forest.

linkage in genetics, the association of hereditary characteristics by the occurrence of genes on a particular chromosome; in sex linkage the genes involved are on a sex chromosome.

lipid any of many kinds of fatlike compounds, including fats and waxes.

lymph plasma-like fluid widespread in animal bodies outside the blood circulatory system.

lymphatic system a one-way system of vessels and enlargements (nodes) conveying lymph.

lysosome an organelle containing enzymes involved in the breakdown of cells.

mamma the milk-producing organ of mammals.

marsupial member of a group of mammals in which the young are born in a relatively early developmental stage and in some but not all cases thereafter protected and nourished in an abdominal pouch (marsupium); contrasted with placental mammal.

maturation final stages in the development of a gamete from a germ cell by meiosis.

meiosis a sequence of cell divisions resulting in reduction of the number of chromosomes, generally from two sets

to one, involved in development of gametes.

membrane a skinlike layer enclosing a region or separating two regions within a cell or organism.

menstrual cycle the estrus cycle with reference to menstruation.

menstruation in female mammals, periodic shedding of the lining of the uterus with accompanying bleeding; part of the estrus cycle.

meristem a tissue composed of unspecialized, dividing cells in plants.

mesoderm an intermediate mass of cells, between outer (ectoderm) and inner (endoderm) layers in an embryo.

metabolism all the functional chemical changes occurring within the cells of an organism.

metaphase the period of preparation for cell division in which the chromosomes become arranged in the midregion of the spindle.

microclimate climatic conditions not of a region as a whole but at a particular spot where a given organism lives.

mimicry resemblance of members of one species to those of another species less subject to predation.

mitochondrion (*plural mitochondria*) an organelle, often rodlike, seat of respiration and energy production in a cell.

mitosis the process of cell division without reduction in number of chromosomes.

mobile said of an organism (for example, in the form of a seed) that is movable but not necessarily under its own power.

modifier a gene that modifies the effects of another gene.

molecule the unit of a chemical substance comprising united atoms of one or more elements.

monoecious said of plants in which both sexes are present in the same individual.

monosaccharide a sugar (carbohydrate) in simplest form, not separable into smaller sugar molecules.

morphogenesis the development of form in the growth of an individual.

morula an embryological stage consisting of a clump of a relatively small number of cells.

motile said of organisms that move under their own power.

mutation broadly, any change in the genetic makeup of a cell; narrowly

(point mutation), substitution of one nucleotide for another in a segment of DNA.

mutualism a symbiosis helpful to both partners.

mycelium the body of a fungus, composed of hyphae.

natural selection the directional factor in evolution caused by differential reproduction of genetically different individuals in a population.

neuron a nerve cell.

neutron an electrically neutral particle in an atom.

niche the whole way of life of an organism, including its habitat, food, habits, and in general its place in a total ecology.

nucleic acid any of an almost indefinitely variable number of large molecules made up of nucleotide units; they include DNA and RNA.

nucleotide any of several kinds of chemical units formed by linkage of a nitrogen-containing base, a sugar, and phosphoric acid.

nucleoprotein a compound of one or more proteins with a nucleic acid.

nucleus in biology, a more or less central part of a cell, usually enclosed in a membrane, containing the chromosomes; in physics, the central mass of protons and neutrons in an atom.

nutrient a substance derived from outside a cell and providing it with energy and structural material.

ontogeny the developmental history of an individual organism.

oögenesis the development of an egg (ovum) from a germ cell.

order the next full step above a family in the hierarchy of classification, including one or more families; man belongs to the order Primates.

organ a functional unit within an organism, made up of one or more tissues.

organelle a structurally and functionally differentiated part of a cell.

organism any living thing.

organizer a substance involved in differentiation of embryonic cells, or a tissue secreting such a substance.

osmosis the differential movement of molecules, often water, through a membrane from a region of higher to one of lower relative concentration.

ovary in both animals and plants, the structure that produces eggs (ova, female gametes).

ovum (*plural ova*) a female gamete.

oxidation removal of electrons in a chemical reaction, typically but not necessarily by addition of oxygen.

P in genetic experimentation, designation of the parental group with which breeding is started.

paleontology the study of the history of organisms, especially through examination of fossils.

parallelism acquisition of similar characteristics by different evolving groups of organisms separately but on the basis of original genetic similarity.

parasitism a symbiosis in which one partner profits at the expense of the other.

parenchyma a tissue composed of thin-walled storage and photosynthetic cells in plants.

penis the male copulatory organ.

peptide a chain of amino acids shorter than a protein.

peptide bond a linking together of amino acids by union of CO in one with NH in the other; proteins are thus formed from amino acids.

petiole the stalk attaching a leaf to a stem.

pH a measure of acidity or alkilinity in a solution; 0 is maximum acidity, 14 is maximum alkilinity, and 7 is neutrality.

phagocyte an amoeba-like blood cell capable of digesting bacteria.

phenotype the visibly developed characteristics of an organism, dependent both on its heredity (genotype) and its life history.

phloem a conductive tissue carrying nutrients from photosynthetic cells in plants.

photoreceptor an organ reacting to stimulation by light.

photosynthesis the production of sugar from carbon dioxide and water, utilizing the energy of light.

phylogeny the evolutionary history of a linear sequence of populations.

phylum (*plural phyla*) the next full step above class in the hierarchy of classifica-

tion including one or more classes; man belongs to the phylum Chordata.

pistil the female organ of a flower, including ovary and stigma.

placenta a structure present in most mammals combining embryonic and parental tissues, mediating transfer of oxygen and nutrients from mother to young.

placental mammal any mammalian species with a placenta, or a member of a group of mammals contrasted with the marsupials.

plasma the liquid part of blood, with all its dissolved contents.

plasmolysis contraction of cell contents caused by loss of water through osmosis.

pleiotropy the production of multiple phenotypic effects by action of a single gene.

poikilothermy changeable temperature in an animal, dependent on environmental temperature, exercise, and other irregular factors.

pollen grain in advanced plants, a small spore that after slight further development produces a male gamete.

pollination the transfer of pollen to a stigma where it develops a male gamete and fertilizes an ovum.

polygenes genes that act together, with additive or complementary effect.

polymer a large molecule formed by the linking together of similar smaller units.

polymorphism the presence of distinctly different, genetically determined phenotypic characteristics within a population of a single species.

polyploidy the presence in a cell of three or more sets of chromosomes; such a cell is said to be polyploid.

polysaccharide a complex sugar (carbohydrate) composed of three or more simple sugar (monosaccharide) units.

population a group of organisms, usually understood as a reproducing group of a single species.

predation the capture and consumption of one animal (prey) by another (predator).

prophase the period of microscopically visible preparation for cell division in which the chromosomes condense into discrete form and the nuclear membrane disappears.

protein a large organic molecule consisting wholly or mainly of a chain of amino acids.

protist an organism consisting of a single cell, or with the body not divided into separate cells; the more animal-like protists are often called protozoans.

proton a positively charged particle in an atom.

protoplasm a general term for all the contents of a cell.

pyramid in ecology, the relative numbers or masses of organisms at different positions in a food chain or of different individual sizes.

race a recognizable population within a species; sometimes equivalent to subspecies.

radical a functional group of atoms recurring as part of various different molecules.

rain forest heavy, jungly forest in a region, usually tropical, of year-round growth and heavy precipitation.

recapitulation the rejected hypothesis that ontogeny repeats phylogeny.

receptor an organ that reacts to changes in the environment, usually by generating nerve impulses.

recessive said of an allele the effects of which may be concealed by those of another allele, dominant, of the same gene in the same individual.

recombination the origin of new combinations of genes by any of several processes involved in sexual reproduction.

reduction in biochemistry, addition of electrons in a chemical reaction, typically but not necessarily by the addition of hydrogen atoms; in genetics, division of chromosomes in meiosis.

reflex a relatively direct effector reaction to an impulse originating in a receptor, without necessary involvement of more complex nerve association pathways; the arrangement of neurons producing a reflex is a reflex arc.

respiration the release of energy by oxidation in organisms; also, the process of lung or gill ventilation involved in oxidation in some animals.

ribosome a particle, composed of RNA and protein, frequently in endoplasmic reticulum, site of protein synthesis.

RNA ribonucleic acid, a family of nucleic acids in which the sugar unit is ribose.

sclerenchyma a tissue composed of thick-walled supportive cells in plants.

secretion the process of segregating or

synthesizing and then releasing a functional organic substance or waste product.

seed a reproductive and dispersal unit of advanced plants enclosed in protective coatings and containing an embryonic sporophyte and food.

segregation in genetics, the separation of different forms (alleles) of a gene by the separation of chromosomes in meiosis.

semen a thick liquid containing sperms produced by the sex organs of some male animals.

serum plasma with clotting factors removed.

sessile said of organisms that are attached to a substrate.

sex, sexuality, sexual reproduction reproduction involving the combination of genetic materials from two sources, usually but not always by fusion of male and female gametes.

sex chromosome a chromosome directly involved in determination of sex; in humans and most other mammals an X or Y chromosome.

sol a relatively free-flowing or liquid state of a colloid.

speciation the evolutionary process of splitting of one species into two or more; also sometimes applied to the quite different process by which one species changes so much in the course of time that a new name is given to it.

species (*same in singular and plural*) the basic unit of classification and of evolution; a population of similar animals connected by interbreeding or by rather immediate common ancestry, unitary in evolutionary and ecological role.

sperm or spermatozoan (*plural spermatozoa*) a male gamete.

spermatogenesis the development of a sperm from a germ cell.

spindle the pattern of threadlike structures seen microscopically when chromosomes are separating in cell division.

spiracle in insects, the external opening of a trachea.

spore a usually diploid and asexual cell capable of developing into a new organism.

sporophyte a plant (in diplophase) producing spores.

stamen the pollen-producing part of a flower.

stigma a structure in a flower that receives pollen, part of a pistil.

stoma (*plural stomata*) an opening in a leaf through which gases are exchanged.

strata (*singular, stratum*) in geology and paleontology, layers of sedimentary rocks; in biogeography, sets of biotic elements that have occupied a region for distinctly different lengths of time.

subspecies a geographically delineated population within a species, not reproductively isolated, but with most of its members distinguishable from those of adjacent populations.

substrate in molecular biology, the substance acted on by an enzyme; in ecology, the base or floor on which an organism lives.

succession in ecology, a sequence of communities of different composition in a given area, not involving marked evolutionary change within populations.

surface tension a condition of a surface like that of an elastic skin due to molecular attraction within a liquid.

survivorship the pattern of age relations in a population resulting from death rates at different ages.

sweepstakes dispersal in biogeography, the occasional and more or less random spread of organisms across what is nevertheless a strong barrier to them.

symbiosis the close association of individuals of different species; by some biologists confined to the relationship here called mutualism.

synthetic theory an explanation of evolution derived by synthesis of all branches of the life sciences and explaining evolution as the outcome of the complex interaction of mutation, natural selection, and other factors; it is the theory expounded at length in this book.

synapse a point where nerve cells are nearly in contact and an impulse is conveyed from one to another.

synapsis the pairing of equivalent chromosomes of different sets prior to meiosis.

systole the contracting phase of the heart cycle.

taiga a cold temperate northern or, to less extent, southern region heavily forested, especially with conifers.

teleonomy the usefulness of adaptations to the organisms that have them.

telophase the final period of cell division, in which the daughter cells separate and each develops a nuclear membrane.

territoriality the tendency of some animals to range over a limited area, which is sometimes defended against intruders.

testcross the reproductive crossing of individuals with different genetic characteristics to test dominance and proportions of different forms (alleles) of a gene.

testis the organ producing male gametes in animals; in mammals, a testicle.

theory a hypothesis that has been thoroughly tested and warrants confidence in its probability.

thrombocyte a blood platelet, involved in clotting.

thrombosis stoppage of blood circulation by a clot (thrombus).

tissue a functional aggregate of similar cells in an organism.

trachea in air-breathing vertebrates, the windpipe; in insects, a tube distributing air to internal cells.

transpiration loss of water from an organism by evaporation.

tundra an arctic region, cold and wet, with no upstanding trees.

vagina the female copulatory organ.

vascular said of organisms, especially advanced plants, in which nutrients and other materials are distributed in solution through tubelike tissues.

vein a vessel carrying blood from capillaries to the heart.

virus a DNA or RNA molecule, generally in structural combination with protein, capable of replication in the living cell of an organism to which it is foreign.

vitamin an organic compound required in small amounts by an animal that cannot synthesize it in adequate quantities if at all, often entering into a coenzyme.

warning coloration coloration of animals, obnoxious or harmful as food, that makes them easily identified by animals that would otherwise prey on them.

xylem a conductive tissue carrying sap upward from the roots in plants.

zygote in sexual reproduction, the single cell formed by fusion of two gametes.

ACKNOWLEDGMENTS
FOR ILLUSTRATION SOURCES

Drawings by CARU Studios and others.

Opening to Part 1: photo by Hugh Spencer.

Opening to Part 2: photo by Dr. Margaret R. Murray.

2-4 Adapted from H. Neurath and K. Bailey, eds., *Proteins: Chemistry, Biological Activity, and Methods,* Vol. 1, Part A, Academic Press, 1953.

3-2 Adapted from figures in R. O. Greep, ed., *Histology,* Blakiston, 1954.

3-5 From "The Living Cell," by Jean Brachet. © 1961 by Scientific American, Inc. All rights reserved.

3-9 From J. M. Allen, *The Nature of Biological Diversity,* McGraw-Hill, 1963.

3-10 From K. R. Porter and M. A. Bonneville, *An Introduction to the Fine Structure of Cells and Tissues,* Lea & Febiger, 1963.

3-11 From Allen.

3-12 From "How Cells Transform Energy," by Albert I. Lehninger. Copyright © 1961 by Scientific American, Inc. All rights reserved.

3-13 From Dr. Wilhelm Bernhard, Institute for Cancer Research, Villejuif (Seine).

Opening to Part 3: photo by Dr. L. B. Shettles.

5-1 Top three left photos by Chester F. Reather, FBPA, Johns Hopkins Univ. School of Medicine; right photo by Richard D. Grill, Carnegie Institution of Washington.

5-3 From Dr. A. H. Sparrow, Brookhaven National Laboratory.

7-4 From "The Genetic Code II," by Marshall W. Nirenberg. © 1963 by Scientific American, Inc. All rights reserved.

7-5 From "The Genetic Code II," by Marshall W. Nirenberg. © 1963 by Scientific American, Inc. All rights reserved.

7-10 Adapted from E. W. Sinnott, L. C. Dunn, and Th. Dobzhansky, *Principles of Genetics,* 4th ed., McGraw-Hill, 1950.

7-11 Adapted with permission from H. Reidel, *Arch. Entwicklungsmech. Organ.,* Vol. 132 (1935) (Springer-Verlag).

Opening to Part 4: photo by Dr. Harold C. Bold, The Plant Kingdom, 2nd © 1964, Prentice-Hall, Inc. Englewood Cliffs, N.J.

8-1 Adapted from L. H. Hyman, *The Invertebrates: Protozoa Through Ctenophora,* McGraw-Hill, 1940; L. A. Kenoyer, H. N. Goddard, and D. D. Miller, *General Biology,* 3rd ed., Harper, 1953.

8-2 Adapted with permission from G. M. Smith, E. M. Gilbert, G. S. Bryan, R. J. Evans, and J. T. Stauffer, *A Textbook of General Botany,* 5th ed., Macmillan, 1953.

8-3 Adapted from Smith *et al.;* in part from E. W. Sinnott and K. S. Wilson, *Botany: Principles and Problems,* 5th ed., McGraw-Hill, 1955.

8-4 Adapted from W. H. Brown, *The Plant Kingdom: A Textbook of General Botany,* Ginn, 1935.

8-5 Adapted from Smith *et al.*

8-15 Adapted from H. V. Neal and H. W. Rand, *Chordate Anatomy,* Blakiston, 1939; after Bremer.

8-16 Adapted from Greep; Neal and Rand; P. E. Smith, ed., *Bailey's Textbook of Histology,* 10th ed., Williams & Wilkins, 1940.

8-17 Adapted from A. F. Huettner, *Fundamentals of Comparative Embryology of the Vertebrates,* rev. ed., Macmillan, 1949.

8-18 Adapted from Wilson.

8-19 Adapted from L. G. Barth, *Embryology,* rev. ed., Holt, Rinehart and Winston, 1953.

8-20 Adapted from Huettner.

8-21 Adapted from J. Z. Young, *The Life of Vertebrates,* Oxford Univ. Press, 1950.

8-22 Adapted from Barth.

8-23 Adapted from Barth.

9-1 Adapted from E. Strasburger, *Textbook of Botany,* 6th ed., Macmillan, 1930.

9-4, 9-5, 9-6, 9-7, 9-8, 9-10 Details of plant structure adapted from Smith *et al.*

9-11 Adapted from Sinnot and Wilson.

9-13 Adapted from Buchsbaum.

9-14 Adapted from Rugh, *Vertebrate Embryology.*

9-16 From B. M. Patten, *Human Embryology,* 2nd ed., McGraw-Hill, 1953; after Schroeder.

9-17 Adapted from W. F. Pauli, *The World of Life,* Houghton Mifflin, 1949.

10-4 Adapted from M. Thomas, *Plant Physiology,* Churchill, London, 1940.

10-5 Adapted from G. Hardin, *Biology: Its Human Implications.* 2nd ed., Freeman, 1952.

10-6 Adapted from Buchsbaum.

10-8 Adapted from P. B. Weisz, *Biology,* McGraw-Hill, 1954.

10-11 Adapted from Hardin; L. A. Borradaile and F. A. Potts, *The Invertebrata,* Cambridge Univ. Press, 1938; T. S. Hall and F. Moog, *Life Science,* Wiley, 1955.

10-13 Adapted from Pauli; in part from Hall and Moog.

10-16 Adapted from Hall and Moog.

11-2 Adapted from K. Von Frisch, *Biologie,* Bayerischer Schulbuch-Verlag, Munich, 1952.

11-3 Adapted from *Biological Science: An Inquiry into Life,* Harcourt, Brace & World, 1963, by permission of Biological Sciences Curriculum Study.

11-5 Adapted from C. A. Villee, *Biology,* 2nd ed., Saunders, 1954.

11-8 Adapted from E. Baldwin, *An Introduction to Comparative Biochemistry,* Cambridge Univ. Press, 1948.

11-15 Adapted from M. Demerec, ed., *Biology of Drosophila,* Wiley, 1950.

11-16, 11-17 Adapted from Romer, *The Vertebrate Body.*

11-18 Adapted from L. Plate, *Allgemeine Zoologie und Abstammungslehre,* Fischer, Jena, 1924.

11-19 Adapted from J. S. Rogers, T. H. Hubbell, and C. F. Byers, *Man and the Biological World,* 2nd ed., McGraw-Hill, 1952; from Pace and McCashland; from K. Von Frisch, *The Dancing Bees,* Harcourt, Brace & World, 1955.

Opening to Part 5: photo American Museum of Natural History.

12-4 Adapted with permission from S. C. Reed and E. W. Reed, *Evolution,* Vol. 4 (1950).

13-1 Adapted from Parker and Haswell; Borradaile and Potts; A. D. Imms, *Insect Natural History,* Blakiston, 1951; R. Hesse and F. Doflein, *Tierbau und Tierleben,* Teubner, Leipzig and Berlin, 1914.

13-5 Adapted from J. J. S. Cornes, *Nature,* Vol. 140 (1937).

13-6 Adapted from Hesse and Doflein.

13-9, 13-10, 13-12 Adapted with permission from D. Lack, *Darwin's Finches,* Cambridge Univ. Press, 1947.

14-5 Based with permission on data from W. C. Boyd, *Genetics and the Race of Man,* Little, Brown, 1950.

14-6 Adapted with permission from E. Mayr, *Systematics and the Origin of Species,* Columbia Univ. Press, 1942.

14-7 Adapted with permission from A. H. Miller, *Univ. Calif. (Berkeley) Publ. Zool.,* Vol. 44, No. 3 (1941).

14-8 Adapted with permission from J. Clausen, *Stages in the Evolution of Plant Species,* Cornell Univ. Press, 1951.

Opening to Part 6: photo General Biological Supply House, Chicago.

15-2 Adapted from Romer, *Man and the Vertebrates.*

15-4 Adapted from A. E. Brehms, *Brehms Tierleben, Allgemeine Kunde Des Tierreichs,* 4th ed., Bibliographisches Institut, Leipzig and Vienna, 1912.

16-2, 16-3 Adapted from Smith *et al.*

16-4 Adapted from Kudo; G. M. Smith, *Cryptogamic Botany,* Vol. I, McGraw-Hill, 1938.

16-5, 16-7, 16-8 Adapted from Kudo; Borradaile and Potts.

16-15, 16-19 (A, B, C), Adapted with permission from Smith *et al.*

17-1 Adapted from Hall and Moog.

17-2 Adapted from Parker and Haswell.

17-3 Adapted from Buchsbaum.

17-4 Adapted from Borradaile and Potts.

17-6 Adapted from Parker and Haswell; in part after W. S. Bullough, *Practical Invertebrate Anatomy,* Macmillan, 1950, with permission.

17-7 Adapted with permission from R. W. Hegner and K. A. Stiles, *College Zoology,* 6th ed., Macmillan, 1951.

17-9 Adapted from R. C. Moore, *Treatise on Invertebrate Paleontology,* Univ. of Kansas Press, 1959; L. Størmer; R. M. Fox and J. W. Fox, *Introduction to Comparative Entomology,* Reinhold, 1964; D. E. Beck and L. F. Braithwaite, *Invertebrate Zoology Handbook,* Burgess, 1962.

17-13 Luna moth and ants, Hugh Spencer; stinkbug and housefly, American Museum of Natural History; dragonfly, boll weevil and louse, U.S. Dept. of Agriculture; mosquitoes, wasp, and bumblebee, Lynwood Chace from National Audubon Society; grasshopper, John R. Clawson from National Audubon Society.

17-18 Adapted from Borradaile and Potts; Buchsbaum.

17-20 Adapted from Hall and Moog; Hegner and Stiles; lower photo by Dr. J. E. Webb

from *Proc. Zool. Soc. London,* Vol. 125 (1955).

17-21 Adapted from Romer, *Man and the Vertebrates.*

17-23 From American Museum of Natural History.

17-24 Adapted from J. R. Norman, *A History of Fishes,* Wyn, 1951.

17-28 Terns, Australian Information Service; jay and heron, American Museum of Natural History; kiwi, New Zealand Consulate; goose, U.S. Fish and Wildlife Service; hawk, Charles Halgren.

Opening to Part 7: photo by Edith Reichmann

18-1 Adapted from Wigglesworth.

18-3 Adapted from C. S. Pittendrigh, *Evolution,* Vol. 2 (1948).

19-2 Adapted from E. P. Odum, *Fundamentals of Ecology,* Saunders, 1949.

19-3 Adapted from W. C. Allee, A. E. Emerson, O. Park, T. Park, and K. P. Schmidt, *Principles of Aminal Ecology,* Saunders, 1949; after O. Park, W. C. Allee, and V. E. Shelford, *A Laboratory Introduction to Animal Ecology and Taxonomy,* Univ. of Chicago Press, 1939, with permission.

19-4 Adapted with permission from Lack.

19-5 Parts 1 and 2 adapted from Turtox Key Card, courtesy, General Biological Supply House, Inc., Chicago; part 3 from Alle *et al.;* after Emerson, with permission.

19-6 Adapted from A. K. Lubeck, *Geomorphology,* McGraw-Hill, 1939; after Dachnowski.

19-7 Adapted from Odum.

19-8 Adapted from Allee *et al.;* after R. Pearl, *The Biology of Population Growth,* Knopf, 1930, with permission; J. Davidson, *Trans. Roy. Soc. S. Australia,* Vol. 62 (1938).

19-9 Adapted from Allee *et al.;* after Gause.

19-10 Adapted from Allee *et al.;* after A. Leopold, *Wisconsin Conserv. Dept. Publ.,* No. 321 (1943), with permission.

19-11 Adapted from Allee *et al.;* after Gause.

19-12 Adapted from Allee *et al.;* after D. A. MacLulich, *Univ. Toronto Biol. Ser.,* No. 43 (1937), with permission of Univ. of Toronto Press.

19-13 Drawing reproduced with permission from Dr. Boyd W. Walker, Univ. of California at Los Angeles.

20-2 Based on data by Sinnott, Dunn, and Dobzhansky.

21-2 Adapted from Allee *et al.;* after Wolcott.

21-12, 21-13, 21-14, 21-15 Adapted from G. G. Simpson, *Evolution and Geography,* Oregon State Board of Education, 1953.

21-16 Adapted with permission from W. D. Matthew, *Climate and Evolution* (Spec. Publ., Vol. 1), N.Y. Academy of Sciences, 1950.

Opening to Part 8: photo American Museum of Natural History.

22-4 Adapted from Simpson, *Evolution and Geography.*

23-4 Adapted with permission from E. H. Colbert, *Dinosaur Book,* McGraw-Hill, © 1954, American Museum of Natural History.

24-2 Adapted from G. G. Simpson. *The Meaning of Evolution,* Yale Univ. Press, 1949.

24-4 Adapted from Simpson, *Evolution and Geography.*

24-5 Adapted from Scott.

24-6, 24-7 Adapted from G. G. Simpson, *Horses,* Oxford Univ. Press, 1951.

24-8 Adapted from Romer, *Man and the Vertebrates.*

24-10 Gibbon and gorilla, New York Zoological Society; chimpanzee, American Museum of Natural History; orangutan, San Diego Zoological Garden.

24-13 Adapted from Romer, *Vertebrate Paleontology.*

INDEX

(Page numbers in italics refer to illustrations.)